COLLEGE MISERICORDIA LIBRARY
RECEIVED
APR 3 1973
DALLAS, PENNSYLVANIA
Y0-ACI-096

COMPREHENSIVE BIOCHEMISTRY

ELSEVIER PUBLISHING COMPANY

335 Jan van Galenstraat, P.O. Box 211, Amsterdam

AMERICAN ELSEVIER PUBLISHING COMPANY, INC.

52, Vanderbilt Avenue, New York, N.Y. 10017

ELSEVIER PUBLISHING COMPANY LIMITED

Rippleside Commercial Estate, Barking, Essex

Library of Congress Catalog Card Number 62–10359

With 129 illustrations and 52 tables

PRINTED IN THE NETHERLANDS

COMPREHENSIVE BIOCHEMISTRY

COMPREHENSIVE BIOCHEMISTRY

SECTION I (VOLUMES 1–4)
PHYSICO-CHEMICAL AND ORGANIC ASPECTS OF BIOCHEMISTRY

SECTION II (VOLUMES 5–11)
CHEMISTRY OF BIOLOGICAL COMPOUNDS

SECTION III (VOLUMES 12–16)
BIOCHEMICAL REACTION MECHANISMS

SECTION IV
METABOLISM

SECTION V
CHEMICAL BIOLOGY

GENERAL INDEX

COMPREHENSIVE BIOCHEMISTRY

EDITED BY

MARCEL FLORKIN

Professor of Biochemistry, University of Liège (Belgium)

AND

ELMER H. STOTZ

Professor of Biochemistry, University of Rochester, School of Medicine and Dentistry, Rochester, N.Y. (U.S.A.)

VOLUME 14

BIOLOGICAL OXIDATIONS

ELSEVIER PUBLISHING COMPANY

AMSTERDAM · LONDON · NEW YORK

1966

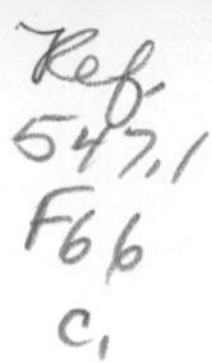

CONTRIBUTORS TO THIS VOLUME

ARTHUR S. BRILL, B.A., PH.D.

Associate Professor of Molecular Biophysics, Department of Molecular Biophysics, The Josiah Willard Gibbs Research Laboratories, Yale University, Box 2166, Yale Station, New Haven, Conn. 06520 (U.S.A.)

SIDNEY P. COLOWICK, PH.D.

Professor, Department of Microbiology, Vanderbilt University School of Medicine, Nashville, Tenn. 37203 (U.S.A.)

KONSTANTINE COST, B.S., M.A., PH.D.

Research Associate, Department of Botany, University of Minnesota, Minneapolis, Minn. 55455 (U.S.A.)

ALBERT W. FRENKEL, B.A., PH.D.

Professor of Botany, Department of Botany, University of Minnesota, Minneapolis, Minn. 55455 (U.S.A.)

DAVID E. GREEN, PH.D.

Institute for Enzyme Research, University of Wisconsin, 1710 University Avenue, Madison, Wis. (U.S.A.)

YOUSSEF HATEFI, PH.D.

Department of Biochemistry, Scripps Clinic and Research Foundation, 476 Prospect Street, La Jolla, Calif. (U.S.A.)

LLOYD L. INGRAHAM, PH.D.

Associate Professor of Biophysics, Department of Biochemistry and Biophysics, University of California, Davis, Calif. 95616 (U.S.A.)

DR. KAZUO OKUNUKI, PH.D.

Professor of Biology, Department of Biology, Faculty of Science, Osaka University, Toyonaka, Osaka (Japan)

JANE H. PARK, PH.D.

Associate Professor, Department of Physiology, Vanderbilt University School of Medicine, Nashville, Tenn. 37203 (U.S.A.)

LESTER J. REED, B.S., PH.D.

Professor of Chemistry and Director, Clayton Foundation Biochemical Institute, Department of Chemistry, The University of Texas, Austin, Texas 78712 (U.S.A.)

THOMAS P. SINGER, PH.D.

Professor of Biochemistry, Department of Biochemistry, University of California, School of Medicine, San Francisco, Calif. 94122; Chief, Molecular Biology Division, Veterans Administration Hospital, San Francisco, Calif. 94121 (U.S.A.)

E. C. SLATER, M.Sc., PH.D., Sc.D.

Professor of Physiological Chemistry, Laboratory of Biochemistry, University of Amsterdam, Jon. Dan. Meijerplein 3, Amsterdam (The Netherlands)

JAN VAN EYS, PH.D.

Associate Professor, Department of Biochemistry, Vanderbilt University School of Medicine, Nashville, Tenn. 37203 (U.S.A.)

GENERAL PREFACE

The Editors are keenly aware that the literature of Biochemistry is already very large, in fact so widespread that it is increasingly difficult to assemble the most pertinent material in a given area. Beyond the ordinary textbook the subject matter of the rapidly expanding knowledge of biochemistry is spread among innumerable journals, monographs, and series of reviews. The Editors believe that there is a real place for an advanced treatise in biochemistry which assembles the principal areas of the subject in a single set of books.

It would be ideal if an individual or small group of biochemists could produce such an advanced treatise, and within the time to keep reasonably abreast of rapid advances, but this is at least difficult if not impossible. Instead, the Editors with the advice of the Advisory Board, have assembled what they consider the best possible sequence of chapters written by competent authors; they must take the responsibility for inevitable gaps of subject matter and duplication which may result from this procedure.

Most evident to the modern biochemist, apart from the body of knowledge of the chemistry and metabolism of biological substances, is the extent to which he must draw from recent concepts of physical and organic chemistry, and in turn project into the vast field of biology. Thus in the organization of Comprehensive Biochemistry, the middle three sections, Chemistry of Biological Compounds, Biochemical Reaction Mechanisms, and Metabolism may be considered classical biochemistry, while the first and last sections provide selected material on the origins and projections of the subject.

It is hoped that sub-division of the sections into bound volumes will not only be convenient, but will find favour among students concerned with specialized areas, and will permit easier future revisions of the individual volumes. Toward the latter end particularly, the Editors will welcome all comments in their effort to produce a useful and efficient source of biochemical knowledge.

Liège/Rochester

M. Florkin
E. H. Stotz

PREFACE TO SECTION III

(VOLUMES 12–16)

Following Section II of Comprehensive Biochemistry on the Chemistry of Biological Compounds, and preceding sections on Metabolism and Chemical Biology, Section III is devoted primarily to Enzymes. Recognizing the encyclopedic nature of any effort to provide even a minimal treatment of all known enzymes, the Editors have chosen instead to select examples from modern enzymology in which advances in reaction mechanisms have been made. Certainly a well-established biochemical reaction mechanism is the carrier function of coenzymes which serve as the prosthetic groups of enzymes, and Section III has a primary purpose of providing treatment of both the chemistry and function of the coenzymes. Other chapters, however, treat thermodynamic and kinetic aspects of enzyme catalysis, hydrolytic enzymes displaying "active center" characteristics, and chelation and stereochemical considerations in enzyme catalysis. A considerable portion of the Section deals with biological oxidation mechanisms. Finally, Section III would seem incomplete without inclusion of the recommendations of the Enzyme Commission of the International Union of Biochemistry and the classified list of Enzymes.

Liège/Rochester

M. FLORKIN
E. H. STOTZ

CONTENTS

VOLUME 14

BIOLOGICAL OXIDATIONS

Chapter I. Dehydrogenation

by Sidney P. Colowick, Jan van Eys and Jane H. Park

Chapter II. Chemistry and Function of Lipoic Acid

by Lester J. Reed

Chapter III. Flavoprotein Dehydrogenases of the Respiratory Chain

by Thomas P. Singer

Chapter IV. The Functional Complexes of the Mitochondrial Electron-Transfer System

by Youssef Hatefi

Chapter V. Cytochromes and Cytochrome Oxidase

by K. Okunuki

A. PREPARATION OF CYTOCHROME COMPONENTS, p. 235

Chapter VI. The Mitochondrial Electron-Transfer System

by D. E. GREEN

Chapter VII. Oxidative Phosphorylation

by E. C. Slater

Chapter VIII. Photosynthetic Phosphorylation

by Albert W. Frenkel and Konstantine Cost

Chapter IX. Enzymatic Activation of Oxygen

by LLOYD L. INGRAHAM

Chapter X. Peroxidases and Catalase

by A. S. Brill

Chapter I

Dehydrogenation

SIDNEY P. COLOWICK, JAN VAN EYS AND JANE H. PARK

Departments of Microbiology, Biochemistry and Physiology, Vanderbilt University School of Medicine, Nashville, Tenn. (U.S.A.)

1. Introduction

(*a*) *Discovery of pyridine nucleotides*

This Chapter will deal with the chemistry of the pyridine-nucleotide coenzymes and their role in biological oxidations. The history of this subject, as reviewed by Warburg and Christian[446] in their classical 1936 paper, goes back to the discovery by Harden and Young in 1904 that fermentation by yeast juice requires a non-dialyzable heat-labile fraction and a dialyzable heat-stable fraction. The heat-stable fraction was later resolved into two coenzymes, one of which was identified by Meyerhof and Lohmann as the phosphate-transferring coenzyme, adenosine triphosphate. The other factor, "cozymase", was also recognized to be an adenine-containing nucleotide through studies in Von Euler's laboratory. However, its exact structure and function remained unknown until Warburg and his collaborators, in 1934–35, identified their "hydrogen-transferring coenzyme" from red blood cells as a dinucleotide of adenine and nicotinamide, containing 3 moles of phosphate per mole[448]. Von Euler's group then presented evidence in 1935–36 that "cozymase" also contained nicotinamide[123]. In 1936, both Von Euler's laboratory[347] and Warburg's laboratory[446] concluded that "cozymase", like the "hydrogen-transferring coenzyme" was a dinucleotide of adenine and nicotinamide, differing only in that it contained 2 moles of phosphate per mole instead of 3. On this basis Warburg and Christian suggested the names "Diphospho-Pyridinnucleotid" and "Triphospho-Pyridinnucleotid".

In the monumental paper by Warburg and Christian[446], many fundamental problems were solved and the groundwork was laid for much of modern

References p. 88

biochemistry. They showed that both coenzymes functioned catalytically in oxidation–reduction reactions. They showed that reduction of the coenzymes was accompanied by appearance of a new absorption band at 340 mμ and by a bluish fluorescence excitable by ultraviolet light. They showed that the kinetics of reduction and reoxidation could be conveniently observed and measured through these properties. They showed that reduction by hydrosulfite or by enzyme-catalyzed reactions led to the same reduced coenzyme. They presented evidence, with the aid of the model compound, N^1-methylnicotinamide iodide, that the reduction consisted in conversion of a quaternary nitrogen of a pyridinium structure to a tertiary nitrogen of a dihydropyridine structure. They demonstrated also the remarkable acid-lability of the reduced coenzyme.

(*b*) *Role in metabolism*

In the same paper of Warburg and Christian, the specific functions of the two coenzymes in respiration and fermentation processes were clearly delineated. In the studies with the "Triphospho-Pyridinnucleotid", they showed that the oxidation of glucose 6-phosphate by molecular oxygen required 2 proteins, one of which (the "Zwischenferment") was required to transfer hydrogen to the coenzyme from the substrate, the second (the "yellow enzyme") being required to catalyze the oxidation of the reduced coenzyme by oxygen. Thus was resolved for that time the old argument about whether oxidizing enzymes activated the substrate or the oxygen; here it was clear that one enzyme (with its coenzyme) activated the substrate, while the other enzyme made possible the reaction with oxygen.

In their studies of fermentation with the "Diphospho-Pyridinnucleotid", Warburg and Christian[446] showed that the coenzyme was reduced by "carbohydrate" upon addition of a protein fraction from yeast, and that the reduced coenzyme could be reoxidized rapidly by acetaldehyde upon addition of another protein fraction from yeast. Thus, the role of "cozymase" in alcoholic fermentation was explained in terms of two oxidation–reduction reactions. The work of Z. Dische and of D. Needham suggested, and the studies of Meyerhof and his collaborators demonstrated in an elegant manner, that the first step involved the reduction of the coenzyme by 3-phosphoglyceraldehyde in a reaction which was apparently obligately "coupled" in some mysterious manner with the synthesis of ATP from ADP and P_i, thus:

$$\text{3-Phosphoglyceraldehyde} + H_2O + \text{coenzyme} \rightleftharpoons \text{3-phosphoglycerate} + \text{reduced coenzyme}$$

$$\text{ADP} + P_i \rightleftharpoons \text{ATP} + H_2O$$

For an early calculation of the energetics of this coupling process, see Meyerhof[280] and Oesper[297]. Subsequent work in Warburg's laboratory[290,447] solved the mystery of the coupling by showing that the apparently coupled reactions were not simultaneous but consecutive, occurring as follows:

3-Phosphoglyceraldehyde + P_i + coenzyme $\rightleftharpoons$ 3-phosphoglyceryl phosphate + + reduced coenzyme

3-Phosphoglyceryl phosphate + ADP $\rightleftharpoons$ ATP + 3-phosphoglycerate

The discovery of these reactions was one of the important milestones in biochemistry, since it established a mechanism whereby the oxidative energy of metabolism could be harnessed as "phosphate bond energy"[258] in ATP. The full significance of this discovery became generally recognized only after the writings of Lipmann[258] and of Kalckar[186] brought it into proper perspective. Since then these reactions have served as a model for all studies of oxidative phosphorylation.

The mechanism of the oxidation step catalyzed by the enzyme 3-phosphoglyceraldehyde dehydrogenase, is discussed in detail in Section 8 (p. 63) of this Chapter. Other dehydrogenases are now known of this complex type, *i.e.* in which the carbonyl group, after oxidation, does not appear as a free carboxyl group but as an acyl derivative. However, the 3-phosphoglyceraldehyde dehydrogenase is the most thoroughly studied one of this group, and will therefore serve as the example. The terminal enzymes of fermentation (alcohol dehydrogenase, lactic dehydrogenase) will serve as the major models used in the discussion of the detailed mechanism of simple dehydrogenases in Section 7 (p. 46). For detailed reviews of these and other dehydrogenases, see Ref. 39.

The widespread role of the pyridine nucleotides in dehydrogenation processes is now well recognized. In combination with specific enzymes, they are involved in the dehydrogenation of hundreds of different natural substrates, especially in the conversion of alcohols and amino compounds to carbonyl compounds, and of the latter to carboxylic acids. In some cases, dehydrogenation of substrates involves a reduction of some electron carrier other than pyridine nucleotide. Thus, the oxidation of α-keto acids (see Chapter II) involves formation of reduced lipoic acid, whereas the desaturation of CH–CH bonds (see Chapter III) involves reduction of flavin coenzymes, and the "oxidation" of water in photosynthesis involves photoreduction of an iron–protein, ferredoxin. These reduced carriers can, under appropriate conditions, reduce the pyridine nucleotides.

The pyridine nucleotides also play a role in biological hydroxylation of substrates by molecular oxygen, catalyzed by "mixed function oxygenases"[163]. In these reactions, one molecule of reduced pyridine nucleotide is oxidized concomitantly with one molecule of the substrate, one atom from the molecular oxygen being incorporated into the hydroxylated product and one atom of oxygen forming water:

$$\underset{\text{(reduced)}}{\text{RH} + \text{coenzyme}} + O_2 + H^+ \rightarrow \text{ROH} + \underset{\text{(oxidized)}}{\text{coenzyme}} + H_2O$$

The pyridine nucleotides are thus concerned in virtually all biosynthetic and degradative processes involving oxidation–reduction steps. In recent years, a distinction has become evident between the functions of the diphospho- and triphospho-forms of the coenzymes. It appears now that the diphospho-form is involved mainly in degradative pathways, in which the hydrogen of the substrate is transferred eventually to oxygen for purposes of energy storage as ATP[208,219], while the triphospho-form is involved mainly in reductive biosynthetic pathways[261]. This "division of labor" has been observed not only in *in vitro* systems but also in intact cells[133].

This separation of function is not absolute, since oxidation–reduction can occur between the triphospho- and diphospho-forms, catalyzed by the enzyme, pyridine nucleotide transhydrogenase[82]. It was suggested[80] shortly after the discovery of this enzyme that it might serve to couple the oxidation of the triphospho form with ATP synthesis, and this proved to be the case[208,219].

A detailed consideration of the various dehydrogenation and transhydrogenation reactions and their physiological significance is beyond the scope of the present Chapter. We will be concerned here primarily with those enzyme reactions in which a pyridine nucleotide reacts directly with a substrate, and the emphasis will be on that information which may be useful for understanding the chemical mechanism of the dehydrogenation process.

(*c*) *Nomenclature and abbreviations*

The following names and abbreviations for the pyridine nucleotides have all been widely used at one time or another.

Cozymase	Hydrogen-transferring coenzyme
Coenzyme I (Co I)	Coenzyme II (Co II)
Diphosphopyridine[a] nucleotide (DPN)	Triphosphopyridine[a] nucleotide (TPN)
Nicotinamide adenine dinucleotide (NAD)	Nicotinamide adenine dinucleotide phosphate (NADP)

[a] Note the undesirable change in translation from Warburg's "Diphospho-pyridin-nucleotid" and "Triphospho-pyridinnucleotid".

At the present time, only the DPN and NAD terminologies are in use. In this article, we will adopt the latter terminology, as recommended by the Commission on Enzymes of the International Union of Biochemistry[121,334].

For the reduced coenzyme, although it is a "dihydropyridine", we will use the recommended abbreviation NADH, in line with the fact that reduction involves the uptake of 2 electrons and one proton (*i.e.* the dihydropyridine tends to be fully dissociated). In order to avoid the implication that NADH represents the product of a 1-electron reduction, the oxidized form will be written with a plus charge (NAD^+), to indicate its quaternary pyridinium structure, whenever balanced equations are written.

Thus, for the electrode reaction, one writes,

$$NAD^+ + H^+ + 2e \rightleftharpoons NADH$$

Then, to show interaction with a system:

$$RH_2 \rightleftharpoons R + 2H^+ + 2e$$

one writes the sum of the above reactions:

$$NAD^+ + RH_2 \rightleftharpoons NADH + R + H^+$$

In cases where oxidation involves formation or disappearance of a new dissociable hydrogen, *e.g.* in aldehyde oxidation, one writes the reaction thus:

$$NAD^+ + RCHO + H_2O \rightleftharpoons RCOO^- + NADH + 2H^+$$

When the state of ionization of all reactants and products is not known, or is not pertinent to the general description of the reaction, one may write the reactants and products without showing correctly the state of ionization of the components, thus:

$$NAD + RCHO + H_2O \rightleftharpoons RCOOH + \text{reduced NAD}$$

The term "reduced NAD" was recommended for this purpose in the second edition of the Report of the Commission on Enzymes[121], in preference to the term $NADH_2$; the use of the latter term in the original report was criticized by W. M. Clark[75], partly on the grounds that such a structure would not exist in the physiological pH range, and, if formed in acid solution, would immediately decompose.

2. Structure and conformation of pyridine nucleotides

(a) *Structures of oxidized forms*

Fig. 1 shows the currently accepted structures of NAD and NADP. The dinucleotide structure for NAD, in which the linkage between the nucleotides occurs by a pyrophosphate bridge, is essentially that originally proposed by Schlenk and Von Euler[347]. The position of the third phosphate group in NADP was established by Kornberg and Pricer[226]. It should be noted that both pentose moieties are D-ribose[346] and that the riboside linkages are β for both the adenine nucleotide[99,174] and the nicotinamide-nucleotide moieties[190]. The evidence for these coenzyme structures has been reviewed

References p. 88

many times in the past (for example, see Kaplan[190], Singer and Kearney[364], Dixon and Webb[105], and LePage[249]). This evidence will not be recounted in detail here. Suffice it to say that the structure of NAD has been proven by synthesis[174]. Major emphasis in this section will be placed on the structure, conformation and electronic configuration of the reduced coenzymes, and on possible changes in these structures when bound to enzymes.

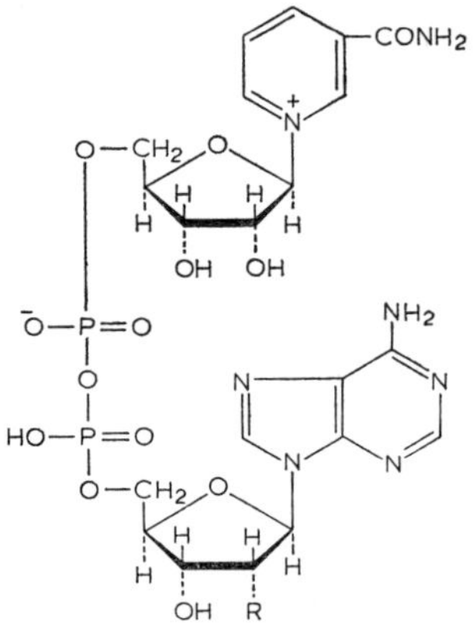

Fig. 1. Structures of pyridine nucleotides. From Levy *et al.*[252]. NAD, R = —OH. NADP, R = $—OPO_3H_2$.

(b) *Structure of reduced coenzymes*

In the studies of Warburg and Christian[446] it was concluded that reduction of the coenzymes in enzyme-catalyzed reactions or by hydrosulfite resulted in an *o*-dihydronicotinamide structure, which was written as the 1,2-dihydro compound (structure I in Fig. 2). This conclusion was based in part on

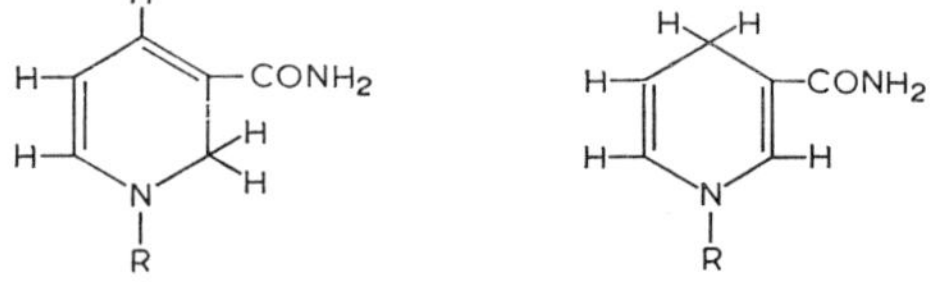

Fig. 2. Structures for the reduced coenzyme as originally formulated (I) and later revised (II).

studies with the model compound, N^1-methylnicotinamide iodide, which was shown to undergo an analogous reduction by hydrosulfite, with the appearance of the characteristic absorption band (at 360 mμ in this case) and fluorescence, coupled with decrease in the pyridinium absorption at 260 mμ. The product was identified by Karrer *et al.* (see Ref. 446) as N^1-methyl-*o*-dihydronicotinamide.

Some 20 years later, it became feasible through the work of Westheimer, Vennesland and their collaborators (see Section 3, p. 17) to label the coenzyme at its reduced site with deuterium. M. E. Pullman *et al.*[318], taking advantage of this development, were able to show that reduction of NAD occurred in the 4- or *p*- rather than in one of the *o*-positions (structure II in Fig. 2). This was demonstrated by the following procedure (see Fig. 3):

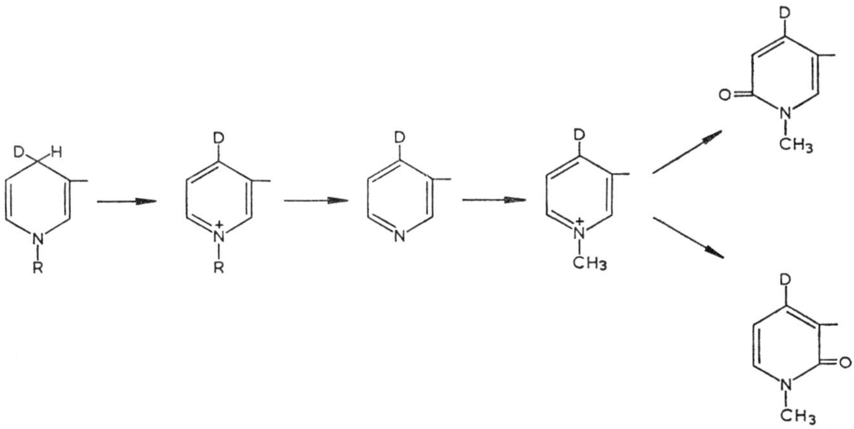

Fig. 3. Scheme of Pullman *et al.*[318] for conversion of labelled reduced coenzyme to the N^1-methylpyridones. From Colowick[79].

(*1*) The coenzyme was labelled with deuterium by a suitable reduction–reoxidation cycle (see Section 4, p. 22); (*2*) The labelled coenzyme was cleaved enzymatically and the labelled nicotinamide released was converted to the *N*-methyl derivative; (*3*) The latter was oxidized with alkaline ferricyanide to form a mixture of the 2- and 6-(*o*-)pyridones which were analyzed for deuterium. Since this oxidation process failed to remove any of the deuterium, it was concluded that the label was in the 4-(*p*-)position.

Similar experiments showed that the product of reduction of the model compound, N^1-methylnicotinamide, by hydrosulfite was also a 1,4-dihydro derivative[327].

Using a more direct approach, Loewus *et al.*[259] established that reduction of the coenzyme occurred in the 4-position by the following procedure: (*1*) Nicotinamide was synthesized with deuterium in the 2-, 4- or 6-position; (*2*) the labelled nicotinamide was incorporated into NAD enzymatically by an exchange reaction (see Section 6, p. 39); (*3*) the labelled coenzymes were reduced with hydrosulfite; (*4*) the reduced coenzymes were allowed to react enzymatically with pyruvate, and the lactate was isolated and analyzed for deuterium. Only when the coenzyme was labelled in the 4-position was there significant labelling of the lactate. Similar experiments by Mauzerall and Westheimer[274] showed that the deuterium-labelled reduced model compound, N^1-benzylnicotinamide, transferred its deuterium to malachite green only when the label was in the 4-position.

Nuclear magnetic resonance (NMR) spectra of reduced *N*-methylnicotinamide have confirmed the C-4 methylene structure[113,175]. The structure has more recently been confirmed by Brown and Mosher[44], using still another method. They showed by infrared spectroscopy that the deuteronicotinamide derived from the deuterium-labelled coenzyme (see Fig. 3) is identical with synthetic 4-deuteronicotinamide and non-identical with 2- or 6-deuteronicotinamide.

Additional evidence in favor of the 1,4-dihydro structure for the coenzyme comes from a consideration of the ultraviolet absorption spectra of the model compounds. Wallenfels[429] has shown that various pyridinium salts, when reduced with hydrosulfite, show a single absorption band around 350 mμ, which is characteristic of the 1,4-dihydro compounds. When the same compounds are reduced with $NaBH_4$, they show two bands, one around 350 mμ and one around 260 mμ, and the products have been identified as 1,6-dihydro compounds. In one case, reduction of a pyridinium salt appeared to yield a 1,2-dihydro compound with either reducing agent; this product showed only a single peak around 420 mμ. The basis for these shifts in absorption (see Fig. 21, p. 32) has been discussed by Wallenfels[429] and by Cilento *et al.*[68].

(*c*) *Conformation of reduced coenzyme*

Recent NMR studies[279] using reduced *N*-benzylnicotinamide (I) have revealed that the 2 hydrogens at C-4 are equivalent. This may mean either a planar ring (Fig. 4A), as recently demonstrated by X-ray diffraction on the crystalline material[209] or 2 puckered ring forms (Fig. 4B) which are mirror images in rapid rotational equilibrium. NMR studies on the reduced coenzyme (II) appeared to confirm this conclusion and indicated furthermore a folded

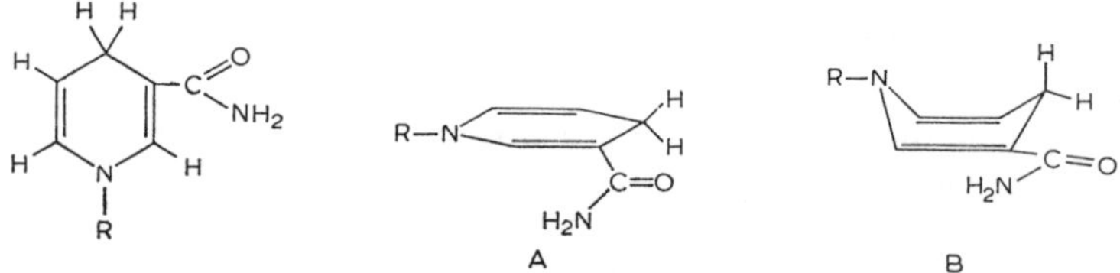

Fig. 4. Possible conformations of reduced pyridine ring of coenzymes or model compounds. From Meyer *et al.*[279]. I, R = $—CH_2C_6H_5$. II, R = —adenosyl-5′-OP_2O_5O-5′-D-ribos-2-β-yl.

configuration of the molecule in which the adenine moiety and the dihydropyridine ring are in juxtaposition.

Such a folded configuration for the reduced coenzyme was first suggested by the studies of G. Weber[451], who demonstrated that the fluorescence emission of NADH at 460 mμ, although known to be due to the dihydropyridine moiety[446] could be excited not only at 340 mμ, where the dihydropyridine moiety absorbs, but also at 260 mμ, where over 90% of the excitation energy is absorbed by adenine. He showed that cleavage of the molecule by nucleotide pyrophosphatase to separate the adenine and reduced nicotinamide-mononucleotide moieties abolished the effectiveness of excitation at 260 mμ, while excitation at 340 mμ remained effective.

Further evidence for the folded nature of the reduced coenzyme came from studies of Shifrin and Kaplan[356,357] who used the enzymatically inactive α isomer of NAD, in which the nicotinamide-riboside moiety is in the α rather than the β configuration. They found that the chemically reduced α isomer showed the same fluorescence as the β form when excited at 340 mμ, but only slight fluorescence when excited at 260 mμ (Fig. 5). This result indicated that the excitation of fluorescence with 260-mμ light was dependent not only on the presence of adenine in the molecule, but on the proper spatial relationship between the adenine and the dihydropyridine ring.

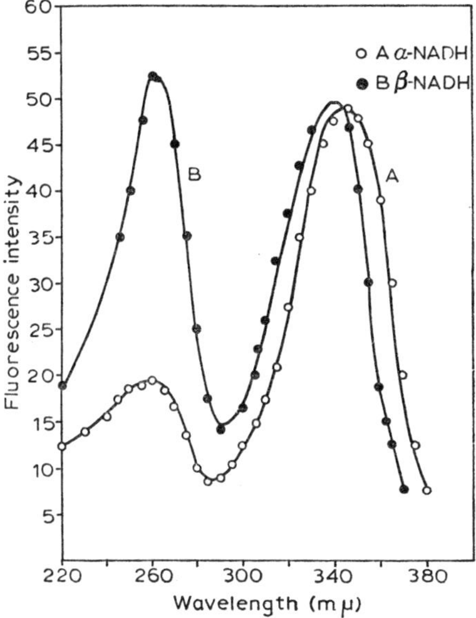

Fig. 5. Corrected fluorescence excitation spectra of α- and β-NADH. $T = 5°$. From Shifrin and Kaplan[356].

References p. 88

Kaplan[189] and Velick[423] have constructed models which show that the reduced form of the active coenzyme (β-NAD) allows juxtaposition of the adenine and dihydropyridine rings more readily than does the α-NAD (Fig. 6). Shifrin and Kaplan[356] and Velick[423] have shown that the amino group of adenine is important in the transfer of excitation energy, since the coenzyme analogue (see Section 6, p. 38) in which the amino group is replaced by a hydroxyl group shows relatively little fluorescence on excitation at the purine absorption maximum. This had led to the view[357] that the adenine amino group may be involved in hydrogen bonding with the oxygen of the carboxamide group of nicotinamide.

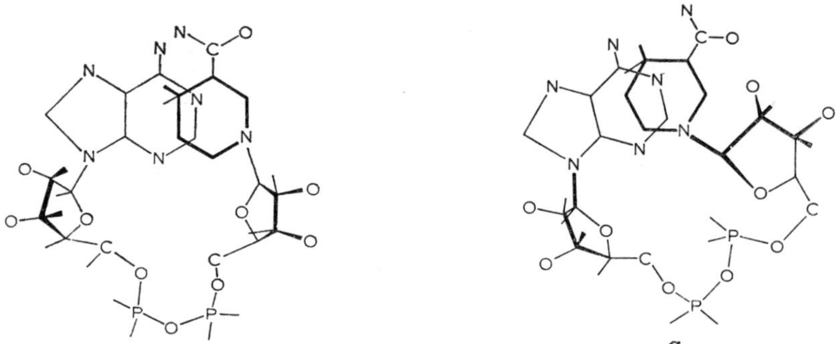

Fig. 6. Folded conformations of NADH with α- and β-isomerism at the pyridine-*N*-riboside bond. These are projections of skeletal models in which the planes of the nitrogen rings are parallel to the plane of the paper, nicotinamide above and adenine below. Other bonds are out of plane and hence appear at varying length in projection. From Velick[423].

Another line of evidence cited by Velick[423] in favor of a folded configuration for the reduced coenzyme is that the 2 hydrogens at C-4 of the dihydropyridine ring are not equivalent with respect to rate of oxidation with chemical oxidizing agents (see Section 4, p. 25). This non-equivalence is difficult to reconcile with the equivalence of the two C-4 hydrogens of the reduced coenzyme observed in the above-mentioned NMR studies of Meyer *et al.*[279].

Velick[423] has studied factors influencing the structure of the folded inner complex of the reduced coenzyme. Raising the temperature apparently dissociates the folded structure, since it lowers the efficiency of energy transfer at 260 mμ much more than at 340 mμ. The effect of changing the solvent is shown in Fig. 7. It can be seen that excitation by 340-mμ light is greatly enhanced in an organic solvent with a moderately lower dielectric constant than water, but that excitation by 260-mμ light is essentially abolished. The fluorescence emission maximum is shifted from 465 mμ in H_2O to 440 mμ in the organic solvent.

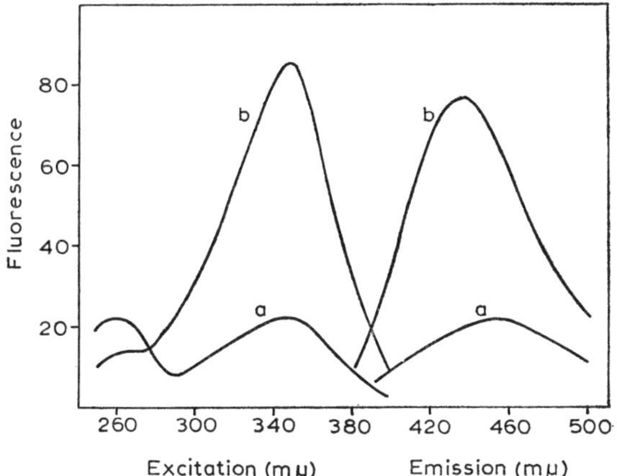

Fig. 7. Corrected fluorescence excitation and emission spectra of NADH at the same concentration in water (a) and in methyl carbitol (b). From Velick[423].

(*d*) *Conformation of reduced coenzyme when bound to protein*

It is remarkable to note that all of the fluorescence changes observed with NADH in organic solvents are also observed when the reduced coenzyme is bound to simple dehydrogenases (Table I). The enhanced fluorescence as well as the enhanced polarization of fluorescence suggest a more rigid structure for the bound NADH, while the failure of 260-mμ excitation to cause fluorescence of the bound dihydropyridine moiety suggests a relatively open conformation for the bound coenzyme. The shift in emission maximum suggests an environment of relatively low dielectric constant. The mode of action of dehydrogenases of this type is discussed in detail in Section 7 (p. 46).

An outstanding exception is the enzyme glyceraldehyde-3-phosphate dehydrogenase. Here there is no enhancement of fluorescence, and correspondingly less polarization of fluorescence, both indicative of more degrees of freedom of the bound coenzyme. The fluorescence emission spectrum suggests a relatively polar environment, and the high efficiency of 260-mμ light in the excitation of fluorescence of the dihydropyridine moiety suggests a closed conformation. The unusual properties of the bound NADH in this case may be related to the complex function of this enzyme, which is discussed in detail in Section 8 (p. 63).

TABLE I

COMPARISON OF ABSORPTION AND FLUORESCENCE PROPERTIES OF FREE AND BOUND NADH

After Velick[423]

Enzyme	*LDH*[a]	*ADH*	*GDH*	*αGPDH*	*GPD*	*Free NADH in:* *Water*	*Free NADH in:* *Methyl Carbinol*
Absorption max. (mμ)	335	325	340	340	340	340	
Fluorescence							
Emission max. (mμ)	440	450	445	447	465	465	440
Polarization	0.47	0.42	0.44	0.43	0.28	0.1	
Enhancement	+	+	+	+	—		+
Excitation max. at 260 mμ[b]	—				+	+	—
Probable conformation of NADH	Open	Open	Open	Open	Closed	Closed	Open

[a] LDH = lactic dehydrogenase of beef heart, ADH = alcohol dehydrogenase of horse liver, GDH = glutamic dehydrogenase of beef liver, αGPDH = α-glycerophosphate dehydrogenase of rabbit skeletal muscle and GPD = glyceraldehyde-3-phosphate dehydrogenase of rabbit skeletal muscle.

[b] Corrected for fluorescence of coenzyme due to energy absorbed by protein at 260 mμ.

(e) *Electronic structure of reduced coenzyme and relationship to ultraviolet absorption spectrum of free and bound forms*

Table I shows that the ultraviolet-absorption peak of the reduced coenzyme may or may not show a shift to lower wavelength on binding to dehydrogenases, whereas the fluorescence-emission band is regularly enhanced and shifted to shorter wavelengths (with the exception previously noted). If the fluorescence shift is taken as evidence of a less polar environment, then it seems that this diminished polarity of the environment does not necessarily cause a shift in ultraviolet absorption. This conclusion is compatible with the findings of Cilento *et al.*[68] who showed that the ultraviolet-absorption maximum of 1-benzyl-dihydronicotinamide was shifted only moderately on passing from water to less polar solvents: water (357 mμ), chloroform (354 mμ), ethanol (354 mμ), benzene (349 mμ), acetone (347 mμ), dioxane (345 mμ), cyclohexane (345 mμ), ethyl ether (340 mμ). This moderate shift, which represents the increased energy required to produce the excited state dipole (Fig. 8B) in less polar solvents, is in line with the moderate value of the dipole moment of the model compound in the ground state[68]. The observed small dipole moment of 3.89 D suggests that in addition to the quinone structure in Fig. 8A, there is a definite though small contribution by the ionic structure B in the ground state. Cilento *et al.*[68] propose that the structure C, which would exhibit completing resonance, makes a more important contribution than structure B, in order to account for the low resonance stability of this compound compared with the acetylpyridine analogue (see Section 6, p. 44). The latter, which could exist only in the forms D and E (Fig. 8), would have a greater resonance stability, thereby accounting for its markedly higher absorption maximum.

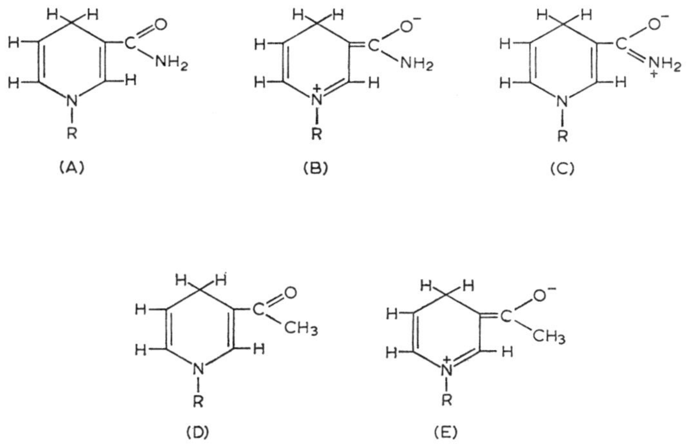

Fig. 8. Possible electronic configurations of reduced NAD and its acetylpyridine analogue.

The question remains as to why, with some dehydrogenases, the binding of the coenzyme is accompanied by a large shift in the absorption maximum toward lower wavelengths. Weber[452] has suggested that this means that the active site is non-polar in character. However, Kosower[228] points out that, in view of the above-mentioned data of Cilento *et al.*[68], this would require a completely hydrophobic area at the active site, which appears unlikely for reasons which he outlines. He therefore proposes an alternative mechanism for the shift in absorption maximum on binding. This proposal is based on the fact that a shift in absorption toward lower wavelengths is observed in certain α,β-unsaturated ketones when a positive charge in the form of a quaternary nitrogen is present near the β carbon of the conjugated system. Kosower proposes that an ε-amino group of lysine in the active site of the dehydrogenase may exert this effect (Fig. 9). He proposes that this amino group, in the case of enzymatic reduction of acetaldehyde (alcohol dehydrogenase) would make hydrogen bonds with the aldehyde oxygen and with the ring oxygen of the ribose to which the dihydropyridine ring is attached, thereby putting the latter into proper position for hydrogen transfer to the aldehyde. This proposed structure would place the ε-amino group of the lysine at about 3 Å from the nitrogen of the pyridine ring, in fair agreement with the distance required to produce the known shift in

References p. 88

absorption maximum of the bound reduced coenzyme. (The function of the proposed "hydrophobic region" in Fig. 9 is to attract the methyl group of the acetaldehyde and thereby determine the stereospecificity for its reduction, see Section 4, p. 30).

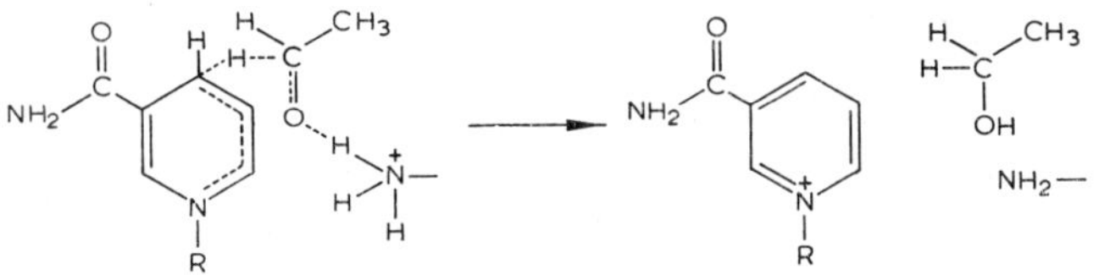

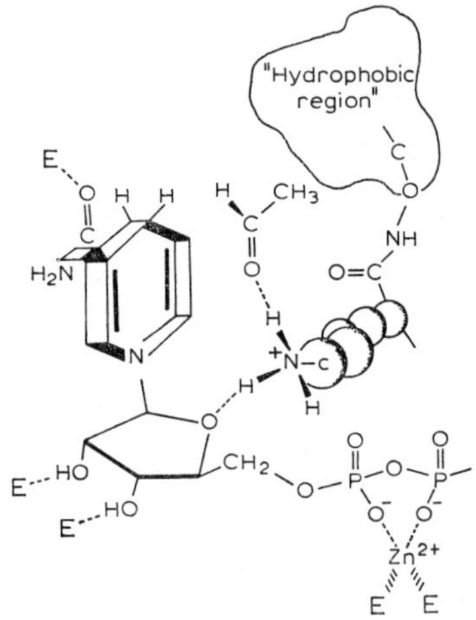

Fig. 9. Illustration of possible role of ε-amino group of lysine in the alcohol dehydrogenase reaction. After Kosower[228].

Kaplan and Ciotti[195] have proposed a somewhat similar mechanism for the shift in absorption on binding of the reduced coenzyme to liver alcohol dehydrogenase. They suggest that a hydrogen-containing group on the protein forms a hydrogen bond directly with the nitrogen of the dihydropyridine ring. Cilento *et al.*[68] have expressed support for this view.

(*f*) *Change in conformation of coenzyme during oxidation–reduction*

Much less can be guessed about the conformation of the oxidized coenzyme than about the reduced coenzyme, because the oxidized form has no useful fluorescence or absorption properties which might serve as indicators of its configuration in solution. However, some generalizations can be made. Velick[423] has pointed out that the reduction of an aromatic pyridinium riboside to a dihydropyridine riboside would result in a marked change in the juxtaposition of the ribose and pyridine ring structures and hence to a marked change in the fit of the coenzyme to the protein, simply on the basis of steric considerations. This is borne out by the fact that there are marked differences in binding constants for the oxidized and reduced coenzymes. As a rule the simple dehydrogenases (see Section 7, p. 55) show much stronger binding of the reduced form than of the oxidized form. Again, the glyceraldehydephosphate dehydrogenase is the exception in that it binds the oxidized coenzyme somewhat more tightly than the reduced coenzyme (see Section 8, p. 66).

There is not much basis for deciding whether or not the oxidized coenzyme exists in the folded configuration postulated for the reduced coenzyme. Since the oxidized coenzyme behaves stereospecifically at C-4 of the pyridine ring upon non-enzymatic reduction by hydrosulfite (see Section 4, p. 24), Velick[423] infers that NAD, like NADH, can occur in a folded conformation. Shifrin and Kaplan[357] draw the same inference from the fact that the adenine moiety can be shown to quench the fluorescence of a coenzyme analogue containing the fluorescent moiety, aminopyridine, in place of nicotinamide.

3. Mechanism of the reduction process

(a) *Reduction of pyridinium salts by hydrosulfite*

When pyridinium salts are reduced by addition of hydrosulfite (dithionite) in bicarbonate solution, a transient yellow intermediate is observed[122]. When the hydrosulfite is added under strongly alkaline conditions, the yellow compound formed is stable, but may be converted to the colorless dihydropyridine product by neutralization[348]. It was generally considered that the yellow compound was a free-radical intermediate until Yarmolinsky and Colowick[472,473] showed that it resulted from an addition reaction with sulfoxylate ion, SO_2^{2-}, to form a sulfinate derivative of NADH, which underwent hydrolysis in neutral solutions to yield NADH (Fig. 10a). Additional evidence that the yellow compound was not a free radical came from measurements of paramagnetism by Swallow[375] and of electron spin resonance by Mauzerall[273].

Since the final product was known to be a 1,4-dihydro compound, it was assumed[473] that the sulfinate moiety of the intermediate was attached at C-4 of the pyridine ring. However, there were certain respects in which the yellow compound did not behave like a typical 4-addition compound (see Section 5, p. 32); it did not show fluorescence, it showed a very high in-

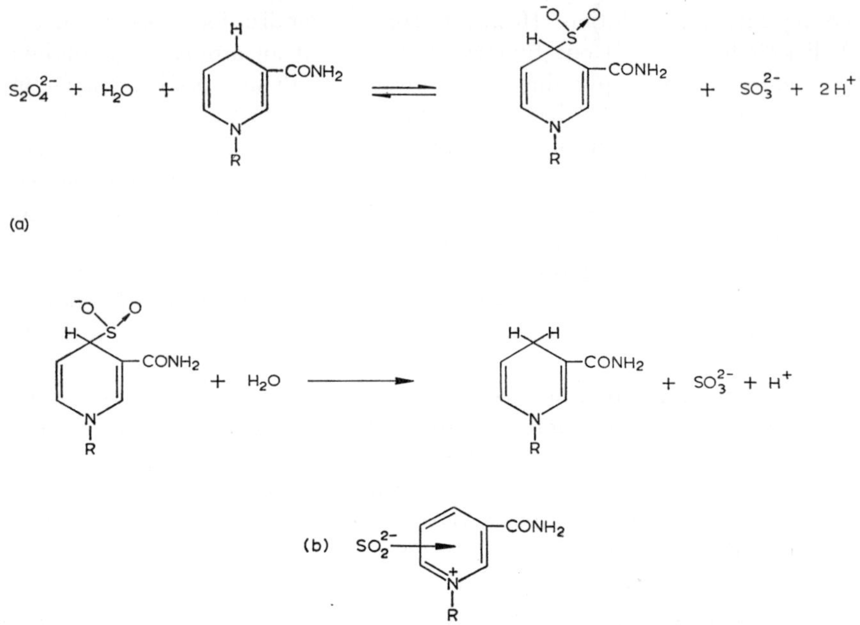

$$S_2O_4^{2-} + H_2O + \text{(1-R-nicotinamide, 4-H)} \rightleftharpoons \text{(4-H, 4-}SO_2^-\text{ adduct)} + SO_3^{2-} + 2H^+$$

(a)

$$\text{(4-sulfinate adduct)} + H_2O \longrightarrow \text{(1,4-dihydro, 4-}H_2\text{)} + SO_3^{2-} + H^+$$

(b) SO_2^{2-} → (pyridinium, N^+–R, CONH$_2$)

Fig. 10. Mechanism of reduction of pyridinium salts by dithionite. (a) Reduction *via* a 4-sulfinate (from Yarmolinsky and Colowick[473]). (b) Proposed charge-transfer complex as intermediate (from Kosower[229]).

crement of absorption at 260 mμ over that due to adenine and it showed a low broad absorption band with a maximum at 360 mμ (Fig. 11), whereas 4-addition compounds as a rule behave like the 1,4-dihydro compound in these respects (*cf.* Fig. 20, p. 32). Wallenfels and Schuly[435], on the basis of the absorption spectrum of the yellow intermediate obtained from 1-(2,6-dichlorobenzyl)-3,5-dicarbamido pyridinium ion, proposed that the sulfinate moiety was attached at C-2 of the pyridine ring, and that hydrolysis was accompanied by a shift of electrons to give the 1,4-dihydropyridine product. Kosower[229] accepted neither the 2- nor the 4-sulfinate structure for the yellow intermediate; he proposed instead that the unusual spectral properties were those of a charge-transfer complex (Fig. 10b). In a recent report by Caughey and Schellenberg[57] on the NMR spectrum of the yellow intermediate obtained from reaction of dithionite with 1-benzyl-nicotinamide ion, they conclude, however, that "the spectra (chemical shifts and coupling constants) appear fully compatible with a 4-sulfinic acid derivative (addition product) structure for the intermediate and exclude the proposed charge-transfer complex structure". The 2-sulfinate structure proposed by Wallenfels and Schuly may be correct for the dicarbamido compound which they

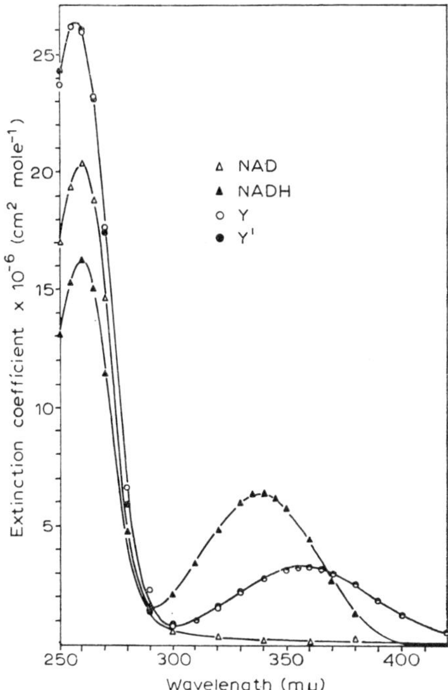

Fig. 11. Absorption spectra of NAD, NADH, and the yellow intermediate (Y or Y') obtained by reaction of NAD with hydrosulfite or formaldehyde sulfoxylate, respectively. From Yarmolinsky and Colowick[473].

studied but not for the monocarbamido structure present in the coenzymes, as Kosower[229] has pointed out.

The mechanism of the chemical reduction by dithionite may serve as a model for the enzymatic reduction in certain systems. Racker (see Section 8, p. 81), has proposed that an adduct of NAD with an SH group of 3-phosphoglyceraldehyde dehydrogenase undergoes "aldehydolysis" to yield NADH.

(b) Direct hydrogen transfer in enzyme systems and model systems

The details of the mechanism of enzymatic reduction are considered in later Sections (7 and 8). We will consider here only some general properties of the dehydrogenase systems and of pertinent model systems.

(i) "Direct hydrogen transfer" in enzyme systems

A major discovery in the field of oxidation–reduction reactions was the finding of Westheimer, Fisher, Conn and Vennesland[126,457] that hydrogen could be directly transferred from a reductant to an oxidant without undergoing exchange with protons in the medium. Their early experiments, carried out with yeast alcohol dehydrogenase, 1,1-dideuteroethanol (CH_3-CD_2OH) and NAD in normal water, revealed that the reduced NAD formed contained 1 atom of deuterium per molecule, proving that a hydrogen atom had been transferred directly from the α-carbon of ethanol to the nicotinamide ring without exchange with the protons of the medium.

This finding came as a great surprise to biochemists because up to that time it was generally accepted that in biological oxidations hydrogen was never transferred directly; rather it was thought that the hydrogen of the donor molecule had to dissociate to produce protons in the medium, after which the dissociated donor could donate electrons directly to the acceptor (see, for example, Clark[74] and Kalckar[186]). Vennesland and Westheimer[428] have pointed out that this earlier misconception was due to the tendency of biochemists to interpret classical theory for the *thermodynamics* of oxidation–reduction systems (see Clark[74]) as if this theory had meaning with respect to *mechanism*. The studies of the Westheimer–Vennesland group provided experimental evidence in support of the old theory of Wieland, proposed in 1912, that oxidation of organic compounds involved removal of hydrogen (see Clark[74]).

(*ii*) *Proteins as possible intermediates in "direct hydrogen transfer"*

Whenever direct enzyme-catalyzed transfer of hydrogen from substrate to coenzyme is observed, without exchange with the medium, this must mean that there are no intermediates containing that hydrogen in a rapidly exchangeable form. This has been taken to mean that the oxidizable groups (*e.g.*, SH groups) of the enzyme proteins themselves probably do not undergo cyclic dehydrogenation–hydrogenation during catalysis[428], since hydrogen bound to sulfur, oxygen or nitrogen is normally rapidly exchangeable with the hydrogen of water. However, hydrogen atoms which are normally rapidly exchangeable may become very slowly exchangeable when they are part of a hydrogen-bonded protein structure, as we know from the work of Linderstrøm-Lang[176].

Evidence against cyclic oxidation–reduction of the dehydrogenase proteins was provided by the studies of Kaplan, Colowick and Neufeld[203], who showed that the protein of alcohol dehydrogenase would not catalyze oxidation–reduction reactions between the oxidized and reduced forms of the pyridine nucleotides when ethanol was omitted. However, these experiments did not rule out the possibility that a reduced protein intermediate was formed only when both the coenzyme and the substrate were simultaneously attached to the protein (see also Section 7, p. 47).

A preliminary report by Schellenberg[344] indicates that the protein is indeed labelled stoichiometrically by the hydrogen that is transferred from ^3H-labelled ethanol to NAD during catalysis by yeast alcohol dehydrogenase. Since the label was found in the acid-hydrolyzed protein on the methylene group of the alanine side-chain of tryptophan, Schellenberg proposes "participation of a tryptophan residue in a dehydrogenation to an indolenine (pseudoindole) during enzymatic reaction". This report comes as a complete surprise to those of us who accepted as dogma the principle of direct transfer of hydrogen from substrate to coenzyme. It would, if shown to be generally applicable, make necessary a complete revolution in our thinking about the mechanism of dehydrogenation, since all models requiring direct juxtaposition of the participating substrate and coenzyme groups (*e.g.* Fig. 9, p. 14, and Fig. 26, p. 61) would have to be re-examined. In any event, the term "direct hydrogen transfer" must be clearly recognized to mean only that there is no exchange with medium water and not that no intermediate hydrogen carriers take part in the transfer process.

A somewhat analogous case in which a protein appears to act as a hydrogen carrier is that[37] of "hydrogen dehydrogenase" which catalyzes the reaction:

$$H_2 + NAD \rightleftharpoons NADH + H^+$$

In this case, either H_2 or NADH can react with a disulfide group of the protein to form an SH group, which is regarded as an intermediate hydrogen carrier.

The idea that certain groups on proteins might serve as carriers in oxidation–reduction reactions is a very old one. For some reason, attention has been focussed largely on the SH groups for this purpose[27,38,40]. However, it is known that other groups, particularly tryptophan, are readily oxidized under mild conditions. In the case of 3-phosphoglyceraldehyde dehydrogenase it has been found that iodine treatment of the protein, under very mild conditions, leads to irreversible loss of most of the dehydrogenase activity by action on groups[115] other than the "essential SH groups". It will be of interest to determine the nature of these groups, especially in the light of the above-mentioned discovery by Schellenberg[344]. That tryptophan may be involved is suggested by spectral evidence for an NAD–indole complex with this enzyme (see Section 8, p. 68).

(*iii*) *Flavins as intermediates in "direct hydrogen transfer"*

Direct hydrogen transfer mediated by flavin coenzymes is demonstrable in certain enzyme systems but not in others (see review by Levy *et al.*[252]). When the flavoprotein, dihydro-orotate dehydrogenase, catalyzes the reduction of orotate by deuterium-labelled reduced NAD in a normal water medium, no deuterium appears in the dihydro-orotate. This is due to the fact that any deuterium on the reduced flavin intermediate would be rapidly exchangeable with the hydrogen of the medium water. This kind of exchange between reduced flavin and water presumably accounts for the frequent observation of exchange between NADH and water catalyzed by purified flavoproteins and by complex oxidation–reduction systems such as mitochondria, microsomes and chloroplasts. One exceptional case is the flavoprotein cytochrome b_5 reductase[112,372], which normally catalyzes the oxidation of NADH by cytochrome b_5. In this case, no exchange is observed between NADH and the medium. When deuterium-labelled NADH is added to this flavoprotein, a complex is formed, apparently consisting of oxidized NAD and a deuterium-labelled reduced flavin. The existence of the latter may be demonstrated either by adding a coenzyme analogue (see Section 6, p. 38) and showing appearance of deuterium in the reduced coenzyme analogue[112], or by adding borate, thereby somehow forcing the reduction of the bound, oxidized NAD by the reduced flavin and causing the re-appearance of the deuterium in the reduced NAD[372]. The borate apparently acts by binding the reduced NAD and thus favoring NAD reduction.

This unequivocal demonstration that a flavoprotein system can catalyze direct hydrogen transfer vitiates the conclusions drawn by others (*e.g.*, see Ref. 330) who have ruled out participation of flavoproteins in certain hydrogen-transfer systems on the grounds that a direct transfer between donor and acceptor was observed.

(iv) Hydrogen atom (1-electron) versus hydride ion (2-electron) transfer

As Westheimer[454,456] has emphasized, the fact that direct hydrogen transfer takes place in dehydrogenase systems has no bearing on the question of whether free-radical intermediates are involved in these reactions. The question at this point is still unresolved, although the balance of the evidence seems to lie in favor of hydride-ion transfer, *i.e.*, transfer of a hydrogen atom with 2 electrons in a single step. A free hydride ion is not implied as an intermediate, but an activated complex with polar properties is thought to be formed.

This is illustrated in Fig. 12 for the model reaction in which hydrogen is transferred directly from 1-benzyl-1,4-dihydronicotinamide to a thio-

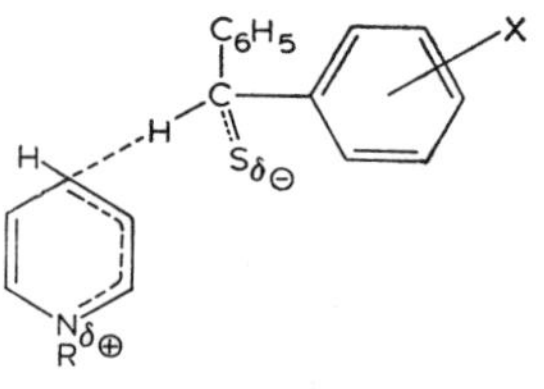

Fig. 12. Proposed activated complex for non-enzymatic hydride-ion transfer. From Westheimer[454].

ketone[454]. A key feature of this proposed mechanism is that the magnitude of the partial positive charge on the carbon in the thioketone group determines the rate of hydride-ion transfer. It is assumed that with ordinary ketones, which are non-reactive in this model system, the partial positive charge on the carbon is insufficient unless an enzyme is present to induce the necessary electron shift. In this system, as well as in other organic-chemical reactions involving direct hydrogen transfer (*e.g.* reduction of organic compounds by lithium aluminum hydride, or the Meerwein–Pondorff reduction in which hydrogen is transferred from an aluminum alkoxide to a ketone) the evidence is good that transfer of a hydride ion is involved[1,454,456]. For example, this reaction is not inhibited by free-radical inhibitors, and substituents in the thiobenzophenone influence the reaction in the manner expected from a hydride transfer. A good yield of NAD^+ models is obtained in these reductions.

In further support of the idea of hydride-ion transfer, Wallenfels[429] reports that addition compounds (see Section 5, p. 31), formed by reaction of certain anions such as cyanide with NAD model compounds, can act as donors of these anions to acceptors, in much the same way as the analogous dihydro compound would act as a hydride-ion donor:

$$\text{NADH} + \text{malachite green} \rightarrow \text{NAD} + \text{leuco malachite green}$$

$$\text{NAD–cyanide} + \text{malachite green} \rightarrow \text{NAD} + \text{leucocyano malachite green}$$

Additional evidence in favor of a 1-stage hydride-ion transfer is afforded by the fact that free-radical reduction yields dimers of quaternary nicotinamide derivatives[431,432]. These dimers are more readily oxidized by free-radical oxidants than is the dihydropyridine. In addition the 1,4-dihydropyridine derivatives are more rapidly oxidized by malachite green than are the 1,6- or 1,2-derivatives while the reverse is true when 1-electron dyes are used. In fact benzyl-viologen will not attack 1-(2,6-dichlorobenzyl)-1,4-dihydronicotinamide at all[431].

However, there is also evidence for radical mechanisms in systems showing direct hydrogen transfer. In fact, the very same system of malachite green reduction cited above, which Wallenfels regards as an example of hydride-ion transfer, was originally considered by Mauzerall and Westheimer[274] to proceed by a radical mechanism.

It has been possible to oxidize NADH by a variety of reagents, such as ferricyanide[319], 2,6-dichlorophenol indophenol[108], riboflavin[365,373], quinones[106], phenazines[101], spirocyclohexyl porphyrexide[345], Fenton's reagent[345], peroxide and copper[53], and methylene blue in air[345]. These oxidations could all be one-electron processes. However, the yield of NAD^+ is not quantitative. The results could also be explained as hydride-ion transfer in some cases, such as for the oxidation by riboflavin[373].

References p. 88

These examples illustrate the difficulty in deciding the question of 1-electron *versus* 2-electron transfer even for a given model reaction, and the difficulty is of course compounded if one attempts to answer this question for enzyme-catalyzed hydrogen-transfer reactions on the basis of data from model reactions.

The only direct approach which has been made to the question of 1-electron *versus* 2-electron processes in the dehydrogenase systems is the measurement of electron spin resonance by Commoner and his collaborators[83]. During the reduction of NAD by ethanol in the presence of alcohol dehydrogenase, they found evidence for a low concentration of free radicals, corresponding to about 10^{-6} of the total NAD present. Westheimer[454] points out that this may alternatively represent a true intermediate, a side-reaction or even an artifact in the system.

(*v*) *Role of metal ions*

Two factors have led to the assignment of a role for metal ions in dehydrogenase mechanisms. One is the fact that in the Meerwein–Pondorff model reaction, as well as in reductions involving Grignard reagents, a metal is involved. The other is the finding of Vallee that many dehydrogenases contain metal ions, notably zinc. This subject has been thoroughly reviewed elsewhere in this series[399] and will not be considered in detail here.

There is no agreement as to the function of the metal in dehydrogenase reactions. In some schemes (see Fig. 9, p. 14, and Fig. 26, p. 61, mechanisms Ia, IIa, IIb) it is given a role only in the binding of the pyridine nucleotide to the protein. In others (see Fig. 26, mechanism Ib), it is given a vital role in the interaction of the pyridine ring with the substrate. Since metals are not universally required for hydrogen-transfer reactions in either model systems[454] or dehydrogenase reactions (see Sections 7, p. 60, and 8, p. 70), it seems more likely that the metals, when present, play a role in binding rather than in the intimate mechanism of the reaction.

4. Stereochemistry of reduction process

(*a*) *Stereochemistry with respect to pyridine nucleotide*

In their studies on direct transfer of hydrogen from 1,1-dideuteroethanol to NAD by yeast alcohol dehydrogenase, Westheimer, Vennesland and their collaborators[126,428,457], noted that the reduced NAD at equilibrium contained only 1 atom of deuterium per mole. Since a value of 2 would be expected if the 2 hydrogens at C-4 were equivalent, this result indicated that the enzymatic reduction specifically transferred hydrogen from the alcohol to one side of the pyridine ring, and that the reverse reaction specifically removed the hydrogen from the same side of the pyridine ring (Fig. 13a). This conclusion confirmed the revolutionary view of Ogston that 2 identical substituents on a carbon atom are distinguishable in space and can therefore react differentially with asymmetric reagents such as enzymes. The stereochemistry of reactions at carbon atoms having the configuration

```
    b
    |
a—C—a
    |
    d
```

("meso carbon atoms"[350]) has been reviewed by Levy *et al.*[252] and by Westheimer[455].

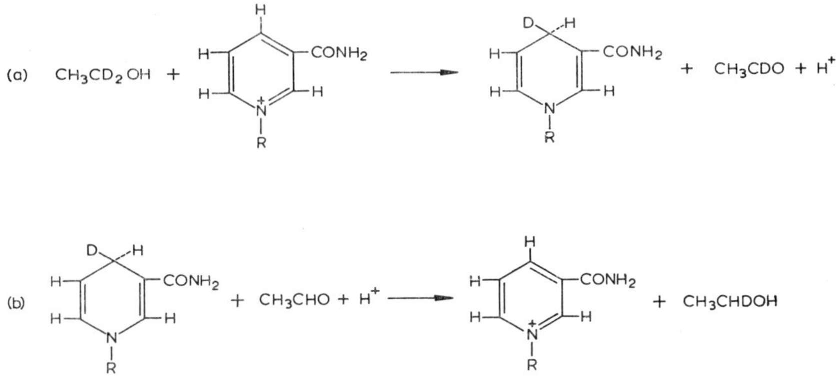

(a) CH_3CD_2OH + [NAD⁺ pyridinium ring: H, CONH₂, H, N⁺–R] ⟶ [reduced ring: D, H, CONH₂, H, N–R] + CH_3CDO + H^+

(b) [reduced ring: D, H, CONH₂, H, N–R] + CH_3CHO + H^+ ⟶ [pyridinium ring: H, CONH₂, H, N⁺–R] + CH_3CHDOH

Fig. 13. Reactions for demonstrating stereospecificity of yeast alcohol dehydrogenase for side A of the nicotinamide ring. After Fisher *et al.*[126].

The conclusion, that alcohol dehydrogenase would specifically remove the hydrogen only from that side of the pyridine ring to which it had originally been added, was confirmed as follows (Fig. 13b): The reduced NAD containing 1 atom of D per molecule, prepared enzymatically as described above, was re-oxidized with acetaldehyde and the same enzyme. The oxidized NAD was shown to be deuterium-free.

When the reduction of the coenzyme was carried out with hydrosulfite in D_2O, the product was shown to be a mixture of the two possible forms of monodeutero reduced NAD since, when this product was re-oxidized enzymatically with acetaldehyde and alcohol dehydrogenase, the oxidized NAD was found to be a mixture of deuterium-free and deuterium-containing molecules (Fig. 14).

The two isomers of monodeutero reduced NAD have been called "form A" and "form B"[343], form A being the isomer produced by yeast alcohol dehydrogenase when transferring deuterium from dideutero-ethanol to NAD. Without reference to the use of isotopes, one can also define side A of the nicotinamide ring of the coenzyme as that side to and from which hydrogen is transferred by yeast alcohol dehydrogenase. The terms α and β, formerly

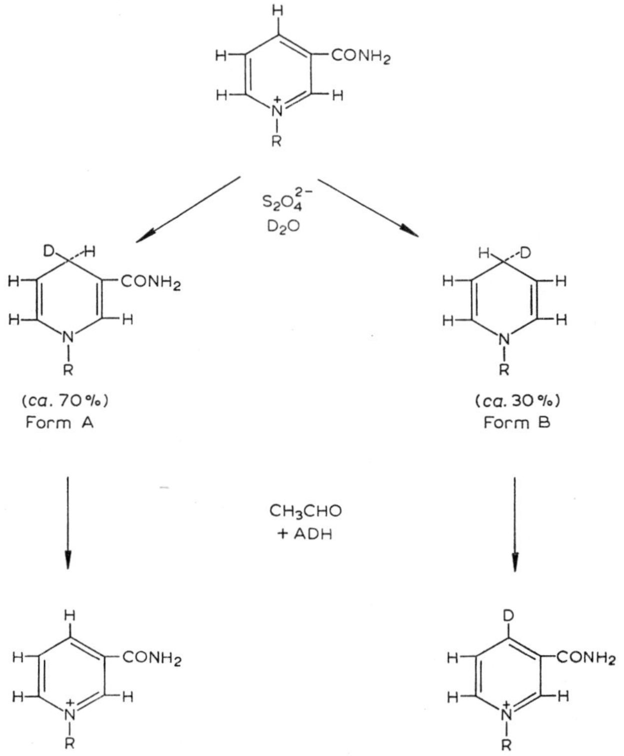

$S_2O_4^{2-}$
D_2O

(ca. 70%)
Form A

(ca. 30%)
Form B

CH_3CHO
+ ADH

Fig. 14. Reactions showing partial stereospecificity of reduction of NAD by hydrosulfite. Data from Pullman *et al.*[318]. See also earlier data of Fisher *et al.*[126].

used to designated sides A and B, have now been abandoned to avoid confusion with the terms α and β NAD, which refer to the configuration of the ribosyl-nicotinamide linkage.

One can see from Fig. 14 that even the chemical reduction by hydrosulfite shows a clear preference (about 2:1) for reduction[126,318] on side A. Fig. 15 shows that chemical oxidation of the reduced coenzyme by neutral ferricyanide[343] also shows a clear preference for side A, presumably of the order of about 5:1, since even in the face of a presumed 5:1 isotope effect favoring C–H over C–D cleavage, the C–D and C–H bonds were cleaved at equal rates when the C–D bond was on side A; when the C–D bond was on side B, it was hardly cleaved at all during oxidation by ferricyanide.

A survey of the stereospecificity of a large number of pyridine nucleotide-linked dehydrogenases has shown that some enzymes act on side A, others on side B, but in every case there is an essentially absolute specificity for a given side of the pyridine ring. A partial list of the enzyme systems which

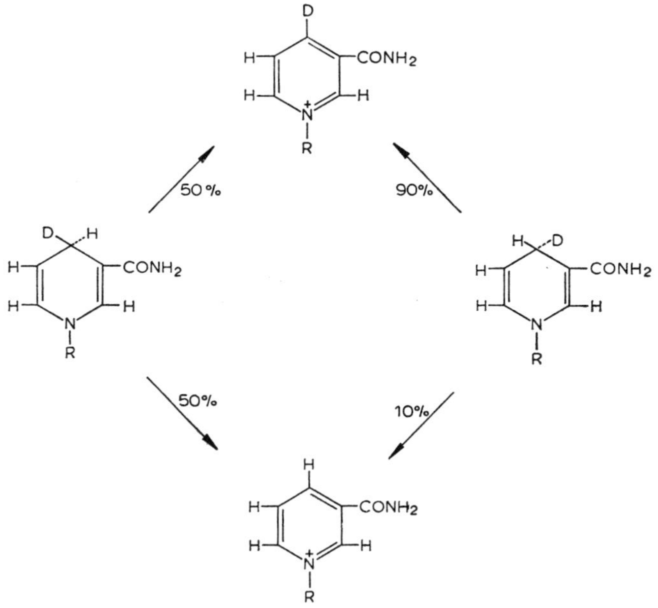

Fig. 15. Reactions showing partial stereospecificity of oxidation of reduced NAD by neutral ferricyanide, favoring side A of pyridine ring[343].

have been so classified is shown in Table II. One of the interesting generalizations which can be made is that the stereospecificity for a given hydrogen-transfer reaction is always the same, regardless of the source of the enzyme. For example, the alcohol dehydrogenases from yeast, *Pseudomonas* and liver show the same A-stereospecificity. Sources of enzymes are therefore not listed in Table II. Another generalization is that the dehydrogenation of a given substrate shows the same stereospecificity whether the nucleotide involved[237] is NAD or NADP. This is true both for the case of a single non-specific enzyme which can use either nucleotide (indicated in Table II as "NAD *or* NADP"), and for the case of 2 different enzymes specific for NAD and NADP respectively (indicated in Table II as "NAD *and* NADP"). A third generalization is that an enzyme which is non-specific with respect to substrate will show the same stereospecificity when different substrates are used[252].

References p. 88

TABLE II

STEREOSPECIFICITY OF SOME NICOTINAMIDE NUCLEOTIDE-LINKED DEHYDROGENASES

In each column, enzymes are listed in approximate order of increasing size of substrate. Sources of enzymes are not given, since the results to date have been the same for a given enzyme from different sources

Enzymes showing A-stereospecificity		*Enzymes showing B-stereospecificity*	
Dehydrogenase	*Nicotinamide nucleotide*	*Dehydrogenase*	*Nicotinamide nucleotide*
Formate[e]	NAD	Hydrogen[c,g]	NAD
Alcohol[d]	NAD	α-Glycerophosphate[d]	NAD
Acetaldehyde[d]	NAD	Triosephosphate[d]	NAD
Glyoxylate[b,e]	NAD *and* NADP	L-Glutamate[a,d]	NAD *or* NADP
D-Lactate[d]	NAD	D-Glucose[d]	NAD
L-Lactate[d]	NAD	D-Glucose 6-phosphate[d]	NADP
D-Glycerate[d]	NAD	6-Phospho-D-gluconate[d]	NADP
L-Malate[d,e]	NAD	Dihydrolipoate (= "diaphorase")[c,d]	NAD
L-Malate (decarboxylating)[d]	NADP	Glutathione (reductase)[a,b,d]	NAD *and/or* NADP
D_s-Isocitrate[d]	NADP	L-β-Hydroxybutyryl CoA[d]	NAD
Dihydro-orotate[b,c,d,e]	NAD *and* NADP	UDPG[e]	NAD
Dihydrofolate (reductase)[f]	NADP	Transhydrogenase[d]	NAD, NADP
Methylene tetrahydrofolate[f]	NADP	β-Hydroxysteroid[d]	NAD
Cytochrome b_5 (reductase)[d]	NAD	3-α-Hydroxysteroid[d]	NAD
		17-β-Hydroxysteroid[a,d]	NAD *or* NADP
		Cytochrome *c* (reductase)[c,d]	NAD

[a] Single enzyme acting with either NAD or NADP.
[b] Different enzymes acting on NAD and NADP respectively.
[c] Hydrogen exchange occurs between water and reduced coenzyme and shows same stereospecificity.
[d] From results compiled by Levy *et al.*[252].
[e] From data of Krakow *et al.*[237].
[f] From Ramasastri and Blakley[330].
[g] From Bone[37].

These generalizations would all appear to point to the nature of the substrate reaction as the feature determining A or B stereospecificity. However, when one compares the various reactions catalyzed by enzymes in group A with those in group B, it is difficult to make clear-cut correlations between the nature of the reactions and their stereospecificity. Krakow *et al.*[237] have noted that enzymes acting on carbohydrates and "carbohydrate derivatives" are found in class B, but that enzymes acting on the α-hydroxy groups of the α-hydroxy acids are found in class A. They noted further that the A-stereospecificity found with the α-hydroxy acids was observed regardless of the stereospecificity with respect to the hydroxyl group (*e.g.* compare D-lactate and L-lactate dehydrogenases in Table II). They also pointed out that a rough correlation existed between size of substrate and stereospecificity class, the enzymes in group A in general acting on the smaller substrates. However, the recent reports placing "hydrogen dehydrogenase" in class B[37], and methylenetetrahydrofolate dehydrogenase in class A[330], have weakened this correlation considerably. There is also no apparent correlation between stereospecificity and coenzyme binding (compare Tables I and II, see also Refs. 253 and 423).

Velick[419] was the first to suggest a possible correlation between A- and B-stereospecificity and physiological function. This suggestion was based on the finding[85] that the bound reduced coenzyme on triosephosphate dehydrogenase can apparently be oxidized by pyruvate and lactate dehydrogenase without prior dissociation from the triosephosphate dehydrogenase. Velick[419] pointed out that this observation, if valid, might mean that physiological hydrogen transfer could be regulated by simultaneous attachment of two dehydrogenases to the same coenzyme molecule. He indicated that this would present steric problems unless the two dehydrogenases acted on opposite sides of the pyridine ring. When Levy and Vennesland[253] found that the two enzymes concerned did indeed act on opposite sides of the pyridine ring (triosephosphate dehydrogenase on side B, lactic dehydrogenase on side A), they proposed that this type of protein–protein interaction might indeed be the basis for the existence of A- and B-stereospecificity. The studies of Nygaard and Rutter[294] and of Astrachan *et al.*[21] confirmed that the bound NADH of triosephosphate dehydrogenase could be oxidized direct by the lactic dehydrogenase system and showed that it could also be oxidized directly by the alcohol dehydrogenase systems of yeast or liver. These findings were in agreement with the views of Velick and of Levy and Vennesland, since alcohol dehydrogenases show A-stereospecificity. However, direct oxidation of the bound NADH of triosephosphate dehydrogenase is also brought about by the cytochrome *c* reductase system[265] and by the glutamate dehydrogenase system[21], both of which show B-stereospecificity. Although these latter results do not fit the predictions of Levy and Vennesland, it should be kept in mind that direct oxidation is difficult to prove when the extent of dissociation of the NADH-triosephosphate dehydrogenase to give free NADH is not accurately known (see discussion by Astrachan *et al.*[21]). In the case of the results with cytochrome *c* reductase[265], recalculation[253] indicates that direct oxidation did not actually occur.

Levy and Vennesland[253] have proposed a model for the action of two dehydrogenases on opposite sides of the pyridine ring of a coenzyme molecule. In this model (Fig. 16), the reduced pyridine ring is shown to undergo a change in conformation from one boat form to another. It is proposed that such a shift may facilitate coupling between dehydrogenases of opposite stereospecificity. Whether or not such boat-shaped configurations actually

References p. 88

occur is still open to question. Evidence pro[252] and con[228,279] has been presented (see Section 2, p. 8).

One of the most important recent developments in the field has been the determination by Cornforth *et al.*[84] of the absolute configuration corresponding to A- and B-stereospecificity. They accomplished this by degrading

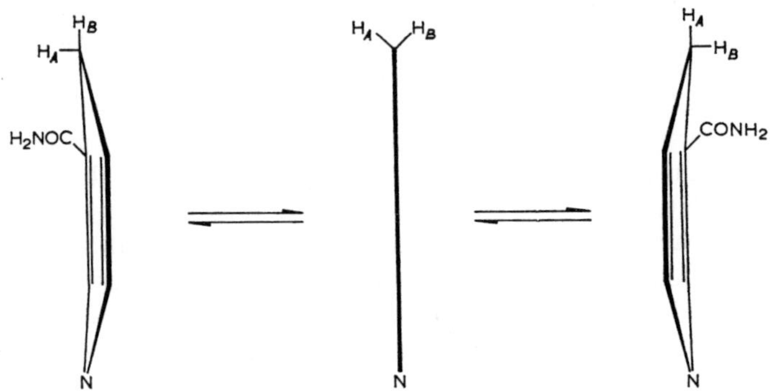

Fig. 16. Proposed shift in conformation of reduced NAD accompanying interaction with dehydrogenases of opposite stereospecificities. From Levy *et al.*[252].

the A and B forms of monodeutero reduced NAD to yield the respective deutero-succinates and determining their optical rotatory dispersion. They have expressed their rule for absolute configuration as follows:

> "When an enzyme of class A transfers hydrogen from a substrate to a pyridine nucleotide, the hydrogen is added to that side of the nicotinamide ring on which the ring atoms 1 to 6 appear in anti-clockwise order."

By good fortune, the structures which have been arbitrarily called form A and form B in the literature (reproduced in Figs. 13 and 14) have turned out to be correctly drawn in terms of absolute configuration.

(b) *Stereospecificity with respect to alcohol groups*

Fig. 17 shows the probable absolute configurations of a series of alcohols which are substrates or products of alcohol dehydrogenases. All of the structures are in the same configuration as the (+)-octan-2-ol first isolated by Neuberg and Nord[291] in 1919 from the action of fermenting yeast on 2-octanone. It is interesting to note that in all cases shown, the less polar of the two substituents on the carbonyl group undergoing reduction is found in the same relative position in each of the alcohols formed. It is remarkable that even when the two substituents are as alike as the methyl and ethyl groups in methyl ethyl ketone, there is an absolute specificity in producing only one of the two possible enantiomorphs[314]. The reduction of the deutero-aldehydes is also stereospecific, leading to the formation of optically active deutero-alcohols[5,251,260]. The enzymatic re-oxidation of the deutero-ethanol has been shown to be absolutely specific in removing the hydrogen rather

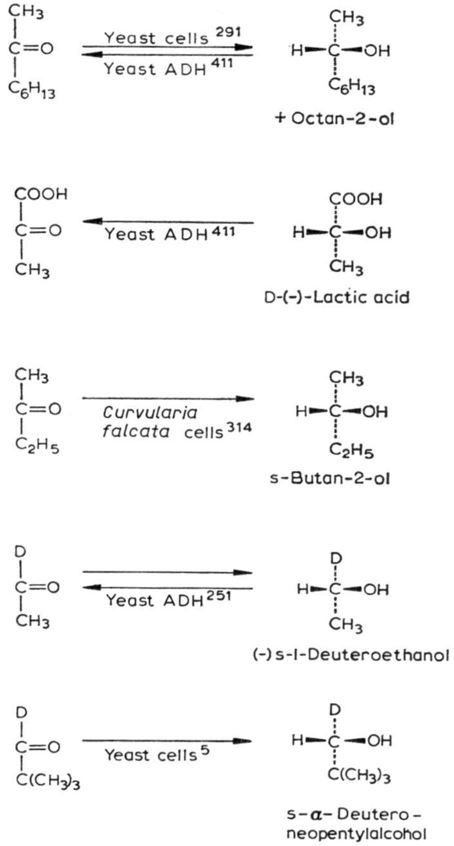

CH3 | C=O | C6H13 ⇌ (Yeast cells[291] →; ← Yeast ADH[411]) CH3 | H–C–OH | C6H13
+ Octan-2-ol

COOH | C=O | CH3 ← (Yeast ADH[411]) COOH | H–C–OH | CH3
D-(-)-Lactic acid

CH3 | C=O | C2H5 → (*Curvularia falcata* cells[314]) CH3 | H–C–OH | C2H5
s-Butan-2-ol

D | C=O | CH3 ⇌ (Yeast ADH[251]) D | H–C–OH | CH3
(-) s-1-Deuteroethanol

D | C=O | C(CH3)3 → (Yeast cells[5]) D | H–C–OH | C(CH3)3
s-α-Deutero-neopentylalcohol

Fig. 17. Probable absolute configurations of alcohols which are substrates or products of alcohol dehydrogenases. The arrows show directions in which each process has been demonstrated.

than the deuterium[251] at the "meso carbon atom". For the assignment of the configuration of the deuteroalcohols, see Refs. 5, 252 and 411. Some cases in which the reduction of ketones by fermenting yeast is only partially stereoselective have been reported by MacLeod *et al.*[262].

The completely stereospecific reduction of carbonyl compounds has also

References p. 88

been accomplished in non-enzymatic reactions of the Grignard and Meerwein–Ponndorf types, in which the reducing agent is optically active (see review by Levy *et al.*[252]). The stereospecificity here is attributed to steric hindrance which favors a lining up of the smaller substituent on the carbonyl compound with the larger substituent on the reducing agent, and *vice versa* (Fig. 18).

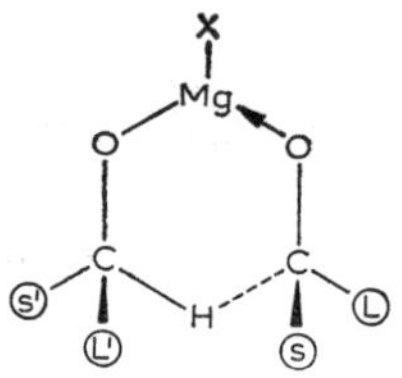

Fig. 18. Proposed intermediate in stereospecific non-enzymatic reduction of a carbonyl compound, containing small (s) and large (L) substituents, by an optically active Grignard reagent containing small (s′) and large (L′) substituents. Adapted from Levy *et al.*[252].

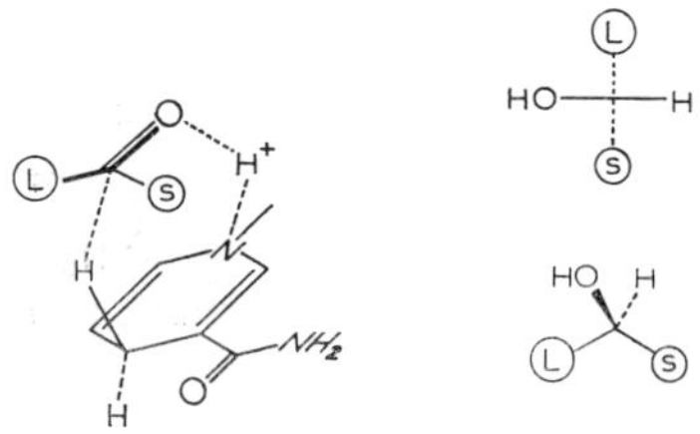

Fig. 19. Proposed intermediate in stereospecific enzymatic reduction of a carbonyl compound. The dihydropyridine ring and the carbonyl compound are drawn in parallel planes. From Prelog[314]. Note that in this drawing, the reaction is indicated with side B of the pyridine ring, according to the absolute configuration of NADH[84].

Prelog[314] has proposed that similar considerations can help to explain stereospecific reductions in enzyme systems. Fig. 19 shows his model for the interaction of a reduced pyridine nucleotide on an enzyme surface with a carbonyl compound, in which the large lipophilic substituent L of the substrate has been placed opposite the hydrogen of the coenzyme and the small substituent opposite the hydrophilic carboxamide group. However, it is clear that no simple scheme involving only interaction of the oriented pyridine nucleotide and the substrate can explain the observed enzymatic stereospecificity, since two different enzymes can produce different enantiomorphs from the same carbonyl compound even though in both cases interaction is with the same side of the pyridine ring (*cf.* D- and L-lactic dehydrogenases in Table II). It is therefore necessary to postulate specific interaction of a region of the protein with either the L or s substituent on the carbonyl compound, and it is usually postulated that a hydrophobic region on the protein interacts with the L substituent on the carbonyl compound (see Fig. 9, p. 14). However, Van Eys and Kaplan[411] have presented kinetic evidence that in alcohol dehydrogenase the L substituent may be directed away from the enzyme surface.

5. Addition reactions

(a) *Addition reactions to pyridinium derivatives*

Meyerhof and co-workers[282] attempted in 1938 to use the carbonyl reagents cyanide and bisulfite in a study of the stoichiometry of the triosephosphate dehydrogenase catalyzed reaction. As a result of that investigation they were the first to observe the interaction of these reagents with oxidized NAD to form a complex which was spectrally reminiscent of reduced NAD. This interaction between cyanide and NAD was restudied several years later by Colowick *et al.*[81]. Since that time many compounds have been found to interact with quaternary pyridinium compounds of physiological interest. They now include: alkali ions[201,271], cyanide[81,282], bisulfite ions[81,282,309], carbonyl compounds[51,171], sulfinate ions[435,473], hydroxylamine[52], hydrazine[416], pyrazole[393], mercaptans[412], aromatic amines[149], imidazoles[406], indoles[7,70], and nitromethane[242,437]. In addition, the interactions between these pyridinium derivatives and iodide[230,232,236] and phosphate[397] ions need mention. Identical type reactions are seen between pyridinium rings and acetylenic compounds[3]. The subject of these complexes has been reviewed on several occasions[190,191,229,234,429]. In general the spectral characteristics of the reaction products in solution are those of dihydropyridine derivatives. The addition compounds derived from analogues of NAD or from NAD model compounds also have spectra similar to their reduced forms. Fig. 20 illustrates the cyanide addition reaction of NAD contrasted to oxidized and reduced NAD.

There has been a discussion in the literature about the precise nature of the interaction between the nucleophilic agents and the pyridinium ring, specifically whether the interaction represents an ion pair, a complex or an actual covalent bond. In many instances the evidence for complex formation is only based on spectral observations which do not always allow distinguishing between a charge-transfer complex and an actual reversible covalent bond formation. In several instances products of the interactions have been isolated and derivatives have been made, the properties of which argue strongly in favor of a localized interaction between the nucleophilic agent and the pyridinium ring. Spectral evidence alone is also not sufficient to involve a charge-transfer complex, since the addition at different positions of the ring will give spectrally distinguishable compounds[429,439] (Fig. 21).

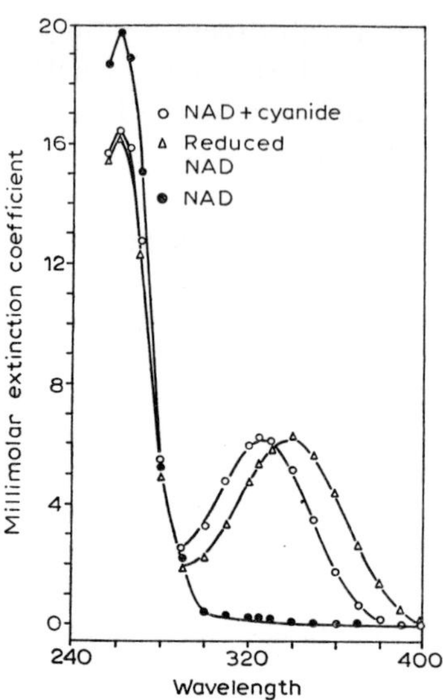

Fig. 20. Absorption spectra of NAD, reduced NAD and NAD–cyanide addition compound at pH 11. From Colowick *et al.*[81].

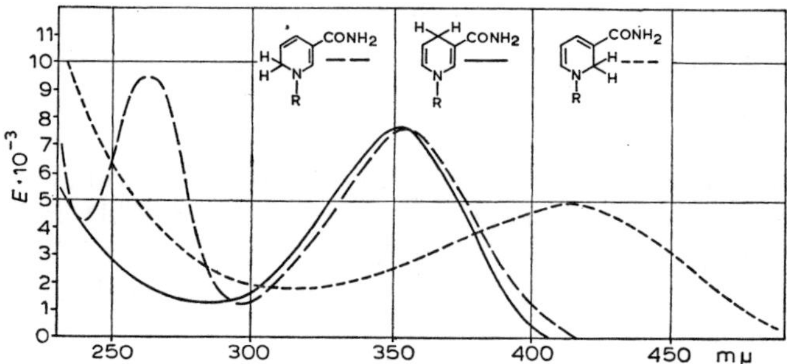

Fig. 21. Ultraviolet spectra of three isomeric dihydronicotinamide derivatives. From Wallenfels[429].

As an example, see the discussion in Section 3 (p. 15) of the nature of the sulfinate derivative of NAD, an intermediate in the reduction of NAD by hydrosulfite, which has been identified on various grounds as a 4-adduct[57,473], a 2-adduct[429,435,438,439] or a charge-transfer complex[229,234]. Of course the interactions need to be individually examined for the actual mechanisms involved and the product formed. Interesting intramolecular interactions have been studied by Shifrin[353,354]. In the compounds in which the β carbon of 1-ethyl nicotinamide was substituted with indole[354], phenol, benzene, imidazole, thiomethyl, or trimethyl ammonium[353], in many instances indications of energy-transfer interactions were evident.

As alluded to, in addition to a charge-transfer complex (non-localized addition) the pyridinium ring can react at both 2- and 4-positions. This gives in the asymmetrical nicotinamide ring 3 possible adduct isomers (Fig. 22). The anion affinity for any site depends of course on the nature of the nitrogen substituent, and, in model compounds and NAD analogues, on the side-chain of the pyridine ring.

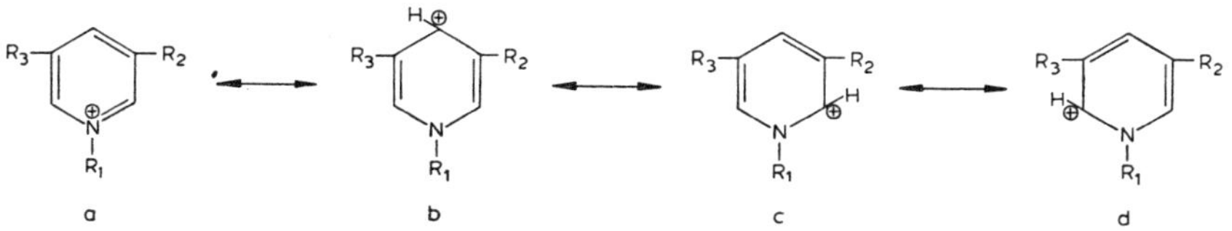

Fig. 22. Mesomeric forms of pyridinium cation capable of adduct formation with anions. From Wallenfels[429].

The most extensively studied reactions are the cyanide and carbonyl addition reactions. The cyanide addition reaction is a reversible interaction between the pyridine ring and cyanide ion[81,282] which is not instantaneous[201] nor instantaneously reversible. This latter property made it possible to isolate the adduct of *N*1-methylnicotinamide and cyanide[270]. While no decision could be made at that time as to the actual localization of the addition, the 2-position was ruled out because the addition compound gave on reduction the product 1,4,5,6-tetrahydronicotinamide[270]. The addition-reaction product between cyanide and *N*1-2,6-dichlorobenzylnicotinamide has also been isolated[437]. The spectrum of that adduct resembles the 1,4-dihydro derivative. Proof of the localization other than on spectral

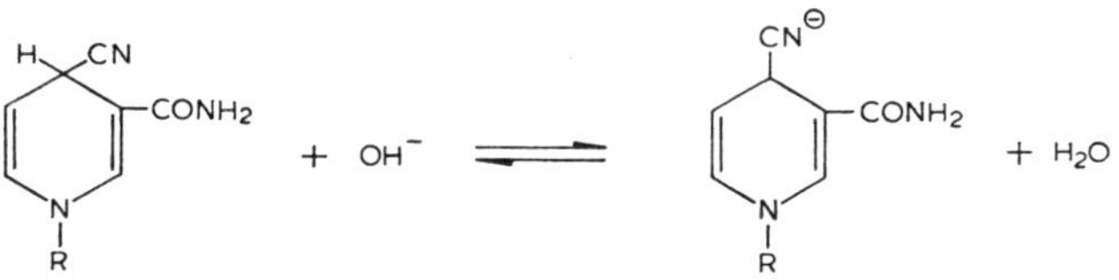

Fig. 23. Exchangeable hydrogen at C-4 in NAD–cyanide addition compound. From San Pietro[341].

grounds came from the work of San Pietro[341] on the NAD–cyanide reaction. He showed that in cyanide solution NAD exchanged deuterium with the medium at position 4 of the ring (Fig. 23). Similar localized interactions were shown between cyanide and pyridinium rings for the *N*1-alkyloxy derivatives of nicotinamide. The cyanide adducts of these compounds spontaneously

References p. 88

decompose into the corresponding alcohols and 4-, or 6-cyano-3-carbamido pyridines. In water, the 4-adduct predominates for the 1-ethoxy derivative[184]. The reaction between cyanide and pyridine derivatives is very strongly dependent on the dielectric constant of the solvent[184,230,245]. There is also a very large effect of both the side-chain and the nitrogen substituent of the pyridine ring. This correlation suggests a relation between redox potential and cyanide affinity[430].

The cyanide addition reaction has become useful as a method for measuring NAD[72,81]. However, this method is not a microdetermination. The carbonyl addition reaction has become more widely used for the determination of oxidized pyridinium derivatives because it has been adapted to fluorimetric techniques. The addition reaction between pyridinium compounds and carbonyl derivatives has been known a long time and has a rather interesting history. This addition reaction in effect is interwoven with the discovery of N^1-methylnicotinamide as a normal metabolite. Najjar and Wood[288] discovered a fluorescent substance in urine which resulted from niacin ingestion. This substance turned out to be a derivative of N^1-methylnicotinamide[172,287]. Najjar *et al.* found that this compound gave, with acetone in alkali, a strongly fluorescent product[287]. Later Huff[171] isolated the fluorescent compound and suggested an acetone adduct of the structure 1,7-dimethyl-5-keto-8,9-dihydro-1,6-naphthyridine which on oxidation in acid gives 1,7-dimethyl-5-hydroxy-1,6-naphthyridine chloride. Now the acetone addition is considered to arise through the 4-position. This would give the 1,6-dimethyl-8-hydroxy-1,7-naphthyridine chloride[243] (Fig. 24). This stabilized acetone adduct has been the basis for the fluorimetric determination of N^1-methylnicotinamide[173], and pyridine nucleotides[250]. Nowadays a product obtained from methyl-ethyl ketone has been found preferable over acetone for that purpose[47,56].

This carbonyl addition reaction with pyridine nucleotides was also accidentally discovered in enzymatic studies. Although not realized at the time, Needham *et al.*[289], and Warburg *et al.*[450] observed the product between glyceraldehyde and NAD. Later Burton and Kaplan[51] found the product between dihydroxyacetone and NAD during a study of a glycerol dehydrogenase. A similar reaction appears to be the basis of the interaction[285] between C_{21} steroids and NAD. Burton and Kaplan[51] investigated the dihydroxyacetone reaction in great detail. The reaction is, compared to the cyanide reaction, slow and, while it is reversible, it is not readily so. Therefore, it has been possible to actually chromatograph the adducts on paper[54,55]. Through alcohol and ether precipitation, compounds could be prepared which had the same spectral qualities as the adducts in solution[55]. Ferricyanide oxidation converted these to oxidized analogues with a dihydroxyacetone side-chain on the nicotinamide, though products with a partially degraded side-chain were also formed[55]. The actual site of the adduct was not ascertained, but the ready hydrolysis of the analogue by animal tissue NADases[50] makes it likely that the substitution is at the 4-position, since 2- or 6-substitution would probably result in a less readily hydrolyzed

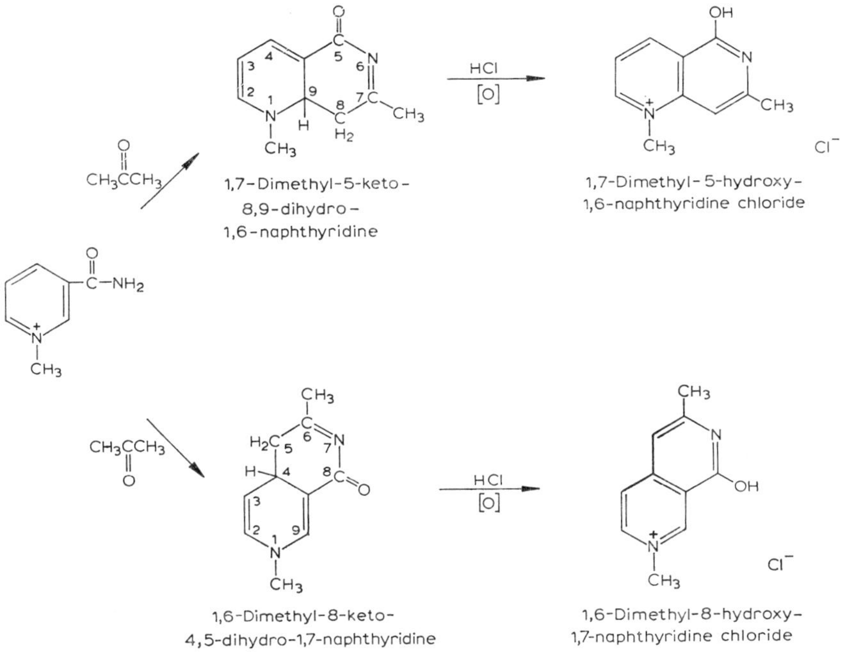

1,7-Dimethyl-5-keto-8,9-dihydro-1,6-naphthyridine

1,7-Dimethyl-5-hydroxy-1,6-naphthyridine chloride

1,6-Dimethyl-8-keto-4,5-dihydro-1,7-naphthyridine

1,6-Dimethyl-8-hydroxy-1,7-naphthyridine chloride

Fig. 24. Chemistry of formation of acetone adduct with N^1-methylnicotinamide.

analogue. This projection is based on the behavior of pyridine bases in the NADase base exchange reaction (see Section 6, p. 38). The relative lack of effect of 2- or 6-substituted bases make it likely that the enzymes cannot handle such compounds readily[200]. This 4-position addition is the more likely since that is the position of attack of acetophenone. This was shown by the observation that the acetophenone and 1-benzoyl-pyridinium ion gave 4-phenacylpyridine after oxygen oxidation[107].

It is of considerable interest that present-day commercial NAD contains enough acetone to give, in solution, the acetone adduct of NAD and, through auto-oxidation, the oxidized acetone adduct of NAD[109], both of which are identical with those prepared by Burton *et al.*[55]. Oxidation of addition products is possible, of course, in those cases where (*1*) a localized adduct exists, and (*2*) the reaction is either not rapidly reversible or the nucleophile is not subject to oxidation itself. The latter condition made it possible to prepare the oxidized derivatives of the imidazole adduct of 1-benzyl-3-acetylpyridinium bromide and of NAD[406]. Again, the actual position of the addition is not certain but the ready hydrolysis of the analogue with pig-brain NADase suggests a 4-position addition. The adduct between nitromethane and 1-dichlorobenzyl-3-carboxamidopyridinium bromide has similarly been oxidized[242,437].

The other addition reactions known are only observable through the spectrum of the complexes, though recently the H_2S adduct of 1′,6′-dichlorobenzylnicotinamide has been isolated[437]. The interest in these other adducts stems largely from the fact that the adduct formation is favored many fold in the presence of the appropriate dehydrogenase[195,197,384,408,417]. Furthermore, since the enzyme exhibits specificity towards the complexing nucleophile in the case of hydroxylamine[195,408,417] and mercaptans[59,417], the study of the addition reaction can shed light on the mechanism of the dehydrogenases. This will be discussed somewhat later in Section 7 (p. 46).

The interaction of alkali ions with NAD or NAD model compounds is less clearly defined. Dilute alkali causes NAD to split at the nicotinamide–ribose linkage. Strong (5 *N*) alkali yields a highly fluorescent product but this may be a secondary product after an initial hydroxyl adduct. In general, one would expect a pseudo-base to give a 1- or 6-position substitution. Indeed, oxidation of N^1-methylnicotinamide with ferricyanide in alkali yields both the 2- and 6-pyridones[316], while alkali also labilizes the hydrogen at the 2-position of the NAD molecule[342]. Enzymatic oxidation of N^1-methylnicotinamide yields predominantly the 6-pyridone[222,223]. In fact, this is a major excretory product of niacin metabolism[223], while the 2-pyridone cannot be detected in urine, even after niacin ingestion[170]. Recently, however, the 4-pyridone of N^1-methylnicotinamide has also been isolated from rat urine[64,458], which could be an oxidation product of the hydroxyl adduct at the 4-position. In alkali, therefore, addition reactions (pseudo-base formation) appear to occur at all 3 possible positions (*cf.* Ref. 13).

It is of interest here to reiterate the fact that the original discovery of N^1-methylnicotinamide as the fluorescent[288] compound F_2 represented probably an alkali addition product. Therefore N^1-methylnicotinamide was found as a natural product of NAD long after Karrer and Warburg[212] prepared it as a model for NAD. Similarly 1-methyl-nicotinamide-6-pyridone was prepared *in vitro*[222] before it was found to be a normal metabolite[222,223].

Double additions are possible, especially on oxidized adducts. Thus the analogue of NAD prepared by oxidizing the imidazole adduct, will still add cyanide, though the maximum is shifted towards longer wavelengths[406]. This is probably an addition at another position in analogy to the 1,2-reduction which one observes in 1-(2,6-dichlorobenzyl)-3-carboxamide-4,6-dimethyl pyridinium chloride[439].

(b) *Addition reactions to reduced pyridinium derivatives*

The reactions so far discussed pertained to oxidized NAD and, in general, quaternary pyridinium derivatives. However, reduced pyridine rings also are capable of addition reactions, essentially similar to the reactions shown by olefins. This property of dihydropyridines provides the explanation of the extreme acid lability of reduced pyridine nucleotides, which was already noted by Warburg[448]. In acid, the spectrum of NADH changes from a 340-mμ absorption band to a band at 295 mμ which is further changed, with complete loss of absorption due to nicotinamide[150]. However, if the acid used is sulfurous acid, the first product (the so-called primary acid product) is stable[150].

The mechanism of the acid reaction was first recognized by Karrer to be an olefin addition[210,211]. However, proof of this was not obtained until Anderson and Berkelhammer[13] obtained the primary acid product of 1-benzyl-3-acetyl-1,4-dihydropyridine. They showed this to be 1-benzyl-2-hydroxy-5-acetyl-1,2,3,4-tetrahydropyridine. This then establishes a proton attack on C-3 and an anion attack on C-2 (Fig. 25). Independently Wallenfels and Schuly studied this reaction. They isolated the bisulfite adduct of 1-(2,6-dichlorobenzyl)-5-carbamido-1,4-dihydropyridine and the corresponding 1,6-dihydro derivative[434,436]. Since the sulfite adduct was identical in both cases they deduced[436] an anion attack on C-2. This identity may have been the result of double-bond migration however.

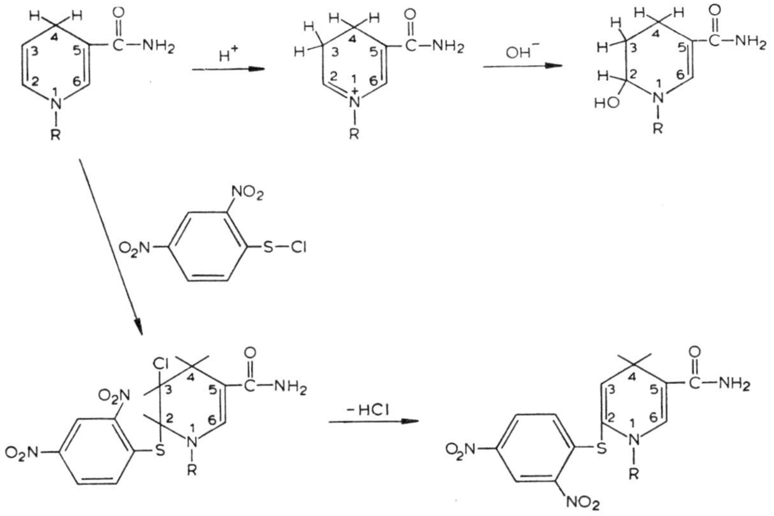

Fig. 25. Representative addition reactions to dihydronicotinamide.

References p. 88

The sulfite addition product is not the only stable addition compound one can obtain. Thiophenol and 1-(2,6-dichlorobenzyl)-5-carbamido-1,4-dihydropyridine give a crystalline adduct of a 1,2,3,4-tetrahydro structure. However, in this case the product of the reaction of 1-(2,6-dichlorobenzyl)-3-carbamido-1,6-dihydropyridine and thiophenol is different. This means that no decision can be made as to the position of anion attack. An interesting reaction is the one with dinitro-sulfenylchloride which gives for the above model compound 1-(2,6-dichlorobenzyl)-2(3)-dinitrophenylthio-3(2)-chloro-5-carbamido-1,2,3,4-tetrahydropyridine (Fig. 25). This rapidly loses HCl to regenerate a dihydropyridine but leaving the dinitrothiophenyl group attached[434]. These weak acids may be special cases however, and it has been suggested that the conversion of a 1,4-dihydronicotinamide derivative to a 2-hydroxy-1,2,3,4-tetrahydro derivative is a general acid-catalyzed addition at the 2,3,5,6-position[183]. This suggestion is mainly based on the fact that no anionic intermediate could be demonstrated.

(c) *Significance of addition reactions*

It has already been mentioned that the addition reactions are favored in the presence of dehydrogenases. This is of practical value in the study of the mechanism of action of dehydrogenases. However, in addition, triosephosphate dehydrogenase represents a special case. The muscle enzyme when interacting with NAD shows a broad absorption band around 365 mμ which has been attributed to a mercaptan addition[322] and to a charge-transfer complex between tryptophan and NAD[70,234]. Spectrally, if the absorption represents an addition reaction, it may be a 1,2-addition. The interaction of NAD and this enzyme will be discussed later (see Section 8, p. 64). Interestingly enough an interaction between NADH and the enzyme also occurs, which probably represents an addition reaction. The enzyme forms, from NADH, a new nucleotide, called NADH–X[65,329]. This nucleotide shows great similarity to the acid-modification product of NADH: it is a tetrahydro-NAD with a maximum around 290 mμ. It is, however, not the primary acid product of NADH since NADH–X is reconverted to NADH with an enzyme from yeast[275], while the acid-modification product is not. It may be noted here that NADH–X is actually a constituent of muscle triosephosphate dehydrogenase as ordinarily isolated[312].

6. Preparation and properties of analogues of NAD

The study of the mechanisms of pyridine nucleotide dependent reactions has been greatly aided by the present availability of structural variants of NAD and NADP. There is now available a long list of analogues with structural modifications in the pyridine ring, the purine ring or the carbohydrate and phosphate moieties.

The original analogue was actually prepared quite early by Schlenk *et al.*[348] when they treated NAD with nitrous acid to obtain nicotinamide–hypoxanthine dinucleotide. This derivative was later again prepared by Kaplan *et al.* by both chemical and enzymatic deamination[202]. This analogue was found to be actually capable of replacing NAD in a variety of enzymatic reactions[317,348]. A second observation greatly stimulated the preparation of further analogues. It had long been known that nicotinamide inhibited the splitting of the NAD molecule at the nicotinamide–ribose linkage by NADases from various sources[154,263,264,268]. The mechanism of this inhibition was found to be an exchange reaction between free nicotinamide and the nicotinamide in the NAD molecule[479]. It was possible, in fact, to make ^{14}C-labelled NAD through the action of a NADase on NAD in the presence of ^{14}C-labelled nicotinamide. This exchange reaction prompted the theory that the antituberculous drug, isonicotinic acid hydrazide (INH), might act in a similar way. Indeed, the drug proved to have a strongly inhibitory action on a variety of animal tissue NADases[480]. There was a species difference in sensitivity towards INH but not to nicotinamide: enzymes from ruminants and birds were inhibited by INH much more than those from other animals such as the pig. This prompted a classification into so-called INH-sensitive and -insensitive enzymes, classically represented by the beef-spleen and pig-brain enzymes, respectively. In the latter case it turned out that an isonicotinic acid hydrazide analogue of NAD was formed rapidly in which the INH replaced the nicotinamide in the molecule[480,481]. Since the rate of NAD disappearance was equal to the rate of NADase reaction, the pig-brain enzyme appeared to be "insensitive" to INH. The basis of the inhibition of the "sensitive" enzymes by INH is not certain. However, some analogue is formed and it is possibly the formed analogue which is the actual inhibitor of the enzymes[145,481]. One NAD-splitting enzyme remained apparently fundamentally different: *Neurospora* NADase. The inhibition of this enzyme by nicotinamide was very slight and was not based on an exchange reaction. However, the addition of ergothioneine imparts nicotinamide sensitivity to this enzyme also, and the enzyme will exchange labelled nicotinamide in the presence of this betaine[148]. The specificity of the *Neurospora* enzyme in the absence of ergothioneine has been of great benefit for the removal of residual NAD from analogue preparations.

The effect of a variety of bases has been tested on the splitting of NAD and NADP by animal tissue pyridine nucleotidases. Not only do a very large number of pyridine derivatives exert an effect[200,263,480], but also a number of pyrimidines, pyrazines, pyridazines, imidazoles, pyrazoles, thiazoles, triazoles and thiadiazoles affect the rate of NAD splitting[263,480]. When such

References p. 88

TABLE III

ANALOGUES OF NAD PREPARED

Compound number	Substituent	Reference[a]	Method of preparation[b]	Enzymatically active[c]
(I) Alteration in nicotinamide mononucleotide moiety				
(A) Altered pyridine rings				
(a) Substituents on pyridine ring in place of 3-carboxamide group				
1	3 —H	196	A-1	No
2	3 —C(=O)H	196, 198	A-1	Yes
3	3 —C(=O)—CH_3	196, 198	A-1	Yes
4	3 —C(=O)—$CH(CH_3)_2$	15, 16	A-1	Yes
5	3 —C(=O)—CH_2CH_3	192	A-1	Yes
6	3 —C(=O)—$CH_2CH_2CH_3$	192	A-1	Yes
7	3 —C(=O)—C_6H_5	15, 16	A-1	Yes
8	3 —C(=O)OH	246	B-4(9) C	No
9	3 —C(=O)—OC_2H_5	246	A-1	No
10	3 —C(=O)—NHOH	15, 16	A-1	Yes
11	3 —C(=O)—$NHNH_2$	15, 16	A-1	Yes
12	3 —CH_3	196	A-1	No
13	3 —CHOH—CH_3	196	A-1	No

TABLE III (*continued*)

Compound number	*Substituent*	*Reference*[a]	*Method of preparation*[b]	*Enzymatically active*[c]
14	3 —CH=NOH	15, 16	A-1	Yes
15	3 $—NH_2$	15, 16, 443	A-1	No
16	3 $—NH—C(=O)CH_3$	15, 16	A-1	No
17	3 $—C(=S)—NH_2$	15, 16	A-1	Yes
18	3 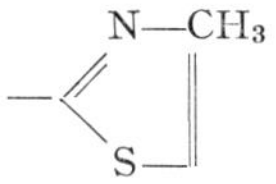 — (thiazolyl ring: N—CH_3, S)	433	A-1	No
19	3 $—CH=CH—C(=O)—NH_2$	15, 16	A-1	No
20	3 $—C(=O)—NH—CH_2CH_3$	196	A-1	No
21	4 $—C(=O)—NHNH_2$	480	A-1	No
22	4 $—C(=O)—NHNH—CH(CH_3)_2$	480	A-1	No
(b) Substituents on pyridine ring in addition to 3-carboxamide group				
23	4 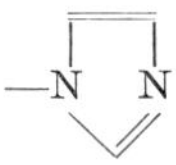 —N (imidazolyl ring, N)	406	B-1	No
24	4 $—CHOH—C(=O)—CH_2OH$	50, 55	B-1	No
25	4 $—CH_2—C(=O)—CH_3$	50, 55	B-1	No
26	4 $—OCH_3$	307	A-1	No
27	4 $—CH_2—CHOH—C(=O)H$	50, 55	B-1	No

References p. 88

TABLE III (*continued*)

Compound number	Substituent	Reference[a]	Method of preparation[b]	Enzymatically active[c]
28	4 —CH_3	443	A-1	No
29	5 —CH_3	192, 443	A-1	No
30	5 —NH_2	443	A-1	No
31	6 —NH_2	102	A-1	No
	(B) Replacement of the pyridine ring			
32	4-amino-5-carboxamide-imidazole	10	A-2	No
33	5-(β-ethylamino)-imidazole (histamine)	8	A-2	No
34	imidazole	6	A-2	No
35	5-(2-amino-2-carboxyethyl)-imidazole (histidine)	6	A-2	No
36	5-(2-acetylaminoethyl)-imidazole (acetylhistamine)	6	A-2	No
37	2-(β-ethylamino)-thiadiazole	71	A-1	No
38	4-methyl-5-(β-hydroxyethyl)-thiazole	412	A-1	No
39	benzimidazole	6	A-2	No
40	hypoxanthine	6	A-2	No
41	adenine	362	B-3	No
42	3-carboxamido-4-keto-1,4-dihydro-pyridine (4-pyridone)	308	B-1	No
43	2- and 6-pyridones: 3-carboxamido-2-keto-1,2-dihydropyridine	248	B-2	No
	(II) Alterations in the adenylic acid moiety			
	(A) Replacement of the adenine ring			
44	hydrogen	310, 362	A-5 (45)	Yes
45	nicotinamide	124, 310, 362	B-3	Yes
46	hypoxanthine	202, 348	B-4 (NAD)	Yes

TABLE III (*continued*)

Compound number	*Substituent*	*Reference*[a]	*Method of preparation*[b]	*Enzymatically active*[c]
47	6-(β-hydroxyethylamino)-purine	460	B-2	Yes
48	1-(β-hydroxyethyl)-6-aminopurine	460	B-2	Yes
49	6-mercaptopurine	22	A-3, B-3	Yes
50	uracil	124	B-3	Yes
51	cytosine	310	B-3	Yes
(B) Replacement of the ribose moiety				
52	deoxyribose	124, 221	A-3, B-3	Yes
(III) Double alteration in the molecule				
(A) Pyridine and purine				
53	3-acetylpyridine–hypoxanthine dinucleotide	363, 409	B-4 (3)	Yes
54	3-carbonylpyridine–hypoxanthine dinucleotide	363, 409	B-4 (2)	Yes
55	3-carboxamido-4-(1-imidazolyl)-pyridine–hypoxanthine dinucleotide	406	B-4 (23)	No
56	3-acetylpyridine-riboside-diphosphate ribose	310	B-4 (3)	Yes
(B) Ribose and purine				
57	nicotinamide–thymidylate dinucleotide	124	B-3	?
(IV) Alteration in the pyrophosphate part				
58	NAD-monomethyl ester	311	B-4	No
59	NAD-dimethyl ester	311	B-4	No
60	insertion of a third phosphate	124	B-3	?
(V) Miscellaneous analogues tested for enzymatic activity				
61	nicotinamide mononucleotide	310	A-4	Yes

References p. 88

TABLE III (*continued*)

Compound number	*Substituent*	*Reference*[a]	*Method of preparation*[b]	*Enzymatically active*[c]
62	nicotinamide mononucleotide dimethylester	311	B-4 (59)	No
63	3-acetylpyridine mononucleotide	310	B-4 (3)	Yes
64	the α-isomer of NAD	199	C	No

[a] The reference refers to the publication in which the analogue preparation is described in some detail or in which the enzymatic testing is reported. Literature included through May, 1964.

[b] *Preparation methods employed.* Parentheses when used enclose number of parent compound shown elsewhere in table.

A. Enzymatic

1. The exchange of the nicotinamide portion of NAD through the action of pig-brain NADase.
2. Same, using the beef-spleen enzyme.
3. Synthesis using NAD-pyrophosphorylase.
4. Degradation from the corresponding pyridine–purine dinucleotide.
5. Hydrolysis with NADase from the analogue indicated in parenthesis.

B. Chemical

1. Oxidation of the corresponding addition product to the nucleotide.
2. Reaction of the nucleotide with the appropriate small chemical.
3. Synthesis through the linkage of monophosphates.
4. Alteration of the corresponding nucleotide.

C. By isolation from natural sources

[c] Enzymatically active indicates that the analogue can replace NAD in at least some of the dehydrogenase reactions. Many are, in addition, substrates for pig-brain or beef-spleen NADase and all dinucleotides that have been tested are substrates for nucleotide pyrophosphatase.

an inhibition is observed with a "sensitive" enzyme, in many cases a rapid exchange can be demonstrated with an "insensitive" enzyme. With this exchange reaction and the large structural liberty allowed by the pig-brain enzyme it has been possible to make a variety of NAD analogues. Table III lists the various analogues so far prepared. Many analogues are not reducible by chemical means; however, many others can be reduced chemically and even enzymatically, though the reactivity of analogues varies with different enzymes. The outstanding analogue in this group has been the 3-acetylpyridine analogue[196] which is quite often capable of replacing NAD[198].

The great usefulness of this derivative and of a later analogue, thionicotinamide–AD[15] which is also enzymatically active[16], lies in the fact that they have a more positive redox potential and thus favor oxidation of alcohols in alcohol dehydrogenase-like reactions. Thus the oxidation–reduction potential[196] of the acetylpyridine–adenine dinucleotide system is

−0.248 V, the thionicotinamide–adenine dinucleotide has a redox potential[16] of −0.285 V, both to be based[23,48,74,335,336] on a value for NAD of −0.320 V. While the data on the analogues are not yet certain it appears that similar relative figures hold for the corresponding analogues of NADP. Although equilibrium data indicate that NADP itself is somewhat higher than NAD, direct measurements indicate no significant difference[337].

After the success with both deamino-NAD and 3-acetylpyridine-AD it was a logical extension to prepare doubly altered analogues through chemical deamination of the corresponding adenine containing analogues[363], resulting in such derivatives as acetylpyridine–hypoxanthine dinucleotide. The general method for preparation of the nucleotides has been described[207] and several are commercially available.

In addition to the analogues derived through exchange, further type analogues have been made. It proved to be feasible to synthesize NAD analogues chemically through the coupling of nicotinamide mononucleotides to nucleoside 5′-monophosphates[124] such as deoxy-adenylic acid, thymidylic acid, and uridylic acid. Even an NADP analogue has been made where the third phosphate is between the two phosphates to give nicotinamide–ribose-phosphate–phosphate–phosphate-ribose–adenine. During these studies there was obtained as a by-product the symmetrical anhydride of nicotinamide: nicotinamide–ribose-phosphate–phosphate-ribose–nicotinamide. That derivative had previously been found as a product of the action of trifluoroacetic anhydride on NAD[362]. The deoxyadenylic acid-containing analogue had also been prepared enzymatically through the reaction of nicotinamide mononucleotide with deoxy-ATP[221].

In addition to the synthetic analogues a number have been prepared through chemical modification of NAD. Thus the oxidation of addition-reaction products with ferricyanide has resulted in the 4-(1,3-dihydroxy-2-keto-propyl)-pyridine-3-carboxamide–adenine dinucleotide from the addition product between dihydroxyacetone and NAD[50,55] and in the 4-(1-imidazolyl)-pyridine-3-carboxamide–adenine dinucleotide and 4-(1-imidazolyl)-pyridine-3-carboxamide–hypoxanthine dinucleotide from the addition product between imidazole and NAD[406]. Direct oxidation of NAD gave the NAD-pyridones[248].

The reaction between ethylene oxide and NAD also produces stable modifications. In this manner one obtains nicotinamide-1-(2-hydroxyethyl)–adenine dinucleotide and nicotinamide-6-(β-hydroxyethyl)–adenine dinucleotide[460].

It is of special interest that there are a number of naturally occurring analogues of NAD. The α-isomer[199] has been discussed previously (Section 2, p. 9). However, in addition one may find the nicotinic acid analogue in nature[26,246,247,313]. This analogue is implicated in the biosynthesis of NAD[313] but it has been very difficult to prepare by an exchange reaction through NADases[26,200,313]. The yield is so small that a more efficient means of preparation is the chemical hydrolysis of the ethylnicotinate–adenine dinucleotide[247]. All the analogues prepared so far for which data are reported have been summarized in Table III.

There is no certain indication for the majority of these analogues that there might exist a physiological role. The acetylpyridine analogue may exist *in vivo* after the administration of acetylpyridine[206]. There are some interesting speculations that the histamine analogue, in which nicotinamide is replaced by histamine through a ribose-ring-nitrogen bond[8] may be formed *in vivo* since ring-ribosylated histamine and histamine degradation products are major excretory products of these imidazole derivatives. There has also been some speculation[146,188] that the pyridone derivative of NAD may be involved in oxidative phosphorylation. However, pyridones prepared by oxidation of NAD with ferricyanide showed no biological activity[248].

While the analogues of NAD are very numerous indeed, the analogues of NADP have not been as widely studied. Since pig-brain NADase will attack both NAD and NADP, analogues of the latter coenzyme may be and have been formed in a corresponding manner. There is, however, one analogue peculiar to NADP and that is the 3′-phosphate isomer[361]. This isomer is active with a number of, but not all, dehydrogenases which normally require NADP.

7. Mechanism of action of simple dehydrogenases

There is a class of NAD and NADP-dependent dehydrogenases where the oxidizable substrate is an alcohol, primary amine or hemi-acetal. The product of dehydrogenation is the corresponding aldehyde, ketone, or lactone. These enzymes are generally classified as *simple dehydrogenases* in contrast to *complex dehydrogenases*. In the oxidation catalyzed by the latter, phosphorylation accompanies the reaction (see Section 8, p. 63). The simple dehydrogenases have a number of properties in common and it is often thought that the mechanism of catalysis is based on a single principle. This idea is maintained here, since it is by far the most likely.

There are obviously levels of understanding of the mechanism by which dehydrogenases, and any other enzyme for that matter, exert their catalytic influence. The first is the participation of enzyme–coenzyme and enzyme–substrate complexes and the stoichiometry of these interactions. Later one may inquire into the nature of the linkage and the functional groups involved in such binding. Finally one may hope to ascertain the actual process on a molecular level. Progress at all 3 levels has been made and the order in which this will be discussed is the one given above.

(a) *Kinetics and mechanism*

It is possible to consider, *a priori*, reaction sequences for a dehydrogenase where the overall reaction is:

$$S_1 + S_2 \rightleftharpoons S_1' + S_2'$$

catalyzed by the enzyme. Two main types of mechanisms can be given. First, the enzyme proper participates in the overall reaction. Thus the sequence of reactions would be:

$$\text{Enzyme} + \text{substrate} \rightleftharpoons \text{product} + \text{reduced enzyme}$$
$$\text{Reduced enzyme} + \text{NAD} \rightleftharpoons \text{enzyme} + \text{NADH}$$

Since a direct hydrogen transfer is involved (see Section 3, p. 17) this would imply a stable enzyme–hydrogen bond. Such a reaction sequence appears unlikely on the basis of available evidence. First of all the kinetics of the reaction rule this mechanism out as will be described a little later. There is more direct evidence: such a sequence would require that the dehydrogenase catalyzed a transhydrogenase reaction, but none of the dehydrogenases tested so far has ever catalyzed the transfer of hydrogen from one NAD molecule to another[203,205,453]. There are, both in bacterial preparations[82] and animal tissues[151,204,369], transhydrogenases, enzymes which catalyze the transfer of hydrogen from one pyridine nucleotide to another without the intervention of substrate. However, these enzymes are not dehydrogenases. On the other hand, the steroid-stimulated transhydrogenase reactions in cytoplasm are probably a series of dehydrogenases working on a common steroid hormone substrate[459].

A modified enzyme would also require an oxidation–reduction reaction between substrates. Such reactions do occur, especially with horse-liver alcohol dehydrogenase[2,193,218,407]. However, in all cases NAD is a requirement.

The alternative to a free reduced enzyme as intermediate is that, during catalysis, a ternary complex between enzyme, coenzyme and substrate is formed, so that the direct hydrogen transfer can be mediated. As mentioned previously (see Section 3, p. 18), the possibility remains open that a reduced enzyme may be an intermediate when hydrogen is transferred within the ternary complex. There are two major possible reaction sequences for formation of the ternary complex. A random order of addition of the substrate and cofactor may occur so that all possible permutations of enzyme, coenzyme and substrate combinations exist. Alternatively, an ordered sequence of events might occur so that the substrate binds only to the enzyme—coenzyme complex or *vice versa*.

There are strong indications that the latter principle of ordered addition holds. The first evidence for a compulsory binding order was given by the studies of Schwert on lactic dehydrogenase. He showed, using ultracentrifugational separation techniques, that beef-heart lactic dehydrogenase bound NAD or NADH readily but that no lactate–enzyme or pyruvate–enzyme complexes could be demonstrated[380]. This did not necessarily indicate the absence of such an intermediate in the process of catalysis, however. Many attempts have been made, therefore, to formalize the kinetics of reactions between two substrates catalyzed by an enzyme, so that kinetic criteria could be used to determine the reaction order[4,35,76–78,90,96,352,470]. The material described by such theoretical papers is often difficult to compare since no agreement exists on the symbols used. This makes evaluation of experimental results a difficult task. Bloomfield *et al.*[36] have summarized the data obtained by kinetic means and have translated some of them into uniform notation. A similar summary may be found in the paper by Cleland[76]. However, for the present purpose the principle involved in distinguishing reaction sequences by kinetic means can be illustrated better using the method and notation introduced by Dalziel[90]. Dalziel assumes that a specific number of enzyme–coenzyme or enzyme–substrate complexes exist, an assumption which simplifies the theoretical approach. Bloomfield *et al.* elaborate for an unspecified number of intermediates[35]. In Dalziel's notation the general rate equation of the reaction becomes:

$$\frac{E_0}{v} = \Phi_0 + \frac{\Phi_1}{[S_1]} + \frac{\Phi_2}{[S_2]} + \frac{\Phi_{12}}{[S_1]\,[S_2]} \qquad (1)$$

where S_1 and S_2 denote substrates, E the enzyme and Φ_0 etc. kinetic constants. The reverse reaction obeys the same type equation but with different constants, designated by primes. This general equation covers a number of possible reaction sequences. In each possible reaction sequence the constants Φ have a different relation to the kinetic rate constants of the intermediate steps involved in the catalysis. In Table IV the different types of reaction sequences which obey Eqn. 1 are tabulated together with the meaning of the kinetic constants. Two of these possibilities have already been discussed and rejected, namely: a reversible oxidation–reduction of the enzyme, whether a binary complex is formed or not. The equation will also cover both a totally random order of addition of substrate and coenzyme, provided all complexes are in rapid equilibrium except one*, and a compulsory substrate-binding order. The latter can be subdivided into types based on whether one or more kinetically significant ternary complexes exist or whether no kinetically significant ternary complex exists (the so-called Theorell–Chance mecha-

* If these criteria are not met, then the random order of addition yields non-linear rate equations[76,96,470]. Such general cases are treated in a complete manner by Wong and Hanes[470].

nism[388]). These many mechanisms can be distinguished on theoretical grounds on the basis of the relationships between the kinetic constants Φ and the equilibrium constant, and from relationships between the kinetic constants[90]. This is again shown in Table IV. As an example: for the Theorell–Chance mechanism and only for that mechanism the following three relationships are fulfilled:

$$\Phi_0' = \frac{\Phi_1 \Phi_2}{\Phi_{12}}$$

$$\Phi_0 = \frac{\Phi_1' \Phi_2'}{\Phi_{12}'}$$

$$K_{\text{eq.}} = \frac{\Phi_{12}'}{\Phi_{12}} = \frac{\Phi_0' \Phi_1' \Phi_2'}{\Phi_0 \Phi_1 \Phi_2}$$

Similar relationships were pointed out by Alberty[4,35]. It is clear, that from a determination of the constants Φ_0, Φ_1, Φ_2 and Φ_{12} one can theoretically make a decision regarding the mechanism. In theory the constants are derived fairly well. A plot of E/v_0 *vs.* $1/[S_1]$ holding $[S_2]$ constant gives a straight line. Several of these plots at varying S_2 concentrations give a family of straight lines each with its own intercept and slope. If one then plots the intercepts *versus* $1/[S_2]$, one again obtains a straight line with a slope of Φ_2 and an intercept of Φ_0. If the slopes of the original lines are plotted against $1/[S_2]$ one obtains a straight line* with a slope of Φ_{12} and an intercept of Φ_1. The practical difficulties in the kinetic method lie in the accuracy required. Dalziel himself applied his criteria to horse-liver alcohol dehydrogenase and concluded that there were deviations from the originally accepted Theorell–Chance mechanism[92]. He was aware of the difficulties inherent in the experiment due to the purity of the reagents, especially NADH[91], but the magnitude of such effects was not realized until later[93] when the presence of a powerful inhibitor in NADH preparations became known. Thus the

* When one plots E/v_0 *vs.* $1/S_1$ one has a plot of

$$\frac{E}{v_0} = \Phi_0 + \frac{\Phi_2}{S_2} + \left(\Phi_1 + \frac{\Phi_{12}}{S_2}\right)\frac{1}{S_1}$$

Two secondary plots then give the following:

$$\text{since} \quad \text{slope} = \Phi_1 + \frac{\Phi_{12}}{S_2}$$

a plot of slope *vs.* $1/S_2$ gives a straight line with slope Φ_{12} and intercept Φ_1; and

$$\text{since} \quad \text{intercept} = \Phi_0 + \frac{\Phi_2}{S_2}$$

a plot of intercept *vs.* $1/S_2$ gives a straight line with slope Φ_2 and intercept Φ_0.

References p. 88

TABLE IV

ALTERNATIVE MECHANISMS FOR DEHYDROGENASE ACTION, AS EXPRESSED BY DALZIEL'S EQUATION

$$\frac{E_0}{v} = \Phi_0 + \frac{\Phi_1}{[S_1]} + \frac{\Phi_2}{[S_2]} + \frac{\Phi_{12}}{[S_1][S_2]}$$

Mechanism	Kinetic coefficients				Relationships between coefficients	Equilibrium constants
	Φ_0	Φ_1	Φ_2	Φ_{12}		
I. *Random-order addition, rate-limiting step interconversion of ternary complexes* $E+S_1 \rightleftharpoons ES_1\ (K_1)$; $ES'_1 \rightleftharpoons E_1+S'_1\ (K'_1)$ $E+S_2 \rightleftharpoons ES_2\ (K_2)$; $ES'_2 \rightleftharpoons E+S'_2\ (K'_2)$ $ES_1+S_2 \rightleftharpoons ES_1S_2\ (K_3)$; $ES'_1S'_2 \rightleftharpoons ES'_1+S'_2\ (K'_3)$ $ES_2+S_1 \rightleftharpoons ES_1S_2\ (K_4)$; $ES'_1S'_2 \rightleftharpoons ES'_2+S'_1\ (K'_4)$ $ES_1S_2 \underset{k'}{\overset{k}{\rightleftharpoons}} ES'_1S'_2$	$\frac{1}{k}$	$\frac{K_4}{k}$	$\frac{K_3}{k}$	$\frac{K_1K_3}{k}$		Φ'_{12}/Φ_{12}
I'. *Binding of substrates is independent but random-order addition exists:* This is case I where $K_1=K_4$ and $K_2=K_3$	$\frac{1}{k}$	$\frac{K_4}{k}$	$\frac{K_3}{k}$	$\frac{K_3K_4}{k}$	$\frac{\Phi_1\Phi_2}{\Phi_{12}} = \Phi_0$	$\Phi'_{12}/\Phi_{12} = \frac{\Phi_0\Phi'_1\Phi'_2}{\Phi'_0\Phi_1\Phi_2}$
II. *Compulsory order of reaction, two ternary complexes exist* $E+S_1 \underset{k_2}{\overset{k_1}{\rightleftharpoons}} ES_1$ $ES_1+S_2 \underset{k_4}{\overset{k_3}{\rightleftharpoons}} ES_1S_2$ $ES_1S_2 \underset{k'}{\overset{k}{\rightleftharpoons}} ES'_1S'_2$ $ES'_1S'_2 \underset{k'_3}{\overset{k'_4}{\rightleftharpoons}} ES'_1+S'_2$ $ES'_1 \underset{k'_1}{\overset{k'_2}{\rightleftharpoons}} E+S'_1$	$\frac{1}{k'_2}+\frac{1}{k'_4}+\frac{k'}{kk'_4}+\frac{1}{k}$	$\frac{1}{k_1}$	$\frac{k_4k'_4+k_4k'+k'_4k}{k_3k'_4k}$	$\frac{k_2(k_4k'_4+k_4k'+k'_4k)}{k_1k_3k'_4k}$	$\frac{\Phi_1\Phi_2}{\Phi_{12}} < \Phi'_0$	$\frac{\Phi'_{12}}{\Phi_{12}}$

II′. *Compulsory order of reaction but only one ternary complex exists* $E+S_1 \underset{k_2}{\overset{k_1}{\rightleftharpoons}} ES_1$ $ES_1+S_2 \underset{k_4}{\overset{k_3}{\rightleftharpoons}} EXY \underset{k'_3}{\overset{k'_4}{\rightleftharpoons}} E\,S'_1+S'_2$ $ES'_1 \underset{k'_1}{\overset{k'_2}{\rightleftharpoons}} E+S'_1$	$\frac{1}{k'_2}+\frac{1}{k'_4}$	$\frac{1}{k_1}$	$\frac{k_4+k'_4}{k_3k'_4}$	$\frac{k_2(k_4+k'_4)}{k_1k_3k'_4}$	$\frac{\Phi_1\Phi_2}{\Phi_{12}} < \Phi'_0$	$\frac{\Phi'_{12}}{\Phi_{12}}$
II″. *Compulsory order of reaction but no kinetically significant ternary complex (Theorell–Chance mechanism)* $E+S_1 \underset{k_2}{\overset{k_1}{\rightleftharpoons}} ES_1$ $ES_1+S_2 \underset{k'_3}{\overset{k_3}{\rightleftharpoons}} ES'_1+S'_2$ $ES'_1 \underset{k'_1}{\overset{k'_2}{\rightleftharpoons}} E+S'_1$	$\frac{1}{k'_2}$	$\frac{1}{k_1}$	$\frac{1}{k_3}$	$\frac{k_2}{k_1k_3}$	$\frac{\Phi_1\Phi_2}{\Phi_{12}} = \Phi'_0$ $\frac{\Phi'_1\Phi'_2}{\Phi'_{12}} = \Phi_0$	$\frac{\Phi'_{12}}{\Phi_{12}} = \frac{\Phi'_0\Phi'_1\Phi'_2}{\Phi_0\Phi_1\Phi_2}$
III. *A single ternary complex exists* $E+S_1+S_2 \underset{k_4}{\overset{k_3}{\rightleftharpoons}} EXY \underset{k'_3}{\overset{k'_4}{\rightleftharpoons}} E+S'_1+S'_2$	$\frac{1}{k'_4}$	0	0	$\frac{k_4+k'_4}{k_3k'_4}$	—	$\frac{\Phi'_{12}}{\Phi_{12}}$
IV. *The enzyme is modified in the course of reaction* $E+S_1 \underset{k_2}{\overset{k_1}{\rightleftharpoons}} EX \underset{k'_1}{\overset{k'_2}{\rightleftharpoons}} E'+S'_1$ $E'+S_2 \underset{k_4}{\overset{k_3}{\rightleftharpoons}} EY \underset{k'_3}{\overset{k'_4}{\rightleftharpoons}} E+S'_2$	$\frac{1}{k'_2}+\frac{1}{k'_4}$	$\frac{k_2+k'_2}{k_1k'_2}$	$\frac{k_4+k'_4}{k_3k'_4}$	0	—	$\frac{\Phi'_1\Phi'_2}{\Phi_1\Phi_2}$
IV′. *No enzyme substrate compounds; modified enzyme* $E+S_1 \underset{k'_1}{\overset{k_1}{\rightleftharpoons}} E'+S'_1$ $E'+S_2 \underset{k'_2}{\overset{k_2}{\rightleftharpoons}} E+S'_2$	0	$\frac{1}{k_1}$	$\frac{1}{k_2}$	0	—	$\frac{\Phi'_1\Phi'_2}{\Phi_1\Phi_2}$

References p. 88

Theorell–Chance mechanism became again more acceptable. Later kinetic analyses have substantiated this[94,389].

Although interpretation is often difficult, nevertheless, many interesting kinetic studies have been made on dehydrogenases. Already mentioned have been the studies of Theorell on liver-alcohol dehydrogenase[94,388,389]. It might be of interest to name a few more: Raval and Wolfe on malic dehydrogenase[331], the thorough studies of Schwert on heart lactic dehydrogenase[380,462], on muscle lactic dehydrogenase by Zewe and Fromm[482], on rabbit erythrocyte lactic dehydrogenase by Ottolenghi and Denstedt[300], yeast alcohol dehydrogenase by Nygaard and Theorell[295], and on ribitol dehydrogenase by Fromm and coworkers[141,292]. It is possible nowadays to use computer solutions of kinetic data[25]. The work of Mahler and others[24,267,360,395] has shown how additional information can be derived evaluating the isotope effects which can be observed when the transferred hydrogen is a deuterium atom.

In all the studies quoted it may be fair to state than an ordered addition scheme is not violated kinetically and that at least malic dehydrogenase and liver alcohol dehydrogenase obey the simplified Theorell–Chance mechanism under the conditions so far examined while other dehydrogenases may be more complex.

In all this discussion an oversimplification has been introduced, namely the participation of a hydrogen ion has been ignored. Most experiments are run with a constant hydrogen-ion concentration, so that this complication does not arise. Inclusion of hydrogen ion as a variable makes kinetic investigation exceedingly complex. An elaborate study of pH effects has been made for lactic dehydrogenase[462], and malic dehydrogenase[332] while for other dehydrogenases kinetic constants at several pH values are known. One type enzyme in this class, however, cannot be treated in this simplified manner, namely glutamic dehydrogenase, because an ammonium ion is also involved*.

$$\text{Glutamate}^- + \text{NADP}^+ \rightleftharpoons \alpha\text{-ketoglutarate}^{2-} + \text{NADPH} + \text{NH}_4^+ + \text{H}^+$$

This system has been studied in some detail by Frieden[137–139]. Again a definite order of reaction: enzyme→enzyme–coenzyme→ternary complex, seemed indicated. In the reverse reaction it seemed that the ammonium ion was bound *prior* to TPNH.

It is clear that the analysis of kinetic behavior of dehydrogenases is only useful if the enzyme concentration is kept constant. More recently it is becoming clear that the simple dehydrogenases are composed of several

* Bloomfield *et al.*[36] suggest that for glutamic dehydrogenase "... the stoichiometry is like that of all the dehydrogenase-catalyzed reactions, but NH_4^+ is produced rather than H^+." This is however incorrect at pH values where the enzyme is active.

chains. These chains, for certain enzymes, associate and dissociate under a variety of conditions. Therefore the actual amount of active enzyme present can vary during kinetic investigations. Thus glutamic dehydrogenase actually dissociates in the presence of NADH[136,138], thus making the use of NADP mandatory in the kinetic experiments[137]. But such dissociation of glutamic dehydrogenase is also found through the action of acid[129,131], detergents[182], alkali[130,131,140], urea[469], *o*-phenanthroline[136], steroids[476,477], phenanthrene and other hydrocarbons[474], silver ions[338], thyroxin[469], dilution[128,244], and dioxane[67]. Similar ready dissociation has been observed for glucose-6-phosphate dehydrogenase[220], lactic dehydrogenase[19,284], yeast alcohol dehydrogenase[165,185] and α-glycerophosphate dehydrogenase[405,410]. Claims have been made that the dissociated form of glutamic dehydrogenase has a different substrate specificity from the undissociated form[475–477], though this has been disputed[127]. Be that as it may, all the above makes it clear that kinetic evaluation of reaction mechanisms is very difficult indeed and with the present state of experimentation almost an impossible undertaking.

(b) *Enzyme–coenzyme interaction*

From the above it is safe, however, to assume that there are enzyme–coenzyme complexes which are important in the enzyme catalysis. As has been hinted at before, enzyme–coenzyme complexes can be demonstrated by physical means as well. Four methods have been used: (*1*) ultracentrifugational separation and equilibrium dialysis; (*2*) spectrophotometric analysis of enzyme–coenzyme complexes; (*3*) fluorimetric analysis of reduced coenzyme–enzyme mixtures, and (*4*) optical rotatory dispersion[254].

The first is the most general but technically less precise. It has been successfully applied to lactic dehydrogenase[380], yeast alcohol dehydrogenase[164], liver alcohol dehydrogenase[385], α-glycerophosphate dehydrogenase[414], and glutamic dehydrogenase[244].

The second method used is the spectrophotometric one .This is based on the fact that certain dehydrogenases (but not all) bind reduced NAD in such a way as to alter the absorption spectrum of the nucleotide through a shift of the 340-mμ maximum to shorter wavelengths (see Section 2, p. 12). This was first observed for liver alcohol dehydrogenase[387] and was later found to occur with beef-heart lactic dehydrogenase as well when low temperature was used[63]. These studies have been greatly benefited through the introduction of the NAD analogues. For instance, the shift in spectrum of beef-heart lactic dehydrogenase is much more readily observed with acetylpyridine–AD or pyridine-3-aldehyde–AD as coenzyme[197]. This type of spectral shift is not general. However, its usefulness is extended when, instead of the reduced

References p. 88

coenzymes, certain NAD-adducts are used, such as those obtained with cyanide, sulfide or bisulfite. One can see a complex between NAD, cyanide and horse-liver alcohol dehydrogenase. This complex is related to the NAD–cyanide complex in the same way that the reduced NADH–enzyme complex is related to the NADH[195,197]. Because of the tight binding, however, the addition reaction between NAD and cyanide appears to be actually favored through the presence of the enzyme. One can observe similar complexes between beef-heart lactic dehydrogenase and the NAD–bisulfite adduct[309,417], the rat-liver lactic dehydrogenase and the NAD–sulfide adduct[384,417] and the rabbit-muscle lactic dehydrogenase and pig-heart malic dehydrogenase and the NAD–bisulfite adduct[308,417].

These studies received a great impetus when it was found that not only the absorption spectrum shifts, but that the fluorescence of NADH is modified as well. The first instance discovered was again liver alcohol dehydrogenase[41]. It was soon found that fluorescence of NADH changes in any or all of several possible ways, which made fluorescence studies very profitable indeed, and extended its usefulness to enzymes which could not be studied spectrophotometrically. Thus one sees fluorescence enhancement, fluorescence quenching, fluorescence-emission shifts and fluorescence polarization (see Section 2, p. 12). A review is given by Velick[423]. Many data have been accumulated from these studies. The fluorescence studies on horse-liver alcohol dehydrogenase[41,390,466], on beef-heart lactic dehydrogenase[358,359,422,461] and skeletal-muscle lactic dehydrogenase[464], rat-liver lactic dehydrogenase[464], malic dehydrogenase[306], and α-glycerophosphate dehydrogenase[17] may be mentioned. From all the studies one generalization can be made (except maybe for glutamic dehydrogenase) namely that *one mole of NAD or NADH binds per unit molecular weight of 35000–40000*. There may be one other exception to this rule, namely α-glycerophosphate dehydrogenase[17], though there is disagreement on the stoichiometry for that enzyme[305,414,423]. Beef-heart glutamic dehydrogenase is a special case, but the size of the actual catalytically active unit is not certain.

That NAD and NADH occupy the same site is clearly shown from an abundance of competition studies in the reports just quoted. Suggestive evidence that this stoichiometry is a true property of the catalytically active molecule is the fact that it corresponds with the metal content of the many dehydrogenases which contain zinc. Thus, alcohol dehydrogenases contain zinc as an intrinsic part of the molecule in amounts stoichiometrically equivalent to the NADH bound. This is 2 per molecule for horse-liver alcohol dehydrogenase and 4 for yeast alcohol dehydrogenase. (For a review, see Vallee[400]). This stoichiometric equivalence seems to hold also for glutamic dehydrogenase and malic dehydrogenase. The finite number of enzyme–coenzyme binding sites determined by physical means suggests that these may be the ones which are intermediates in the catalytic reaction sequence.

A second generalization can be made. *In general, all binding sites appear equal and independent.* Therefore it is possible to derive dissociation constants for the enzyme–NAD and enzyme–NADH complexes. The agreement between the physically determined and kinetically determined values (Table V) leave very little doubt that the binding of NAD is indeed at the "active site" of the dehydrogenase. For horse-liver alcohol dehydrogenase data obtained from equilibrium studies are in general agreement[23]. From the inspection of Table V a third generalization suggests itself, namely that *NADH binds stronger than does NAD* (however, see Section 8, p. 66).

TABLE V

DISSOCIATION CONSTANTS OF ENZYME–COENZYME COMPLEXES[a]

Enzyme	*Coenzyme*	*pH*	*Dissociation constant (molar)*	
			From kinetic data	*From physical data*
Yeast alcohol dehydrogenase	NAD	6.0	$1.7 \cdot 10^{-4}$ (374)	—
		7.15	$2.6 \cdot 10^{-4}$ (374)	$2.6 \cdot 10^{-4}$ (374)
	NADH	6.0	$4.2 \cdot 10^{-5}$ (374)	—
		7.15	$7.1 \cdot 10^{-5}$ (374)	$13.0 \cdot 10^{-5}$ (374)
Liver alcohol dehydrogenase	NAD	7	$1.41 \cdot 10^{-4}$ (374)	$1.6 \cdot 10^{-4}$ (374)
		9	$1.60 \cdot 10^{-5}$ (374)	$1.2 \cdot 10^{-5}$ (374)
	NADH	7	$2.8 \cdot 10^{-7}$ (374)	$3.1 \cdot 10^{-7}$ (374)
		9	$8.6 \cdot 10^{-7}$ (374)	$6.5 \cdot 10^{-7}$ (374)
Lactic dehydrogenase (beef heart)	NAD	7.05	$2.24 \cdot 10^{-4}$ (462)	$3.2 \cdot 10^{-4}$ (380)
		9.05	$1.6 \cdot 10^{-4}$ (462)	—
	NADH	6.98	$3.8 \cdot 10^{-6}$ (462)	—
		9.01	$1.13 \cdot 10^{-5}$ (462)	—
		9.80	—	$1.87 \cdot 10^{-6}$ (464)

[a] Figures between parentheses designate literature references.

The chemistry of the binding site of NAD has not been studied in great detail. There is rather suggestive evidence for the participation of a mercaptan in the binding of NADH since the fluorescence and spectral shifts are abolished by sulfhydryl reagents. This is, however, rather indirect evidence for the participation of sulfhydryl groups. Only recently has direct evidence for a sulfhydryl group *at the active site* appeared. Horse-liver alcohol dehydrogenase can be inhibited by two moles of iodoacetic acid and this inhibition is prevented by NADH[256]. In addition, on the same enzyme it has been possible to covalently attach the analogue 4-methyl-5-(β-hydroxyethyl)-thiazole–AD through oxidation with ferricyanide. Again NAD and NADH protect against the formation of this linkage. The evidence seems to favor a disulfide linkage between analogue and enzyme[413]. However the iodoacetate and analogue bind at different loci, since both can be introduced in the same enzyme molecule. Suggestive evidence of participation of a sulfhydryl group at the active site exists for the lactic dehydrogenase from a variety of sources, since one mole of *p*-chloromercuribenzoate (*p*-CMB) per mole of NAD bound inhibits activity[340]. The confusion which usually exists around such stoichiometry data is readily explained by the fact that the *p*-CMB reaction is very slow with many dehydrogenases. Lactic dehydrogenase is a classical example of such difficulties but they are also encountered with α-glycerophosphate dehydrogenase[312]. On the other hand, yeast alcohol dehydrogenase has an overabundance of sulfhydryl groups which are all very reactive[168].

Not only is there conflict about the role of sulfhydryl groups as binding sites for NAD and NADH but such conflict is also present for the role of the metal as a binding site. *o*-Phenanthroline is an inhibitor of dehydrogenases, competitive with the coenzymes[403]. It has been suggested that *o*-phenanthroline and adenosine-diphosphate ribose do not compete for the same site, even though both compete with NAD and NADH[478]. Many structures for a binary or ternary complex involving the zinc have been postulated.

Attempts have been made to deduce the protein environment of the NADH from the alterations in the fluorescence and from the observed spectral shifts (see Section 2, p. 11). On this basis a positive grouping, such as ε-amino group of lysine has been implicated[228,353]. Previously it was suggested that this shift was due to a hydrophobic environment[355]; while this suggestion was not verified experimentally[353] the existence of a hydrophobic environment on yeast alcohol dehydrogenase is implicated from inhibition studies with N^1-alkyl nicotinamide derivatives[14].

The effect of pH on the binding of NADH shows participation[254] of a group on horse-liver alcohol dehydrogenase with a pK about 10. This group must belong to the protein since no dissociable group on NADH is titratable[355] between pH 5–10. This protein group may be the sulfhydryl group implicated earlier[257,413]. From binding of NAD analogues it can be inferred that neither the carboxamide grouping nor the adenine-amino grouping are essential for binding, though this does not imply that they do not participate. Thus yeast alcohol dehydrogenase becomes labile in the presence of nicotinamide hypoxanthine dinucleotide[409], while horse-liver alcohol dehydrogenase does not distinguish NAD and NHD.

(c) *Substrate binding*

We may, after the foregoing discussion, infer that there is no ready binding site for the substrate on the free dehydrogenase molecule while there is one on the enzyme–coenzyme complex. This then raises the question whether there is an induced alteration in the protein due to the coenzyme, and that such alteration generates a binding site, or whether the coenzyme participates more directly in the binding of the substrate.

There are a number of substances which behave as competitive inhibitors for the substrates on the dehydrogenases. One of the first that was found in this regard is hydroxylamine for horse-liver alcohol dehydrogenase[194]. This compound is an inhibitor, competitive with alcohol. Since the combination of hydroxylamine–NAD–enzyme forms a complex in the case of horse-liver alcohol dehydrogenase which seems to be related to the non-enzymatic NAD–hydroxylamine complex[52], one may suggest that the processes of complex formation and substrate binding are related. Yeast alcohol dehydrogenase forms a similar hydroxylamine–pyridine-3-aldehyde–AD–enzyme complex[408].

Hydroxylamine will only inhibit *alcohol* dehydrogenase in this manner. Thus there is a specificity analogous to a substrate specificity in the action of hydroxylamine. This same phenomenon is even more strikingly shown by the mercaptans which are analogous to the substrates. Thus both yeast and liver alcohol dehydrogenase are inhibited competitively by *n*-alkyl mercaptans in proportion to the activity of the corresponding alcohol and there is a ternary complex between enzyme–coenzyme and mercaptan, some million times more favorable than the interaction between coenzyme and mercaptan alone[417]. α-Mercaptoacids inhibit lactic dehydrogenases[417], and again corresponding with the activity of the substrates of equivalent carbon-chain length[59]. Here, too, a ternary complex, enzyme–coenzyme–mercaptan, can be demonstrated[417]. In addition, formate, which is a competitive inhibitor for ethanol on liver alcohol dehydrogenase lowers the dissociation constant for NAD on that enzyme kinetically, suggesting a ternary enzyme–NAD–formate complex[394]. This is generally true for fatty acids. In addition fatty acid amides are inhibitors for aldehyde and kinetically enzyme–NADH–amide complexes appear likely[394,471] as do enzyme–NAD–amide complexes[471]. Similar conclusions can be drawn for imidazole kinetically.

With the advent of fluorimetric methods the effect of inhibitors was further investigated. By fluorescence techniques ternary complexes have been implicated for enzyme–NADH and –imidazole and –fatty acid amides[390,465,466]. However, completely contrary interpretations have been made of the effect of imidazole and formate[255]. Pyrazole also forms a ternary pyrazole–enzyme–NAD complex[393]. In this case a pyrazole–NAD complex can be implicated spectrophotometrically, and the action of pyrazole may well be completely analogous to mercaptans. This could indeed also be the case for imidazole which also gives addition complexes in the absence of enzyme[406]. Lactic dehydrogenase also shows evidence fluorimetrically for interaction of inhibitors of the substrate with the enzyme–coenzyme complexes. A large number of α-hydroxy carboxylic acids enhance the fluo-

References p. 88

rescence of the NADH–lactic dehydrogenase complex[463]. However oxamate, which is a competitive inhibitor of pyruvate, decreases the fluorescence[463].

The evidence for ternary complexes is further substantiated by the fact that the inhibitor, oxamate, will bind to NAD– or NADH–lactic dehydrogenase complexes as indicated by ultracentrifugational separation techniques, but not to free enzyme[293]. Approximately one mole of oxamate per mole of coenzyme is bound. The dissociation constant for oxamate from the enzyme–NADH complex is measured by ultracentrifugational separation techniques to be $1.1 \cdot 10^{-5}M$, while fluorimetrically a value of $1.2 \cdot 10^{-5}M$ is found[463]. Interestingly, the dissociation of oxamate from the enzyme–NAD complex is much greater, namely $1.7 \cdot 10^{-4}M$. These stoichiometry data for oxamate are different from the ones arrived at through spectrophotometric titration of inhibitors, since for the mercaptan analogues and hydroxylamine usually only half the number of complexes are formed as there are binding sites for coenzyme[417]. The difference is not resolved, though it is possible that the answer lies in the fact that in the one case only the binding of the inhibitor as a complex with NAD is measured while in the case of oxamate and oxalate the actual binding of the molecule to the enzyme is ascertained.

The substrates themselves can be inhibitory, in fact this is fairly common for dehydrogenases. There are major exceptions: thus for glutamic dehydrogenase[137] and for yeast alcohol dehydrogenase[295] increases in substrate concentrations result in deviations from the predicted rates toward higher activities. Other enzymes, though, are subject to substrate inhibition, such as liver alcohol dehydrogenase[388,392], lactic dehydrogenases[153], and malic dehydrogenase[98,333] for oxaloacetate, while malate produces substrate activation[98,331]. The data obtained to date are too sparse to draw conclusions about the mechanism of this inhibition. Suggestions can be made from the data: the effect of oxaloacetate on malic dehydrogenase seems to indicate that there are two types of inhibitions exerted by oxaloacetic acid. One could envision at least two plausible explanations for substrate inhibition: In a compulsory order sequence of enzyme→enzyme–coenzyme→enzyme–coenzyme–substrate the formation of an "abortive" enzyme–substrate complex would be inhibitory, and also the formation of ternary complexes between enzyme–reduced coenzyme–oxidized substrate (or *vice versa*) could be formed*. In malic dehydrogenase both might apply. It is obvious that

---

* In the Dalziel notation the first possibility would give the rate equation

$$\frac{E}{v_0} = \Phi_0 + \frac{\Phi_2}{[S_2]} + \left(1 + \frac{[S_2]}{K_1}\right)\left(\Phi_1 + \frac{\Phi_{12}}{[S_2]}\right)\frac{1}{[S_1]}$$

where K_1 is the dissociation constant of the inactive complex ES_2. It is clear that, when $S_2/K_1 \ll 1$ the equation reverts to the regular equation. The second possibility would give these observations of substrate inhibition and activation compound the difficulties of kinetic analysis. One must hope that our assumptions about the mechanism are not so erroneous that the whole structure of kinetic analysis becomes a trivial exercise.

It is profitable, however, before we proceed to the consideration of the actual mechanism to summarize what we can deduce so far: (*a*) There is a compulsory reaction sequence in that the enzyme binds coenzyme first. This complex combines with the substrate. (*b*) The enzyme does not participate as a free reduced intermediate in the transfer of hydrogen. (*c*) The environment of NADH is sufficiently distorted by enzyme and by substrate analogues to give spectral alterations.

(*d*) *Mechanism of reaction*

From the above, coupled with our knowledge about direct hydrogen transfer, we have to conclude that on the enzymatic surface a more or less direct contact between substrate and coenzyme is effected in a stereospecific manner. The transfer of the hydrogen could occur in this manner either in one step (hydride-ion transfer) or in a two-stage process, with free radicals as intermediates.

During enzymatic action of alcohol dehydrogenases no free radicals can be detected[266] or at best a minute trace[83]. While it is not conclusively proven it appears likely from these studies and from model reactions (see Section 3, p. 20) that the hydrogen-transfer reaction catalyzed by dehydrogenases does not proceed through a free-radical intermediate. This leaves a hydride-ion transfer or the borderline case of hydrogen-atom transfer with an intermediate charge-transfer complex.

In any mechanism the substrate, be it alcohol, lactate, glycerophosphate, or others, must be brought into close proximity to the pyridine nucleotide. The binding must activate the substrate as well as the coenzyme. From the discussion of binding given previously one may envision *a priori* 4 possible structures for an active ternary complex. These 4 possible complexes are distinguished by the mode of binding of substrate.

$$\frac{\mathrm{E}}{v_0} = \Phi_0 + \frac{[\mathrm{S}_2]}{K_\mathrm{I} k_x} + \frac{\Phi_2}{[\mathrm{S}_2]} + \frac{\Phi_1}{[\mathrm{S}_1]} + \frac{\Phi_{12}}{[\mathrm{S}_1][\mathrm{S}_2]}$$

where K_I is the dissociation constant of S_2 from the inactive complex $\mathrm{ES}_1'\mathrm{S}_2$ and k_x is the dissociation rate constant of the enzyme–coenzyme complex that forms the inhibitory ternary complex. The same formula applies when the inhibitory substrate combines with the ternary complex to form an inactive complex, except then that k_x has the value of the dissociation rate of the ternary complex into product–enzyme–coenzyme complex. A kinetic treatment has also been given by Bloomfield and Alberty[34] and by Cleland[77].

Thus we can postulate:

(*I*) The protein provides at least one separate binding site for the substrate.

(*Ia*) This binding site is not shared by the coenzyme.

(*Ib*) This binding site is shared by the coenzyme.

(*II*) The coenzyme proper is the binding site for the substrate.

(*IIa*) The coenzyme serves both as binding site and as hydride-ion (hydrogen-atom) acceptor.

(*IIb*) One molecule of the coenzyme serves as binding site and another as hydride-ion acceptor.

Limitations need be placed on several of these possible ternary complexes, specifically *Ia*. If a compulsory binding order really exists, mechanism *Ia* implies that binding of coenzyme causes the generation of a site for the substrate. Also, the dehydrogenases are often metallo-proteins. One is tempted to use the zinc as the focal point in the dehydrogenase mechanism. However, for lactic dehydrogenase this cannot be used since at least one rat-liver lactic dehydrogenase does not contain this metal (C. S. Vestling, personal communication).

Winer and Schwert[463] have postulated an imidazole grouping on the enzyme as a binding and activating site on the enzyme. The imidazole was postulated on the strength of the finding of a grouping on the protein which behaves kinetically as a proton donor/acceptor and which has a pK of about 7.0. In addition a positively charged grouping is postulated at the enzyme surface. This grouping has a pK of about 9.4 (may be the ε-amino group of a lysine) (Fig. 26-1a). This mechanism will require, as said before, some difference in protein structure between the free enzyme and the enzyme–coenzyme complex.

The mechanism designated *Ib* has primarily been postulated for alcohol dehydrogenase. In such a mechanism (Fig. 26-1b) the zinc plays a vital role. It is the binding site for alcohol and the binding site for the adenine-amino group. The ternary complex then reaches an equilibrium between redox forms as in a Meerwein–Ponndorf–Oppenhauer reduction. This type of mechanism has been proposed in various forms by Mahler and Douglas[267], Theorell[386,391], and Wallenfels and Sund[441,442]. In these mechanisms NAD is bound through a chelate form, specifically[386,441] through the adenine-amino group and ring nitrogen. This type of linkage has been made plausible through the crystallization of model compounds, such as adenosine–zinc–thiophenol[440]. This kind of mechanism would readily predict a competitive inhibition between NAD and *o*-phenanthroline, as is indeed found[169,403]. Because zinc also binds to alcohol in this mechanism an argument against this mechanism has been that *o*-phenanthroline is not competitive with alcohol, though in a compulsory binding order one would not necessarily expect such competition[95]. However, one would expect under certain

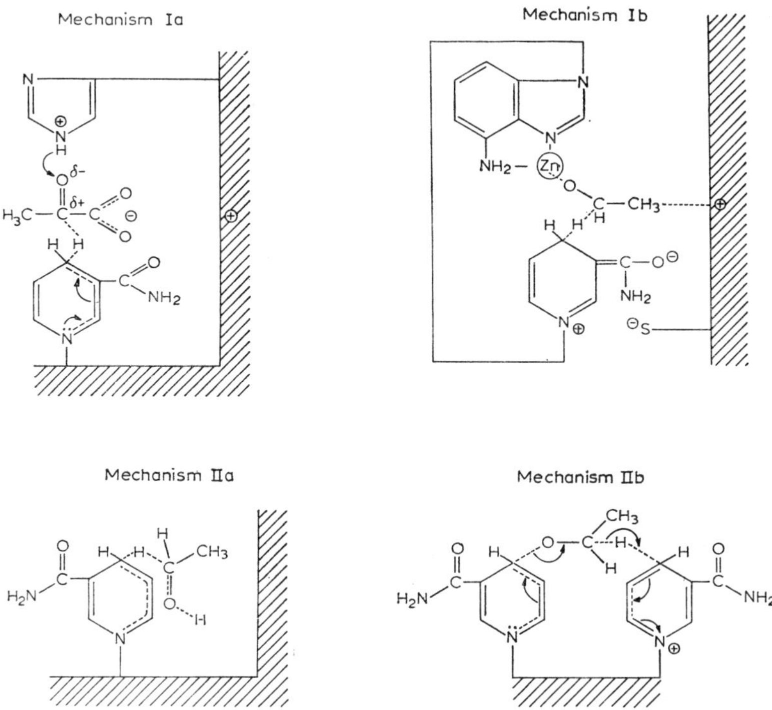

Fig. 26. Representative transition states proposed for dehydrogenase mechanisms. Mechanism Ia from Ref. 463, Ib from Ref. 441, IIa from Ref. 228 and IIb from Ref. 415.

conditions a ternary complex between enzyme–NAD and a chelator. It has been thought that one can indeed observe such a complex from the effects of imidazole[390] and pyrazole[393]. From fluorescence data and from kinetic data a ternary complex of imidazole–enzyme–NADH has been inferred. In fact, multiple complexes have been postulated[89]. These imidazole–enzyme complexes were likened to the enzyme–coenzyme–substrate complexes. Recently, however, through the use of optical rotatory-dispersion techniques, evidence has been presented that imidazole displaces NADH from the liver alcohol dehydrogenase[255]. It is clear therefore that there remains uncertainty over this mechanism as well. Furthermore, in this and the previous mechanism the formation of ternary complexes between coenzyme and nucleophilic substances will have to reflect a preferential binding of the coenzyme–nucleophilic substance over the coenzyme alone, rather than the analogy of the nucleophilic substance to the substrate.

The mechanisms designated *IIa* and *IIb*, where the substrate is directly bound to the coenzyme, give a more readily understandable reason for an ordered addition sequence. Burton and Kaplan suggested an addition reaction of ethanol to bound NAD followed by a hydride-ion transfer[52]. Kosower[231,234] suggested a charge-transfer complex between ethanol and bound NAD (Fig. 26-IIa). In this case the adducts of nucleophilic substances which are competitive with the substrate, such as hydroxylamine and ethylmercaptan on alcohol dehydrogenase, are truly analogous to the binding of substrate. This kind of mechanism does not explain the role of zinc; therefore in this and the following mechanism a binding of NAD to the zinc is implied without suggesting a mechanistic role of the metal.

To accommodate the addition reactions of substrate analogues and the fact that the stoichiometry of binding of these analogues under certain conditions was one for each *two* NAD molecules, there has been suggested the mechanism *IIb* (Fig. 26) in which one NAD molecule binds the substrate through an addition complex, while a second accepts the hydrogen[415]. In this mechanism each NAD is equal until the substrate binds. It has been suggested that in this mechanism the reverse reaction would also require NAD, which cannot be demonstrated[166], though conceivably two NADH molecules could serve the function in the reverse direction. It is of some interest that triosephosphate dehydrogenase, which was excluded originally from this mechanism[415] may actually proceed through the participation of both NAD and NADH for the reduction of substrate[167] (however, see Section 8, p. 82). In addition, against this mechanism is the evidence that in a multi-chain enzyme like lactic dehydrogenase, the chains seem to act independently[187] while this mechanism requires the chains to act in concert if each chain binds one NAD.

In all the mechanisms discussed it is evident that the substrate site shows little specificity. This is true for yeast alcohol dehydrogenase[18,28,114,144,213,411], lactic dehydrogenase[269,277], horse-liver alcohol dehydrogenase[33,278,466,467] and malic dehydrogenase[98]. However, some are more specific, such as α-glycerophosphate dehydrogenase, which so far has only attacked α-glycerophosphate and D-erythrulose 1-phosphate[66].

It is also becoming clear that there are non-protein compounds associated with dehydrogenases, the function of which is not clear. Thus such compounds are associated with α-glycerophosphate dehydrogenase[17,58,404], malic dehydrogenase[308] and triosephosphate dehydrogenase[58,312]. These substances are not required for activity. Several have been identified: adenosine diphosphate–ribose[17], NADH–X[312], and a substance for which the structure 4-methyl-5-(β-hydroxyethyl)-thiazolyl succinic acid has been suggested[404], though this structure is disputed and may be in error[58,410]. It appears likely that at least some of these derivatives, especially adenosine diphosphate–ribose and NADH–X are degradation products from the parent dinucleotide. Such degradation products could easily arise as a result of the special environment the catalytically active site generates.

8. Mechanism of action of 3-phosphoglyceraldehyde dehydrogenase

3-Phosphoglyceraldehyde dehydrogenase (GPD) is unique among the dehydrogenases in that the crystalline preparations from muscle contain firmly bound NAD. There are approximately 3 moles of NAD bound per mole of enzyme—in other words, one mole of NAD for each of the 3, or possibly 4, active centers of the enzyme. Since the dehydrogenase is often regarded as an enzyme–coenzyme complex, the first section of this review of GPD is concerned with the interactions between the enzyme and the coenzyme. The following topics will be considered: (*1*) The stoichiometry of NAD binding; (*2*) Binding constants; and (*3*) Chemistry of binding.

The second part of this discussion is a description of the various reactions catalyzed by the dehydrogenase. The so-called physiological reaction catalyzed by GPD is the oxidation of 3-phosphoglyceraldehyde in the presence of NAD and phosphate to yield 1,3-diphosphoglyceric acid and NADH. The energy of the oxidation reaction is conserved in the high-energy phosphate bond of the product. The dehydrogenase departs from the "conventional" metabolic pathways as it can also catalyze 6 other reactions: (*1*) a transacylase reaction in which the acyl group of an acyl-phosphate is transferred to inorganic ^{32}P, arsenate, or sulfhydryl compounds; (*2*) an acyl-phosphatase reaction involving the hydrolysis of acyl-phosphates; (*3*) an esterase reaction in which *p*-nitro-phenylacetate is hydrolyzed; (*4*) an addition reaction in which the pyridine ring of NADH is hydrated, with the formation of NADHX; (*5*) a diaphorase-like activity, in which a suitable dye is reduced by NADH and; (*6*) a transphosphorylase reaction between ATP and IMP. These reactions are associated with the highly purified crystalline dehydrogenase and differ considerably with regard to pH optima and requirements for NAD and sulfhydryl groups on the enzyme.

Against this background of enzyme versatility a number of catalytic mechanisms has been proposed, most of which involve an *S*-acyl enzyme as an intermediate in the oxidation reaction. These suggestions are dealt with in some detail in the third part of the review. The molecular explanation for the oxidation reactions of the simple dehydrogenases, *e.g.*, lactic or alcohol dehydrogenase, has been difficult to visualize with accuracy. In the case of the more complex GPD, the definition of the intermediate steps in the catalysis must be compatible with an even greater variety of information. However, the diversity of activities has occasionally rendered the problems of the catalytic mechanisms more accessible to experimentation.

References p. 88

(*a*) *The binding of NAD to the enzyme*

(*i*) *Stoichiometry of binding*

In the crystallization of rabbit-muscle GPD with ammonium sulfate and 0.001 *M* cysteine, two molecules of NAD remained tightly bound to one molecule of enzyme with an assumed[382] molecular weight of 120000. The enzyme-bound NAD was not removed by dialysis or recrystallization. However, the coenzyme was not thought to be covalently bound as it could be removed by charcoal treatment[383] and was exchangeable[426] with NAD labelled with ^{32}P. The amount of bound NAD varies with the crystallization procedure. Ferdinand[125] has prepared a highly active crystalline dehydrogenase from rabbit muscle which has less than 1 mole of NAD per mole of enzyme. Fox and Dandliker[135] have shown that an enzyme crystallized in the presence of versene rather than cysteine binds 3 moles of NAD per mole of enzyme. The molecular weight[97,134] was determined as 140000. The still higher value of 3.6 moles bound NAD was cited by Racker, Klybas and Schramm[320]. These authors have not as yet published the experimental details and calculations for this study, so it is difficult to compare their work with that of others. Murdock and Koeppe[286] have recently indicated that 4 molecules of NAD are bound to the crystals of the rabbit-muscle dehydrogenase. This improved ratio of 4:1 was obtained by re-determining the extinction coefficients of the NAD-free protein at 280 mμ and 260 mμ, after modifying the charcoal treatment so as to effect a more complete removal of bound NAD. The native enzyme with its full complement of NAD has an $E_{280}:E_{260}$ ratio of 1.05. Charcoal treatment removes the NAD which absorbs primarily at 260 mμ so that the ratio is raised to 2.13. The previously reported values[125,426] after charcoal treatment were 1.7 and 1.92. The value of 4 moles of NAD per mole of enzyme is consistent with the value of 3.6 as the maximum number of binding sites for the substrate[303] PNPA, the end-group analysis of 4 valines[155] (*cf.* Ref. 420), and the combined amino acid and peptide analyses which have shown the dehydrogenase to be a tetramer with 4 equivalent subunits[156] with molecular weight 35000. These calculations leading to the conclusion of a tetramer are based on a molecular weight[97,134] of approximately 140000. In differentiating between 3 and 4 sites, the molecular weight is a critical factor; the use[382] of the lower value 120000 can, for example, lower the calculated number of binding sites from 3.5 to 3.0 per molecule. The available evidence favors the concept of a tetramer with four identical subunits.

The enzymes from skeletal muscle or heart from various mammalian[119,120,178] and crustacean[11,379] species show no striking differences from rabbit muscle in NAD content. With fishes and birds, however, relatively low values have been obtained, some species showing essentially no binding[11].

It is curious that chicken, turkey and pheasant have the same amino acid content, physical and immunological properties and that, of these, only the chicken muscle binds appreciable NAD. One fish, the halibut, binds NAD, but sturgeon does not. When studied in detail, such differences may reflect subtle modifications in protein structure or more obvious evolutionary modifications.

Crystalline GPD from yeast has no bound NAD when prepared according to the methods of Warburg and Christian[447] or Krebs, Rafter and Junge[239]. However, by adding NAD and measuring NAD–enzyme interaction by methods described below, it has been possible to demonstrate the binding of 2 moles of NAD to the yeast enzyme[370,421]. Chance[61] has shown that NAD is bound to the yeast GPD *in vivo*. Actually this dehydrogenase constitutes 5% of the dry weight of yeast[239] and by calculation binds up to 20% of the NAD of the cells[61]. The calculation assumes that the absorption band at 360 mμ of the NAD–glyceraldehyde phosphate dehydrogenase complex, which is abolished by IAA treatment (see below), is the only one of its kind in the cell to be so affected.

The dehydrogenase has been isolated from roots[143], seeds[152] and leaves [20,143,339] of green plants. However, there has been no mention of bound NAD in these cases.

(*ii*) *Binding constants for NAD and NADH*

The binding constants for NAD were determined by ultracentrifugation methods by Velick, Hayes and Harting[426]. The dissociation constant for the enzyme–NAD complex of crystals prepared in presence of cysteine was $K'_{\text{NAD}} = 10^{-7}$ moles/l, where

$$K' = \frac{(\text{free enzyme sites})\ (\text{NAD})}{(\text{bound enzyme sites})}$$

This value has been verified by an enzymatic method of Astrachan *et al.*[21] using the enzyme–NAD complex as substrate for takadiastase deaminase, which attacks only the free NAD. The experiments of Velick *et al.*[426] indicated that the NAD is equally dissociable from a fully active enzyme in the presence of cysteine or an inactive protein requiring cysteine for activation. When NAD is added to a charcoal-treated, NAD-free enzyme and the K' measured in the ultracentrifuge, the K'_{NAD} decreases from a value of $6.4 \cdot 10^{-6}$ moles/l when 0.58 moles of NAD are bound to a value of $0.08 \cdot 10^{-6}$ moles/l when 2.9 moles of NAD are bound.

This trend indicates that, under these particular conditions of high protein concentration and low temperature, each NAD appears to increase the affinity for the next. Using this technique, a rough estimate of the

References p. 88

K'_{NADH} was determined as 10^{-6} to 10^{-5} moles/l. The NADHX which formed[329,426] during the course of the experiment, precluded an accurate determination. Studies of the equilibrium constant for the oxidation reaction with stoichiometric amounts of enzyme–NAD complex as oxidant, gave the same value as when catalytic amounts of enzyme were used, indicating that GPD–NADH and GPD–NAD are equally dissociable[351,427]. Other data involving the displacement of bound NADH by NAD also indicate that the binding constants are of the same order of magnitude; the K'_{NADH} was determined[85] to be approximately $3 \cdot 10^{-7}$ moles/l.

The dissociation constants for NAD and NADH have been redetermined by Velick using sensitive fluorimetric methods[422,424]. The dissociation constants for NAD and NADH were $0.6 \cdot 10^{-7}$ moles/l and $2.4 \cdot 10^{-7}$ moles/l, respectively, in 0.1 *M* Tris, pH 7.1, 25°. In accordance with these values the bound NADH can be competitively displaced by NAD as must be the case in the enzymatic reaction if the 2 forms of coenzyme have the same binding site. Under these conditions of dilute solution at room temperature there was no interaction between the binding sites of an enzyme which was prepared in presence of versene. As a confirmation of Fox and Dandliker's data[135], the enzyme crystallized in the presence of versene was found to bind 3 molecules of NAD.

The dissociation constants for the GPD–$(NAD)_2$ complex of the yeast dehydrogenase have been determined by ultracentrifugation methods[421] and spectrophotometrically[370]. Velick has shown that the K'_{NAD} is dependent on the amount of bound NAD. The K'_{NAD} is $1.7 \cdot 10^{-5}$ moles/l and $0.19 \cdot 10^{-5}$ moles/l when 0.5 and 2.0 moles of NAD are bound, respectively[421]. This variation in affinity was not observed by Stockell[370], whose spectrophotometric measurements demonstrated that the two sites were equal and independent with a $K'_{NAD} = 0.45 \cdot 10^{-5}$ moles/l. Stockell considers the affinity of NAD for the muscle enzyme to be one hundred times greater than for yeast.

The discrepancy in the results obtained by ultracentrifugation and spectrophotometric methods is as yet unresolved for both the yeast and the muscle enzyme. The equality or inequality of the NAD-binding sites on the enzyme surface may be determined not only by the amino acid sequences of the monomers, which are known to be identical at the active site[157], but by configurational changes induced in the whole enzyme molecule by the stepwise addition of NAD. Other attempts to determine whether or not interaction occurs between binding sites have involved (*a*) studies of the kinetics or extent of reaction of bound NAD or NADH[85,135,224,265,286,351,426,427], and (*b*) studies of the extent of release of bound NAD by acetyl phosphate or *p*-CMB[16,322,421]. However, these results have not been consistent, so that no conclusions can be reached on this question. Reports of incomplete reduction of bound NAD may be due in part to technical difficulties[135,351] including the use of incorrect extinction coefficients[426]. Velick and Furfine[425] have recently suggested a 10% correction in the NADH values due to a hypochromic effect of the enzyme.

A detailed analysis of the binding constants for NAD has not been carried out with enzymes isolated from other species. For further discussion of coenzyme interaction, see the "substrate–coenzyme addition theory" in Section 8c (p. 82).

(iii) Chemistry of NAD binding

The chemistry of the NAD binding to GPD is still in the speculative stage. A number of proposals have been made, *i.e.* covalent bonds, electrostatic bonds, and charge–transfer complexes. Specific sites of attachment have also been suggested, SH groups, tryptophan, tyrosine, histidine, lysine, and Zn^{2+}. The main methods for investigating this problem involve: (*1*) spectrophotometric and fluorimetric changes produced by the formation of the enzyme–$(NAD)_3$ or enzyme–$(NADH)_3$ complexes, (*2*) inhibition of binding by specific reagents, (*3*) pH–titration curves and (*4*) comparative studies using NAD analogues.

(*a*) *Amino acid interactions with NAD.* The sulfhydryl groups on GPD have received the most attention as possible binding sites for NAD. Racker and Krimsky[322] found that the binding of NAD to GPD produced a low, broad spectrum between 310 mμ and 400 mμ with a maximum about 360. Since the spectrum was abolished by IAA, *p*-CMB, acetyl phosphate[322], or H_2O_2 (Refs. 60,62), the sulfhydryl group was implicated. At that time, Krimsky and Racker[241] proposed that glutathione (GSH) was a coenzyme for GPD and thus the GSH was the favored SH group. It is now known that glutathione, when present, is bound to the enzyme only in small amounts (0.2 moles per mole of enzyme) and by a disulfide rather than a peptide linkage[224]. The SH group at the active site has been shown to be a cysteine moiety with peptide linkages to serine and threonine[157]. The linkage of NAD with enzyme was pictured as a covalent bond between the S and the C-4 of the nicotinamide ring[320]. This suggestion was supported by the fact that *p*-CMB removed the enzyme-bound NAD[421] from the enzyme. Although this idea was very attractive, a good deal of evidence has subsequently accumulated which suggests that the spectral properties of the NAD–enzyme complex may not be due to sulfhydryl addition compounds. Model systems involving the addition of sulfhydryl compounds to NAD have been studied[412]. The spectrum of the addition compounds does not resemble that of the NAD–enzyme complex, since the spectrum is shifted more toward the ultraviolet (320–350 mμ) with a maximum at 335 mμ. Moreover, the minimal pH required for the model addition reaction is about pH 8.0 and the maximal effect is reached at pH 10, whereas the greatest affinity of NAD for the yeast enzyme is between 5.5 and 7.5[370]. Further, the dissociation constant for the NAD–sulfhydryl addition compounds is many times higher than for the GPD–NAD complex of rabbit-muscle enzyme. The spectrum of bound 3-acetylpyridine–adenine dinucleotide, which is more pronounced than that of bound NAD, is only partially abolished by IAA[197].

An alternative explanation for the spectrum of the NAD–enzyme complex was first suggested by Kosower, namely, a charge-transfer complex between NAD and the enzyme[228,231,233,235]. The most convincing evidence was the broad featureless quality of the spectrum which closely resembles that of charge-transfer complexes[299]. Experimental evidence was shortly forthcoming as NAD was shown to produce a yellow color with indole, L-tryptophan, glycyl L-tryptophan[69], and tryptamine[7]. NAD gives a spectrum with urea-treated enzymes, such as chymotrypsin[69], trypsin and alcohol dehydrogenase[9]. The NAD spectrum elicited with tryptophan or the urea-treated enzymes is similar to that of the NAD–GPD complex. Tryptophan is the only amino acid to produce the visible spectra. Although tyrosine and phenylalanine could theoretically undergo charge transfer, NAD complexes are not detectable spectroscopically[70]. The tryptophan absorption intensities are similar to those for GPD–NAD complex[70], the dissociation constants are low[70], and the transfer occurs in the pH range from 2.0 to 8.0[9]. The association K is so high that the complex could occur *in vivo*[9]. The nicotinamide portion of the ring is involved, since substitution of the 2 position eliminates the reaction[9]. The theoretical considerations of Pullman predict that only the nicotinamide portion would be involved[315], and the experiments of Isenberg and Szent-Györgyi[177] at low temperature support the charge-transfer possibility.

Fluorimetric studies have also implicated an interaction between tryptophan and NAD. The protein fluorescence, which is almost completely due to tryptophan, is quenched by enzyme-bound NAD or NADH. There is also a direct transfer of energy from the excited aromatic amino acids of the enzyme to the bound NADH which may then be excited to fluoresce[422].

Although the evidence is heavily weighted in favor of tryptophan as the amino acid responsible for the 300–400 mμ spectrum of the enzyme–NAD complex, it is nevertheless reasonable to assume that the sulfhydryl groups are in the vicinity of the bound NAD. The active center for substrate binding contains 2 SH groups[157], and one of these is the site for substrate binding. Since the substrate transfers the H directly to the NAD (see Section 3, p. 17) it follows that the coenzyme must be situated near the active site. This deduction is substantiated by the fact that *p*-CMB stoichiometrically displaces the bound NAD from the enzyme[421]. A smaller molecule, IAA, can abolish the spectrum of the NAD–enzyme complex but does not remove the NAD[302]. Although the NAD is still bound to an *S*-carboxymethylated GPD or to an inactive enzyme prepared in the absence of cysteine or versene, there are differences in the mode of binding of the NAD to inactive and active enzyme[21]. These differences can be detected by sensitive enzymatic methods. For example, snake venom pyrophosphatase splits the NAD bound to inactive GPD somewhat faster than the NAD bound to an active enzyme. Takadiastase deaminase will readily deaminate the bound-NAD bound on an inactive enzyme but will not deaminate the NAD on an active preparation. The NAD bound to an inactive enzyme is reduced, without prior dissociation, by other dehydrogenases, whereas the NAD bound to an active enzyme is not available to the other dehydrogenases. These assays of availability of bound NAD demonstrate that the inactive enzyme with oxidized sulfhydryl groups binds the NAD in a manner so as to alter the position of the nicotinamide, pyrophosphate, and adenine moieties. In general, the NADH bound to an active enzyme is available to other enzymes; *i.e.* it follows the pattern of the NAD complex with an *inactive* enzyme[21]. Thus the reduction of the nicotinamide moiety also produces marked effects on the positioning of all parts of the coenzyme. These studies demonstrate that the SH groups may facilitate NAD binding but are not essential for binding. There certainly appear to be multiple binding sites for the coenzyme.

Several other sites of attachment have been proposed. Velick[422] briefly suggests histidine as a likely site because phosphate, which enhances the fluorescence of the bound NADH at pH 6.5 but not at 8.5, might interact with an imidazole ring. Histidine is probably not responsible for the spectrum of the NAD–enzyme complex because the model NAD–imidazole complex has an ultraviolet spectrum with a high dissociation constant and forms only at high pH values[406].

The pH dependence of the NAD affinity for the yeast enzyme led Stockell to propose that the ionizable groups of the enzyme with pK_a of 5.0 and 8.0 are required in binding. Although the γ-carboxyl group of glutamic acid has a pK_a in the region of 5.0, the calculations of the heats of ionization are not compatible with involvement of this group in binding. Multiple ionizations between pH 8.0 and 9.0 appear to decrease the affinity of the NAD for the enzyme. An α-amino group or a sulfhydryl group might well account for these changes[370].

(*b*) *Zn^{2+} and NAD interaction.* As Zn^{2+} has been shown to be involved in the binding of NAD to alcohol dehydrogenase[402], it naturally comes under consideration for GPD. Vallee *et al.*[401] have found Zn to be present in GPD crystallized from rabbit muscle and yeast. These authors showed that considerable amounts of Cu, Mg, Fe, and Ca were also bound to the yeast and muscle preparations which were commercial samples of questionable purity.

References p. 88

Keleti and his collaborators found Zn in the enzyme preparations from cow, yeast, and crayfish[215]. However, more recent analyses have detected only traces of Zn in active preparations of rabbit-muscle[125] and yeast[418] dehydrogenases. A summary of the data on the ratio of moles of enzyme : Zn : NAD binding sites is shown in Table VI. These ratios do not give a satisfying numerical relationship of Zn: enzyme or Zn: number of NAD-binding sites.

TABLE VI

ZINC CONTENT OF VARIOUS PREPARATIONS OF 3-PHOSPHOGLYCERALDEHYDE DEHYDROGENASE

Source	*Ratio Zn: enzyme*	*Number of NAD-binding sites*	*References for Zn content*
Rabbit muscle	1.7	3 or 4	Vallee *et al.*[401]
	0.05		Ferdinand[125]
Yeast	0.54	2	Vallee *et al.*[401]
	2.0		Keleti *et al.*[215]
	0.05		Vanderheiden *et al.*[418]
Bovine muscle	2.0	2.4	Keleti *et al.*[215]
Crayfish muscle	1.0	3.0	Keleti *et al.*[215]

All these preparations are inhibited by *o*-phenanthroline at concentrations[216,401] varying from $1 \cdot 10^{-3}$ to $1.5 \cdot 10^{-2}$ *M*. Stockell[370] has, on the other hand, done preliminary experiments to indicate that Zn is not involved in the coenzyme binding. When the yeast enzyme was incubated at pH 10 for 30 min the presence of 0.001 *M* *o*-phenanthroline or 0.015 *M* EDTA, the enzyme was still active. If Zn were present in the enzyme preparation, it was not removed by this procedure[370] since the coenzyme binding was unaffected. Thus, the relationship of the Zn to coenzyme binding or dehydrogenase reactions is very tenuous. For considerations of the mechanism of enzyme action it is extremely important to know whether Zn is an active participant in the enzymatic reaction. Therefore, it is hoped that these conflicting data will be somehow reconciled or connected to give a more accurate picture.

(*c*) *Hydrophilic nature of binding site for NADH*. As pointed out in Section 2 (p. 8), NADH in aqueous solution has a closed ("hairpin") conformation, as indicated by the high efficiency of energy transfer from the adenine moiety to the nicotinamide moiety in the excitation of fluorescence. Such studies on the bound NADH of GPD indicate that this conformation is retained, suggesting a relatively polar environment at the binding site, in contrast to LDH. The retention of the 340-mμ absorption band in the NADH–

GPD complex leads to the same conclusion. In agreement with these findings, the octadecapeptide isolated from the catalytically active site for the substrates is hydrophilic[157].

(*d*) *Binding of NAD analogues and derivatives.* Several authors have attempted to determine the features of the NAD structure which are important for binding. Neither the amide group of nicotinamide nor the amino group of the adenine is essential for binding, although acetylpyridine–adenine dinucleotide and nicotinamide–hypoxanthine dinucleotide show a 20- to 30-fold decrease in affinity for the yeast enzyme[371]. However, the combined effect of 2 structural alterations is striking since acetylpyridine–hypoxanthine dinucleotide has a 600-fold decrease in affinity. Similar kinetic studies of binding constants have not been carried out with the muscle enzyme. Acetylpyridine–adenine dinucleotide substitutes for NAD at a level of 50% activity in both the yeast and muscle enzymes. The NAD analogues containing the pyridine bases nicotinyl hydroxamic acid or thionicotinamide are reduced at 20% the rate of NAD[16]. Pyridine-3-aldehyde–adenine dinucleotide inhibits the enzyme, but pyridine-3-aldehyde does not[198].

(*e*) *Coenzyme specificity.* The yeast[447] and muscle[86] enzymes are specific for NAD, not only in their dehydrogenase but also in transferase and phosphatase activities[161,302]. Photosynthetic micro-organisms and higher plants contain, in addition to NAD-specific enzymes[143,152,366], NADP-specific enzymes[20,32,42,142,339], some of which can function without phosphate or arsenate[20,32,339]. Only one species, *Alcaligenis faecalis*[43], has been found to contain a single enzyme which uses NAD or NADP, but here the affinity is 100 times higher for NADP.

(*f*) *Properties conferred on enzyme by bound NAD.* The NAD-free enzyme from muscle is relatively unstable[426] and more sensitive than the enzyme–NAD complex to inactivation by heat[147], proteolysis[240,321,376,378], antibodies[117,238], organic solvents[100,118] or a specific lipid inhibitor isolated from the dehydrogenase itself[377]. These properties are correlated with the more ordered configuration of the NAD–enzyme complex[40,73,119], as measured by optical rotatory dispersion[398]. The yeast enzyme is more stable and more readily crystallizable than the muscle enzyme in the absence of NAD[447]. The addition of *p*-CMB, which removes bound NAD, causes the expected changes in rotatory dispersion[73,119] and susceptibility to proteolytic enzymes[376,378]. The apparent rate and extent of reaction of *p*-CMB with the SH groups of the enzyme is the same for the NAD-free enzyme and for the NAD–enzyme complex[426]. In the case of iodoacetate, the rate of inactivation is actually higher with the NAD–enzyme complex[322,351].

In contrast to NAD, the reduced coenzyme causes inactivation of the enzyme[12,396]. This inactivation, which is oxygen-dependent and irreversible by cysteine, appears to involve primarily the generation of H_2O_2 from air

References p. 88

oxidation of two SH groups on the enzyme, followed by further oxidative action by the generated H_2O_2. The question of the physiological significance of this inactivation process remains open.

It is clear from the above that combination of the enzyme with the coenzyme must result in a considerably altered protein conformation. That this is the case may also be deduced from a consideration of the different types of catalytic activities observed in the presence and absence of coenzyme. An enzyme with bound NAD may function not only as a dehydrogenase but also as a transferase or phosphatase. However, removal of the NAD releases an esterase activity that is non-existent in the presence of bound NAD[161,302,303,322]. These effects will be discussed in detail in the following section on the multiple functions of the enzyme.

(b) *Multiple functions of the dehydrogenase*

(i) *Dehydrogenase activity*

The major physiological role of the enzyme is oxidative phosphorylation. The general features of the hydrogen-transfer process have been discussed in Section 3 (p. 17), and the stereochemistry has been described in Section 4 (p. 27). It has been pointed out that in the GPD reaction, a direct transfer of hydrogen occurs from the substrate to side B of the pyridine ring, and the possible significance of this with respect to direct oxidation of the bound NADH by A-specific dehydrogenases has been discussed. Before examining in further detail the mechanism of the dehydrogenase reaction, we will consider here the other catalytic functions of the enzyme, so that this information can be used in attempting finally to formulate a reaction mechanism for the over-all oxidative phosphorylation process (see Section 8c, p. 79).

(ii) *Transacylase activity*

In substrate-specificity studies acetaldehyde was shown to be oxidized by the dehydrogenase in a reaction comparable to that of the natural substrate, 3-phosphoglyceraldehyde, and to yield acetyl phosphate[161]:

$$CH_3CHO + H_3PO_4 + NAD^+ \rightleftharpoons CH_3\overset{\overset{\displaystyle O}{\|}}{C}OPO_3H_2 + NADH + H^+$$

The overall reaction resembled the oxidation of acetaldehyde by extracts of *Clostridium kluyveri*[49,367] and suggested that the dehydrogenase by analogy might also function as a transacetylase. When the dehydrogenase was tested, it was found that inorganic $^{32}PO_4$ could exchange with the organic phosphate of acetyl phosphate and that arsenate could effect an irreversible arsenolysis of acetyl phosphate[160,323].

$$CH_3\overset{\overset{\displaystyle O}{\|}}{C}OPO_3H_2 + H_3{}^{32}PO_4 \underset{}{\overset{E(NAD)_3}{\rightleftharpoons}} CH_3\overset{\overset{\displaystyle O}{\|}}{C}O^{32}PO_3H_2 + H_3PO_4$$

$$CH_3\overset{\overset{\displaystyle O}{\|}}{C}OPO_3H_2 + H_3AsO_4 \xrightarrow{E(NAD)_3} [CH_3\overset{\overset{\displaystyle O}{\|}}{C}OAsO_3H_2] + H_3PO_4$$

$$\downarrow H_2O$$

$$CH_3COOH + H_3AsO_4$$

Similar reactions were shown to occur with the natural substrate, 1,3-diphosphoglyceric acid[161,296,323]. By analogy with the case of bacterial transacetylase[368] and sucrose phosphorylase[110,111], these reactions suggested the possibility of an acyl–enzyme intermediate. One of the criteria for this type of intermediate is that the acyl group be transferable to other acceptors. Consequently, a number of sulfhydryl compounds were tested as acceptors, namely, coenzyme A, glutathione, cysteine, and thioglycolate[161,322]. In the presence of the dehydrogenase, the acetyl group of acetyl phosphate could be transferred to sulfhydryl acceptors to form thioesters, *e.g.* *S*-acetyl–coenzyme A and *S*-acetylglutathione:

$$CH_3\overset{\overset{\displaystyle O}{\|}}{C}OPO_3H_2 + CoASH \overset{E(NAD)_3}{\rightleftharpoons} CH_3\overset{\overset{\displaystyle O}{\|}}{C}OSCoA + H_3PO_4$$

With 1,3-diphosphoglyceric acid the enzyme can only transfer the glyceryl group to methylmercaptan and not to coenzyme A or glutathione[468].

One unusual feature of the transacylase reactions is a requirement for bound NAD. The removal of bound coenzyme results in a complete loss of transferase activity which can be restored by addition of NAD[161,322]. The requirement and function of the NAD in the transferase reactions is not understood. The possibility has been considered that the NAD might contain traces of NADH which could initiate the reversible reduction of the acyl phosphates to the aldehyde and thereby account for the ^{32}P exchange and arsenolysis. However, this explanation of the transfer reactions with acetyl phosphate appears very unlikely in view of the following observations: (*a*) The rates of phosphate exchange and arsenolysis with acetyl phosphate are both greatly in excess of the rate of acetaldehyde oxidation under comparable conditions[161,296]; (*b*) the exchange reaction can be further separated from the oxidation by lowering the pH from 8.1 to 7.0. This reduces the exchange rate by 50% and the rate of oxidation by about[161] 95%; (*c*) In those cases in which NAD was added to the NAD-free enzyme the coenzyme was purified chromatographically under acid conditions which destroy NADH[161]. Thus NAD may act in some manner, other than oxidation

References p. 88

and reduction, as a direct participant in the exchange reactions, or it may be required to maintain an active configuration at the catalytic site.

The other characteristic of the transfer reactions is the requirement for reduced sulfhydryl groups on the enzyme. The SH groups are essential because the transferase reactions proceed *via* a thioester acetyl–enzyme intermediate. The existence of this intermediate is substantiated by the following data. In the presence of IAA the arsenolysis of acetyl phosphate is inhibited[197,323]. Racker and Krimsky[323] noted that glutathione could partially reverse the IAA inhibition of arsenolysis without restoring any of the oxidation properties. The explanation for the glutathione effect remains somewhat obscure. The actual isolation of an acetyl–enzyme, which was prepared by Racker and Krimsky[324] with acetyl phosphate and a NAD-free preparation of muscle dehydrogenase, afforded definite proof for the existence of such an intermediate. The ratio of bound acetyl groups to enzyme ranged from 0.8:1 to 2:1. The acetyl–enzyme complex was shown to be an enzymatically active intermediate since the acetyl group could be reduced by NADH to give acetaldehyde and NAD or decomposed by arsenate and NAD.

$$CH_3CHO \xleftarrow{\text{NADH}} CH_3\overset{\overset{\displaystyle O}{\|}}{C}\text{-SE} \xrightarrow[\text{NAD}]{H_3AsO_4} CH_3COOH$$

In this very original investigation, the acetyl–enzyme complex was characterized as heat stable at pH 4.5 and reactive with hydroxylamine, yielding a hydroxamic acid. The formation of the complex was inhibited by IAA. These properties are consistent with the proposal of a thioester linkage between the acetyl group and the enzyme. The importance of the SH group was further indicated in the work of Boyer and his coworkers[224,225,286] who found that either acetyl phosphate or IAA reduces the number of total titratable SH groups by about 2.3 groups. In the presence of both IAA and acetyl phosphate the disappearance of SH groups is still only 2.3 indicating that IAA and acetyl phosphate probably react at the same site, namely, cysteine. The protein chemistry of the acetyl–enzyme complex has been further studied by Harris, Meriwether and Park[157]. A radioactive [^{14}C]acetyl–enzyme complex was digested with proteolytic enzymes and the analysis of the peptides of the active center showed that the acetyl group labelled a specific cysteine moiety forming *S*-acetylcysteine. The same cysteine group is specifically carboxymethylated with [^{14}C]iodoacetic acid[157]. The detailed structure of the active center is discussed in the section on mechanism (see Section 8c, p. 79).

(iii) Acyl phosphatase activity

In the absence of cysteine or other reducing agents, the dehydrogenase from muscle and yeast catalyzes a NAD-dependent hydrolysis of acetyl phosphate[158,301].

$$CH_3\overset{\overset{O}{\|}}{C}OPO_3H_2 + H_2O \xrightarrow{E_{(NAD)_3}} CH_3COOH + H_3PO_4$$

The original rates observed with this so-called "oxidized" preparation of enzyme were increased 6-fold by treating the enzyme with iodosobenzoate (IOB)[325]. When more favorable conditions are used for the oxidation with IOB and for the acylphosphatase assay, the rate of hydrolysis of acetyl phosphate is at least 100 times as high as that originally reported for the enzyme without IOB treatment. With 10^{-5} *M* 1,3-diphosphoglycerate (enzymatically generated) as substrate the rate was about 3 times that with 10^{-2} *M* acetyl phosphate, and in fact reached one-tenth of the turnover number observed for the normal dehydrogenase function[116]. Since the IOB procedure is known to oxidize the SH groups required for dehydrogenase activity[115], the phosphatase reaction must be catalyzed at a site not involving these SH groups. The phosphatase structure produced by the IOB treatment is apparently present only in traces in the "oxidized enzyme" as formerly isolated, and is virtually absent from the native enzyme.

The phosphatase activity is inhibited by cysteine, glutathione, cyanide, bisulfite[158,301], hydroxylamine, semicarbazide, and phenylhydrazine[324]. Only the first 4 compounds can cleave disulfide bonds, whereas all can combine with the essential NAD, or with a possibly essential metal. Other metal-binding agents, such as pyrophosphate[328], glycine[116] or thyroxine derivatives[301] are also inhibitory. It is noteworthy that the various inhibitors of phosphatase activity do not inhibit the dehydrogenase function and are in many cases actually used to promote the hydrogen-transfer function.

The phosphatase reaction can also be differentiated from the dehydrogenase and transferase activities on the basis of pH optimum. The hydrolytic activity is increased[301] about 50% by lowering the pH from 8.2 to 7.0, whereas the rate of oxidation of aldehydes is greatly accelerated by raising the pH above 7.0. Rafter and Colowick[328] reported that the maximal phosphatase activity was found at pH 5.9 in 0.1 *M* succinate buffer.

Studies with ^{18}O showed that the dehydrogenase preparations ("oxidized enzyme"), unlike all other phosphatases, catalyzed a C–O split of acetyl phosphate[301]. The non-enzymatic hydrolysis of acetyl phosphate proceeds predominantly by an O–P split at neutral pH, but changes to a C–O split in both 3.0 *M* HCl and 3.0 *M* KOH[301]. It was thought that an investigation of the properties of the hydrolysis of acetyl phosphate with pyridine at pH 8.6 might shed some light on the function of the NAD in the enzymatic hydrolysis. However, the attack of pyridine in aqueous solution is on the

References p. 88

phosphorus of acetyl phosphate in preference to attack on carbon. Attack by other nitrogen containing compounds on acetyl phosphate is well known[227]. Therefore, the NAD may either act to assure the proper conformation of another carbonyl-attacking group on the protein, *e.g.* imidazole, or else the protein maintains an acetyl phosphate–NAD geometry which assures C–O cleavage. Both alternatives are compatible with the ^{18}O data and involve a combined NAD–protein interaction.

NADH was only about half as active as NAD in the restoration of the hydrolytic activity to a NAD-free enzyme. An accurate comparison of NADH and NAD is complicated by the fact that acetyl phosphate causes the oxidation of NADH[301] when enzyme preparations retaining some dehydrogenase function are used.

(iv) Esterase activity

The fact that the hydrolysis of acetyl phosphate catalyzed by the dehydrogenase proceeds by a C–O split rather than a P–O split suggested a possible relationship between this enzyme and proteolytic enzymes which show esterolytic activity. Indeed the dehydrogenase from both muscle[302,303] and yeast[381] was shown to catalyze the hydrolysis of *p*-nitrophenyl acetate, a substrate well studied with trypsin and chymotrypsin. Although the turnover number with the muscle dehydrogenase is only 5 moles/mole enzyme/min, it is nonetheless 5 times greater than the value for chymotrypsin which is considered to have substantial esterase activity[162]. The dehydrogenase is 700 times more effective than cysteine or GSH in cleaving *p*-NPA. The esterolysis occurs at or near the active site since the hydrolysis is inhibited by 3-phosphoglyceraldehyde, glyceraldehyde, acetyl phosphate, NAD, IAA, and iodosobenzoate[298,303,381]. These inhibitions of the esterolytic activity are in striking contrast to the phosphatase reaction which requires NAD and is not inhibited by oxidation of the sulfhydryl groups. The two hydrolytic activities are, therefore, mutually exclusive.

The dehydrogenase can hydrolyze a number of analogues of *p*-nitrophenyl acetate such as *o*-nitrophenyl acetate, *m*-nitrophenyl acetate, *o*-chlorophenyl acetate, *m*-chlorophenyl acetate, 2-chloro-4-nitrophenyl acetate, ethyl *p*-nitrophenyl carbonate, etc.[298]. The rate of the reaction is related to the electron-withdrawing capacity of the phenolic moiety. The esterolytic activity is restricted to aryl esters; thus, acetyltyrosine ethyl ester and aliphatic esters do not act as substrates.

The esterolytic activity of the dehydrogenase certainly appears to be remote in terms of the metabolic role of the enzyme in skeletal muscle or yeast. However, *p*-nitrophenyl acetate and its analogues have proved to be quite useful in the investigation of the catalytic mechanism of the dehydrogenase. Under proper conditions the reaction of *p*-nitrophenyl acetate with the dehydrogenase results in the formation of an acetyl–enzyme complex which has been isolated and shown to have 3–4 acetyl groups bound per mole of muscle protein and 3 per mole of yeast enzyme[302,303,381]. The amino acid sequence of the active center has been determined[88,157] and will be discussed in detail in the Section on mechanism (p. 79).

(v) NADHX formation

Rafter, Chaykin and Krebs[329] noticed that the yeast enzyme at a low pH (*ca.* 5.0) produced a decrease in the absorption of NADH at 340 mμ and an increase at 290 mμ. The product of the reaction was designated DPNHX, which by the new terminology becomes NADHX. Polyvalent anions, such as pyrophosphate, phosphate, or citrate, were required. NAD at a ratio of 2 NAD:1 NADH inhibited the NADHX formation. The turnover number was 2 moles/mole enzyme/min as compared to 28 000 moles/mole enzyme/min for the oxidation reaction. NADHX can also be formed by the rabbit-muscle dehydrogenase but the reaction rate is even lower, possibly due to the enzyme-bound NAD or the greater instability of the muscle enzyme at lower pH[426]. With the muscle enzyme, Rafter *et al.*[329] noted a cysteine requirement for NADHX formation, but this is difficult to reconcile with the results of Grisolia and his coworkers[12] who found no inhibition with H_2O_2 or IAA, which completely inhibit the SH-dependent oxidation function. NADHX formation appears to be specific for 3-phosphoglyceraldehyde dehydrogenase since alcohol dehydrogenase and lactic dehydrogenase do not show this activity[329]. Acetyl phosphate, which ordinarily causes oxidation of NADH to NAD, promotes NADHX formation instead when pyrophosphate is present[328].

Isotope studies[276,329] with D_2O and $^{32}PO_4$ showed that only D_2O is incorporated into NADHX. This information plus hydrogenation data[65] and spectral evidence[276] lead to the proposed structure shown in Fig. 27. It is interesting to note that yeast juice contains an enzyme which converts NADHX to NADH with an ATP and Mg^{2+} requirement[275].

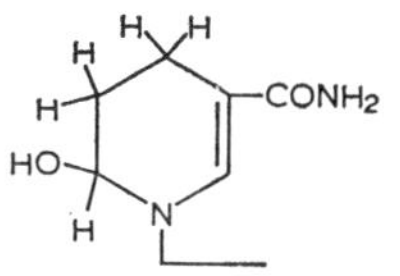

H H
H
H
CONH2
HO
H
N

Fig. 27. Probable structure of NADH–X.

(vi) Diaphorase

The dehydrogenase from rabbit muscle or yeast combines with 2,6-dichlorophenolindophenol, producing a decrease in absorption of the dye at

525 mμ. The protein–dye complex develops a diaphorase activity, *i.e.* upon the addition of NADH the excess dye is reduced and NAD accumulates[326]. Pretreatment of the enzyme with the dye is a prerequisite for diaphorase activity. All reagents, such as 3-phosphoglyceraldehyde, acetyl phosphate, NADH, *p*-CMB, IAA, which inhibit the combination of the enzyme and the dye, also inhibit the appearance of diaphorase activity. After the complex is formed only *p*-CMB is inhibitory, suggesting that the dye is covering the active site for the substrates. The turnover number for the diaphorase reaction is 20 moles/mole protein/min and the pH optimum 4.8. The NAD is somehow involved in the initial stages of the combination of dye and protein. An enzyme with bound NAD produces a more active diaphorase function than a NAD-free enzyme. The protein–dye complex has reduced activity for dehydrogenase, phosphatase, arsenolysis and NADHX formation. The biological significance of the diaphorase activity, like the NADHX formation, is vague, at best, but it may prove useful in understanding the mechanism of hydrogen transfer.

(vii) Transphosphorylase

A transphosphorylase reaction has been attributed to the dehydrogenase[217]:

$$\text{ATP} + \text{IMP} + \text{NAD} + \text{E(SH)}_2 \rightarrow \text{ADP} + \text{IDP} + \text{NADH} + \text{ES–S}$$

In this reaction, the phosphate is transferred from ATP to IMP, the NAD is reduced, and the sulfhydryl groups of the enzyme are oxidized. Stoichiometrically, the reaction cannot be made to go beyond the number of bound NAD molecules by the addition of NAD or cysteine[214]. The SH group at the active site may not be involved as the enzyme can still oxidize 3-phosphoglyceraldehyde after the transphosphorylation is completed. The authors offer no suggestions as to the significance of this reaction in terms of the overall mechanism or function of the dehydrogenase.

(viii) Summary of activities

In order to facilitate the comparison of the various activities of the dehydrogenase, the 7 reactions are tabulated (Table VII) on the basis of two criteria; first, the involvement of NAD or NADH in the reaction and second, the requirement for sulfhydryl groups. For each criterion, a hydrolytic reaction stands out as an exception in the group of reactions. The esterolysis of *p*-nitrophenyl acetate is the only instance in which the coenzyme is not a participant in the reaction or required for activity as an enzyme-bound cofactor. The hydrolysis of acyl phosphate is uniquely insensitive to sulfhydryl-blocking agents and does not require reduced SH groups on the enzyme surface. The conditions required for the hydrolytic activities are

TABLE VII

SUMMARY OF ACTIVITIES OF 3-PHOSPHOGLYCERALDEHYDE DEHYDROGENASE

Activity	*NAD or NADH involved in reaction*	*SH groups on enzyme required*
1. Oxidation and phosphorylation	+	+
2. Transferase, ^{32}P exchange, or arsenolysis	+	+
3. Hydrolysis of acetyl phosphate	+	o
4. Hydrolysis of *p*-nitrophenyl acetate	o	+
5. NADHX formation	+	+
6. Diaphorase	+	+
7. Transphosphorylase	+	+

such that when either type of hydrolysis is proceeding at maximal rate, the other activity can not be evoked simultaneously.

Thus, by changing the experimental conditions the triose dehydrogenase enzyme can be converted into a transferase, phosphatase, esterase, hydratase, diaphorase, or transphosphorylase. The biological significance of these conversions is only speculative. However, the study of the multiple functions has been useful in the consideration of the intermediate steps in the catalytic mechanism. The ideas of various investigators concerning the mechanism of action are presented in the following section.

(*c*) *The mechanism of catalysis*

(*i*) *Sequence of oxidation and phosphorylation*

Warburg and Christian originally proposed that, in the oxidation of 3-phosphoglyceraldehyde, the aldehyde group was first phosphorylated non-enzymatically and then enzymatically oxidized to produce the high-energy acyl phosphate, 1,3-di-phosphoglyceric acid[444,445,447,449].

$$\begin{matrix} R \\ | \\ C{-}H \\ \| \\ O \end{matrix} + H_3PO_4 \rightleftharpoons H{-}\begin{matrix} R \\ | \\ C \\ | \\ OPO_3H_2 \end{matrix}{-}OH + NAD \xrightleftharpoons{\text{Enzyme}} \begin{matrix} R \\ | \\ C{=}O \\ | \\ OPO_3H_2 \end{matrix} + NADH$$

where $R = \begin{matrix} CH_2OP \\ | \\ CHOH \\ | \end{matrix}$

A second, more generally accepted hypothesis has been proposed by a number of authors. The reaction is schematically represented as an oxidation followed by a phosphorylation, and the main focus of activity on the enzyme

References p. 88

surface is the active SH group.

$$\text{HS–E–NAD} + \text{RCHO} \rightleftharpoons \text{R}\overset{\overset{\text{O}}{\|}}{\text{C}}\text{S–E–NADH} + \text{H}^+$$

$$\text{R}\overset{\overset{\text{O}}{\|}}{\text{C}}\text{S–E–NADH} + \text{NAD} \rightleftharpoons \text{R}\overset{\overset{\text{O}}{\|}}{\text{C}}\text{S–E–NAD} + \text{NADH}$$

$$\text{R}\overset{\overset{\text{O}}{\|}}{\text{C}}\text{S–E–NAD} + \text{H}_3\text{PO}_4 \rightleftharpoons \text{HS–E–NAD} + \text{R}\overset{\overset{\text{O}}{\|}}{\text{C}}\text{OPO}_3\text{H}_2$$

The bulk of the evidence now indicates that a non-enzymatic reaction of the aldehyde substrate with phosphate does not occur. Evidence of Warburg[449] and Needham[289] for a phosphate-stimulated non-enzymatic reduction of NAD by glyceraldehyde proved later to be an artifact caused by an aldehyde–NAD addition reaction[51]. Meyerhof and co-workers[281] showed that no appreciable non-enzymatic aldehyde–phosphate addition occurs, but presented evidence that such a reaction might occur to a small extent in the presence of enzyme[283]. Additional evidence against a non-enzymatic aldehyde–arsenate addition reaction has been based on the widely divergent K_m values for glyceraldehyde and arsenate[351].

The major argument of Warburg and his co-workers is a kinetic one, based on their observation[444,449], that the *initial* rate of enzymatic reduction of NAD by glyceraldehyde is higher when phosphate is present. However, the interpretation of this finding is complicated by the fact that the binding of NAD by the protein is promoted by phosphate and inhibited by other buffers in a competitive manner[62]. Thus, the phosphate (or arsenate[427]) effect on the initial rate may be due simply to an increase in the concentration of bound NAD available for reaction. In support of this view, when excess NAD is added to the muscle enzyme, the rate of reduction becomes as high in the absence as in the presence of phosphate[427]. Warburg has objected to the use of added NAD on the grounds that this introduces sufficient inorganic phosphate, as a contaminant, to promote the oxidation reaction. However, studies of the reaction of phosphoglyceraldehyde with excess NAD in the absence of phosphate show that the oxidation does not proceed beyond 2 or 3 moles of NADH formed per mole of enzyme present, as expected for a reaction limited by the accumulation of an acyl–enzyme intermediate[224,427]. The subsequent addition of phosphate permits resumption of oxidation. Thus, the phosphate appears to be necessary for a late step rather than an initial step in the sequence, and this view is supported by the close fit of the observed kinetics with the equations developed on the assumption of an acyl–enzyme intermediate[224,427].

Apart from the kinetic arguments, which still leave some room for doubt as to the sequence of events, there is a large body of evidence which favors the view that oxidation precedes phosphorylation. The acyl-transfer reactions, ^{32}P exchange, arsenolysis and the formation of thio esters take place in the absence of any oxidation–reduction steps and clearly indicate an acyl–enzyme intermediate[161,322]. The most convincing evidence is found in the previously mentioned work of Racker and Krimsky, who have isolated an acetyl–enzyme, formed from acetyl phosphate and the dehydrogenase, and demonstrated that this enzyme–substrate complex could be reduced with NADH to give acetaldehyde[324].

(ii) Separation of oxidation and phosphorylation

Krimsky and Racker have suggested that there may be two active heads on the dehydrogenase—one for the dehydrogenation and the other for the phosphorylation reaction. The most recent evidence for this proposal was obtained with a dehydrogenase which was partially digested with chymotrypsin[240]. The digested dehydrogenase could oxidize glyceraldehyde as rapidly as the native enzyme in the absence of phosphate. Addition of phosphate had no effect on the digested enzyme but markedly stimulated the native enzyme. The digestion of the enzyme did not alter the oxidation of 3-phosphoglyceraldehyde using monothioglycerol as the acyl acceptor but with arsenate as acceptor 95% of the activity was lost. The authors cautiously point out alternative explanations, such as a "crippled enzyme", instead of the proteolytic release of a phosphorylation head. The possibility of a crippled enzyme is very likely because the chymotrypsin produced an altered mode of binding and a reduced affinity of the NAD for the dehydrogenase which could thereby interfere with the NAD-dependent acyl-transfer reaction.

(iii) "Aldehydolysis" theory

There have been several attempts to expand in somewhat more detail the mechanisms proposed above. Racker and Krimsky have suggested that the oxidation of 3-phosphoglyceraldehyde involved an "aldehydolysis" of the

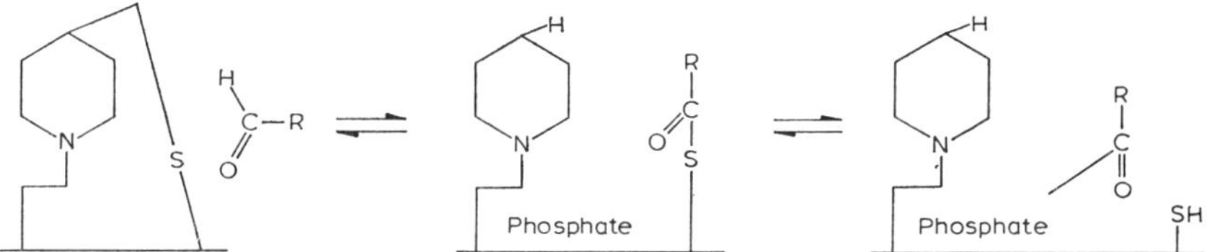

Fig. 28. "Aldehydolysis" mechanism for 3-phosphoglyceraldehyde dehydrogenase. Adapted from Racker and Krimsky[322].

References p. 88

covalent bond between the coenzyme NAD and a sulfhydryl group (see Section 8a, p. 67). The hydrogen of the aldehyde group would thus be transferred to the NAD to yield NADH and an acylthioester, 3-P glyceryl–enzyme[322] as shown in Fig. 28. The data in support of "aldehydolysis" is derived mainly from the spectrophotometric experiments involving the spectrum of the NAD–enzyme complex[322]. Since this spectrum is most probably a reflection of an interaction with a tryptophan moiety and not a sulfhydryl group (see Section 8a, p. 68), the proposal as diagrammed in Fig. 28 may need modification. Nonetheless this proposal has been very provocative in the consideration of the role of the essential sulfhydryl groups.

(iv) Substrate–coenzyme addition theory

A mechanism for alcohol dehydrogenase has been proposed by Van Eys, San Pietro and Kaplan[415], in which the essential feature is that one NAD molecule serves to bind the alcohol and a second NAD is the H acceptor (see Section 7, p. 62, and Fig. 26, mechanism IIb, p. 61). These authors specifically state that the mechanism is not to be applied to aldehyde dehydrogenases, as one can see by comparing assumptions quoted below with the known experimental facts for GPD.

(*1*) "It must be emphasized that no bond between substrate and protein is required." In the case of the GPD, an enzyme–substrate complex has been shown to occur between 3-phosphoglyceraldehyde, 1,3-diphosphoglyceric acid, acetyl phosphate, or *p*-nitrophenyl acetate.

(*2*) ". . . substances which resemble the substrate are bound with a stoichiometry of 1 mole per 2 mole of NAD bound maximally." In the case of GPD the number of binding sites for the substrate is equivalent to the number of NAD, *i.e.* 3–4. Moreover, the stoichiometric inhibitors of GPD, namely, IAA, *p*-CMB, IOB, and tetrose diphosphate[132,320], completely inhibit when 3 or 4 moles are bound per mole enzyme.

Nonetheless this mechanism has been applied to GPD by Hilvers and Weenen[167]. They claim that the reduction of acetyl phosphate by NADH is accelerated by the presence of NAD. According to the theory, NAD should facilitate the positioning of the acetyl phosphate during the transfer of the H from the NADH to the substrate. When the enzyme-bound NAD of the muscle enzyme is hydrolyzed by *Neurospora* nucleosidase the reduction reaction is inhibited. After this treatment, addition of NAD stimulates the reduction. However, the yeast enzyme behaves in just the opposite manner, *i.e.* the rate of the reduction with NADH is not decreased by treatment of the enzyme with nucleosidase but rather increased. It is not very satisfactory to be obliged to propose two mechanisms for the enzymes from different sources. This is particularly true since the active center octadecapeptides have been shown to be identical for the yeast and muscle enzymes[304].

The second line of evidence in favor of the mechanism of Van Eys *et al.* was that the reduction of enzyme-bound NAD with glyceraldehyde in the presence of arsenate was not complete. It is unfortunate that glyceraldehyde was selected as substrate because Velick and Hayes[427] have shown that glyceraldehyde gives lower results than 3-phosphoglyceraldehyde in the assay of the number of catalytic sites of the enzyme. Boyer and his co-workers[224] have shown that 3-phosphoglyceraldehyde gives complete reduction of 3 moles of NAD bound per mole of muscle enzyme. If an experiment gives less than the maximal number of bound NAD molecules, the interpretation must be made with caution. Boyer has also found that at low pH, the NADH can be converted to NADHX which does not absorb at 340 mμ and gives an erroneous estimate of the NADH formed. At the moment there seems to be more evidence against the hypothesis than for it, as far as 3-phosphoglyceraldehyde dehydrogenase is concerned.

(v) Structure of the active site

The dehydrogenase, transferase and esterase activities have been shown to involve the formation of an acyl–enzyme intermediate. An acid-stable covalent acyl–enzyme compound has actually been isolated as an intermediate by the reaction of acetyl phosphate[324] or *p*-nitrophenyl acetate[303] with the NAD-free dehydrogenase. The work with the acetyl–enzyme prepared with *p*-nitrophenyl acetate was pursued at the level of amino acid sequence studies[88,157]. Since the formation of the acetyl–enzyme is inhibited by 3-phosphoglyceraldehyde, glyceraldehyde, NAD and phosphate, which are the substrates and cofactors of the classical dehydrogenase reaction, the active site for esterolysis must involve a portion of the active site for oxidation. Moreover, both the esterase and the dehydrogenase activities are inhibited by iodoacetic acid.

In order to investigate the structure of the active site, the enzyme was labelled with [^{14}C]iodoacetic acid (IAA) or [^{14}C]*p*-nitrophenyl acetate (*p*-NPA). The labeled peptides obtained after digestion with trypsin and pepsin, respectively are shown below[157].

([^{14}C]IAA):

$^{14}CH_2COOH$ (on the first *Cys*)

Ileu·Val·Ser·Asn·Ala·Ser·*Cys*·Thr·Thr·Asn·*Cys*·Leu·Ala·Pro·Leu·Ala·Lys

([^{14}C]*p*-NPA):

$^{14}COCH_3$ (on *Cys*)

Lys·Ileu·Val·Ser·Asn·Ala·Ser·*Cys*(Thr,Thr,Asn)

There is sufficient overlap to indicate that the carboxymethyl site[157] and acetyl site[88,157] are identical. Labelling studies with the yellow sulfhydryl reagent, *N*-(4-dimethylamino-3,5-dinitrophenyl)-maleimide, give compatible

References p. 88

results[144a]. Moreover, for each molecule of enzyme having a molecular weight of 140 000 there are 3 or possibly 4 identical sites, indicating that the enzyme is a trimer or tetramer. It is interesting that only one cysteine in the larger peptide reacts with iodoacetic acid or *p*-nitrophenyl acetate while the other cysteine, which is only 4 amino acids away, is unreactive. The remaining 2 sulfhydryl groups present per monomer of the muscle enzyme do not react with IAA unless the protein is treated with urea. Absence of negative charges may also be significant in view of the fact that the substrates and cofactors of the dehydrogenase such as 3-phosphoglyceraldehyde, NAD, and phosphate are themselves negatively charged. The presence of hydroxyl and amide side-chains in the vicinity of the reactive SH group provides a hydrophilic environment favorable to the formation of ancillary bonds with aldehyde substrates. This work has been extended by Perham and Harris[304] who showed that the same unique octadecapeptide sequence of amino acids occurred in the dehydrogenase enzyme isolated from pig muscle and yeast. Although the catalytic sites of the yeast and muscle enzymes are identical, there are significant differences at distant loci, since the yeast enzyme monomer has only 2 cysteines, both at the active site, whereas the muscle enzyme has 4, of which 2 are at the active site. This particular sequence of amino acids at the active site may be mandatory for the oxidative phosphorylation. Certainly this dehydrogenase, by virtue of formation of high-energy phosphate compounds, is a critical enzyme in those species where the Embden–Meyerhof cycle operates.

(vi) A proposed mechanism for esterase activity

Fig. 29 shows the mechanism proposed by Olson and Park[298] for the

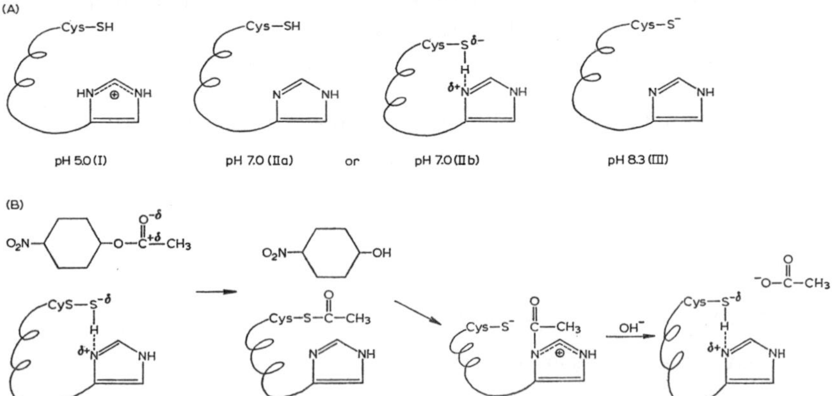

Fig. 29. Proposed mechanism for esterase activity of 3-phosphoglyceraldehyde dehydrogenase. From Olson and Park[298]. (A) Diagrammatic representation of the enzyme at different pH values. (B) Suggested mechanism for hydrolysis of *p*-nitrophenyl acetate.

esterase activity of the enzyme. The first step is a nucleophilic attack of the active-center SH group of the enzyme on the acetyl ester, resulting in the formation of an acetyl thioester. The second step is a hydrolysis of the acetyl thioester, proceeding through an acetyl imidazole intermediate. The proposal is analogous in some respects to that for the esterase activity of chymotrypsin[87,104].

In the mechanism proposed, the attack by the sulfur in the first step is promoted at neutral pH by an adjacent imidazole, which acts by attracting a proton and thereby increasing the negative charge on the sulfur. This mechanism for the acylation step is based in part on model reactions for the non-enzymatic cleavage of nitrophenyl acetate by thiols[29,103,179,349]; furthermore, the esterase system shows the predicted enhancing effect of electron-withdrawing substituents on the benzene ring which increase the positive charge on the carbonyl carbon[30,298]. The proposed role of the imidazole in the acylation step is based in part on the finding of Jencks and Carriuolo[181] that imidazole can catalyze acetyl transfer from acetyl imidazole to thiol acceptors.

The participation of the imidazole of histidine in both the acylation and deacylation steps is indicated by the pH dependence of these steps[298], and the correspondence of the spectrum of the acetyl–enzyme and acetylimidazole[159]. The proposed role of histidine in the deacylation step, *i.e.* in the hydrolysis of the thio ester, is in line with the well-established role of imidazole in catalyzing acyl transfer, presumably *via* an acyl–imidazole intermediate[31,180]. Such a catalytic effect is very striking in those model systems in which an intramolecular hydrolysis of a *p*-nitrophenyl ester is catalyzed by a sterically restricted imidazole group[45,46].

(vii) A proposed mechanism for dehydrogenase activity

In this proposal (Fig. 30) the first step is analogous to that for the esterase reaction, again characterized by a nucleophilic attack by the SH group, this time upon the aldehyde carbon to form a thiohemiacetal. After dehydrogenation of the latter to form a thioester and replacement of the NADH by the more tightly bound NAD[422], the next step proposed is again a cleavage of the thioester *via* an acetyl–imidazole intermediate, but this time with phosphate or arsenate as the acceptor rather than water. This step, in contrast to the hydrolytic reaction, requires NAD[161,322] and it may be that the positive charge on the pyridinium moiety plays a role in attracting the phosphate anion[298] or that a more complex effect of NAD^+ on the conformation of the protein is involved[119]. The reversal of this second step has an exact counterpart in a model reaction in which imidazole catalyzes the transfer of an acetyl group from acetyl phosphate to a thiol acceptor[180].

The proposed model, involving cooperation between a cysteine and a

References p. 88

histidine at the active center, requires the assumption that these two amino acids are brought together by a folding of the peptide chain, since there is no histidine in the active-center peptide obtained by tryptic digestion. This model can explain satisfactorily the oxidative phosphorylation as well as

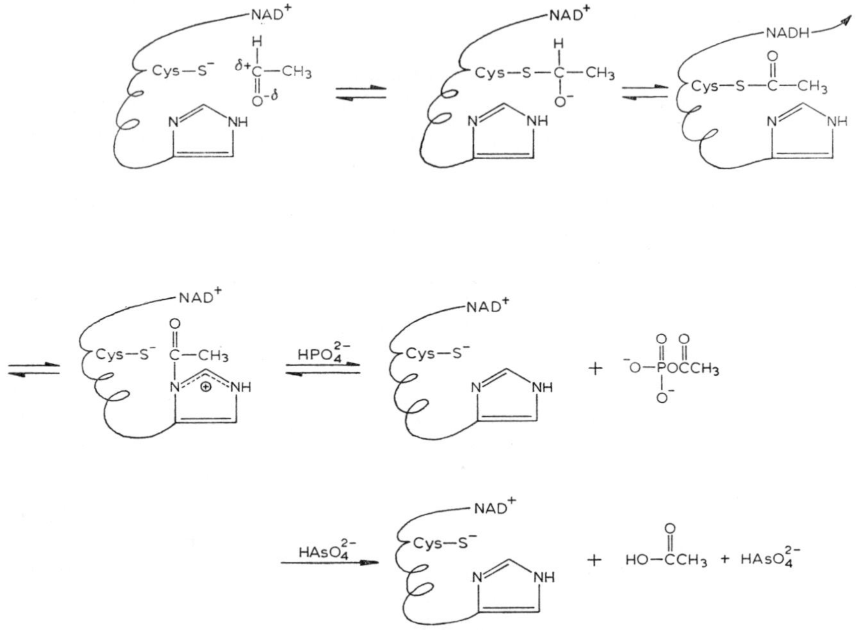

Fig. 30. Proposed mechanism for dehydrogenase reaction using acetaldehyde as the model substrate in place of 3-phosphoglyceraldehyde. From Olson and Park[298].

the transferase and esterase activities of the enzyme. It is also compatible with Racker and Krimsky's finding of selective retention of the oxidation function during proteolytic modification of the enzyme, since this could be accompanied by an unfolding which separated the histidine and cysteine sites. The model may also be compatible with the acylphosphatase function of the oxidized protein, since the imidazole may catalyze hydrolysis of the acylphosphates when no SH is available to perhaps stabilize the acyl–enzyme. However, the increase in acylphosphatase with decreasing pH is puzzling[328]. No attempt has been made to include in the model the nature of the binding of NAD or of the mechanisms of the NADHX formation, diaphorase-like activity, or transphosphorylation.

It should be emphasized that the above proposal is only a working hypothesis, and that there is as yet no direct chemical evidence for the existence of an acetyl–imidazole intermediate. If such an intermediate exists, the conditions of isolation of the labelled peptides must favor its conversion to an *S*-acyl derivative. Under certain conditions it has been possible to prepare an acyl–enzyme which yields upon digestion an *N*-acetyl-lysine containing peptide[272], but this form of acyl–enzyme appears not to be catalytically active.

References p. 88

REFERENCES

1 R. H. Abeles, R. F. Hutton and F. H. Westheimer, *J. Am. Chem. Soc.*, 79 (1957) 712.
2 R. H. Abeles and H. A. Lee Jr., *J. Biol. Chem.*, 235 (1960) 1499.
3 T. Agawa and S. I. Miller, *J. Am. Chem. Soc.*, 83 (1961) 449.
4 R. A. Alberty, *J. Am. Chem. Soc.*, 75 (1953) 1928.
5 V. E. Althouse, K. Ueda and H. S. Mosher, *J. Am. Chem. Soc.*, 82 (1960) 5938.
6 S. G. A. Alivisatos and L. LaMantia, *Biochem. Biophys. Res. Commun.*, 2 (1960) 164.
7 S. G. A. Alivisatos, G. A. Mourkides and A. Jibril, *Nature*, 186 (1960) 718.
8 S. G. A. Alivisatos, F. Ungar, L. Luckas and L. LaMantia, *J. Biol. Chem.*, 235 (1960) 1742.
9 S. G. A. Alivisatos, F. Ungar, A. Jibril and G. A. Mourkides, *Biochim. Biophys. Acta*, 51 (1961) 361.
10 S. G. A. Alivisatos and D. W. Woolley, *J. Am. Chem. Soc.*, 77 (1955) 1065.
11 W. S. Allison and N. O. Kaplan, *J. Biol. Chem.*, 239 (1964) 2140.
12 R. Amelunxen and S. Grisolia, *J. Biol. Chem.*, 237 (1962) 3240.
13 A. G. Anderson and G. Berkehammer, *J. Am. Chem. Soc.*, 80 (1958) 992.
14 B. M. Anderson and C. D. Anderson, *Biochem. Biophys. Res. Commun.*, 16 (1964) 258.
15 B. M. Anderson, C. J. Ciotti and N. O. Kaplan, *J. Biol. Chem.*, 234 (1959) 1219.
16 B. M. Anderson and N. O. Kaplan, *J. Biol. Chem.*, 234 (1959) 1226.
17 H. Ankel, T. Bucher and R. Czok, *Biochem. Z.*, 332 (1960) 315.
18 Y. Aone, *Osaka Daigaku Igaku Zasshi*, 10 (1950) 619.
19 E. Apella and C. L. Markert, *Biochem. Biophys. Res. Commun.*, 6 (1961) 171.
20 D. I. Arnon, L. L. Rosenberg and F. R. Whatley, *Nature*, 173 (1954) 1132.
21 L. Astrachan, S. P. Colowick and N. O. Kaplan, *Biochim. Biophys. Acta*, 24 (1957) 141.
22 M. A. Atkinson, J. F. Jackson, R. K. Morton and A. W. Murray, *Nature*, 196 (1962) 35.
23 K. I. Bäcklin, *Acta Chem. Scand.*, 12 (1958) 1279.
24 R. H. Baker, *Biochemistry*, 1 (1962) 41.
25 R. M. Baker and H. R. Mahler, *Biochemistry*, 1 (1962) 35.
26 A. Ballio and G. Serlupi-Crescenzi, *Nature*, 180 (1957) 1203.
27 E. S. G. Barron, *Advan. Enzymol.*, 11 (1951) 201.
28 E. S. G. Barron and S. Levine, *Arch. Biochem. Biophys.*, 41 (1952) 175.
29 M. L. Bender, *J. Am. Chem. Soc.*, 82 (1960) 1904.
30 M. L. Bender and K. Nakamura, *J. Am. Chem. Soc.*, 84 (1963) 2577.
31 M. L. Bender and B. W. Turnquest, *J. Am. Chem. Soc.*, 79 (1956) 1656.
32 C. P. Benedict and H. Beavers, *Nature*, 191 (1961) 71.
33 A. E. Bliss, *Arch. Biochem. Biophys.*, 31 (1951) 197.
34 V. Bloomfield and R. A. Alberty, *J. Biol. Chem.*, 238 (1963) 2817.
35 V. Bloomfield, L. Peller and R. A. Alberty, *J. Am. Chem. Soc.*, 84 (1962) 4367.
36 V. Bloomfield, L. Peller and R. A. Alberty, *J. Am. Chem. Soc.*, 84 (1962) 4375.
37 D. H. Bone, *Biochim. Biophys. Acta*, 67 (1963) 589.
38 P. D. Boyer, in P. D. Boyer, H. Lardy and K. Myrbäck (Eds.), *The Enzymes*, Vol. 1, Academic Press, New York, 1959, p. 511.
39 P. D. Boyer, H. Lardy and K. Myrbäck (Eds.), *The Enzymes*, Vol. 7, Academic Press, New York, 1963.
40 P. D. Boyer and A. R. Schulz, in R. Benesch *et al.* (Eds.), *Sulfur in Proteins*, Academic Press, New York, 1959, p. 199.
41 P. D. Boyer and H. Theorell, *Acta Chem. Scand.*, 10 (1955) 447.
42 G. Brawerman and N. Konigsberg, *Biochim. Biophys. Acta*, 43 (1960) 374.
43 F. N. Brenneman and W. A. Volk, *J. Biol. Chem.*, 234 (1959) 2443.
44 M. C. Brown and H. S. Mosher, *J. Biol. Chem.*, 235 (1960) 2145.
45 T. C. Bruice, *J. Am. Chem. Soc.*, 81 (1959) 5444.
46 T. C. Bruici and J. M. Sturtevant, *J. Am. Chem. Soc.*, 81 (1959) 2860.
47 H. B. Burch, C. A. Storvick, R. L. Bicknell, H. C. Kung, L. G. Alejo, W. A.

EVERHART, O. H. LOWRY, C. G. KING AND O. A. BESSEY, *J. Biol. Chem.*, 212 (1955) 897.
48 K. BURTON AND T. H. WILSON, *Biochem. J.*, 54 (1953) 86.
49 R. M. BURTON, *Federation Proc.*, 11 (1952) 193.
50 R. M. BURTON AND N. O. KAPLAN, *Arch. Biochem. Biophys.*, 70 (1957) 107.
51 R. M. BURTON AND N. O. KAPLAN, *J. Biol. Chem.*, 206 (1954) 283.
52 R. M. BURTON AND N. O. KAPLAN, *J. Biol. Chem.*, 211 (1954) 447.
53 R. M. BURTON AND M. LAMBORG, *Arch. Biochem. Biophys.*, 62 (1956) 369.
54 R. M. BURTON AND A. SAN PIETRO, *Arch. Biochem. Biophys.*, 48 (1954) 184.
55 R. M. BURTON, A. SAN PIETRO AND N. O. KAPLAN, *Arch. Biochem. Biophys.*, 70 (1957) 87.
56 K. J. CARPENTER AND E. KODICEK, *Biochem. J.*, 46 (1950) 421.
57 W. S. CAUGHEY AND K. A. SCHELLENBERG, *Federation Proc.*, 23 (1964) 479.
58 P. G. CELLIERS, A. STOCK AND G. PFLEIDERER, *Biochim. Biophys. Acta*, 77 (1963) 577.
59 R. R. J. CHAFFEE AND W. L. BARTLETT, *Biochim. Biophys. Acta*, 39 (1960) 370.
60 B. CHANCE, in W. D. MCELROY AND H. B. GLASS (Eds.), *The Mechanism of Enzyme Action*, Johns Hopkins, Baltimore, 1954, p. 399.
61 B. CHANCE, in W. D. MCELROY AND H. B. GLASS (Eds.), *The Mechanism of Enzyme Action*, Johns Hopkins, Baltimore,1954, p. 445.
62 B. CHANCE AND J. HARTING, *Federation Proc.*, 12 (1953) 188.
63 B. CHANCE AND J. B. NEILANDS, *J. Biol. Chem.*, 199 (1952) 383.
64 M. L. W. CHANG AND B. C. JOHNSON, *J. Biol. Chem.*, 234 (1959) 1817.
65 S. CHAYKIN, J. O. MEINHART AND E. G. KREBS, *J. Biol. Chem.*, 220 (1956) 811.
66 N. J. CHU AND C. E. BALLOU, *J. Am. Chem. Soc.*, 83 (1961) 1711.
67 J. E. CHURCHICH AND F. WOLD, *Biochemistry*, 2 (1963) 781.
68 G. CILENTO, E. DECARVALHO FILHO AND A. C. GIORA ALBANESE, *J. Am. Chem. Soc.*, 80 (1958) 4472.
69 G. CILENTO AND P. GIUSTI, *J. Am. Chem. Soc.*, 81 (1959) 3802.
70 G. CILENTO AND P. TEDESCHI, *J. Biol. Chem.*, 236 (1961) 907.
71 M. M. CIOTTI, S. R. HUMPHREYS, J. M. VENDITTI, N. O. KAPLAN AND A. GOLDIN, *Cancer Res.*, 20 (1960) 1195.
72 M. M. CIOTTI AND N. O. KAPLAN, in S. P. COLOWICK AND N. O. KAPLAN (Eds.), *Methods in Enzymology*, Vol. 3, Academic Press, New York, 1957, p. 890.
73 M. CLARK AND J. H. PARK, unpublished experiments.
74 W. M. CLARK, *Oxidation–Reduction Potentials of Organic Systems*, Chapter 1, Williams and Wilkins, Baltimore, 1960, p. 440.
75 W. M. CLARK, *Science*, 141 (1963) 995.
76 W. W. CLELAND, *Biochim. Biophys. Acta*, 67 (1963) 104.
77 W. W. CLELAND, *Biochim. Biophys. Acta*, 67 (1963) 173.
78 W. W. CLELAND, *Biochim. Biophys. Acta*, 67 (1963) 188.
79 S. P. COLOWICK, in W. D. MCELROY AND H. B. GLASS (Eds.), *The Mechanism of Enzyme Action*, Johns Hopkins, Baltimore, 1954, p. 381.
80 S. P. COLOWICK, in W. D. MCELROY AND H. B. GLASS (Eds.), *Phosphorus Metabolism*, Vol. 1, Johns Hopkins, Baltimore, 1951, p. 436.
81 S. P. COLOWICK, N. O. KAPLAN AND M. M. CIOTTI, *J. Biol. Chem.*, 191 (1951) 447.
82 S. P. COLOWICK, N. O. KAPLAN, E. F. NEUFELD AND M. M. CIOTTI, *J. Biol. Chem.*, 195 (1952) 95.
83 B. COMMONER, J. J. HEISE, B. B. LIPPINCOTT, R. E. NORBERG, J. V. PASSONEAU AND J. TOWNSEND, *Science*, 126 (1957) 57.
84 J. W. CORNFORTH, G. RYBACK, G. POPJAK, C. DONNINGER AND G. SCHROEPFER, *Biochem. Biophys. Res. Commun.*, 9 (1962) 371.
85 C. F. CORI, S. F. VELICK AND G. T. CORI, *Biochim. Biophys. Acta*, 4 (1950) 160.
86 G. T. CORI, M. W. SLEIN AND C. F. CORI, *J. Biol. Chem.*, 159 (1945) 565.
87 L. W. CUNNINGHAM, *Science*, 125 (1957) 1145.
88 L. W. CUNNINGHAM AND A. SCHEPMAN, *Biochim. Biophys. Acta*, 73 (1963) 406.
89 G. CZERLINSKI, *Biochim. Biophys. Acta*, 64 (1962) 199.
90 K. DALZIEL, *Acta Chem. Scand.*, 11 (1957) 1706.

91 K. Dalziel, *Biochem. J.*, 84 (1962) 240.
92 K. Dalziel, *Biochem. J.*, 84 (1962) 244.
93 K. Dalziel, *J. Biol. Chem.*, 238 (1963) 1538.
94 K. Dalziel, *J. Biol. Chem.*, 238 (1963) 2850.
95 K. Dalziel, *Nature*, 197 (1963) 462.
96 K. Dalziel, *Trans. Faraday Soc.*, 54 (1958) 1247.
97 W. B. Dandliker and J. B. Fox, *J. Biol. Chem.*, 214 (1955) 275.
98 D. D. Davies and E. Kun, *Biochem. J.*, 66 (1957) 307.
99 J. Davoll, B. Lythgoe and A. R. Todd, *J. Chem. Soc.*, (1946) 833.
100 T. Devenye, T. Keleti, B. Szorenyi and M. Saggo, *Acta Physiol. Acad. Sci. Hung.*, 18 (1960) 271.
101 F. Dickens and H. McIlwain, *Biochem. J.*, 32 (1938) 1615.
102 L. S. Dietrich, J. M. Friedland and L. A. Kaplan, *J. Biol. Chem.*, 233 (1958) 964.
103 B. M. Dirks and P. D. Boyer, *Cereal Chem.*, 28 (1951) 483.
104 G. H. Dixon and H. Neurath, *J. Am. Chem. Soc.*, 79 (1957) 4558.
105 M. Dixon and E. C. Webb, *The Enzymes*, Academic Press, New York, 1958, p. 394.
106 M. Dixon and L. G. Zerfas, *Biochem. J.*, 34 (1940) 371.
107 W. Doering and W. McEwen, *J. Am. Chem. Soc.*, 73 (1951) 2104.
108 M. I. Dolin, *Arch. Biochem. Biophys.*, 55 (1955) 415.
109 M. I. Dolin and K. B. Jacobson, *Biochem. Biophys. Res. Commun.*, 11 (1963) 102.
110 M. Doudoroff, H. A. Barker and W. Z. Hassid, *J. Biol. Chem.*, 168 (1947) 725.
111 M. Doudoroff, H. A. Barker and W. Z. Hassid, *J. Biol. Chem.*, 170 (1947) 147.
112 G. R. Drysdale, M. J. Spiegel and P. Strittmatter, *J. Biol. Chem.*, 236 (1961) 2323.
113 H. E. Dubb, M. Saunders and J. H. Wang, *J. Am. Chem. Soc.*, 80 (1958) 1767.
114 K. Ebisuzaki and E. S. G. Barron, *Arch. Biochem. Biophys.*, 69 (1957) 555.
115 R. Ehring and S. P. Colowick, *Federation Proc.*, 23 (1964) 424.
116 R. Ehring and S. P. Colowick (in preparation).
117 P. Elodi, *Acta Physiol. Acad. Sci. Hung.*, 13 (1958) 219.
118 P. Elodi, *Acta Physiol. Acad. Sci. Hung.*, 20 (1961) 311.
119 P. Elodi and G. Szabolcsi, *Nature*, 184 (1959) 56.
120 P. Elodi and E. Szorenyi, *Acta Physiol. Acad. Sci. Hung.*, 9 (1956) 339.
121 *Enzyme Nomenclature: Recommendations (1964) of the International Union of Biochemistry on the Nomenclature and Classification of Enzymes, together with their Units and the Symbols of Enzyme Kinetics*, Elsevier, Amsterdam, 1965.
122 H. von Euler, E. Adler and H. Hellstrom, *Z. Physiol. Chem.*, 241 (1936) 239.
123 H. von Euler, H. Albers and F. Schlenk, *Z. Physiol. Chem.*, 237 (1935) 180 I; 240 (1936) 113.
124 C. P. Fawcett and N. O. Kaplan, *J. Biol. Chem.*, 237 (1962) 1709.
125 W. Ferdinand, *Biochem. J.*, 92 (1964) 578.
126 H. F. Fisher, E. E. Conn, B. Vennesland and F. H. Westheimer, *J. Biol. Chem.*, 202 (1953) 687.
127 H. F. Fisher and D. G. Cross, *Federation Proc.*, 22 (1963) 289.
128 H. F. Fisher, D. G. Cross and L. L. McGregor, *Nature*, 196 (1962) 895.
129 H. F. Fisher, L. L. McGregor and D. G. Cross, *Biochim. Biophys. Acta*, 65 (1962) 175.
130 H. F. Fisher, L. L. McGregor and U. Power, *Biochem. Biophys. Res. Commun.*, 8 (1962) 402.
131 H. F. Fisher, L. L. McGregor and U. Power, *Federation Proc.*, 21 (1961) 56.
132 A. L. Fluharty and C. E. Ballou, *J. Biol. Chem.*, 234 (1959) 2517.
133 D. W. Foster and B. Bloom, *J. Biol. Chem.*, 236 (1961) 2548.
134 J. B. Fox and W. B. Dandliker, *J. Biol. Chem.*, 218 (1956) 53.
135 J. B. Fox and W. B. Dandliker, *J. Biol. Chem.*, 221 (1956) 1005.
136 C. Frieden, *Biochim. Biophys. Acta*, 27 (1958) 431.
137 C. Frieden, *J. Biol. Chem.*, 234 (1959) 809.
138 C. Frieden, *J. Biol. Chem.*, 234 (1959) 815.
139 C. Frieden, *J. Biol. Chem.*, 234 (1959) 2891.
140 C. Frieden, *J. Biol. Chem.*, 237 (1962) 2396.
141 H. J. Fromm and O. R. Nelson, *J. Biol. Chem.*, 237 (1962) 215.

[142] R. C. Fuller and M. Gibbs, *Plant Physiol.*, 34 (1953) 329.
[143] M. Gibbs, *Nature*, 170 (1952) 164.
[144] A. Gierer, *Biochim. Biophys. Acta*, 17 (1955) 111.
[144a] A. H. Gold and H. L. Segal, *Biochemistry*, 3 (1964) 778.
[145] D. S. Goldman, *J. Am. Chem. Soc.*, 76 (1954) 2841.
[146] D. E. Griffiths, *Federation Proc.*, 22 (1963) 1064.
[147] S. Grisolia and B. J. Joyce, *Biochem. Biophys. Res. Commun.*, 1 (1959) 280.
[148] L. Grossman and N. O. Kaplan, *J. Biol. Chem.*, 231 (1958) 727.
[149] A. L. Guardiola, D. Paretsky and W. McEwen, *J. Am. Chem. Soc.*, 80 (1958) 418.
[150] E. Haas, *Biochem. Z.*, 288 (1936) 123.
[151] D. D. Hagerman and C. A. Villee, *J. Biol. Chem.*, 234 (1959) 2031.
[152] R. H. Hagerman and D. I. Arnon, *Arch. Biochem. Biophys.*, 55 (1955) 162.
[153] M. T. Hakala, A. J. Glaid and G. W. Schwert, *J. Biol. Chem.*, 221 (1956) 191.
[154] P. Handler and J. R. Klein, *J. Biol. Chem.*, 143 (1942) 49.
[155] J. I. Harris and R. N. Perham, *Biochem. J.*, 89 (1963) 60P.
[156] J. I. Harris and R. N. Perham, *Proc. 6th Intern. Congr. Biochem.*, New York, 1964, p. 293.
[157] J. I. Harris, B. P. Meriwether and J. H. Park, *Nature*, 197 (1963) 154.
[158] J. Harting, in W. D. McElroy and H. B. Glass (Eds.), *The Mechanism of Enzyme Action*, Johns Hopkins, 1953, p. 536.
[159] J. Harting and B. Chance, *Federation Proc.*, 12 (1953) 714.
[160] J. Harting and S. F. Velick, *Federation Proc.*, 11 (1952) 226.
[161] J. Harting and S. F. Velick, *J. Biol. Chem.*, 207 (1954) 857; 207 (1954) 867.
[162] B. S. Hartley and B. A. Kilby, *Biochem. J.*, 56 (1954) 288.
[163] O. Hayaishi, *Oxygenases*, Academic Press, New York, 1962, p. 1.
[164] J. E. Hayes Jr. and S. F. Velick, *J. Biol. Chem.*, 207 (1954) 225.
[165] R. T. Hersh, *Biochim. Biophys. Acta*, 58 (1962) 353.
[166] A. G. Hilvers, *Biochim. Biophys. Acta*, 54 (1961) 186.
[167] A. G. Hilvers and J. H. M. Weenen, *Biochim. Biophys. Acta*, 58 (1962) 380.
[168] F. L. Hoch and B. L. Vallee, in R. Benesch, R. E. Benesch, P. D. Boyer, I. M. Klotz, W. R. Middlebrook, A. G. Szent-Gyorgyi and D. R. Schwarz (Eds.), *Sulfur in Proteins*, Academic Press, New York, 1959, p. 245.
[169] F. L. Hoch, R. J. P. Williams and B. L. Vallee, *J. Biol. Chem.*, 232 (1958) 453.
[170] W. I. M. Holman and D. J. deLange, *Biochem. J.*, 45 (1949) 559.
[171] J. W. Huff, *J. Biol. Chem.*, 167 (1947) 151.
[172] J. W. Huff and W. A. Perlzweig, *J. Biol. Chem.*, 150 (1943) 395.
[173] J. W. Huff and W. A. Perlzweig, *J. Biol. Chem.*, 167 (1947) 157.
[174] N. A. Hughes, G. W. Kenner and A. R. Todd, *J. Chem. Soc.*, (1957) 3733.
[175] R. F. Hutton and F. H. Westheimer, *Tetrahedron*, 3 (1958) 73.
[176] A. Hvidt and K. Linderstrøm-Lang, *Biochim. Biophys. Acta*, 14 (1954) 574.
[177] I. Isenberg and A. Szent-Györgyi, *Proc. Natl. Acad. Sci., (U.S.)*, 45 (1959) 1229.
[178] G. Jecsai, *Acta Physiol. Acad. Sci. Hung.*, 17 (1960) 161.
[179] W. P. Jencks and J. Carriuolo, *J. Am. Chem. Soc.*, 82 (1960) 1778.
[180] W. P. Jencks and J. Carriuolo, *J. Biol. Chem.*, 234 (1959) 1272.
[181] W. P. Jencks and J. Carriuolo, *J. Biol. Chem.*, 234 (1959) 1280.
[182] B. Jirgensons, *J. Am. Chem. Soc.*, 83 (1961) 3161.
[183] C. C. Johnston, J. L. Gardner, C. H. Suelter and D. E. Metzler, *Biochemistry*, 2 (1963) 689.
[184] Y. Kagawa, *J. Biochem. (Tokyo)*, 47 (1960) 104.
[185] J. H. R. Kagi and B. L. Vallee, *J. Biol. Chem.*, 235 (1960) 3188.
[186] H. M. Kalckar, *Chem. Rev.*, 28 (1941) 71.
[187] N. O. Kaplan, *Brookhaven Symp. Biol.*, 17 (1964) 131.
[188] N. O. Kaplan, in W. D. McElroy and H. B. Glass (Eds.), *Phosphorus Metabolism*, Johns Hopkins, Baltimore, 1955, p. 428.
[189] N. O. Kaplan, in F. E. W. Wolstenholme and C. M. O'Connor (Eds.), *Steric Course of Microbiological Reactions*, Churchill, London, 1959, p. 37.
[190] N. O. Kaplan, in P. D. Boyer, H. Lardy and K. Myrbäck (Eds.), *The Enzymes*, Vol. 3, Academic Press, New York, 1960, p. 105.

[191] N. O. KAPLAN, *Record Chem. Progr. (Kresge-Hooker Sci. Lib.)*, 16 (1955) 176.
[192] N. O. KAPLAN AND M. M. CIOTTI, *Ann. N.Y. Acad. Sci.*, 94 (1961) 701.
[193] N. O. KAPLAN AND M. M. CIOTTI, in S. P. COLOWICK AND N. O. KAPLAN (Eds.), *Methods in Enzymology*, Vol. 3, Academic Press, New York, 1957, p. 253.
[194] N. O. KAPLAN AND M. M. CIOTTI, *J. Biol. Chem.*, 201 (1953) 785.
[195] N. O. KAPLAN AND M. M. CIOTTI, *J. Biol. Chem.*, 211 (1954) 431.
[196] N. O. KAPLAN AND M. M. CIOTTI, *J. Biol. Chem.*, 221 (1956) 823.
[197] N. O. KAPLAN, M. M. CIOTTI AND F. E. STOLZENBACH, *Arch. Biochem. Biophys.*, 69 (1957) 441.
[198] N. O. KAPLAN, M. M. CIOTTI AND F. E. STOLZENBACH, *J. Biol. Chem.*, 221 (1956) 833.
[199] N. O. KAPLAN, M. M. CIOTTI, F. E. STOLZENBACH AND N. R. BACHUR, *J. Am. Chem. Soc.*, 77 (1955) 815.
[200] N. O. KAPLAN, M. M. CIOTTI, J. VAN EYS AND R. M. BURTON, *J. Biol. Chem.*, 234 (1959) 134.
[201] N. O. KAPLAN, S. P. COLOWICK AND C. C. BARNES, *J. Biol. Chem.*, 191 (1951) 461.
[202] N. O. KAPLAN, S. P. COLOWICK AND M. M. CIOTTI, *J. Biol. Chem.*, 194 (1952) 579.
[203] N. O. KAPLAN, S. P. COLOWICK AND E. F. NEUFELD, *J. Biol. Chem.*, 195 (1952) 107.
[204] N. O. KAPLAN, S. P. COLOWICK AND E. F. NEUFELD, *J. Biol. Chem.*, 205 (1953) 1.
[205] N. O. KAPLAN, S. P. COLOWICK, L. J. ZATMAN AND M. M. CIOTTI, *J. Biol. Chem.*, 205 (1953) 31.
[206] N. O. KAPLAN, A. GOLDIN, S. R. HUMPHREYS, M. M. CIOTTI AND J. M. VENDITTI, *Science*, 120 (1954) 437.
[207] N. O. KAPLAN AND F. E. STOLZENBACH, in S. P. COLOWICK AND N. O. KAPLAN (Eds.), *Methods in Enzymology*, Vol. 3, Academic Press, New York, 1957, p. 899.
[208] N. O. KAPLAN, M. N. SWARTZ, M. E. FRECH AND M. M. CIOTTI, *Proc. Natl. Acad. Sci., (U.S.)*, 42 (1956) 481.
[209] J. L. KARLE, *Acta Cryst.*, 14 (1961) 497.
[210] P. KARRER, F. W. KAHNT, R. EPSTEIN, W. JAFFE AND T. ISHII, *Helv. Chim. Acta*, 21 (1938) 223.
[211] P. KARRER AND F. J. STARE, *Helv. Chim. Acta*, 20 (1937) 418.
[212] P. KARRER AND O. WARBURG, *Biochem. Z.*, 285 (1936) 297.
[213] T. KELETI, *Acta Physiol. Acad. Sci. Hung.*, 13 (1958) 309.
[214] T. KELETI, personal communication.
[215] T. KELETI, S. GYORGYI, M. TELEGDI AND H. ZALUSKA, *Acta Physiol. Acad. Sci. Hung.*, 22 (1962) 11.
[216] T. KELETI AND M. TELEGDI, *Acta Physiol. Acad. Sci. Hung.*, 15 (1959) 281.
[217] T. KELETI AND M. TELEGDI, *Acta Physiol. Acad. Sci. Hung.*, 17 (1960) 141.
[218] L. P. KENDALL AND A. N. RAMANATHAN, *Biochem. J.*, 52 (1952) 430.
[219] W. W. KIELLY AND J. R. BRONK, *J. Biol. Chem.*, 230 (1958) 521.
[220] H. N. KIRKMAN AND E. M. HENDRICKSON, *J. Biol. Chem.*, 237 (1961) 2371.
[221] H. KLENOW AND B. ANDERSEN, *Biochim. Biophys. Acta*, 23 (1957) 92.
[222] W. E. KNOX, *J. Biol. Chem.*, 163 (1946) 699.
[223] W. E. KNOX AND W. I. GROSSMAN, *J. Biol. Chem.*, 168 (1947) 363.
[224] O. J. KOEPPE, P. D. BOYER AND M. P. STULBERG, *J. Biol. Chem.*, 219 (1956) 569.
[225] O. J. KOEPPE, A. L. MURDOCK AND D. S. SHEPPARD, *Federation Proc.*, 18 (1959) 263.
[226] A. KORNBERG AND W. E. PRICER, *J. Biol. Chem.*, 186 (1950) 557.
[227] D. E. KOSHLAND, *J. Am. Chem. Soc.*, 73 (1951) 4103.
[228] E. M. KOSOWER, *Biochim. Biophys. Acta*, 56 (1962) 474.
[229] E. M. KOSOWER, in P. D. BOYER, H. LARDY AND K. MYRBÄCK (Eds.), *The Enzymes*, Vol. 3, Academic Press, New York, 1960, p. 171.
[230] E. M. KOSOWER, *J. Am. Chem. Soc.*, 77 (1955) 3883.
[231] E. M. KOSOWER, *J. Am. Chem. Soc.*, 78 (1956) 3497.
[232] E. M. KOSOWER, *J. Am. Chem. Soc.*, 80 (1958) 3253.
[233] E. M. KOSOWER, *J. Am. Chem. Soc.*, 80 (1958) 3261.
[234] E. M. KOSOWER, *Molecular Biochemistry*, McGrawHill, New York, 1962.
[235] E. M. KOSOWER, *Tetrahedron*, 5 (1959) 281.
[236] E. M. KOSOWER AND P. E. KLINEDINST JR., *J. Am. Chem. Soc.*, 78 (1956) 3493.

237 G. KRAKOW, J. LUDOWIEG, J. MATHER, W. NORMORE, L. TOSI, S. UDAKA AND B. VENNESLAND, *Biochemistry*, 10 (1963) 1009.
238 E. G. KREBS AND V. A. NAJJAR, *J. Exptl. Med.*, 88 (1948) 569.
239 E. G. KREBS, G. W. RAFTER AND J. M. JUNGE, *J. Biol. Chem.*, 200 (1953) 479.
240 I. KRIMSKY AND E. RACKER, *Biochemistry*, 2 (1963) 512.
241 I. KRIMSKY AND E. RACKER, *J. Biol. Chem.*, 198 (1952) 721.
242 F. KROHNKE AND K. ELLENGAST, *Ann. Chem.*, 600 (1956) 176.
243 F. KROHNKE AND K. ELLENGAST, *Ann. Chem.*, 600 (1956) 198.
244 H. KUBO, M. IWATSUBO, H. WATARI AND T. SOYAMA, *J. Biochem.*, 46 (1959) 1171.
245 M. R. LAMBORG, R. M. BURTON AND N. O. KAPLAN, *J. Am. Chem. Soc.*, 79 (1957) 6173.
246 M. R. LAMBORG, F. E. STOLZENBACH AND N. O. KAPLAN, *J. Biol. Chem.*, 231 (1958) 685.
247 T. A. LANGAN JR., N. O. KAPLAN AND L. SHUSTER, *J. Biol. Chem.*, 234 (1959) 2161.
248 S. B. LEIGHTON, *Thesis*, The Johns Hopkins University, Baltimore, 1957.
249 G. A. LEPAGE, in H. A. LARDY (Ed.), *Respiratory Enzymes*, Burgess, Minneapolis, 1949, p. 88.
250 N. LEVITAS, J. ROBINSON, F. ROSEN, J. W. HUFF AND W. A. PERLZWEIG, *J. Biol. Chem.*, 167 (1947) 169.
251 H. R. LEVY, F. A. LOEWUS AND B. VENNESLAND, *J. Am. Chem. Soc.*, 79 (1957) 2949.
252 H. R. LEVY, P. TALALAY AND B. VENNESLAND, in P. B. D. DE LA MARE AND W. KLYNE (Eds.), *Progress in Stereochemistry*, Vol. 3, Butterworth, London, 1962, p. 239.
253 H. R. LEVY AND B. VENNESLAND, *J. Biol. Chem.*, 228 (1957) 85.
254 T. K. LI, O. D. ULMER AND B. L. VALLEE, *Biochemistry*, 1 (1963) 114.
255 T. K. LI, O. D. ULMER AND B. L. VALLEE, *Biochemistry*, 2 (1963) 482.
256 T. K. LI AND B. L. VALLEE, *Biochem. Biophys. Res. Commun.*, 12 (1963) 44.
257 T. K. LI AND B. L. VALLEE, *Biochemistry*, 3 (1964) 869.
258 F. LIPMANN, *Advan. Enzymol.*, 1 (1941) 99; 6 (1946) 231.
259 F. A. LOEWUS, B. VENNESLAND AND D. C. HARRIS, *J. Am. Chem. Soc.*, 77 (1955) 3391.
260 F. A. LOEWUS, F. H. WESTHEIMER AND B. VENNESLAND, *J. Am. Chem. Soc.*, 75 (1953) 5018.
261 J. M. LOWENSTEIN, *J. Biol. Chem.*, 236 (1961) 1213.
262 R. MACLEOD, H. PROSSER, L. FIKENTSCHER, J. LANYI AND H. S. MOSHER, *Biochemistry*, 3 (1964) 838.
263 H. MCILWAIN, *Biochem. J.*, 46 (1950) 612.
264 H. MCILWAIN AND R. RODNIGHT, *Biochem. J.*, 44 (1949) 470.
265 H. R. MAHLER, *Biochim. Biophys. Acta*, 14 (1954) 100.
266 H. R. MAHLER, in *Symposium on Free Radicals in Biological Systems*, Stanford Biophysics Lab., California, 1960.
267 H. R. MAHLER AND J. DOUGLAS, *J. Am. Chem. Soc.*, 79 (1957) 1159.
268 P. J. G. MANN AND J. H. QUASTEL, *Biochem. J.*, 35 (1941) 502.
269 C. L. MARKERT AND F. MOLLER, *Proc. Natl. Acad. Sci., (U.S.)*, 45 (1959) 753.
270 W. MARTI, M. VISCONTINI AND P. KARRER, *Helv. Chim. Acta*, 39 (1956) 1451.
271 R. B. MARTIN AND J. G. HULL, *J. Biol. Chem.*, 289 (1964) 1237.
272 E. MATHEW, C. F. AGNELLO AND J. H. PARK, *J. Biol. Chem.*, 240 (1965) 3232.
273 D. MAUZERALL, referred to by F. WESTHEIMER, in W. D. MCELROY AND H. B. GLASS (Eds.), *The Mechanism of Enzyme Action*, Johns Hopkins, Baltimore, 1954, p. 356.
274 D. MAUZERALL AND F. H. WESTHEIMER, *J. Am. Chem. Soc.*, 77 (1955) 2261.
275 J. O. MEINHART, S. CHAYKIN AND E. G. KREBS, *J. Biol. Chem.*, 220 (1956) 821.
276 J. O. MEINHART AND M. C. HINES, *Federation Proc.*, 16 (1956) 425.
277 A. MEISTER, *J. Biol. Chem.*, 184 (1950) 117.
278 A. D. MERRITT AND G. M. TOMKINS, *J. Biol. Chem.*, 234 (1959) 2778.
279 W. H. MEYER, H. R. MAHLER AND R. H. BAKER JR., *Biochim. Biophys. Acta*, 64 (1962) 353.
280 O. MEYERHOF, *Ann. N.Y. Acad. Sci.*, 45 (1944) 377.
281 O. MEYERHOF AND R. JUNOWICS-KOCHOLATY, *J. Biol. Chem.*, 149 (1943) 71.
282 O. MEYERHOF, P. OHLYMEYER AND W. MOHLE, *Biochem. Z.*, 297 (1938) 113.
283 O. MEYERHOF AND P. OESPER, *J. Biol. Chem.*, 170 (1949) 1.

284 D. B. S. Millar, *J. Biol. Chem.*, 237 (1962) 2135.
285 C. Monder, *Biochemistry*, 2 (1963) 684.
286 A. L. Murdock and O. J. Koeppe, *J. Biol. Chem.*, 239 (1964) 1983.
287 V. A. Najjar, V. White and D. B. McNair-Scott, *Bull. Johns Hopkins Hosp.*, 74 (1944) 378.
288 V. A. Najjar and N. W. Wood, *Proc. Soc. Exptl. Biol. Med.*, 44 (1940) 386.
289 D. M. Needham, L. Siminovitch and S. M. Rapkine, *Biochem. J.*, 49 (1951) 113.
290 P. Negelein and W. Bromel, *Biochem. Z.*, 303 (1939) 132.
291 C. Neuberg and F. F. Nord, *Ber.*, 52 (1919) 2237.
292 R. C. Nordlie and H. J. Fromm, *J. Biol. Chem.*, 234 (1959) 2523.
293 W. B. Novoa and G. W. Schwert, *J. Biol. Chem.*, 236 (1961) 2150.
294 A. P. Nygaard and W. J. Rutter, *Acta Chem. Scand.*, 10 (1956) 37.
295 A. P. Nygaard and H. Theorell, *Acta Chem. Scand.*, 9 (1955) 1300.
296 P. Oesper, *J. Biol. Chem.*, 207 (1954) 421.
297 P. Oesper, in W. D. McElroy and H. B. Glass (Eds.), *Phosphorus Metabolism*, Vol. 1, Johns Hopkins, Baltimore, 1951, p. 523.
298 E. J. Olson and J. H. Park, *J. Biol. Chem.*, 239 (1964) 2316.
299 L. E. Orgel, *Quart. Rev. (London)*, 8 (1954) 422.
300 P. Ottolenghi and O. F. Denstedt, *Can. J. Biochem. Physiol.*, 36 (1958) 1093.
301 J. H. Park and D. E. Koshland, *J. Biol. Chem.*, 233 (1958) 986.
302 J. H. Park, B. P. Meriwether, P. Clodfelder and L. W. Cunningham, *Federation Proc.*, 19 (1960) 29.
303 J. H. Park, B. P. Meriwether, P. Clodfelder and L. W. Cunningham, *J. Biol. Chem.*, 236 (1961) 136.
304 R. Perham and J. I. Harris, *J. Mol. Biol.*, 7 (1963) 316.
305 G. Pfleiderer and F. Auricchio, *Biochem. Biophys. Res. Commun.*, 16 (1964) 53.
306 G. Pfleiderer and E. Hohnholz, *Biochem. Z.*, 331 (1959) 245.
307 G. Pfleiderer, T. T. Holbrook and T. Wieland, *Biochem. Z.*, 338 (1963) 52.
308 G. Pfleiderer, E. Hohnholz-Merz and D. Gerlach, *Biochem. Z.*, 336 (1962) 371.
309 G. Pfleiderer, D. Jeckel and T. Wieland, *Biochem. Z.*, 328 (1956) 187.
310 G. Pfleiderer, E. Sann and F. Ortanderl, *Biochim. Biophys. Acta*, 73 (1963) 39.
311 G. Pfleiderer, E. Sann and A. Stock, *Chem. Ber.*, 93 (1960) 3083.
312 G. Pfleiderer and A. Stock, *Biochem. Z.*, 336 (1962) 56.
313 J. Preiss and P. Handler, *J. Biol. Chem.*, 233 (1958) 488.
314 V. Prelog, in G. E. W. Wolstenholme and C. M. O'Connor (Eds.), *Steric Course of Microbiological Reactions*, Churchill, London, 1959, p. 79.
315 B. Pullman and A. Pullman, *Proc. Natl. Acad. Sci., (U.S.)*, 45 (1959) 136.
316 M. E. Pullman and S. P. Colowick, *J. Biol. Chem.*, 206 (1954) 121.
317 M. E. Pullman, S. P. Colowick and N. O. Kaplan, *J. Biol. Chem.*, 194 (1952) 593.
318 M. E. Pullman, A. San Pietro and S. P. Colowick, *J. Biol. Chem.*, 206 (1954) 129.
319 J. H. Quastel and A. H. M. Wheatley, *Biochem. J.*, 32 (1938) 936.
320 E. Racker, V. Klybas and M. Schramm, *J. Biol. Chem.*, 234 (1959) 2510.
321 E. Racker and I. Krimsky, *Federation Proc.*, 17 (1958) 1135.
322 E. Racker and I. Krimsky, *J. Biol. Chem.*, 198 (1952) 731.
323 E. Racker and I. Krimsky, *Nature*, 169 (1952) 1043.
324 E. Racker and I. Krimsky, *Science*, 122 (1955) 319.
325 G. W. Rafter, *Arch. Biochem. Biophys.*, 67 (1957) 267.
326 G. W. Rafter and S. P. Colowick, *Arch. Biochem. Biophys.*, 66 (1957) 190.
327 G. W. Rafter and S. P. Colowick, *J. Biol. Chem.*, 209 (1954) 773.
328 G. W. Rafter and S. P. Colowick, *J. Biol. Chem.*, 224 (1957) 373.
329 G. W. Rafter, S. Chaykin and E. G. Krebs, *J. Biol. Chem.*, 208 (1954) 799.
330 B. V. Ramasastri and R. L. Blakley, *J. Biol. Chem.*, 239 (1964) 112.
331 D. N. Raval and R. G. Wolfe, *Biochemistry*, 1 (1962) 263.
332 D. N. Raval and R. G. Wolfe, *Biochemistry*, 1 (1962) 1118.
333 D. N. Raval and R. G. Wolfe, *Biochemistry*, 2 (1963) 220.
334 Report of the Commission on Enzymes of the International Union of Biochemistry, Revised Edition, in M. Florkin and E. H. Stotz (Eds.), *Comprehensive Biochemistry*, Vol. 13, Elsevier, Amsterdam, 1965.

335 F. L. Rodkey, *J. Biol. Chem.*, 213 (1955) 777.
336 F. L. Rodkey, *J. Biol. Chem.*, 234 (1959) 188.
337 F. L. Rodkey and J. A. Donovan Jr., *J. Biol. Chem.*, 234 (1959) 677.
338 K. S. Rogers, T. E. Tompson and L. Hellerman, *Biochim. Biophys. Acta*, 64 (1962) 202.
339 L. L. Rosenberg and D. I. Arnon, *J. Biol. Chem.*, 217 (1955) 361.
340 G. D. Sabato and N. O. Kaplan, *Biochemistry*, 2 (1963) 776.
341 A. San Pietro, *J. Biol. Chem.*, 217 (1955) 579.
342 A. San Pietro, *J. Biol. Chem.*, 217 (1955) 589.
343 A. San Pietro, N. O. Kaplan and S. P. Colowick, *J. Biol. Chem.*, 212 (1955) 941.
344 K. A. Schellenberg, *Federation Proc.*, 24 (1965) 233.
345 K. A. Schellenberg and L. Hellerman, *J. Biol. Chem.*, 231 (1958) 547.
346 F. Schlenk, *J. Biol. Chem.*, 146 (1942) 619.
347 F. Schlenk and H. von Euler, *Naturwissenschaften*, 24 (1936) 794.
348 F. Schlenk, H. Hellström and H. von Euler, *Ber.*, 71 (1938) 1471.
349 G. R. Schonbaum and M. L. Bender, *J. Am. Chem. Soc.*, 82 (1960) 1900.
350 P. Schwarz and H. E. Carter, *Proc. Natl. Acad. Sci., (U.S.)*, 40 (1954) 499.
351 H. L. Segal and P. D. Boyer, *J. Biol. Chem.*, 204 (1953) 265.
352 H. L. Segal, J. F. Kachmar and P. D. Boyer, *Enzymologia*, 15 (1952) 187.
353 S. Shifrin, *Biochemistry*, 3 (1964) 829.
354 S. Shifrin, *Biochim. Biophys. Acta*, 81 (1964) 205.
355 S. Shifrin and N. O. Kaplan, *Advan. Enzymol.*, 22 (1960) 337.
356 S. Shifrin and N. O. Kaplan, in W. D. McElroy and H. B. Glass (Eds.), *Light and Life*, Johns Hopkins, Baltimore, 1961, p. 144.
357 S. Shifrin and N. O. Kaplan, *Nature*, 183 (1959) 1529.
358 S. Shifrin and N. O. Kaplan, *Proc. Natl. Acad. Sci., (U.S.)*, 44 (1958) 177.
359 S. Shifrin, N. O. Kaplan and M. M. Ciotti, *J. Biol. Chem.*, 234 (1959) 1555.
360 V. J. Shriner Jr., H. R. Mahler, R. H. Baker Jr. and R. R. Hiatt, *Ann. N.Y. Acad. Sci.*, 84 (1960) 583.
361 L. Shuster and N. O. Kaplan, *J. Biol. Chem.*, 215 (1955) 183.
362 L. Shuster, N. O. Kaplan and F. E. Stolzenbach, *J. Biol. Chem.*, 215 (1955) 195.
363 J. M. Siegel, G. A. Montgomery and R. M. Bock, *Arch. Biochem. Biophys.*, 82 (1959) 288.
364 T. P. Singer and E. B. Kearney, *Advan. Enzymol.*, 15 (1954) 79.
365 T. P. Singer and E. B. Kearney, *J. Biol. Chem.*, 183 (1950) 409.
366 R. M. Smillie and R. C. Fuller, *Biochem. Biophys. Res. Commun.*, 3 (1960) 368.
367 E. R. Stadtman and H. A. Barker, *J. Biol. Chem.*, 180 (1949) 1095.
368 E. R. Stadtman and H. A. Barker, *J. Biol. Chem.*, 184 (1950) 769.
369 A. M. Stein, N. O. Kaplan and M. M. Ciotti, *J. Biol. Chem.*, 234 (1959) 979.
370 A. Stockell, *J. Biol. Chem.*, 234 (1959) 1286.
371 A. Stockell, *J. Biol. Chem.*, 234 (1959) 1293.
372 P. Strittmatter, *J. Biol. Chem.*, 239 (1964) 3043.
373 C. H. Suelter and D. Metzler, *Biochim. Biophys. Acta*, 44 (1960) 23.
374 H. Sund and H. Theorell, in P. D. Boyer, H. Lardy and K. Myrbäck (Eds.), *The Enzymes*, Vol. 7, Academic Press, New York, 1963, p. 25.
375 A. J. Swallow, *Biochem. J.*, 60 (1955) 443.
376 G. Szabolcsi, *Acta Physiol. Acad. Sci. Hung.*, 13 (1958) 213.
377 G. Szabolcsi, E. Biszku and M. Saggo, *Acta Physiol. Acad. Sci. Hung.*, 17 (1960) 183.
378 G. Szabolcsi, E. Biszku and E. Szorenyi, *Biochim. Biophys. Acta*, 35 (1959) 327.
379 E. Szorenyi, P. Elodi and T. Deveye, *Acta Physiol. Acad. Sci. Hung.*, 9 (1956) 351.
380 Y. Takenaka and G. W. Schwert, *J. Biol. Chem.*, 223 (1956) 157.
381 E. Taylor, B. P. Meriwether and J. H. Park, *J. Biol. Chem.*, 238 (1963) 734.
382 J. F. Taylor, *Federation Proc.*, 9 (1950) 237.
383 J. F. Taylor, S. F. Velick, G. T. Cori, C. F. Cori and M. W. Slein, *J. Biol. Chem.*, 173 (1948) 619.
384 H. Tereyama and C. S. Vestling, *Biochim. Biophys. Acta*, 20 (1956) 586.
385 H. Theorell, *Advan. Enzymol.*, 20 (1958) 31.

386 H. Theorell, *Federation Proc.*, 20 (1961) 967.
387 H. Theorell and R. K. Bonnichsen, *Acta Chem. Scand.*, 5 (1951) 1105.
388 H. Theorell and B. Chance, *Acta Chem. Scand.*, 5 (1951) 1127.
389 H. Theorell and J. McKinley-McKee, *Acta Chem. Scand.*, 15 (1961) 1797.
390 H. Theorell and J. McKinley-McKee, *Acta Chem. Scand.*, 15 (1961) 1811.
391 H. Theorell and J. McKinley-McKee, *Acta Chem. Scand.*, 15 (1961) 1834.
392 H. Theorell, A. P. Nygaard and R. Bonnichsen, *Acta Chem. Scand.*, 9 (1955) 1148.
393 H. Theorell and T. Yonetani, *Biochem. Z.*, 338 (1963) 537.
394 H. Theorell and A. D. Winer, *Arch. Biochem. Biophys.*, 83 (1959) 291.
395 J. Thompson, *Biochemistry*, 2 (1963) 224.
396 D. Tucker and S. Grisolia, *J. Biol. Chem.*, 237 (1962) 1068.
397 F. Ungar and S. G. A. Alivisatos, *Biochim. Biophys. Acta*, 46 (1961) 406.
398 P. Urnis and P. Doty, *Advan. Protein Chem.*, 16 (1961) 401.
399 B. L. Vallee and J. E. Coleman, in: M. Florkin and E. H. Stotz (Eds.), *Comprehensive Biochemistry*, Vol. 12, Elsevier, Amsterdam, 1964, p. 165.
400 B. L. Vallee, in P. D. Boyer, H. Lardy and K. Myrbäck (Eds.), *The Enzymes*, Vol. 3, Academic Press, New York, 1960, p. 225.
401 B. L. Vallee, S. J. Adelstein and W. E. C. Wacker, *J. Am. Chem. Soc.*, 78 (1956) 5879.
402 B. L. Vallee and F. L. Hoch, *Proc. Natl. Acad. Sci., (U.S.)*, 41 (1955) 327.
403 B. L. Vallee, R. J. P. Williams and F. L. Hoch, *J. Biol. Chem.*, 234 (1959) 2621.
404 J. van Eys, *Federation Proc.*, 19 (1960) 26.
405 J. van Eys, *Federation Proc.*, 22 (1963) 290.
406 J. van Eys, *J. Biol. Chem.*, 233 (1958) 1203.
407 J. van Eys, *J. Biol. Chem.*, 236 (1963) 1531.
408 J. van Eys, M. M. Ciotti and N. O. Kaplan, *Biochim. Biophys. Acta*, 23 (1957) 581.
409 J. van Eys, M. M. Ciotti and N. O. Kaplan, *J. Biol. Chem.*, 231 (1958) 571.
410 J. van Eys, J. Judd, J. Ford and W. B. Womack, *Biochemistry*, 3 (1964) 1755.
411 J. van Eys and N. O. Kaplan, *J. Am. Chem. Soc.*, 79 (1957) 2782.
412 J. van Eys and N. O. Kaplan, *J. Biol. Chem.*, 228 (1957) 305.
413 J. van Eys, R. Kretszchmar, Nan Sen Tseng and L. W. Cunningham, *Biochem. Biophys. Res. Commun.*, 8 (1962) 243.
414 J. van Eys, J. B. Nuenke and M. K. Patterson Jr., *J. Biol. Chem.*, 234 (1959) 2308.
415 J. van Eys, A. San Pietro and N. O. Kaplan, *Science*, 127 (1958) 1443.
416 J. van Eys and F. E. Stolzenbach, unpublished experiments, quoted in N. O. Kaplan, in P. D. Boyer, H. Lardy and K. Myrbäck (Eds.), *The Enzymes*, Vol. 3, Academic Press, New York, 1960, p. 144.
417 J. van Eys, F. E. Stolzenbach, L. Sherwood and N. O. Kaplan, *Biochim. Biophys. Acta*, 27 (1958) 63.
418 B. S. Vanderheiden, J. O. Meinhart, R. G. Dodson and E. G. Krebs, *J. Biol. Chem.*, 237 (1962) 2095.
419 S. F. Velick, *Ann. Rev. Biochemistry*, 25 (1956) 257.
420 S. F. Velick and S. Udenfriend, *J. Biol. Chem.*, 203 (1953) 575.
421 S. F. Velick, *J. Biol. Chem.*, 203 (1953) 563.
422 S. F. Velick, *J. Biol. Chem.*, 233 (1958) 1455.
423 S. F. Velick, in W. D. McElroy and H. B. Glass (Eds.), *Light and Life*, Johns Hopkins, Baltimore, 1961, p. 108.
424 S. F. Velick, in R. Benesch *et al.* (Eds.), *Sulfur in Proteins*, Academic Press, New York, 1959, p. 267.
425 S. F. Velick and C. Furfine, in H. Lardy and K. Myrbäck (Eds.), *The Enzymes*, Vol. 7, Academic Press, New York, 1963, p. 243.
426 S. F. Velick, J. E. Hayes and J. Harting, *J. Biol. Chem.*, 203 (1953) 527.
427 S. F. Velick and J. E. Hayes, *J. Biol. Chem.*, 203 (1953) 545.
428 B. Vennesland and F. H. Westheimer, in W. D. McElroy and H. B. Glass (Eds.), *The Mechanism of Enzyme Action*, Johns Hopkins, Baltimore, 1954, p. 357.

429 K. WALLENFELS, in G. E. W. WOLSTENHOLME AND C. M. O'CONNOR (Eds.), *Steric Course of Microbiological Reactions*, Churchill, London, 1959, p. 10.
430 K. WALLENFELS AND H. DEIKMAN, *Ann Chem.*, 621 (1959) 166.
431 K. WALLENFELS AND M. GELLRICH, *Chem. Ber.*, 92 (1959) 1406.
432 K. WALLENFELS AND M. GELLRICH, *Ann. Chem.*, 621 (1959) 198.
433 K. WALLENFELS, M. GELLRICH AND F. KUBOWITZ, *Ann. Chem.*, 621 (1959) 137.
434 K. WALLENFELS, D. HORMANN AND H. SCHULY, *Ann. Chem.*, 621 (1959) 188.
435 K. WALLENFELS AND H. SCHULY, *Angew. Chem.*, 70 (1958) 471.
436 K. WALLENFELS AND H. SCHULY, *Biochem. Z.*, 329 (1957) 75.
437 K. WALLENFELS AND H. SCHULY, *Ann. Chem.*, 621 (1959) 86.
438 K. WALLENFELS AND H. SCHULY, *Ann. Chem.*, 621 (1959) 178.
439 K. WALLENFELS AND H. SCHULY, *Ann. Chem.*, 621 (1959) 215.
440 K. WALLENFELS AND H. SUND, *Biochem. Z.*, 329 (1957) 41.
441 K. WALLENFELS AND H. SUND, *Biochem. Z.*, 329 (1957) 59.
442 K. WALLENFELS, H. SUND, M. L. ZARNITZ, O. P. MALHOTRA AND J. FISHER, in R. BENESCH, R. E. BENESCH, P. D. BOYER, I. M. KLOTZ, W. R. MIDDLEBROOK, A. G. SZENT-GYORGYI AND D. R. SCHWARZ (Eds.), *Sulfur in Proteins*, Academic Press, New York, 1959, p. 215.
443 P. WALTER AND N. O. KAPLAN, *J. Biol. Chem.*, 238 (1963) 2823.
444 O. WARBURG, *Naturforsch.*, 12b (1957) 47.
445 O. WARBURG, *Wasserstoffübertragende Fermente*, Aulendorf/Württ, Freiburg i. Br., 1949, p. 39.
446 O. WARBURG AND W. CHRISTIAN, *Biochem. Z.*, 287 (1936) 291.
447 O. WARBURG AND W. CHRISTIAN, *Biochem. Z.*, 303 (1939) 40.
448 O. WARBURG, W. CHRISTIAN AND A. GRIESE, *Biochem. Z.*, 282 (1935) 157.
449 O. WARBURG, H. KLOTZSCH AND K. GAWEHN, *Z. Naturforsch.*, 9b (1954) 271.
450 O. WARBURG, H. KLOTZSCH AND K. GAWEHN, *Z. Naturforsch.*, 9b (1954) 391.
451 G. WEBER, *Nature*, 180 (1958) 1409.
452 G. WEBER, personal communication to N. O. KAPLAN, quoted by S. SHIFRIN AND N. O. KAPLAN, *Advan. Enzymol.*, 22 (1960) 353.
453 M. M. WEBER AND N. O. KAPLAN, *J. Biol. Chem.*, 225 (1957) 909.
454 F. H. WESTHEIMER, in P. D. BOYER, H. LARDY AND K. MYRBÄCK (Eds.), *The Enzymes*, Academic Press, New York, 1959, p. 259.
455 F. H. WESTHEIMER, in G. E. W. WOLSTENHOLME AND C. M. O'CONNOR (Eds.), *Steric Course of Microbiological Reactions*, Churchill, London, 1959, p. 3.
456 F. H. WESTHEIMER, in W. D. MCELROY AND H. B. GLASS (Eds.), *The Mechanism of Enzyme Action*, Johns Hopkins, Baltimore, 1954, p. 321.
457 F. H. WESTHEIMER, H. F. FISHER, E .E. CONN AND B. VENNESLAND, *J. Am. Chem. Soc.*, 73 (1951) 2403.
458 T. WIELAND, C. FEST AND G. PFLEIDERER, *Ann. Chem.*, 642 (1961) 163.
459 H. G. WILLIAMS-ASHMAN, in D. M. BONNER (Ed.), *Control Mechanisms in Cellular Processes*, Ronald Press, New York, 1961, p. 167.
460 H. G. WINDMUELLER AND N. O. KAPLAN, *J. Biol. Chem.*, 236 (1961) 2716.
461 A. D. WINER, W. B. NOVOA AND G. W. SCHWERT, *J. Am. Chem. Soc.*, 79 (1957) 6571.
462 A. D. WINER AND G. W. SCHWERT, *J. Biol. Chem.*, 231 (1958) 1065.
463 A. D. WINER AND G .W. SCHWERT, *J. Biol. Chem.*, 234 (1959) 1155.
464 A. D. WINER, G. W. SCHWERT AND D. B. S. MILLAR, *J. Biol. Chem.*, 234 (1959) 1149.
465 A. D. WINER AND H. THEORELL, *Acta Chem. Scand.*, 13 (1959) 1038.
466 A. D. WINER AND H. THEORELL, *Acta Chem. Scand.*, 14 (1960) 1729.
467 A. D. WINER, *Acta Chem. Scand.*, 12 (1958) 1695.
468 E. C. WOLF AND S. BLACK, *Arch. Biochem. Biophys.*, 80 (1959) 236.
469 J. WOLFF, *J. Biol. Chem.*, 237 (1962) 230.
470 J. T. F. WONG AND C. S. HANES, *Can. J. Biochem. Physiol.*, 40 (1962) 763.
471 C. L. WORONICK, *Acta Chem. Scand.*, 15 (1961) 2062.
472 M. B. YARMOLINSKY, referred to by S. P. COLOWICK, in W. D. MCELROY AND H. B. GLASS (Eds.), *The Mechanism of Enzyme Action*, Johns Hopkins, Baltimore, 1954, p. 353.
473 M. B. YARMOLINSKY AND S. P. COLOWICK, *Biochim. Biophys. Acta*, 20 (1956) 177.

474 K. L. Yielding and G. M. Tomkins, *Biochim. Biophys. Acta*, 62 (1962) 327.
475 K. L. Yielding and G. M. Tomkins, *Federation Proc.*, 22 (1963) 289.
476 K. L. Yielding and G. M. Tomkins, *Proc. Natl. Acad. Sci., (U.S.)*, 46 (1960) 1483.
477 K. L. Yielding, G. M. Tomkins and J. Curran, *Proc. Natl. Acad. Sci., (U.S.)*, 47 (1961) 270.
478 T. Yonetani, *Biochem. Z.*, 338 (1963) 300.
479 L. J. Zatman, N. O. Kaplan and S. P. Colowick, *J. Biol. Chem.*, 200 (1953) 197.
480 L. J. Zatman, N. O. Kaplan, S. P. Colowick and M. M. Ciotti, *J. Biol. Chem.*, 209 (1954) 453.
481 L. J. Zatman, N. O. Kaplan, S. P. Colowick and M. M. Ciotti, *J. Biol. Chem.*, 209 (1954) 467.
482 V. Zewe and H. J. Fromm, *J. Biol. Chem.*, 237 (1962) 1668.

Chapter II

Chemistry and Function of Lipoic Acid

LESTER J. REED

Clayton Foundation Biochemical Institute and Department of Chemistry, University of Texas, Austin, Texas (U.S.A.)

1. Introduction

Lipoic acid was discovered independently in several laboratories in the late 1940's as a growth factor and a requirement for pyruvate oxidation for certain microorganisms. The trivial names "acetate-replacing factor"[1], "pyruvate oxidation factor"[2], "protogen"[3,4] and "B.R. factor"[5] were used to designate the biologically active substance prior to its isolation and identification. When the substance was isolated in crystalline form the trivial name "α-lipoic acid" was proposed[6]. After its structure was established the trivial name "6-thioctic acid" was suggested[7]. The American Society of Biological Chemists has recognized priority of the name "lipoic acid" and has adopted it as the trivial designation of 1,2-dithiolane-3-valeric acid (I).

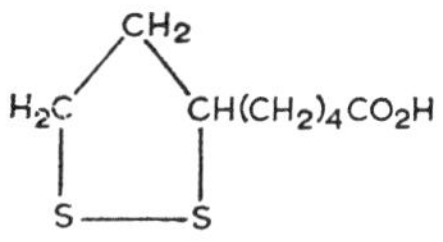

CH_2

H_2C $CH(CH_2)_4CO_2H$

S——S

I

Lipoic acid

Lipoic acid is widely distributed among microorganisms, plants and animals. Most nutritional investigations with higher animals have failed to show a growth response to added lipoic acid. However, there is no doubt that this substance plays a vital role in animal metabolism. At present the only well-defined role of lipoic acid is that of a prosthetic group in multienzyme complexes which catalyze an oxidative decarboxylation of pyruvate and α-ketoglutarate to produce acetyl coenzyme A and succinyl

References p. 125

coenzyme A, respectively, and reduced nicotinamide adenine dinucleotide (NADH). This article will attempt to present an integrated picture in terms of reaction mechanisms of lipoic acid function in α-keto acid oxidation. Brief consideration will be given to the chemistry of lipoic acid, particularly those aspects which are deemed pertinent to its biological role.

2. Isolation and proof of structure

Studies on the distribution of lipoic acid in tissues indicated that it is tightly bound to protein. Thus, it is not extractable by hot water or by lipid solvents and is released only by hydrolysis with acid, alkali, or crude proteolytic enzymes. Lipoic acid was first isolated in crystalline form from the water-insoluble residue of beef liver[6,8]. The assay procedures involved, (*a*) manometric determination of oxygen uptake following activation of the pyruvate oxidation system of lipoic acid-deficient *Streptococcus faecalis* cells, and (*b*) measurement of the growth rate of *Streptococcus lactis* on an acetate-free synthetic medium. In the isolation of lipoic acid, 250-lb. batches of liver residue were hydrolyzed with 6 *N* sulfuric acid, and the filtered hydrolysate was extracted with benzene. The active material was then extracted into aqueous bicarbonate, and the extract was acidified and extracted with benzene. The crude acidic material thus obtained was esterified with diazomethane and the ester mixture was chromatographed on alumina and then on florisil. The most active fractions were saponified with 0.1 *N* sodium hydroxide and the acidic material was crystallized from *n*-hexane to give pale yellow platelets, m.p. 47.5°, $[\alpha]_D^{25}$ +96.7° (*c* 1.88, benzene). A total of approximately 30 mg of the crystalline substance was obtained from 10 tons of liver residue.

Elemental analyses and molecular-weight determinations of lipoic acid[8,9] established the formula $C_8H_{14}O_2S_2$. Lipoic acid does not give a positive nitroprusside test for the thiol group, but a polarographic study established that the sulfur is reducible at the dropping mercury electrode and is therefore present as a disulfide group. Desulfurization with Raney nickel converts lipoic acid to octanoic acid. Lipoic acid does not contain a C-methyl group as shown by absence of an infrared band at 3.37 μ and by a Kuhn–Roth determination. This latter finding indicates that one of the sulfur atoms must be linked to the terminal carbon atom of the octanoic acid skeleton. The pK_a value of 4.7 exhibited by lipoic acid precludes attachment of the second sulfur atom to carbon atoms 2 or 3. These data limit the possible structures to three: 4,8-, 5,8-, or 6,8-dithiooctanoic acid. That the latter structure (*i.e.*, 1,2-dithiolane-3-valeric acid) is the correct structure was established by synthesis[7,10]. The absolute configuration of the natural (+)-form has been established[11].

3. Chemistry of lipoic acid

(a) *Oxidation and reduction*

Mild oxidation of lipoic acid with hydroperoxides or with air converts it to a sulfoxide (β-lipoic acid). Which sulfur atom is in the oxidized state has not been established. However, it appears that the sulfur atom at

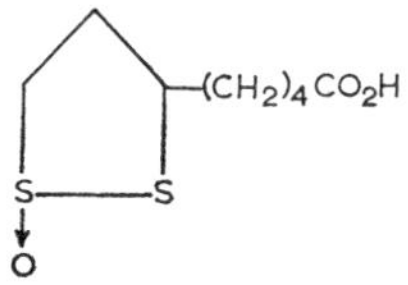

$(CH_2)_4CO_2H$ S—S ↓ O

β-Lipoic acid

C-8 of the carbon skeleton is oxidized, since the specific rotation of the sulfoxide prepared from (+)-lipoic acid is almost identical with that of the latter compound. If the sulfur atom at the asymmetric center (C-6) were oxidized, a marked change in optical properties might be expected. Lipoic acid is oxidized rapidly to the monosulfoxide in the presence of ammonium persulfate. The rate of oxidation is approximately thirty times that of a six-membered cyclic disulfide. A seven-membered cyclic disulfide was barely attacked by persulfate, and a linear disulfide was stable to persulfate under the conditions employed. These observations point up the unique reactivity of the 1,2-dithiolane ring[12].

Oxidation of lipoic acid under more drastic conditions, *e.g.* with performic acid, converts it to 6,8-disulfooctanoic acid[13]. This oxidation played an important role in elucidation of the nature of the functional form of lipoic acid (see Section 4*e*, p. 115).

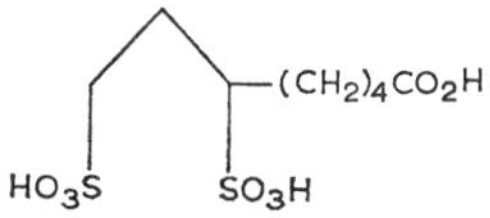

$(CH_2)_4CO_2H$ HO_3S SO_3H

6,8-Disulfooctanoic acid

Lipoic acid is reducible at the dropping mercury electrode. The half-wave potential at pH 7.0 is −0.576 V *versus* the saturated calomel electrode[14]. This value corresponds to a reduction potential of −0.325 V with respect to the standard hydrogen electrode. The reduction potential of the dihydrolipoic acid–lipoic acid system has been calculated from the equilibrium constant of the dihydrolipoic dehydrogenase-catalyzed reaction with the NADH–NAD^+ system (see Section 4*d*, p. 112). The value[15] obtained at pH 7.1 and 22°C is −0.294 V, which is in fair agreement with the polarographic measurement.

Lipoic acid is reduced easily to dihydrolipoic acid (6,8-dithioloctanoic acid) by sodium borohydride. Cleavage of the dithiolane ring by thiols (thiol–disulfide interchange reaction) is discussed in Section 3*c*.

$-(CH_2)_4CO_2H$

HS SH

Dihydrolipoic acid

Dihydrolipoic acid is oxidized readily to lipoic acid by a variety of reagents such as iodine, oxygen in the presence of metal cations, ferricyanide, and *o*-iodosobenzoate. Linear disulfide polymers are often obtained as by-products of the oxidation.

(*b*) *Polymerization*

Photolysis of 1,2-dithiolane in neutral solution with near ultraviolet light results in polymerization[16]. This observation indicates a photochemical fission of the disulfide linkage into thiyl radicals. Photolysis in acidified ethanol does not lead to polymerization, but the 1,2-dithiolane ring is destroyed. Presumably, the dithiyl radical produced by photolysis reacts with the solvent to give an unstable thiol sulfenate, which undergoes further change, even in the dark. Apparently, one photon is required to break the S—S bond in either 1,2-dithiolane or lipoic acid.

Lipoic acid is relatively stable in the solid state. However, when it is heated above its melting point or when its solutions are exposed to light, it shows a tendency to polymerize. Once the crystal lattice of lipoic acid is broken, the molecules tend to polymerize under conditions which provide for opening the 1,2-dithiolane ring, *e.g.* absorption of heat or light. The lipoic acid polymers appear to be linear disulfides[17]. These polymers undergo depolymerization in basic solution, a reaction which apparently involves an intramolecular thiol–disulfide interchange. Recovery of monomer by this procedure is of practical significance, since substantial amounts of polymeric material are produced in the synthesis of lipoic acid and related substances.

(*c*) *Ring strain*

Characteristic ultraviolet absorption maxima have been found for linear disulfides and five-, six-, and seven-membered cyclic disulfides. The absorption maximum for linear disulfides is located at 250 mμ, whereas that of the cyclic disulfides is progressively displaced toward longer wavelengths as the size of the ring decreases. Lipoic acid exhibits an absorption maximum at 330 mμ (ε = 150). This spectral shift is attributed to an increase in ring strain[12,16]. The unique reactivity and instability of 1,2-dithiolane point up this possibility. In view of the suggestion[12,16] (as yet unproved) that lipoic acid participates in the primary quantum conversion reaction of photosynthesis, attempts have been made to determine the strain energy in the 1,2-dithiolane ring. A necessary condition for this hypothesis appeared to be that the strain amounts to 25–30 kcal/mole. Conformational analysis indicates a ring strain of 15 $\pm$ 5 kcal/mole[18]. However, experimental determinations of the strain energy in 1,2-dithiolane and lipoic acid have given smaller values. Equilibrium measurements (as a function of temperature) of the reaction between 1,2-dithiolane and thiols (Eqn. 1) have given values of 4.2–6.3 kcal/mole[16,19]. The free energy (ΔF) of the reaction is approximately -1.67 kcal/mole. Values of 4 kcal/mole

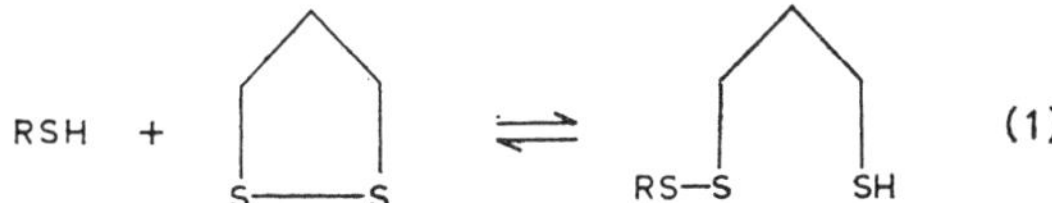

for the strain energy in 1,2-dithiolane and 3.5 kcal/mole for lipoic acid were obtained by measurement of the heats of oxidation of the corresponding dithiols[20]. It appears from these experimental results that the five-membered ring as found in lipoic acid does not exhibit undue strain. From a structural standpoint, the strain in the 1,2-dithiolane ring can be attributed to the fact that the dihedral angle between the two S—S—C planes is much smaller than that in open-chain disulfides, resulting in overlapping of the orbitals of the two non-bonding pairs of p electrons on the sulfur atoms[12,18]. The dihedral angle in open-chain disulfides is approximately 90°, whereas that in 1,2-dithiolane-4-carboxylic acid is only 26.6 $\pm$ 1° (see Ref. 21).

4. Biological function of lipoic acid

Effects of lipoic acid and its derivatives have been noted with a variety of biological systems[22,23]. It appears that a majority of these effects are not due to a vitamin-like function of lipoic acid, but rather to thiol–disulfide interchange reactions with protein disulfide or thiol groups (Eqn. 2). It is pertinent to note that the rate of thiol–disulfide interchange reactions can vary markedly with the nature of the disulfide and thiol involved[24]. Thus trimethylene disulfide (1,2-dithiolane) is cleaved at a faster rate than *n*-butyl disulfide by *n*-butanethiol, and the rate of cleavage of tri-

References p. 125

$$\text{R(SH)(SH)} + \text{S}_2\text{En} \rightleftharpoons \text{R(S—S—En—SH)(SH)} \rightleftharpoons \text{R(S—S)} + \text{(HS)}_2\text{En} \qquad (2)$$

methylene disulfide by *n*-butanethiol is much more rapid than by methyl thioglycolate. Also, it has been observed frequently that thiols differ in their ability to reduce protein disulfide linkages or to activate certain enzymes. For example, thioglycolic acid is about fifty times as effective as cysteine in reducing the lactogenic hormone. These are clearly rate and not equilibrium phenomena since the reduction potentials for the cysteine, thioglycolic acid and dihydrolipoic acid systems are nearly equal, *i.e.*, about −0.32 V at pH 7.0. It seems possible, therefore, that what may appear to be a specific stimulation (or inhibition) of an enzyme or enzyme system by lipoic acid or its derivatives is merely a manifestation of a faster rate of oxidation or reduction of protein sulfhydryl or disulfide groups, *i.e.*, thiol–disulfide interchange, by the lipoic acid–dihydrolipoic acid system than by other disulfides or thiols.

At present there is no convincing evidence of a natural function of lipoic acid other than its established role in the CoA- and NAD-linked oxidative decarboxylation of α-keto acids (Eqn. 3). It is to be noted that

$$RCOCO_2H + CoA\text{—}SH + NAD^+ \rightarrow RCO\text{—}S\text{—}CoA + CO_2 + NADH + H^+ \qquad (3)$$

there are alternate pathways of α-keto acid oxidation which do not involve lipoic acid[25]. Evidence for participation of lipoic acid in reaction 3 is summarized below. First, lipoic acid is essential for oxidation of pyruvate, α-ketobutyrate, β-methyl-α-ketobutyrate, and β-methyl-α-ketovalerate by cells of *S. faecalis* harvested from a lipoic acid-deficient medium[2,25]. Both the aerobic oxidation and the dismutation of pyruvate, Eqns. 4 and 5, are lipoic acid-dependent[2], but not the non-oxidative decarboxylation leading to acetoin formation (Eqn. 6)[26,27]. Second, enzyme systems which catalyze

$$2\ \text{Pyruvate} + O_2 \rightarrow 2\ \text{acetate} + 2\ CO_2 \qquad (4)$$

$$2\ \text{Pyruvate} \rightarrow \text{acetate} + CO_2 + \text{lactate} \qquad (5)$$

$$2\ \text{Pyruvate} \rightarrow \text{acetoin} + 2\ CO_2 \qquad (6)$$

reaction 3 contain significant amounts of "bound" lipoic acid and are arsenite-sensitive[15,25,28–31]. The inhibition by arsenite (at 10^{-5} to 10^{-4} *M*) is reversed by dithiols, but not by monothiols, suggesting the presence of an essential dithiol structure in these enzyme systems[32,33]. Third, release of bound lipoic acid from the *Escherichia coli* pyruvate and α-ketoglutarate dehydrogenation complexes with lipoamidase results in a loss of ability to catalyze[34,34a,35] reaction 3. Reincorporation of lipoic acid into the inactive preparations by incubation with lipoic acid, adenosine triphosphate and a lipoic acid-activating enzyme system restores this activity. These inactivation and reactivation experiments provide direct evidence of lipoic acid involvement in reaction 3.

The available evidence indicates that the oxidative decarboxylation of pyruvate and α-ketoglutarate represented by Eqn. 3 proceeds *via* the reaction sequence shown in Eqns. 7–11, inclusive. This sequence is represented schematically in Fig. 1, where the brackets indicate enzyme-bound compounds.

$$RCOCO_2H + TPP{-}E_1 \longrightarrow [RCHO{-}TPP]{-}E_1 + CO_2 \quad (7)$$

$$[RCHO{-}TPP]{-}E_1 + \text{(S—S lipoyl ring)}{-}(CH_2)_4C(=O){-}E_2 \longrightarrow \text{(HS, S}{-}C(=O)R\text{)}{-}(CH_2)_4C(=O){-}E_2 + TPP{-}E_1 \quad (8)$$

$$\text{(HS, S}{-}C(=O)R\text{)}{-}(CH_2)_4C(=O){-}E_2 + HS{-}CoA \longrightarrow \text{(HS, SH)}{-}(CH_2)_4C(=O){-}E_2 + RC(=O){-}S{-}CoA \quad (9)$$

$$\text{(HS, SH)}{-}(CH_2)_4C(=O){-}E_2 + FAD{-}E_3\text{(S—S)} \longrightarrow \text{(S—S)}{-}(CH_2)_4C(=O){-}E_2 + H\dot{F}AD{-}E_3\text{(}\dot{S}\text{, SH)} \quad (10)$$

$$H\dot{F}AD{-}E_3\text{(}\dot{S}\text{, SH)} + NAD^+ \longrightarrow FAD{-}E_3\text{(S—S)} + NADH + H^+ \quad (11)$$

$$R = CH_3,\ HOOC(CH_2)_2$$

In its functional form lipoic acid is bound in amide linkage to the ε-amino group of a lysine residue (see Section 4 *e*, p. 115). This scheme assigns to the bound lipoic acid acyl-generation, acyl-transfer, and electron-transfer functions[36,37]. Enzyme systems which catalyze reaction 3 have been isolated from mammalian and bacterial cells as organized units (multienzyme complexes) of high molecular weight. Thus, the pyruvate dehydrogenation system of pigeon-breast muscle[38] and the α-ketoglutarate dehydrogenation system of pig-heart muscle[39] were isolated as units with molecular weights

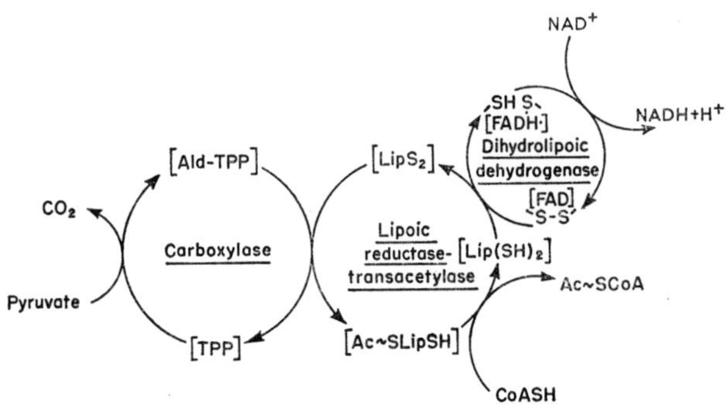

Fig. 1. Schematic representation of the reaction sequence in the lipoyl-linked oxidative decarboxylation of pyruvate. The brackets indicate enzyme-bound compounds.

of approximately 4 million and 2 million, respectively. Pyruvate and α-ketoglutarate dehydrogenation systems were isolated from *E. coli* as multienzyme complexes with molecular weights of 4.8 and 2.4 million, respectively[30]. The *E. coli* pyruvate dehydrogenation complex has been separated into three essential enzymatic components, (*a*) pyruvic carboxylase (E_1), (*b*) lipoic reductase–transacetylase (E_2), and (*c*) dihydrolipoic dehydrogenase (E_3)[40]. It should be emphasized that reactions 7–11 occur within these multienzyme complexes. A high degree of spatial orientation of the enzymes within the complexes must exist to permit interaction of the bound coenzymes (see Section 5, p. 117).

(*a*) *Decarboxylation reaction*

The decarboxylation reaction, Eqn. 7, is visualized as a cleavage of the α-keto acid to yield CO_2 and an enzyme-bound "aldehyde–thiamine pyrophosphate" (RCHO–TPP) compound, *i.e.*, "active aldehyde". In brief, it is generally accepted that thiamine pyrophosphate ionizes at the 2-position of the thiazolium ring, and that the resulting zwitterion (II) reacts with the carbonyl group of pyruvate to form an intermediate (III) which undergoes decarboxylation to produce "active acetaldehyde" (IV). The occurrence of reaction 7 as the first step in the oxidative decarboxylation of pyruvate and α-ketoglutarate can be inferred from the following observations. First, the mammalian and bacterial pyruvate and α-ketoglutarate dehydrogenation

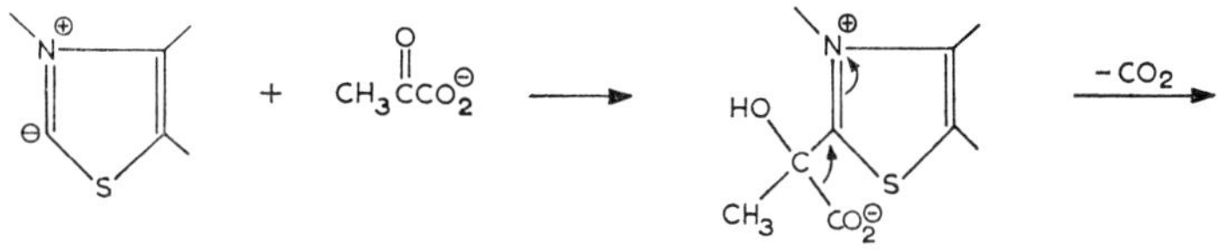

II III

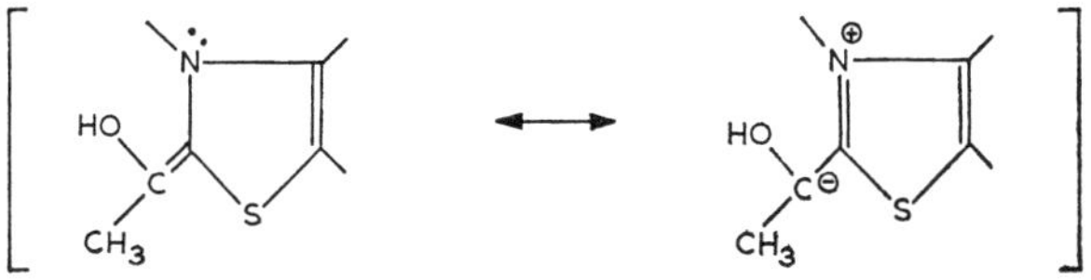

IV
"Active acetaldehyde"

complexes catalyze an exchange reaction between $^{14}CO_2$ and the carboxyl group of the corresponding α-keto acid, which is TPP-dependent and CoA-independent[41,42]. The pyruvate–$^{14}CO_2$ exchange reaction is insensitive to arsenite, indicating that bound lipoic acid is not involved in this reaction[43]. Second, the pyruvate dehydrogenation complexes produce acyloins [$CH_3COCH(OH)R$] from pyruvate and added aldehydes[37,44]. Acyloin synthesis involves condensation of "active acetaldehyde" with a molecule of added aldehyde and is independent of lipoic acid. Third, oxidation of pyruvate and α-ketoglutarate with ferricyanide as electron acceptor, Eqn. 12, observed with the mammalian and bacterial complexes, requires TPP, but not bound lipoic acid, CoA or NAD[31,35,44,45]. Ferricyanide apparently oxidizes the "active aldehyde" to RCO_2H (see Section 4*b*). Fourth, resolution of the *E. coli* pyruvate dehydrogenation complex has yielded an enzymatic component, pyruvic carboxylase (E_1), which catalyzes reaction

$$RCOCO_2H + 2\ Fe(CN)_6^{3-} + H_2O \rightarrow RCO_2H + CO_2 + 2\ Fe(CN)_6^{4-} + 2\ H^+ \qquad (12)$$

12 in the presence of TPP, does not contain bound lipoic acid, and is a requirement for reconstitution of the over-all pyruvate dehydrogenation activity (Eqn. 3)[40].

(*b*) *Acyl-generation reaction*

The acyl-generation reaction, Eqn. 8, is visualized as a reductive acylation of protein-bound lipoic acid. Specifically, "active acetaldehyde" is believed to attack the disulfide linkage of bound lipoic acid in a nucleophilic displacement reaction, followed by a reverse condensation[46], as illustrated below.

References p. 125

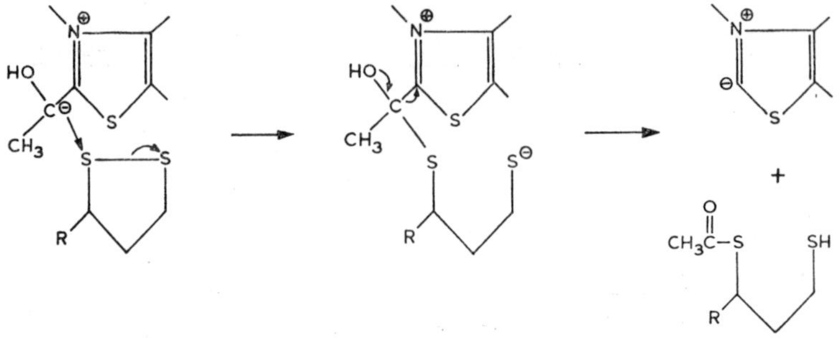

The postulated intermediate is a semi-thioketal of 2-acetylthiamine pyrophosphate (see below). It is presumed that the acyl group is attached to the secondary thiol group, *i.e.*, at C-6, in dihydrolipoyl–E_2, in view of evidence obtained in model reactions with substrate amounts of dihydrolipoic acid (see Section 4 *c*, p. 110).

Evidence for reaction 8 is summarized below. It has been reported[25,47] that a small amount of thioester, presumed to be *S*-acetyldihydrolipoic acid, is produced when *E. coli* fraction A (a complex of enzymes E_1 and E_2) is incubated with pyruvate, a catalytic amount of TPP, and a substrate amount of lipoic acid ($LipS_2$). This observation was interpreted as indicating a reductive acetylation of external lipoic acid. Attempts to confirm this observation have produced conflicting results[29,35,48]. Recently, however, it has been observed (L. J. Reed and M. Koike, unpublished results) that substantial and equivalent amounts of thioester and thiol are produced when the pyruvic carboxylase (E_1) isolated from the *E. coli* pyruvate dehydrogenation complex is incubated with pyruvate, a catalytic amount of TPP, and a substrate amount of lipoic acid or lipoamide. The reaction

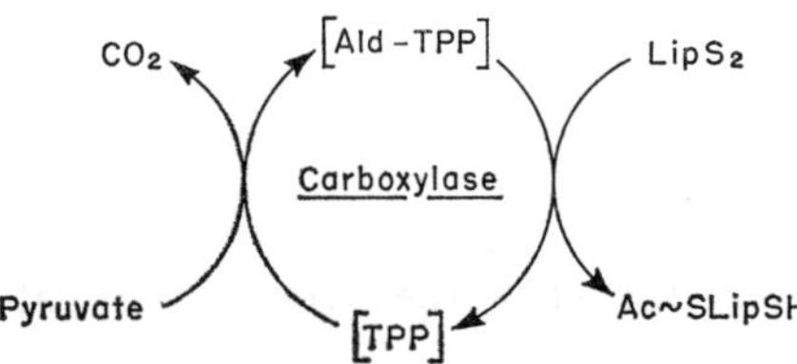

Fig. 2. Schematic representation of the model reductive acetylation reaction between pyruvate and lipoate (or lipoamide) catalyzed by pyruvic carboxylase.

rate is slow, necessitating use of relatively large amounts of pyruvic carboxylase. The reaction, represented schematically in Fig. 2, appears to be a satisfactory model of the physiological reaction (Eqn. 8) involving a catalytic amount of protein-bound lipoic acid.

Ferricyanide can serve as electron acceptor for oxidation of "active aldehyde". With ferricyanide, however, the acyl group appears as the free acid (Eqn. 12) rather than a thioester. When the ferricyanide-linked oxidation of pyruvate, catalyzed by the *E. coli* pyruvic carboxylase, proceeds in the presence of inorganic phosphate, part of the pyruvate is converted to acetyl phosphate[49]. This observation suggests that an energy-rich

$$\text{(HO)(CH}_3\text{)C}^{\ominus}\text{-thiazolium}^{\oplus} + 2\,Fe(CN)_6^{3-} \longrightarrow CH_3\overset{O}{\overset{\|}{C}}\text{-thiazolium}^{\oplus} + 2\,Fe(CN)_6^{4-} + H^+$$

acetyl compound is an intermediate in reaction 12, and that this intermediate undergoes phosphorolysis to produce acetyl phosphate. The postulated intermediate is presumably 2-acetylthiamine pyrophosphate[50], produced by loss of two electrons and a proton from "active acetaldehyde" as illustrated below. The ferricyanide model reaction obtained with pyruvic carboxylase is illustrated schematically in Fig. 3.

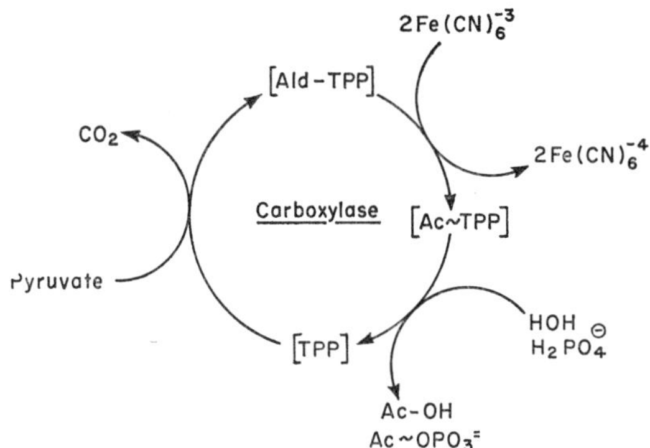

Fig. 3. Schematic representation of the ferricyanide-linked oxidation of pyruvate catalyzed by pyruvic carboxylase.

2-Acylthiazolium salts have been synthesized and shown to be kinetically and thermodynamically unstable[51-53]. These compounds undergo nucleophilic attack by water to give acids, by alcohols to give esters, by hydroxylamine to give hydroxamates, and by mercaptide ions to give thioesters, as illustrated below. The free energy of methanolysis of 2-benzoyl-3,4-dimethylthiazolium iodide is approximately −15 kcal/mole[54]. This value indicates that the free energy of hydrolysis of 2-acylthiazolium salts is more neg-

References p. 125

ative than that found with acetyl phosphate and other classical "high-energy" anhydrides.

(c) *Acyl-transfer reaction*

The acyl-transfer reaction, Eqn. 9, is visualized as a nucleophilic displacement of dihydrolipoyl–enzyme by coenzyme A to produce acyl coenzyme A. An enzymatic component (E_2) which contains bound lipoic acid and apparently catalyzes reactions 8 and 9 has been isolated from the *E. coli* pyruvate dehydrogenation complex[40]. This component is tentatively named lipoic reductase–transacetylase.

Evidence for reaction 9 is based largely on model reactions carried out with substrate amounts of dihydrolipoic acid. Incubation of *E. coli* fraction A (a complex of enzymes E_1 and E_2) and phosphotransacetylase with acetyl phosphate, DL-dihydrolipoic acid, and a catalytic amount of CoA produces a thioester, and an equivalent amount of thiol disappears[37,45]. This result indicates a coupling of the phosphotransacetylase reaction

$$CH_3COOPO_3^{2-} + CoA\text{—}SH \rightarrow CH_3CO\text{—}S\text{—}CoA + HPO_4^{2-} \qquad (13)$$

$$CH_3CO\text{—}S\text{—}CoA + Lip(SH)_2 \rightarrow CH_3CO\text{—}S\text{—}Lip\text{—}SH + CoA\text{—}SH \qquad (14)$$

$$\text{Sum: } CH_3COOPO_3^{2-} + Lip(SH)_2 \xrightarrow{(CoA)} HPO_4^{2-} + CH_3CO\text{—}S\text{—}Lip\text{—}SH \qquad (15)$$

(13) and reaction 14 to give reaction 15. Reaction 14, which is a model of the physiological reaction, Eqn. 9 (reverse direction), is catalyzed by the lipoic reductase–transacetylase component of fraction A[40]. This model reaction is illustrated schematically in Fig. 4. Enzymatically produced *S*-acetyldihydro-

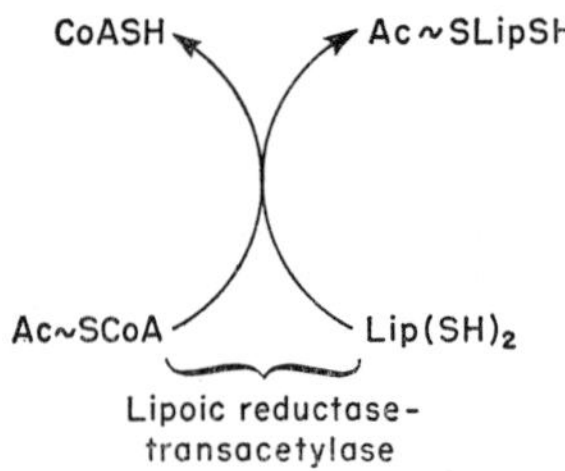

Fig. 4. Schematic representation of the model acetyl transfer reaction between acetyl CoA and dihydrolipoate (or dihydrolipoamide) catalyzed by lipoic reductase–transacetylase.

lipoic acid undergoes arsenolysis in the presence of fraction A, phosphotransacetylase, arsenate, and a catalytic amount of CoA[47]. This result indicates an acetyl transfer from *S*-acetyldihydrolipoic acid to CoA, *i.e.*, a reversal of reaction 14.

It has been reported[55] that (—)-dihydrolipoic acid, derived from the natural (+)-lipoic acid, but not (+)-dihydrolipoic acid is acetylated in reaction 15. However, in recent experiments (L. J. Reed and M. Koike, unpublished data) with the highly purified *E. coli* pyruvate dehydrogenation complex it has been observed that both optical isomers of dihydrolipoic acid are acetylated, although the rate with the natural (—)-isomer is considerably faster than with the (+)-isomer. Reduced glutathione, mercaptoethanol, thioglycolic acid and *N,N*-diethylmercaptoethylamine show little or no activity in reaction 15 with fraction A[29].

The thioester produced in reaction 15 from (—)-dihydrolipoic acid has been isolated and characterized as (+)-6-*S*-acetyldihydrolipoic acid[55] (V). The evidence for the structure assigned to the thioester may be summarized as follows. First, thioester (V) is converted to a crystalline acylurea

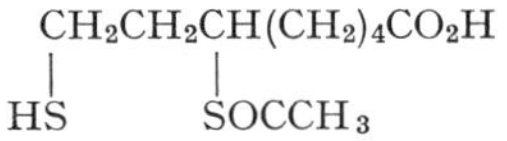

$CH_2CH_2CH(CH_2)_4CO_2H$	$CH_2CH_2CH(CH_2)_4CO_2H$
HS　　SOCCH$_3$	CH$_3$COS　　SH
6-*S*-Acetyldihydrolipoic acid	8-*S*-Acetyldihydrolipoic acid
V	VI

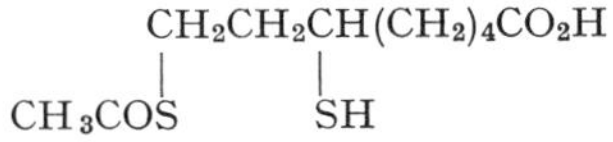

by reaction with di-(*p*-dimethylaminophenyl)carbodiimide. The physical constants of this acylurea are different from those of the corresponding derivative of chemically acetylated dihydrolipoic acid (VI). Second, the methyl ester of (V) reacts smoothly with *N*-propionyldiphenylketimine, whereas the methyl ester of the synthetic *S*-acetyldihydrolipoic acid (VI) does not react with this reagent. Since *N*-propionyldiphenylketimine is apparently specific for primary —SH groups, it is concluded that chemical acetylation (with acetic anhydride and pyridine) occurs preferentially on the primary —SH group of dihydrolipoic acid, whereas the enzymatic reaction results in acetylation of the secondary —SH group.

A mono-*S*-succinyldihydrolipoic acid is produced enzymatically by coupling succinic thiokinase and *E. coli* fraction A′ (derived from the α-ketoglutarate dehydrogenation complex)[47]. Succinic thiokinase generates succinyl CoA (Eqn. 16), and transfer of the succinyl group to dihydro-

$$HO_2C(CH_2)_2CO_2H + ATP + CoA\text{—}SH \rightarrow HO_2C(CH_2)_2CO\text{—}S\text{—}CoA + ADP + HPO_4^{2-} \quad (16)$$

$$HO_2C(CH_2)_2CO\text{—}S\text{—}CoA + Lip(SH)_2 \rightarrow HO_2C(CH_2)_2CO\text{—}S\text{—}Lip\text{—}SH + CoA\text{—}SH \quad (17)$$

References p. 125

lipoic acid (Eqn. 17) is catalyzed by fraction A′. The thioester has been characterized as 6-*S*-succinyldihydrolipoic acid.

The model transacetylation reaction, Eqn. 15, carried out with a substrate amount of dihydrolipoic acid does not involve the catalytically active, protein-bound lipoic acid. This conclusion is based on the observation that removal of bound lipoic acid from the *E. coli* pyruvate dehydrogenation complex by incubation with lipoamidase does not affect the ability of the complex[35] to catalyze reaction 15. Apparently, reductive acetylation of protein-bound lipoic acid (Eqn. 8) occurs at one active site on the lipoic reductase–transacetylase and acetyl transfer to CoA (Eqns. 9 and 14) occurs at a second active site. A possible mechanism for these reactions is presented in Section 5, p. 117.

Evidence for reaction 9 can be adduced from inhibition studies with arsenite[29]. Preincubation of the pig-heart α-ketoglutarate dehydrogenation complex with arsenite in the presence of both α-ketoglutarate and CoA results in inhibition of over-all reaction 3. If it is assumed that the site of arsenite inhibition is the protein-bound dihydrolipoic acid (see Section 4*d*), the requirement for both α-ketoglutarate and CoA to produce the inhibited complex is consistent with reactions 8 and 9, *i.e.*, the reactive succinyl group is transferred to CoA and the dihydrolipoyl-enzyme then interacts with arsenite. The CoA requirement for arsenite inhibition also would appear to preclude attachment of the reactive succinyl group to a site on the enzyme complex other than the bound dihydrolipoic acid.

(*d*) *Electron-transfer reaction*

Oxidation of protein-bound dihydrolipoic acid (Eqn. 10) is accomplished by an FAD-flavoprotein, dihydrolipoic dehydrogenase (lipoamide dehydrogenase). This enzyme has been separated from the other enzymes comprising the α-keto acid dehydrogenation complexes, and its mechanism of action has been the subject of intensive investigation. There is good evidence that dihydrolipoic dehydrogenase contains a reactive disulfide group, presumably that of a cystine residue, which participates in the catalytic cycle of the enzyme. A biradical (*i.e.*, half-reduced) form of the enzyme, comprising a sulfur radical and a flavin semiquinone, is believed to be an intermediate in the over-all two-electron transfer from protein-bound dihydrolipoic acid to NAD (Eqns. 10 and 11)[56,57].

Classic studies with the brain pyruvate-oxidation system showing inhibition by trivalent arsenicals and reversal by the dithiol, 2,3-dimercaptopropanol (BAL), but not by monothiols, led to the postulate that a dithiol structure is involved in pyruvate oxidation[32,33]. It is now known that this dithiol structure is covalently-bound dihydrolipoic acid. The latter substance apparently forms a stable cyclic thioarsenite with trivalent arsenicals[58] (and with arsenite), and thereby its catalytic action in α-keto acid oxidation is inhibited.

HS SH R $+ As(OH)_3 \longrightarrow$ S S As OH R $+ 2\ H_2O$

Separation of the *E. coli* pyruvate and α-ketoglutarate dehydrogenation systems into three protein fractions, one (A) specific for pyruvate and a second (A′) specific for α-ketoglutarate, plus a third fraction (B) common to the two systems, suggested a dehydrogenase function for fraction B[59]. Strong support for this conclusion was provided by the demonstration that fraction B catalyzes the oxidation of dihydrolipoic acid by NAD (Eqn. 18). Dihydrolipoic dehydrogenases have been isolated in highly purified form

$$Lip(SH)_2 + NAD^+ \rightleftharpoons LipS_2 + NADH + H^+ \qquad (18)$$

from the pig-heart α-ketoglutarate dehydrogenation complex[31,60], from the *E. coli* pyruvate and α-ketoglutarate dehydrogenation complexes[40,61], and from *Spinacia oleracea*[61a]. With the pig-heart dihydrolipoic dehydrogenase, reaction 18 is freely reversible[15]. This reaction, illustrated schematically in Fig. 5, furnishes a good model for the physiological reaction involving protein-bound dihydrolipoic acid (see Fig. 1).

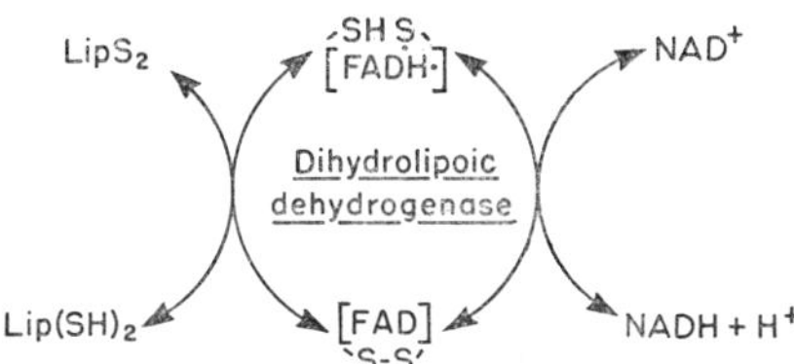

Fig. 5. Schematic representation of the model electron-transfer reaction between dihydrolipoate (or dihydrolipoamide) and NAD catalyzed by dihydrolipoic dehydrogenase.

The discovery[62] that the classic flavoprotein known as "Straub's diaphorase"[63] behaves as a powerful dihydrolipoic dehydrogenase has led to the demonstration that the dihydrolipoic dehydrogenase component of the pig-heart α-ketoglutarate dehydrogenation complex and Straub's diaphorase are one and the same enzyme[31,64]. The pig-heart and *E. coli* dihydrolipoic dehydrogenases contain 2 molecules of FAD per molecule of

References p. 125

enzyme. As observed spectrophotometrically, the flavin of the pig-heart α-ketoglutarate dehydrogenation complex is reduced by α-ketoglutarate + CoASH and is reoxidized by NAD[31]. This reduction is inhibited by arsenite. The flavin in the *E. coli* pyruvate and α-ketoglutarate dehydrogenation complexes also is reduced by pyruvate + CoASH and by α-ketoglutarate + CoASH, respectively[30]. Neither α-keto acid nor CoASH alone causes reduction of the flavin. These results are consistent with the sequence of reactions 7–11.

The reduction potential of the pig-heart dihydrolipoic dehydrogenase has been determined[60] from the extent of its reduction at different NADH/NAD^+ ratios. The value is between −0.332 and −0.320 V at pH 7.0 and 25°C. Thus, the reduction potential of this flavoprotein is close to that of the NADH/NAD^+ system, −0.320 V at pH 7.0 and 25°C, and the $Lip(SH)_2/LipS_2$ system, −0.325 V at pH 7.0 and 25°C. This is consistent with the ready reversibility of reaction 18 as well as the high initial reaction rates in both directions. It would appear that NAD is the physiological electron acceptor for the α-keto acid dehydrogenation complexes and that the NADH formed is oxidized by way of the electron-transport chain. However, the possibility should also be considered that the complexes are linked directly to the electron-transport chain, possibly to a flavoprotein or to cytochrome *b*, without mediation of NAD. This possibility has yet to be investigated.

When the pig-heart dihydrolipoic dehydrogenase is reduced with NADH or with free or protein-bound dihydrolipoic acid, an increase in absorbancy in the region between 500 and 600 mμ is observed (maximum at 530 mμ), concomitant with a decrease[60,65] at 455 mμ. Detailed studies of the stoichiometry of formation of the 530-mμ band and the kinetics of its formation and disappearance under a variety of conditions have led to the conclusion that this band is due to a flavin semiquinone which is an obligatory intermediate in the catalytic cycle of the enzyme. The bound FAD appears to function only between the oxidized and semiquinone levels. Addition of *p*-chloromercuriphenyl sulfonate results in disappearance of the 530-mμ band and further decrease in absorbancy at 455 mμ, indicating that the flavin semiquinone is stabilized by interaction with a protein sulfhydryl group. Dihydrolipoic dehydrogenase is inhibited by arsenite or cadmium ion in the presence of reducing substrate, *i.e.*, NADH[56,57]. This inhibition is reversed by BAL and to a lesser extent by monothiols. The 530-mμ band associated with the partially reduced enzyme is eliminated on addition of arsenite or cadmium ion and further reduction of the flavin is observed (at 455 mμ). Analysis of the enzyme for—SH content shows the appearance of two additional moles of—SH per mole of flavin on reduction with NADH[57,66]. On the basis of these data and other extensive spectrophotometric observations, it appears that the flavoprotein contains a second prosthetic group, *i.e.*, a reactive disulfide, which participates in the catalytic cycle. Reduction of the prosthetic disulfide group by dihydrolipoyl–enzyme to give FAD—E_3—$(SH)_2$ is visualized, followed by interaction of the dithiol and flavin to give the stable intermediate (biradical) responsible for the 530-mμ band. It is to be noted that a free-radical signal cannot be detected by electron paramagnetic resonance spectroscopy on reduction of the enzyme with NADH[57]. However, a biradical of the type shown in Eqns. 10 and 11 might not show a free-radical signal because of electron sharing between the sulfur radical and the flavin semiquinone. The pig-heart dihydrolipoic dehydrogenase contains two active centers per molecule[67]. The enzyme apparently consists of two identical peptide chains which are covalently linked by the two active-center disulfide bonds, presumably those of cystine residues.

Oxidation of NADH by lipoyl derivatives catalyzed by pig-heart and *E. coli* dihydrolipoic dehydrogenases (Eqn. 18) requires the presence of NAD[56]. In this respect, these enzymes are unique among NAD-linked dehydrogenases. The NAD apparently prevents conversion of the flavoprotein to an inactive form in which the flavin is fully reduced, *i.e.*, $FADH_2$—E_3—$(SH)_2$. The bacterial enzyme, in contrast to the mammalian enzyme, is converted readily to the fully reduced form by excess NADH[61]. However, the catalytic mechanisms of both enzymes appear to be identical.

(*e*) *Functional form of lipoic acid*

That the lipoic acid in purified preparations of the pyruvate and α-ketoglutarate dehydrogenation complexes is bound covalently to protein is indicated by the observation that lipoic acid is not released by extraction of the complexes with hot alcohol–ether or with hot trichloroacetic acid[15,30]. Elucidation of the nature of the linkage of lipoic acid to protein was essential for verification of the postulated reactions 7–11 and for further clarification of mechanism. As will be seen below, studies of components and conditions necessary for incorporation of lipoic acid into the apopyruvate dehydrogenation system of *S. faecalis* and for release of bound lipoic acid from the *E. coli* pyruvate and α-ketoglutarate dehydrogenation complexes indicated that in its functional form lipoic acid is bound to protein in covalent linkage through its carboxyl group. Subsequently, a direct approach involving degradation of the *E. coli* complexes containing bound radioactive lipoic acid revealed that the lipoyl moieties are linked to the ε-amino groups of lysine residues.

Incubation of extracts of lipoic acid-deficient *S. faecalis* cells with lipoic acid gives preparations which are capable of oxidizing pyruvate[68,69].

References p. 125

Experiments with ^{35}S-labeled lipoic acid showed that during the incubation lipoic acid is converted to a protein-bound form. Fractionation of the lipoic acid-deficient extracts revealed requirements for adenosine triphosphate (ATP) and two protein fractions for incorporation of lipoic acid into the apopyruvate dehydrogenation system. One of the essential fractions produces lipohydroxamate and pyrophosphate when incubated with lipoic acid, ATP, and hydroxylamine. Lipoic acid and ATP, but neither of the two protein fractions, are replaceable by synthetic lipoyl adenylate. These results can be explained[70,71] by the reaction sequence 19–21. Reaction 19 is visualized as an activation of the carboxyl group of lipoic acid through

$$\mathrm{E_I + ATP + lipoic\ acid \rightarrow E_I—lipoyl—AMP + PP_i} \quad (19)$$

$$\mathrm{E_I—lipoyl—AMP + E_{II} \rightarrow lipoyl—E_{II} + AMP + E_I} \quad (20)$$

$$\mathrm{Lipoyl—E_{II} + APDS \rightarrow lipoyl—APDS + E_{II}} \quad (21)$$

formation of lipoyl adenylate, which appears to be bound to a lipoic acid-activating enzyme (E_I). Reactions 20 and 21 are visualized as a transfer of the lipoyl moiety to the apopyruvate dehydrogenation system (APDS). These latter two reactions are apparently catalyzed by a transfer enzyme of low molecular weight (W. Lippmann and L. J. Reed, unpublished data). A lipoic acid-incorporating system has also been detected in and isolated from extracts of *E. coli*[69], suggesting a general significance for the enzyme system. Attempts to separate the *E. coli* system into two components have been unsuccessful.

Support for the proposal that lipoic acid is bound covalently through its carboxyl group in the *E. coli* pyruvate and α-ketoglutarate dehydrogenation complexes was furnished by studies with a hydrolytic enzyme, "lipoyl-X hydrolase" (lipoamidase), obtained from extracts of *S. faecalis*[34,34a]. Incubation of the complexes with lipoamidase releases approximately 96% of the bound lipoic acid and results in a loss of the NAD-linked α-keto acid dehydrogenation activity (Eqn. 3)[35]. When the inactive complexes are incubated with radioactive lipoic acid, ATP and the lipoic acid-activating system approximately as much radioactive lipoic acid is incorporated into the complexes as is found in the native complexes and the enzymatic activities of the reactivated and native complexes are essentially the same.

When *E. coli* is grown aerobically in the presence of [$^{35}S_2$]lipoic acid, the latter substance is incorporated into the pyruvate and α-ketoglutarate dehydrogenation complexes[13,30]. These radioactive complexes have been isolated in a highly purified state and used to elucidate the nature of the group to which the lipoyl moiety is bound. Both radioactive complexes were oxidized with performic acid and then partially hydrolyzed with 12 *N* hydrochloric acid (3 h at 105°C). From the hydrolysates was isolated in good yield a ninhydrin-positive, radioactive conjugate which was identi-

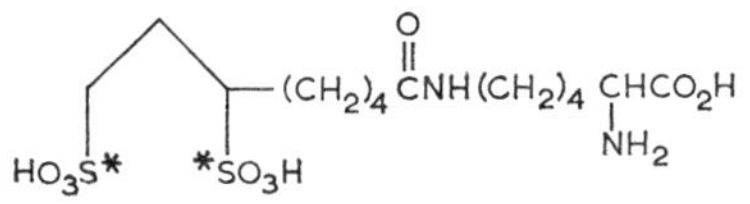

$$\underset{HO_3S^*}{|}\ \ \underset{*SO_3H}{|}\!-\!(CH_2)_4\overset{O}{\overset{\|}{C}}NH(CH_2)_4\underset{NH_2}{\underset{|}{C}}HCO_2H$$

VII

fied as N^{ε}-(6,8-disulfooctanoyl)-L-lysine (VII) by degradation and synthesis[13]. The amino acid sequence around the N^{ε}-lipoyllysine residues in the two enzyme complexes has been determined[72]. The sequence Gly–Asp–ε-Lipoyl-Lys–Ala is present in the pyruvate dehydrogenation complex and the sequence Thr–Asp–ε-Lipoyl-Lys–Val–(Val,Leu)–Glu is present in the α-ketoglutarate dehydrogenation complex. It is thus apparent that both complexes contain the sequence Asp–ε-Lipoyl-Lys, but otherwise the sequences are different. This difference in amino acid sequence is probably responsible, at least in part, for the substrate specificity of the two complexes.

The evidence presented above demonstrates that in the *E. coli* pyruvate and α-ketoglutarate dehydrogenation complexes the lipoyl moieties are bound in amide linkage with protein ε-aminolysine groups. That this linkage may also be present in mammalian α-keto acid dehydrogenation complexes is suggested by the observation[73] that a hydrolytic enzyme from baker's yeast, which resembles lipoamidase, releases bound lipoic acid from the former complexes. In the *E. coli* systems it appears that lipoamidase cleaves the covalent bond between lipoic acid and a protein ε-aminolysine group. Reactivation of the apoenzyme presumably involves re-forming this bond and requires incubation with lipoic acid, ATP, and a lipoic acid-activating enzyme system.

5. Structural organization of α-keto acid dehydrogenation complexes

The pyruvate and α-ketoglutarate dehydrogenation systems which catalyze over-all reaction 3 have been isolated from mammalian and bacterial cells as multienzyme complexes of high molecular weight. The *E. coli* pyruvate dehydrogenation complex has been separated into three essential components[40], (*a*) pyruvic carboxylase (reaction 7), (*b*) lipoic reductase–transacetylase (reactions 8 and 9), and (*c*) dihydrolipoic dehydrogenase (reactions 10 and 11). Pyruvic carboxylase and dihydrolipoic dehydrogenase can be selectively dissociated from the pyruvate dehydrogenation complex. The former enzyme is released at a pH above 9.0, leaving a complex of lipoic reductase–transacetylase (E_2) and dihydrolipoic dehydrogenase (E_3). Dissociation of dihydrolipoic dehydrogenase from the pyruvate dehydrogenation complex is accomplished by fractionation on calcium phosphate gel suspended on cellulose in the presence of 4 *M* urea. Release of dihy-

References p. 125

drolipoic dehydrogenase leaves a complex of lipoic reductase–transacetylase (E_2) and pyruvic carboxylase (E_1). Separation of lipoic reductase–transacetylase from pyruvic carboxylase is accomplished by fractionation on gel–cellulose at pH 9.5. Separation of lipoic reductase–transacetylase from dihydrolipoic dehydrogenase is accomplished by fractionation on gel–cellulose in the presence of 4 *M* urea. Reconstitution experiments indicate that pyruvic carboxylase and dihydrolipoic dehydrogenase do not combine with each other, but these two components do combine independently of each other with the lipoic reductase–transacetylase component. In other words, lipoic reductase–transacetylase appears to possess separate binding sites for pyruvic carboxylase and dihydrolipoic dehydrogenase. When pyruvic carboxylase, lipoic reductase–transacetylase and dihydrolipoic dehydrogenase are mixed in a ratio of 3 : 2 : 1 by weight, which corresponds to the relative ratio of these components in the native complex, a large unit is produced which resembles the native complex in composition and enzymatic activities.

Lipoic reductase–transacetylase comprises approximately 34% of the protein of the pyruvate dehydrogenation complex, indicating that its "molecular weight" is about 1.6 million. Its high lipoic acid content (approximately 33 mμmoles/mg protein) suggests that it is an aggregate of a small subunit. If it is assumed that there is 1 molecule of bound lipoic acid per subunit, the minimal molecular weight of the subunit would be about 30 000. This conclusion is supported by the finding that in the presence of 0.83 *M* acetic acid lipoic reductase–transacetylase is dissociated into a subunit with a molecular weight of approximately 26 600[74].

The molecular weights of pyruvic carboxylase and dihydrolipoic dehydrogenase, calculated from sedimentation and diffusion measurements, are approximately 183 000 and 112 000, respectively. From the available data on the composition of the *E. coli* pyruvate dehydrogenation complex and the molecular weights of the complex and its constituent enzymes the number of molecules of the constituent enzymes per molecule of complex has been calculated. These numbers are about 16 for the carboxylase, 64 for the lipoic reductase–transacetylase subunit, and about 8 for the dihydrolipoic dehydrogenase. The structural arrangement of these enzymatic components in the complex is discussed below.

The ratio of bound lipoic acid to FAD in the pyruvate dehydrogenation complex is about 4 : 1. There is apparently an "excess" of bound lipoic acid. All of the lipoic acid in the complex is bound to the lipoic reductase–transacetylase aggregate. It is evident from Fig. 1 that the lipoyl moiety undergoes a cyclic series of transformations, *i.e.*, reductive acetylation, acetyl transfer, and reoxidation. These transformations apparently involve interaction of the lipoyl moiety, which is covalently bound to one enzyme (lipoic reductase–transacetylase), with "acetaldehyde–thiamine pyrophosphate", which is bound to a second enzyme (carboxylase), and with the prosthetic disulfide group of a third enzyme (dihydrolipoic dehydrogenase). The lipoyl moiety must also interact with CoA at an as yet unidentified site on the lipoic reductase–transacetylase. These interactions between prosthetic groups of separate enzymes occur within a complex in which there is apparently restricted movement of the individual enzymes and no dissociation of intermediates (with the exception of acetyl CoA).

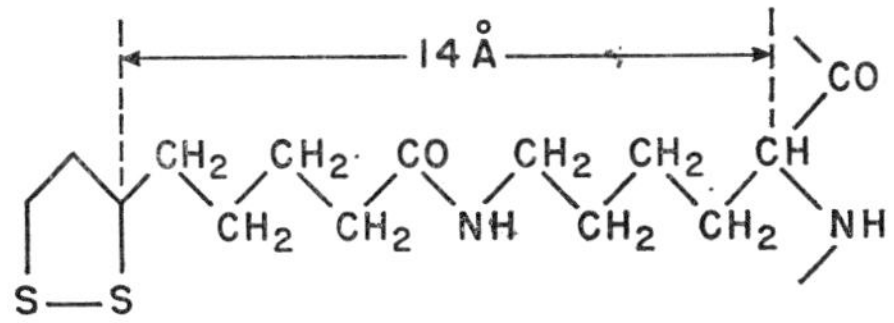

Fig. 6. N^{ε}-Lipoyllysine residue.

Highly specific positioning of the three enzymatic components of the complex, and by inference the prosthetic groups of these components, is indicated by the resolution and reconstitution experiments discussed above. Granted this assumption, it still appears impossible for the three prosthetic groups (and the CoA) to be in close enough molecular proximity to interact. A possible solution to this enigma is provided by the discovery[13] that the lipoyl moieties are bound to the ε-amino groups of lysine residues. This attachment provides a flexible arm of approximately 14 Å for the reactive dithiolane ring (Fig. 6), conceivably permitting rotation of the

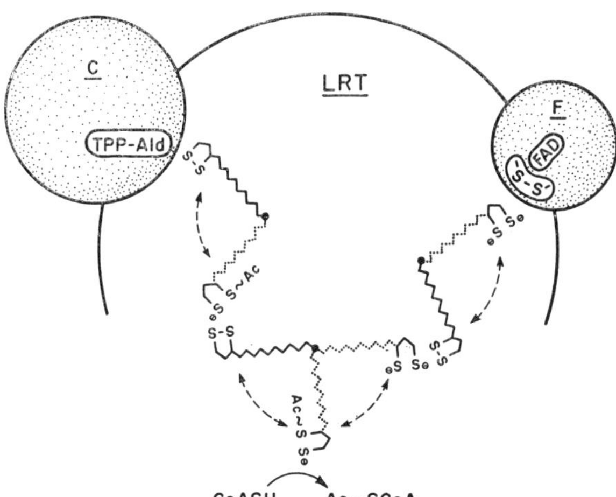

Fig. 7. A schematic representation of possible interactions between N^{ε}-lipoyllysyl moieties in the *E. coli* pyruvate dehydrogenation complex. The arrows describe the area covered by each lipoyllysyl moiety. C, LRT, and F represent, respectively, carboxylase, lipoic reductase–transacetylase, and flavoprotein.

References p. 125

latter between the bound "acetaldehyde–thiamine pyrophosphate" of the carboxylase, the site for acetyl transfer to CoA, and the prosthetic group of the flavoprotein. It is also conceivable that the distances between these three sites are too large to be encompassed by the rotation of a single lipoyllysyl moiety, necessitating interaction between several such moieties (Fig. 7). This possibility could account for the "excess" of bound lipoic acid in the complex. Interaction of the lipoyllysyl moieties is visualized as comprising thiol–disulfide interchange and acetyl transfer as illustrated below.

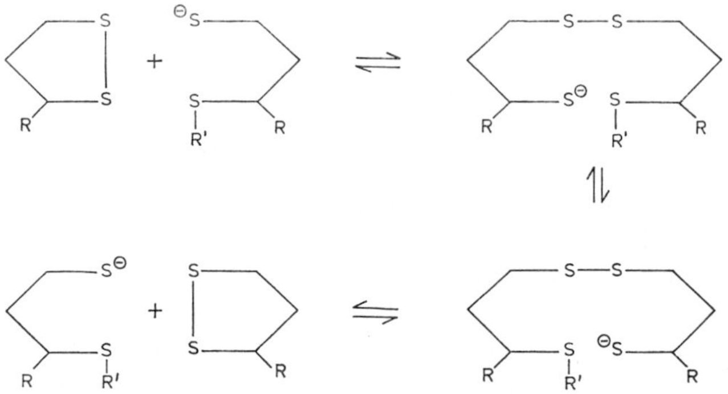

$R = (CH_2)_4CO$-enzyme $R' = H$ or CH_3CO

As yet the mammalian and bacterial α-ketoglutarate dehydrogenation complexes have been separated into only two components, dihydrolipoic dehydrogenase (E_3) and what appears to be a complex of α-ketoglutaric carboxylase (E_1) and lipoic reductase–transsuccinylase (E_2)[31,75]. It is to be noted that the ratio of bound lipoic acid to FAD in both α-ketoglutarate dehydrogenation complexes is approximately 1 : 1, whereas this ratio is about 4 : 1 in the bacterial pyruvate dehydrogenation complex[30,31]. These ratios and the fact that the molecular weight of the α-ketoglutarate dehydrogenation complex is only one-half that of the pyruvate dehydrogenation complex indicate differences in the structural organization of these two α-keto acid dehydrogenation complexes. At present little is known of the composition of the mammalian pyruvate dehydrogenation complex.

The *E. coli* pyruvate dehydrogenation complex has provided a unique opportunity to correlate functional properties as revealed by biochemical analysis with ultrastructure as revealed by electron microscopy. Recent methodological advances in high-resolution electron microscopy of biological systems[76–79] have made it possible to visualize directly structural detail of the order of 6 to 8 Å under favorable conditions, thereby furnishing access to the molecular domain where structure and function are indissolubly blended. Electron microscopy has disclosed the substructure of cell membranes[76,79] and of viruses[77], yielding results that can profitably be compared with X-ray data and biochemical information to deduce the actual arrangement of the protein subunits in certain spherical virus particles[77].

The picture of the structural organization of the pyruvate dehydrogenation complex which emerged from biochemical studies[40], *i.e.* an organized mosaic of enzymes in which each of the component enzymes is uniquely located to permit efficient implementation of a consecutive reaction sequence, has been confirmed and extended by correlative electron microscopic studies carried out in collaboration with Dr. H. Fernández-Morán[80]. Moreover, through systematic application of improved preparation techniques[78,79] important structural details of the individual multienzyme

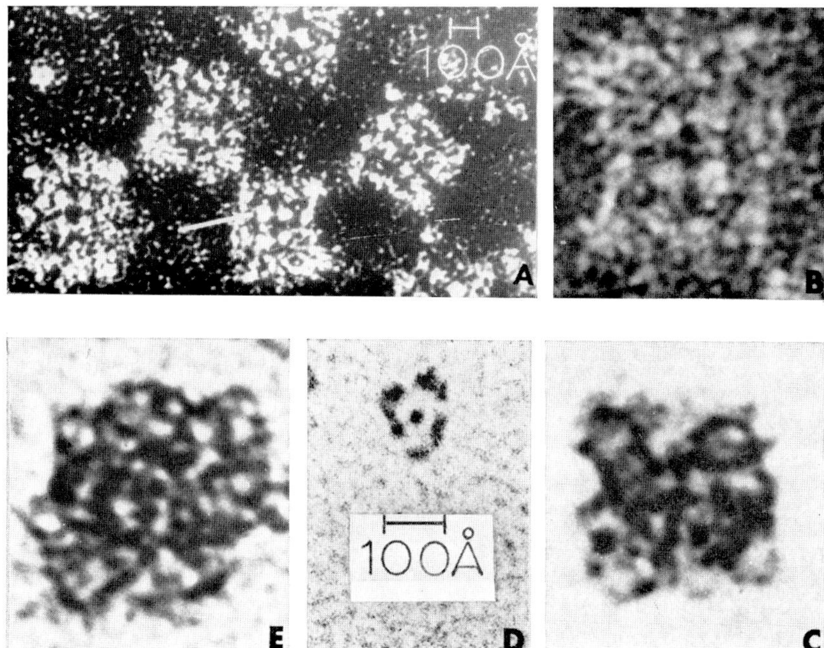

Fig. 8. High-resolution electron micrographs of *E. coli* pyruvate dehydrogenation complex and pyruvic carboxylase. (A) Complex negatively stained with 1% phospnotungstate (pH 7.4) using microdroplet cross-spraying technique (× 350 000); (B) enlargement of complex showing four central subunits and associated structures (× 750 000); (C,E) complex positively stained with 2% uranyl acetate using modified microdroplet cross-spraying technique. Subunit structure with characteristic fine structure shown in positive contrast (× 750 000); (D) pyruvic carboxylase molecule positively stained with uranyl acetate (× 750 000). (H. Fernández-Morán, Massachusetts General Hospital, Boston, and University of Chicago.)

References p. 125

complexes could be directly observed, thereby disclosing novel features of their molecular architecture[80].

Electron micrographs of the complex negatively stained with phosphotungstate (Fig. 8A,B) show various aspects of a regular polyhedral structure about 300 to 400 Å in diameter. Each of the polyhedral structures corresponding to the multienzyme complexes embedded in different orientations features an orderly array of subunits, 60 to 90 Å in diameter. There appear to be four well-defined subunits in the central portion of the structural complex (Fig. 8A, arrow), and additional uniform subunits along each of the edges. These subunits are clearly depicted in preparations of the complex stained with uranyl acetate under special conditions (Fig. 8C,E). Many of these subunits are similar in appearance and dimensions (Fig. 8C) to those observed in electron micrographs of the isolated pyruvic carboxylase component of the complex (Fig. 8D). Examination of electron micrographs of various subfractions and of controlled modifications of

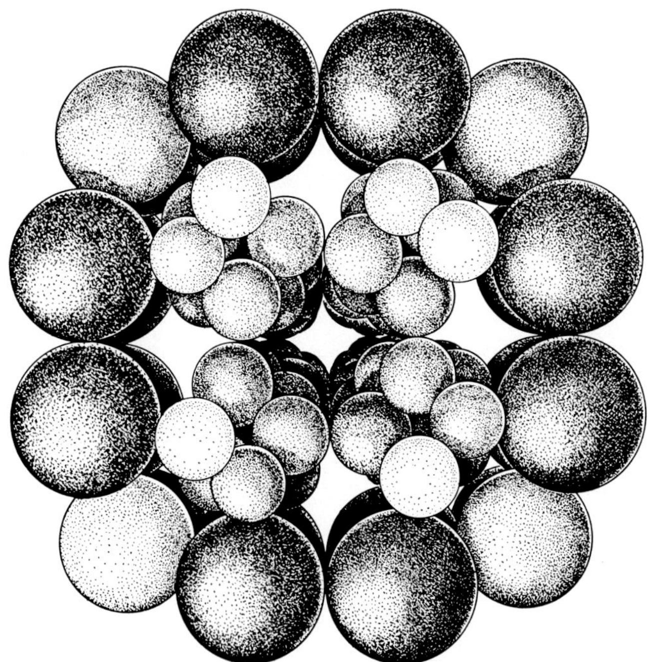

Fig. 9. Diagram showing a possible arrangement of the components of the *E. coli* pyruvate dehydrogenation complex. The model consists of 16 molecules of pyruvic carboxylase (large spheres) and 8 molecules of dihydrolipoic dehydrogenase (medium-size spheres) disposed in an orderly arrangement around the 64 subunits comprising the lipoic reductase–transacetylase aggregate (small spheres).

the complex has led to the tentative conclusion that the four central subunits (Fig. 8A,B) correspond essentially to the lipoic reductase–transacetylase aggregate. The molecules of pyruvic carboxylase and dihydrolipoic dehydrogenase are disposed in an orderly arrangement around this aggregate. A possible arrangement of the enzymatic components of the complex is shown in Fig. 9.

These correlative studies of the pyruvate dehydrogenation complex are of particular significance because this multienzyme complex has been the first to yield concurrently to direct biochemical and ultrastructural analysis at an operational level of resolution adequate for elucidation of its macromolecular organization.

ADDENDUM

The two years which have passed since this review was written have witnessed significant advances in our understanding of the macromolecular organization, function and biosynthesis of the α-keto acid dehydrogenation complexes. The *E. coli* α-ketoglutarate dehydrogenation complex has been separated into three enzymes analogous to those obtained from the pyruvate dehydrogenation complex[81,82]. The three enzymes are (*a*) α-ketoglutaric carboxylase, (*b*) lipoic reductase–transsuccinylase and (*c*) dihydrolipoic dehydrogenase. The three isolated enzymes combine spontaneously when mixed to produce a large unit resembling the native α-ketoglutarate dehydrogenation complex. The appearance in the electron microscope of the isolated lipoic reductase–transsuccinylase negatively stained with phosphotungstate is similar to that of the lipoic reductase–transacetylase aggregate obtained from the pyruvate dehydrogenation complex[80], *i.e.*, the subunits are arranged into four stacks, comprising a tetrad. Various permutations of the enzymes comprising the *E. coli* pyruvate and α-ketoglutarate dehydrogenation complexes have been examined. The two carboxylases and the two transacylases are not functionally interchangeable, nor do these components form "hybrid" complexes. However, the two flavoproteins (dihydrolipoic dehydrogenases) are interchangeable with respect to both complex formation and function. Whether or not the two flavoproteins are chemically identical has yet to be determined.

Significant studies on the biosynthesis of the *E. coli* pyruvate dehydrogenation complex have been reported[83–85]. A series of acetate-less mutants of *E. coli* K12 lacking pyruvate dehydrogenation activity (Eqn. 3, p. 104) were obtained: (*I*) those lacking carboxylase activity, (*II*) those lacking lipoic reductase–transacetylase activity and (*III*) those lacking all of the activ-

References p. 125

ities associated with the pyruvate dehydrogenation complex. Thus far no mutants lacking only dihydrolipoic dehydrogenase have been recovered. Class *I* mutants produce a partial complex consisting of the lipoic reductase–transacetylase aggregate and dihydrolipoic dehydrogenase. Class *II* mutants synthesize uncomplexed carboxylase. Genetic analysis of the acetate-less mutants indicates that the structural genes for the carboxylase and the lipoic reductase–transacetylase are closely linked and that the biosynthesis of the pyruvate dehydrogenation complex begins with the synthesis of the carboxylase. It appears that the constituent enzymes of the complex are synthesized at different rates to produce precisely the amounts of these enzymes required for formation of the complex. Furthermore, it appears that these disproportional rates of synthesis are set at the level of polypeptide-chain formation. Studies on possible genetic relationships between the pyruvate and α-ketoglutarate dehydrogenation complexes indicate that the two complexes most likely do not share any genetic determinant. The results of the genetic analysis and of the biochemical analysis of the native pyruvate and α-ketoglutarate dehydrogenation complexes are in excellent agreement thus far. It can be anticipated that continued correlation of the results of biochemical, electron microscopic and genetic analyses of the pyruvate and α-ketoglutarate dehydrogenation complexes will provide deeper insight into the "supramolecular" organization of enzyme systems.

Pyruvate-dehydrogenation systems which catalyze reaction 3 have been isolated recently from pig-heart muscle[86] and from beef-kidney mitochondria (E. Ishikawa and L. J. Reed, unpublished data) as multienzyme complexes of high molecular weight. Both multienzyme complexes exhibit carboxylase, lipoic reductase–transacetylase and dihydrolipoic dehydrogenase activities. A comparative study of the mammalian and bacterial α-keto acid dehydrogenation complexes should lead to further understanding of the macromolecular organization of these complexes and of the principles which underlie the fitting together and functioning of the individual enzymes in the complexes.

Some progress has been made in elucidating the biosynthesis of lipoic acid[87]. Tracer experiments with *E. coli* indicate that octanoic acid can function as a precursor of lipoic acid. [1-^{14}C]Octanoic acid appears to be incorporated into lipoic acid as a unit, C-1 of the biosynthesized lipoic acid corresponding to C-1 of the octanoic acid. No ^{14}C was incorporated into lipoic acid when [1-^{14}C]hexanoic acid, [1,6-$^{14}C_2$]adipic acid or [1-^{14}C]-8-hydroxyoctanoic acid were included in the growth medium.

Comprehensive reviews of dihydrolipoic dehydrogenase[88] and of the pyruvate and α-ketoglutarate oxidation enzymes[89] have been published.

REFERENCES

1 B. M. Guirard, E. E. Snell and R. J. Williams, *Arch. Biochem.*, 9 (1946) 381.
2 D. J. O'Kane and I. C. Gunsalus, *J. Bacteriol.*, 56 (1948) 499.
3 G. W. Kidder and V. C. Dewey, *Arch. Biochem.*, 20 (1949) 433.
4 E. L. R. Stokstad, C. E. Hoffman, M. A. Regan, D. Fordham and T. H. Jukes, *Arch. Biochem.*, 20 (1949) 75.
5 L. Kline and H. A. Barker, *J. Bacteriol.*, 60 (1950) 349.
6 L. J. Reed, B. G. DeBusk, I. C. Gunsalus and C. S. Hornberger Jr., *Science*, 114 (1951) 93.
7 M. W. Bullock, J. A. Brockman Jr., E. L. Patterson, J. V. Pierce and E. L. R. Stokstad, *J. Am. Chem. Soc.*, 74 (1952) 3455.
8 L. J. Reed, I. C. Gunsalus, G. H. F. Schnakenberg, Q. F. Soper, H. E. Boaz, S. F. Kern and T. V. Parke, *J. Am. Chem. Soc.*, 75 (1953) 1267.
9 J. A. Brockman Jr., E. L. R. Stokstad, E. L. Patterson, J. V. Pierce and M. E. Macchi, *J. Am. Chem. Soc.*, 76 (1954) 1827.
10 L. J. Reed, in N. Kharasch (Ed.), *Organic Sulfur Compounds*, Vol. 1, Pergamon, London, 1961, p. 443.
11 K. Mislow and W. C. Meluch, *J. Am. Chem. Soc.*, 78 (1956) 5920.
12 M. Calvin, *Federation Proc.*, 13 (1954) 697.
13 H. Nawa, W. T. Brady, M. Koike and L. J. Reed, *J. Am. Chem. Soc.*, 82 (1960) 896.
14 B. Ke, *Biochim. Biophys. Acta*, 25 (1957) 650.
15 D. R. Sanadi, M. Langley and R. L. Searls, *J. Biol. Chem.*, 234 (1959) 178.
16 J. A. Barltrop, P. M. Hayes and M. Calvin, *J. Am. Chem. Soc.*, 76 (1954) 4348.
17 R. C. Thomas and L. J. Reed, *J. Am. Chem. Soc.*, 78 (1956) 6148.
18 G. Bergson and L. Schotte, *Arkiv Kemi*, 13 (1958) 43; G. Bergson, *Arkiv Kemi*, 19 (1962) 265.
19 A. Fava, A. Iliceto and E. Camera, *J. Am. Chem. Soc.*, 79 (1957) 833.
20 S. Sunner, *Nature*, 176 (1955) 217.
21 O. Foss and O. Tjomsland, *Acta Chem. Scand.*, 12 (1958) 1810.
22 L. J. Reed, *Advan. Enzymol.*, 18 (1957) 319.
23 L. J. Reed, in R. S. Harris and I. G. Wool (Eds.), *Vitamins and Hormones*, Vol. 20, Academic Press, New York, 1962, p. 1.
24 P. D. Boyer, in P. D. Boyer, H. Lardy and K. Myrbäck (Eds.), *The Enzymes*, 2nd ed., Vol. 1, Academic Press, New York, 1959, p. 511.
25 I. C. Gunsalus, *Federation Proc.*, 13 (1954) 715.
26 D. J. O'Kane, *J. Bacteriol.*, 60 (1950) 449.
27 M. I. Dolin and I. C. Gunsalus, *J. Bacteriol.*, 62 (1951) 199.
28 R. S. Schweet and K. Cheslock, *J. Biol. Chem.*, 199 (1952) 749.
29 D. R. Sanadi, M. Langley and F. White, *J. Biol. Chem.*, 234 (1959) 183.
30 M. Koike, L. J. Reed and W. R. Carroll, *J. Biol. Chem.*, 235 (1960) 1924.
31 V. Massey, *Biochim. Biophys. Acta*, 38 (1960) 447.
32 R. A. Peters, H. M. Sinclair and R. H. S. Thompson, *Biochem. J.*, 40 (1946) 516.
33 R. A. Peters, *Symposia Soc. Exptl. Biol.*, 3 (1949) 36.
34 L. J. Reed, M. Koike, M. E. Levitch and F. R. Leach, *J. Biol. Chem.*, 232 (1958) 143.
34a K. Suzuki and L. J. Reed, *J. Biol. Chem.*, 238 (1963) 4021.
35 M. Koike and L. J. Reed, *J. Biol. Chem.*, 235 (1960) 1931.
36 L. J. Reed, *Physiol. Revs.*, 33 (1953) 544.
37 I. C. Gunsalus, in W. D. McElroy and B. Glass (Eds.), *The Mechanism of Enzyme Action*, Johns Hopkins, Baltimore, 1954, p. 545.
38 R. S. Schweet, B. Katchman, R. M. Bock and V. Jagannathan, *J. Biol. Chem.*, 196 (1952) 563.
39 D. R. Sanadi, J. W. Littlefield and R. M. Bock, *J. Biol. Chem.*, 197 (1952) 851.
40 M. Koike, L. J. Reed and W. R. Carroll, *J. Biol. Chem.*, 238 (1963) 30.
41 S. Korkes, *Brookhaven Symp. Biol.*, 5 (1953) 192.
42 M. Goldberg and D. R. Sanadi, *J. Am. Chem. Soc.*, 74 (1952) 4972.
43 A. D. Gounaris and L. P. Hager, *J. Biol. Chem.*, 236 (1961) 1013.

[44] R. S. Schweet, M. Fuld, K. Cheslock and M. Paul, in W. D. McElroy and B. Glass (Eds.), *Phosphorus Metabolism*, Vol. 1, Johns Hopkins, Baltimore, 1951, p. 246.
[45] L. P. Hager, *Ph. D. Dissertation*, University of Illinois, Urbana, Ill. 1953.
[46] L. L. Ingraham, *Biochemical Mechanisms*, Wiley, New York, 1962, p. 85.
[47] I. C. Gunsalus and R. A. Smith, *Proc. Intern. Symp. Enzyme Chem., Tokyo–Kyoto, 1957*, Academic Press, New York, 1958, p. 77.
[48] D. S. Goldman, *Biochim. Biophys. Acta*, 45 (1960) 279.
[49] M. L. Das, M. Koike and L. J. Reed, *Proc. Natl. Acad. Sci. U. S.*, 47 (1961) 753.
[50] R. Breslow, *J. Cellular Comp. Physiol.*, Suppl. 1 (1959) 100.
[51] R. Breslow and E. McNelis, *J. Am. Chem. Soc.*, 82 (1960) 2394.
[52] F. G. White and L. L. Ingraham, *J. Am. Chem. Soc.*, 82 (1960) 4114.
[53] K. Daigo and L. J. Reed, *J. Am. Chem. Soc.*, 84 (1962) 666.
[54] C. P. Nash, C. W. Olsen, F. G. White and L. L. Ingraham, *J. Am. Chem. Soc.*, 83 (1961) 4106; F. G. White and L. L. Ingraham, *J. Am. Chem. Soc.*, 84 (1962) 3109.
[55] I. C. Gunsalus, L. S. Barton and W. Gruber, *J. Am. Chem. Soc.*, 78 (1956) 1763.
[56] V. Massey and C. Veeger, *Biochim. Biophys. Acta*, 48 (1961) 33.
[57] R. L. Searls, J. M. Peters and D. R. Sanadi, *J. Biol. Chem.*, 236 (1961) 2317.
[58] O. K. Reiss, *J. Biol. Chem.*, 233 (1958) 789.
[59] L. P. Hager and I. C. Gunsalus, *J. Am. Chem. Soc.*, 75 (1953) 5767.
[60] R. L. Searls and D. R. Sanadi, *J. Biol. Chem.*, 235 (1960) 2485.
[61] M. Koike, P. C. Shah and L. J. Reed, *J. Biol. Chem.*, 235 (1960) 1939.
[61a] J. Matthews and L. J. Reed, *J. Biol. Chem.*, 238 (1963) 1869.
[62] V. Massey, *Biochim. Biophys. Acta*, 30 (1958) 205.
[63] F. B. Straub, *Biochem. J.*, 33 (1939) 787.
[64] R. L. Searls and D. R. Sanadi, *J. Biol. Chem.*, 236 (1961) 580.
[65] V. Massey, Q. H. Gibson and C. Veeger, *Biochem. J.*, 77 (1960) 341.
[66] G. Palmer and V. Massey, *Biochim. Biophys. Acta*, 58 (1962) 349.
[67] V. Massey, T. Hofmann and G. Palmer, *J. Biol. Chem.*, 237 (1962) 3820.
[68] F. R. Leach, K. Yasunobu and L. J. Reed, *Biochim. Biophys. Acta*, 18 (1955) 297.
[69] L. J. Reed, F. R. Leach and M. Koike, *J. Biol. Chem.*, 232 (1958) 123.
[70] L. J. Reed, *Proc. Intern. Symp. Enzyme Chem., Tokyo–Kyoto, 1957*, Academic Press, New York, 1958, p. 71.
[71] L. J. Reed, in P. D. Boyer, H. Lardy and K. Myrbäck (Eds.), *The Enzymes*, Vol. 3, 2nd ed., Academic Press, New York, 1960, p. 195.
[72] K. Daigo and L. J. Reed, *J. Am. Chem. Soc.*, 84 (1962) 659.
[73] G. R. Seaman, *J. Biol. Chem.*, 234 (1959) 161.
[74] C. R. Willms and L. J. Reed, *Federation Proc.*, 23 (1964) 264.
[75] L. J. Reed and M. Koike, *Federation Proc.*, 20 (1961) 238.
[76] H. Fernández-Morán, *Rev. Mod. Phys.*, 31 (1959) 319.
[77] R. W. Horne and P. Wildy, *Virology*, 15 (1961) 348.
[78] H. Fernández-Morán, in R. J. C. Harris (Ed.), *The Interpretation of Ultrastructure*, Academic Press, New York, 1962, p. 411.
[79] H. Fernández-Morán, *Proc. Assoc. Res. Nerv. Ment. Dis.*, 40 (1962) 235.
[80] H. Fernández-Morán, L. J. Reed, M. Koike and C. R. Willms, *Science*, 145 (1964) 930.
[81] L. J. Reed, B. B. Mukherjee and J. Matthews, *Federation Proc.*, 24 (1965) 229.
[82] B. B. Mukherjee, J. Matthews, D. L. Horney and L. J. Reed, *J. Biol. Chem.*, 240 (1965) PC 2268.
[83] U. Henning, C. Herz and K. Szolyvay, *Z. Vererbungslehre*, 95 (1964) 236.
[84] U. Henning and C. Herz, *Z. Vererbungslehre*, 95 (1964) 260.
[85] U. Henning, K. Szolyvay and C. Herz, *Z. Vererbungslehre*, 95 (1964) 276.
[86] T. Hayakawa, H. Muta, M. Hirashima, S. Ide, K. Okabe and M. Koike, *Biochem. Biophys. Research Communs.*, 17 (1964) 51.
[87] L. J. Reed, T. Okaichi and I. Nakanishi, *Intern. Symp. Chem. Natural Products, Abstr., Kyoto*, 1964, p. 218.
[88] V. Massey, in P. D. Boyer, H. Lardy and K. Myrbäck (Eds.), *The Enzymes*, Vol. 7, 2nd ed., Academic Press, New York, 1963, p. 275.
[89] D. R. Sanadi, in P. D. Boyer, H. Lardy and K. Myrbäck (Eds.), *The Enzymes*, Vol. 7, 2nd ed., Academic Press, New York, 1963, p. 307.

Chapter III

Flavoprotein Dehydrogenases of the Respiratory Chain

THOMAS P. SINGER

Edsel B. Ford Institute for Medical Research, Henry Ford Hospital, Detroit (Mich.)

1. Definition, and general properties

The term "respiratory chain-linked dehydrogenase" has come into use in recent years to describe a group of flavoproteins which are structurally and functionally associated with the terminal electron-transport system and which serve as the primary reaction sites of oxidizable metabolites with the respiratory chain. The best known and most extensively studied enzymes in this category are succinate and reduced NAD dehydrogenases. In fact, most of the special properties of this group of enzymes were first recognized as a result of investigations of the behavior of these two enzymes in respiratory-chain preparations. In addition to succinate and reduced NAD dehydrogenases the following enzymes are usually included in this group: mitochondrial α-glycerophosphate dehydrogenase, choline dehydrogenase, and the electron-transferring flavoprotein (ETF). The evidence that all 5 of these enzymes are structurally and functionally linked to the cytochrome system appears to be sound[1].

The inclusion of certain other enzymes in this group, such as the D(—)-lactate cytochrome reductase and L(+)-lactate dehydrogenase of yeast and the L-galactono-γ-lactone dehydrogenase of plant mitochondria, is provisional and somewhat arbitrary. The main reason for this is that although these proteins have been highly purified (the two lactate-oxidizing enzymes have been obtained in homogeneous form), there is as yet no conclusive evidence that they are structurally bound to the respiratory chain and react directly with it, rather than by way of a mediator, such as external cytochrome *c*. Further, as discussed in a recent review[1], the criteria which set apart this group of enzymes from other flavoproteins have never been rigorously

References p. 194

defined and, hence, with some enzymes (such as the D(—)-lactate cytochrome reductase of yeast), which share many but not all the characteristics of the respiratory chain-linked dehydrogenases, it is difficult to decide from available evidence whether their inclusion in this category is justifiable.

As already mentioned, the main distinguishing feature of these enzymes is their structural and functional linkage to the respiratory chain. This tight functional union of the flavoprotein with the cytochrome system is undoubtedly of great physiological importance, since it may account for the relatively high degree of efficiency of electron transfer from reduced flavoprotein to the cytochrome chain and may also provide the machinery for cross reactions between individual oxidase chains. Examples of the latter are the energy-dependent reduction of NAD by succinate[2,3] and the inhibition exerted by either member of a pair of respiratory chain-linked metabolites (*e.g.*, succinate and α-glycerophosphate, reduced NAD and succinate, succinate and choline) on the rate of oxidation of the other one in mitochondria[4,5].

One consequence of this tight linkage is that the extraction of these flavoproteins in the free form without obvious modification of the enzymes is a difficult task which calls for special techniques. As is well known, until about 10 years ago all attempts at solubilization of any of these enzymes met with consistent failure, despite the fact that they had been extensively studied in particulate preparations several decades earlier. The only known method for the extraction of reduced NAD, α-glycerophosphate and choline dehydrogenases in soluble form is digestion with phospholipase A, while all procedures available for extraction of succinate dehydrogenase from mammalian or yeast mitochondria in significant yield involve dehydration with an organic solvent, followed by brief exposure to moderately alkaline pH. The electron-transferring flavoprotein appears to be an exception to this rule, since it is readily extracted[6] from acetone powders at neutral pH.

The respiratory chain-linked dehydrogenases are flavoproteins, in which the flavin prosthetic group is relatively tightly bound to the apoenzyme. In succinate dehydrogenase the FAD moiety is covalently linked to the peptide chain[7]. Further, except for ETF, they all contain non-heme iron. The presence of the latter grossly modifies the typical absorption spectrum of simple flavoproteins.

An interesting property of dehydrogenases of this class is their relatively high selectivity for electron carriers. None of the 5 enzymes mentioned is significantly autooxidizable; except for ETF which appears to react with soluble cytochrome *c* (although the question remains open even for that protein[8]), none of them shows more than a trace reaction with cytochrome *c* either in respiratory-chain preparations or in the soluble, purified form. As examples of the high degree of specificity of these enzymes for artificial electron acceptors one may quote succinate, choline, and reduced NAD dehydrogenases, for each of which only one oxidant has been found to react rapidly with the reduced flavoprotein (phenazine methosulfate in the first two cases; ferricyanide in the case of reduced NAD dehydrogenase). This specificity may be inherent in the native structure of the proteins, since agents which modify the intact structure often enhance the reactivity with certain dyes to a remarkable extent. Thus a wide variety of treatments, including prolonged incubation with the substrate in aerobic condition, cause the appearance of cytochrome *c* and indophenol reductase activities in reduced NAD dehydrogenase[9–11] and preparative modification of succinate dehydrogenase elicits a dramatic increase[12,13] in reactivity with $FMNH_2$.

Despite major efforts in many laboratories the primary reaction partner of these flavoproteins in the intact respiratory chain has not been unambiguously established. Cytochrome *b*, cytochrome c_1, and coenzyme Q have all been considered the primary oxidants of succinate and reduced NAD dehydrogenases (either directly or by way of protein-bound non-heme irons) in mitochondria, but at this writing the sequence of electron transport from the flavoproteins to the respiratory chain has not been unambiguously established. So far no rapid reaction has been observed between the isolated flavoproteins and coenzyme Q or any of the cytochromes on mixing purified preparations of the two potential reactants. It is impossible to decide whether this is due to modification of the flavoprotein in the course of isolation, to preparative modification of the cytochrome component, to the fact that an additional substance is needed to catalyze the interaction, or to the circumstance that interaction between the components requires an integrated structure which is not established on simple mixing of the components. Considerably greater success has attended efforts to reconstitute the respiratory chain from *particulate* fragments thereof[14].

While, in view of these facts, assays based on the use of artificial electron carriers have been the only means available for the purification and characterization of dehydrogenases of this type, certain problems are inherent in their use. Problems on the technical plane are numerous; their importance for meaningful assays have been amply emphasized[1,13]. Among theoretical problems entailed in the use of dye assays perhaps the most important requirements are to ascertain that the particular electron carrier reacts directly with the dehydrogenase in both particle-bound and soluble form, rather than by way of another catalyst, and that the assay selected measures the full or nearly full turnover rate of the dehydrogenase. If the latter requirement is not met, *i.e.*, if the reaction rate of the dehydrogenase with the dye lags considerably behind the rate of the substrate–flavoprotein reaction, studies of kinetics, inhibitors, and activators are apt to yield quantitatively misleading data. Yet, only in rare instances can one be

References p. 194

certain that this particular requirement has been met. The fact that in respiratory-chain preparations, under appropriate conditions, the same turnover number is measured for succinate dehydrogenase with coenzyme Q_{10} and phenazine methosulfate as electron acceptors, while all other assays measure a considerably lower turnover number, offers a measure of assurance that these electron carriers may be measuring the full activity[13]. Similarly, the correlation of reduced NAD–ferricyanide activity and the rate of appearance of reduced NAD–induced EPR signal[15] suggest that the ferricyanide assay[16] may be a measure of the full activity of reduced NAD dehydrogenase.

The view has also been voiced[17] that assays based on the use of artificial electron acceptors may be hazardous, since they may mask protein modifications which might be detected if the natural electron acceptor were used. It has been observed, for instance, that the reactivity of soluble succinate dehydrogenase with phenazine methosulfate declines more rapidly than the ability of the enzyme to reconstitute the succinoxidase activity of alkali-treated heart muscle particles[17]. While, in principle, this view is correct, the alternative suggested is frought with experimental and theoretical complications. (*1*) As already mentioned, the "natural" electron acceptors of respiratory chain-linked dehydrogenases are not definitely known; (*2*) reconstitution experiments, in lieu of catalytic assays, are not practical, since success along these lines has been reported only for succinate dehydrogenase[18]; (*3*) even in the case of succinate dehydrogenase several types of reconstituted preparations are formed with a given sample of succinate dehydrogenase, none of which is completely identical with untreated respiratory-chain preparations[19,20]. Further, differential loss of activity of succinate dehydrogenase in one type of catalytic assay but not in another is commonly encountered and may be detected without reconstitution experiments[13].

Another property of this group of enzymes which should be emphasized is their unusual lability in the soluble, purified state. An extreme example is succinate dehydrogenase which loses activity within a few hours after extraction, regardless of the precautions taken, probably as a result of damage incurred in the extraction procedure. Succinate, reduced NAD, choline, and α-glycerophosphate dehydrogenases are all readily destroyed by organic solvents; they withstand only a very limited pH range, and reduced NAD dehydrogenase is fragmented at temperatures in excess of 30°. Coupled with the fact that these proteins have a tendency to be irreversibly adsorbed on a variety of materials and that their concentration in mitochondria is usually very low, their isolation in sufficient quantity and purity to permit characterization of their structure by contemporary methods or the delineation of their mechanism of action presents a truly formidable task.

The present Chapter summarizes current knowledge of reduced NAD and succinate dehydrogenases. For a survey of the properties of the other respiratory chain-linked dehydrogenases the reader is referred to recent reviews[1,21].

2. Reduced NAD dehydrogenase

(a) *Historical*

Ever since the discovery of pyridine-nucleotide catalysis in Warburg's laboratory in the early 1930's, there has been a steady and wide-spread interest in enzymes concerned with the oxidation of reduced NAD and reduced NADP, primarily those which might function in the aerobic oxidation of the reduced coenzymes. A large number of preparations have been isolated from animal and plant tissues and microorganisms which link the oxidation of reduced NAD or reduced NADP to dyes, cytochrome *c* or H_2O_2. In each instance examined the enzymes concerned turned out to be flavoproteins, a fact which may be related to the marked ability of riboflavin and its nucleotides to catalyze the non-enzymatic oxidation of reduced nicotinamide nucleotides in model systems[22].

Systematic attempts at the isolation and characterization of the reduced NAD dehydrogenase of the respiratory chain had to await, however, recognition of the facts that a unique system — the reduced NAD oxidase chain — exists within mitochondria, that only that fraction of reduced NAD oxidation which proceeds by way of this system results in significant ATP synthesis, and that in the mitochondrial environment the reduced NAD dehydrogenase component of this chain does not react significantly either with external cytochrome *c* or with O_2 but transfers electrons directly to the respiratory chain. Since the criteria which were known to distinguish the respiratory chain-linked reduced NAD dehydrogenase from the various other reduced NAD oxidizing enzymes of animal tissues (antimycin A- and amytal-sensitivity, functional linkage to the respiratory chain and to the energy-conservation system) were properties of an organized multi-enzyme system and not of the flavoprotein itself, and since no specific assay for this enzyme was available, prior to its isolation there was no way of knowing whether any of the reduced NAD oxidizing enzymes described in the literature represented the respiratory chain-linked dehydrogenase in purified form, or a modified form thereof, or an enzyme of altogether different origin.

The dilemma was eventually circumvented by utilizing the most specific starting materials available for the isolation of the enzyme: ETP[23] and the so-called "reduced NAD oxidase"[24] particles. These very similar particle preparations are considerably enriched with respect to reduced NAD dehydrogenase, as compared with mitochondria, and appear to be virtually

References p. 194

free from reduced NAD-oxidizing flavoproteins other than the respiratory chain-linked enzyme. The dehydrogenase was quantitatively extracted from these sources by digestion with snake venom phospholipase A at 30° and neutral pH, a mild procedure which does not appear to cause known modification of the dehydrogenase[16,25,26]. The dehydrogenase was then isolated in highly purified form from beef heart[27,28] and in partially purified state from beef liver mitochondria[29,30]. The resulting preparations showed the same kinetic properties, substrate specificity, and response to inhibitors and protein-modifying agents as metabolically intact samples of the reduced NAD oxidase system[1,26,27].

A remarkable property of reduced NAD dehydrogenase, which came to light[31] only in the course of its purification, is its tendency to be fragmented under the influence of acid pH and organic solvents as well as by temperatures in excess of about 30°. This degradation is accompanied by extensive loss of the characteristic reactivity of the enzyme with ferricyanide and of substrate-reducible EPR signal[15] at $g = 1.94$, the emergence of cytochrome *c* and indophenol reductase activities, changes in substrate specificity, labilization of the flavin moiety, etc.[9,10]. Once these facts were recognized, it could be readily shown[9,10] that the numerous reduced NAD–cytochrome reductase preparations isolated from mammalian mitochondria were not naturally-occurring enzymes but degradation products of reduced NAD dehydrogenase, since all of them had been extracted under conditions which degraded both particle-bound and soluble reduced NAD dehydrogenase (prolonged incubation at 37°, extraction with aqueous ethanol at acid pH at 42–44° or digestion with thiourea[32–37]). The various cytochrome-reducing preparations, although presumed to be different, were experimentally indistinguishable from each other or from the main cytochrome reductase component of preparations extracted at 37°, and, further, application of the procedures used in the extraction and purification of these cytochrome reductases to purified reduced NAD dehydrogenase resulted in degradation of the enzyme to the same product[9,10]. Thus in retrospect it is quite clear that in the isolation of these cytochrome reductases and diaphorases extraction methods were selected which created maximal activity toward cytochrome *c* or 2,6-dichlorophenolindophenol (DCIP).

An example of the demonstration that reduced NAD–cytochrome reductases hitherto isolated from mitochondria are degradation products of reduced NAD dehydrogenase is given in Scheme 1. In this experiment a sample of ETP (a purified preparation of the respiratory chain) was extracted with phospholipase A until essentially all the reduced NAD dehydrogenase became soluble, as judged by the ferricyanide assay (*cf.* below). The residue was then subjected to the acid-ethanol extraction used in the isolation of the reduced NAD–cytochrome reductase of Mahler *et al.*[32]. As shown in Scheme 1, almost no cytochrome reductase was obtained on acid-ethanol treatment after prior removal of reduced NAD dehydrogenase. When, however, the ETP preparation was first subjected to the acid-ethanol treatment, a con-

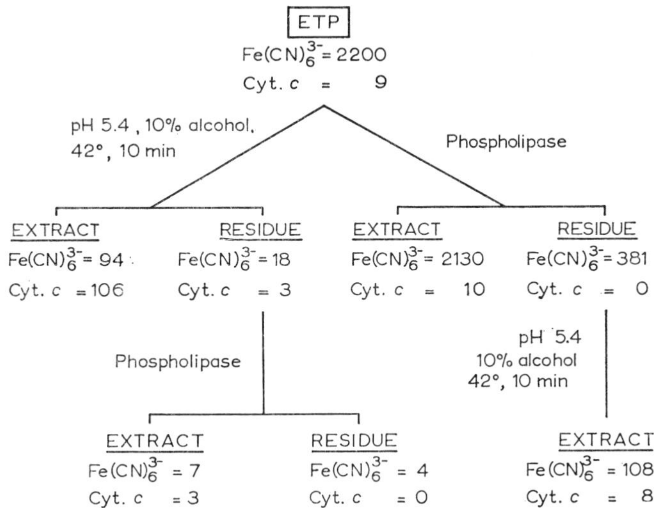

Scheme 1. Common origin of reduced NAD dehydrogenase and reduced NAD–cytochrome reductase. The numbers denote total activities with ferricyanide and cytochrome *c* as acceptors at V_{max} derived from 100 mg of ETP (protein basis), expressed as micromoles of reduced NAD oxidized per min and are average figures for 5 experiments, with only minor variations between individual experiments. Phospholipase digestion was carried out at a ratio of 1 mg of *Naja naja* venom per 25 mg of protein at pH 7.4, 30°, for 90 min. After removal of the extracted protein, the residue was digested a second time under identical conditions. Data from Watari *et al.*[9].

siderable cytochrome reductase activity was extracted, in fact, far more than that present in the starting material. At the same time extensive destruction of ferricyanide activity occurred so that on subsequent digestion of the enzyme with phospholipase A only a trace of reduced NAD dehydrogenase was recovered.

Similar balance studies have shown that cytochrome reductase preparations extracted by digestion with snake venom[36] at 37° or with thiourea[37] are also breakdown products of reduced NAD dehydrogenase, rather than naturally-occurring enzymes.

These observations have greatly simplified the problem of the pathway of reduced NAD oxidation in mammalian mitochondria. At least for heart muscle, the tissue most extensively explored in this respect, and probably also for liver, it is no longer necessary to postulate the presence of the large number of reduced NAD oxidizing enzymes of undetermined function as

References p. 194

were thought to be present in the mitochondria at one time. At present it appears that reduced NAD oxidation in these mitochondria proceeds entirely by way of the respiratory chain-linked dehydrogenase. The only other reduced NAD-oxidizing enzymes of established occurrence in these mitochondria are lipoyl dehydrogenase[38], the only known function of which is NAD *reduction* in the course of α-keto acid metabolism[39,40] and DT diaphorase[41–43] (primarily an extramitochondrial enzyme but also reported to be present in mitochondria[44]), the role of which remains conjectural.

(*b*) *Assay*

The only assay known to be a satisfactory measure of reduced NAD dehydrogenase from mammalian mitochondria is based on the use of ferricyanide as electron acceptor[16]. Activity must be calculated from extrapolation to infinite ferricyanide concentration (V_{max}), since the apparent K_m for the oxidant changes during extraction and is strongly pH-dependent and since both the substrate (reduced NAD) and the product (NAD) are competitive inhibitors with respect to ferricyanide. Further, in respiratory-chain preparations dual reaction sites exist for ferricyanide, one at the dehydrogenase level (low affinity for ferricyanide) and one in the cytochrome c to c_1 region (high affinity for ferricyanide). Thus the concentration of the dehydrogenase can be calculated only from V_{max} data[16].

In the original method the assay was carried out in phosphate buffer at pH 7.4, since at higher pH values the slope relating reciprocal activities to reciprocal ferricyanide concentration was too steep. Subsequently[26] it was found that the substitution of triethanolamine buffer, pH 7.8, provides more moderate slopes and permits accurate measurements at the pH optimum (pH 7.8). With this modification and with the aid of a fast recording spectrophotometer equipped with suitable scale expansion features[16], the ferricyanide assay has proved to be rapid, accurate, and reliable in heart and liver preparations from a variety of species.

It seems likely that the flavoprotein–ferricyanide interaction is not the rate-limiting step in the catalytic cycle and, further, that the ferricyanide assay may measure the full activity of the dehydrogenase, since with two substrates, which are oxidized at quite different rates, the half-time of appearance of the EPR signal at $g = 1.94$ (a measure of the catalytically active iron components of the enzyme) corresponds exactly to one catalytic cycle in the ferricyanide assay[15,45]. Also, on thermal inactivation of the enzyme, ferricyanide activity and substrate-reducible EPR signal are lost in a parallel manner (Fig. 1).

As in all assays involving the use of artificial electron carriers, the applicability of the method must be checked for each tissue studied, since the experimental conditions required for a valid assay may vary with the tissue and species. Thus preliminary results suggest that the ferricyanide assay, at least in its present form, does not measure the full activity of the dehydrogenase from yeast mitochondria[46].

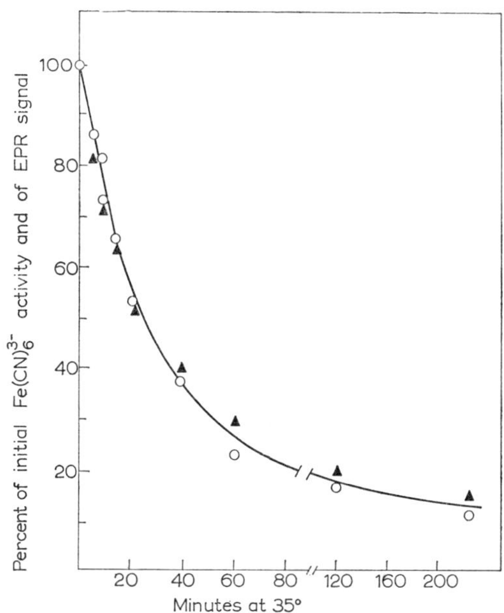

Fig. 1. Parallelism of loss of $Fe(CN)_6^{3-}$ activity (○—○) and of EPR signal (▲—▲) on thermal inactivation of reduced NAD dehydrogenase at 35° (modified from Beinert *et al.*[15]). Purified reduced NAD dehydrogenase (27.3 mg/ml) was incubated in 0.03 *M* phosphate, pH 7.8, in the dark and samples were removed and assayed for reduced NAD dehydrogenase activity and for substrate-induced EPR signal at the times indicated.

Transhydrogenation between reduced NAD and suitable oxidized pyridine nucleotide analogues provides an alternative assay of the enzyme[16]. This method is, however, less specific than the reduced NAD–ferricyanide reaction, since even considerably purified preparations of the enzyme contain flavoprotein impurities which catalyze transhydrogenation[28] between reduced NAD and acetylpyridine NAD.

(c) *Isolation*

The dehydrogenase was first isolated from phospholipase extracts of beef heart ETP by $(NH_4)_2SO_4$ and protamine precipitation and differential ultracentrifugation[27]. The resulting product possessed a very high specific activity (375 μmoles reduced NAD oxidized/min/mg at 30°) and was electrophoretically homogeneous, but the tendency of the enzyme to aggregate in purified preparations at neutral pH prevented both further purification and the meaningful application of other criteria of homogeneity[28]. Subsequently it was found that this aggregation is prevented at alkaline pH values, where the enzyme is fairly stable. On the basis of these observations a considerably improved purification procedure was devised[28,47], the terminal steps of which include two sucrose-gradient centrifugations at pH 10. This preparation is free from flavoprotein impurities and, as judged by sedimentation analysis, is about 65–70% homogeneous. The specific activity of the best preparations is 940–970 μmoles reduced NAD/min/mg and that of the homogeneous enzyme is estimated to be 1400.

The enzyme has also been extracted and purified from liver mitochondria by methods similar to those used for the isolation of the heart enzyme[29,30,48]. Because of its very low concentration in liver mitochondria and the unavailability of a convenient starting material comparable to heart ETP, preparations beyond a specific activity of about 100 are difficult to obtain from this source.

(d) *Molecular properties*

At pH 10, where aggregation of the flavoprotein is prevented, the sedimentation coefficient of the beef heart enzyme is $s_{20,w} = 14 \pm 0.5$ in the concentration range[28] of 6–10 mg protein per ml. A preliminary estimate of the molecular weight, based on FMN content and corrected for the impurity detected by ultracentrifugation, has been reported to be of the order of 550000. This value may be a lower limit since in recent preparations of very high specific activity (over 1400) a somewhat lower FMN content has been noted[49]. Further, it appears from gradient-centrifugation studies that the enzyme might exist in several polymeric forms. The dehydrogenase contains 16–18 gramatoms of non-heme iron per mole of FMN[27,47] and 1.6 mole of "labile sulfide" per gramatom of non-heme iron[49].

The identity of the flavin component of the enzyme was for a long time a matter of controversy[27,50]. On the basis of the composition of particulate complexes[51] and other indirect evidence[52], some authors concluded that it was FAD, while analysis of other particles[53] and of the derived reduced NAD–cytochrome reductases[31,36,54] suggested that it was FMN. The latter evidence, while suggestive, was inconclusive, since in the course of the transformation of the dehydrogenase to reduced NAD–cytochrome reductase a net conversion of FAD to FMN has been observed[10]. Electrophoretically monodisperse preparations of the soluble enzyme yielded both FAD and FMN on deproteinization and this behavior was interpreted to suggest that FAD might be the natural prosthetic group but that, owing to an unusual type of linkage to the protein, the act of deproteinization might cause partial breakdown of the FAD moiety to FMN[27]. It has been recently demonstrated, however, that gradient centrifugation of the enzyme at pH 10 yields a preparation containing only FMN, and that the FAD present at earlier stages of purification belongs to impurities which are tenaciously associated with the dehydrogenase at neutral pH but are separable at alkaline pH values[28]. It may be concluded, therefore, that the dehydrogenase from heart mitochondria is an FMN enzyme, since analysis of highly purified preparations of the flavoprotein itself, of the "reduced NAD–coenzyme Q reductase complex" of which it is a component, and of derived cytochrome reductases yield concordant results[28,31,53,54]. The only recent conclusion to the contrary is that of Massey and Swoboda[52], who noted a gradual breakdown of FAD to FMN on storage of Keilin–Hartree preparations and therefore suggested that FMN enzymes from heart mitochondria may be artifactual. This conclusion is not correct, however, since it has now been shown that this type of hydrolysis of FAD to FMN occurs only in the extramitochondrial compartment and that the FMN content is the same in strictly fresh as in aged mitochondria[55,56].

The flavoprotein is brown colored and shows a generalized absorption over the entire visible range, with a maximum[27] at 410 mμ. As in many other iron-flavoproteins[1,58] the spectrum of the flavin component is masked by the large absorbance contributed by iron-protein bonds. Fig. 2 illustrates the difference spectrum of the enzyme following reduction by reduced NAD. As expected from the very high turnover number of the enzyme, bleaching by reduced NAD is too rapid to be followed by stopped-flow measurements, but the rate of bleaching by reduced NADP, a very poor substrate[11], is several orders of magnitude slower.

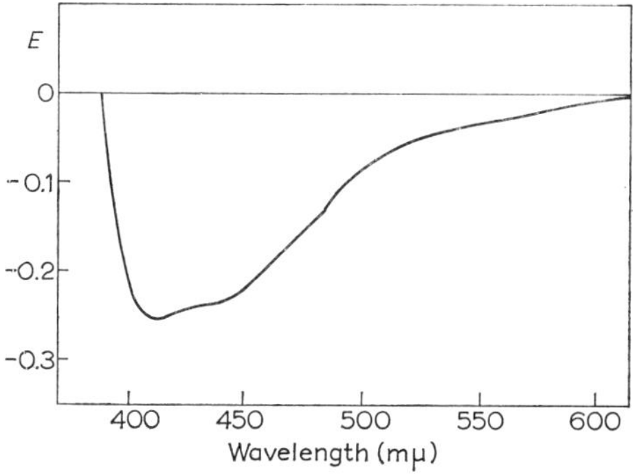

Fig. 2. Difference spectrum of reduced NAD dehydrogenase (9.25 mg protein/ml) obtained immediately after the addition of $8 \cdot 10^{-4}$ *M* reduced NAD to the enzyme. Negative values denote decolorization. From Ringler *et al.*[27].

Both the iron and flavin moieties are tightly bound and are not dissociable in the pH range where the enzyme is stable. On fragmentation of the dehydrogenase to cytochrome reductases, however, most of the non-heme iron is lost[9,10]. In the reduced NAD–cytochrome reductase fragments the iron: flavin ratio is of the order of 2–4 and the flavin is readily dissociable[31,54,57].

In view of the constant proportion of non-heme iron and "labile sulfide" found for this protein, as for ferredoxin[59] and photosynthetic pyridine nucleotide reductase[60], it is tempting to speculate that the sulfur group and the non-heme iron are linked in a structural unit in all these cases. A similar suggestion has recently been made by Handler *et al.*[58] on the basis of studies of the non-heme iron and "labile sulfide" content of dehydroorotic dehydrogenase, xanthine oxidase, and aldehyde oxidase.

(*e*) *Catalytic properties*

(*i*) *Beef heart reduced NAD dehydrogenase*

The turnover number of the enzyme[28], based on FMN content, is 800000 moles reduced NAD oxidized per minute, one of the highest values for a flavoprotein recorded in the literature. The substrate specificity and Michaelis constants of the enzyme are summarized in Table I. Although all reduced NAD analogues tested serve as substrates, only deamino reduced NAD is oxidized at a rate approaching that given by reduced NAD. When tested at catalytic enzyme concentrations no activity was observed with reduced NADP as substrate[26] but more recently it was found that at very high enzyme concentrations oxidation of reduced NADP becomes measurable[11]. This

TABLE I

SUBSTRATE SPECIFICITY AND MICHAELIS CONSTANTS OF REDUCED NAD DEHYDROGENASE[a]

Substrate	*Beef heart enzyme*		*Beef liver enzyme*	
	Relative rate of oxidation[b] (%)	K_m (*M*)	*Relative rate of oxidation*[b] (%)	K_m (*M*)
Reduced NAD	100	$1.08 \cdot 10^{-4}$	100	$1.02 \cdot 10^{-4}$
Deamino reduced NAD	48	$4.0 \cdot 10^{-5}$	56	$1.0 \cdot 10^{-4}$
Acetylpyridine reduced NAD	1.6	$7.9 \cdot 10^{-5}$	0.39	$1.0 \cdot 10^{-4}$
Acetylpyridine deamino reduced NAD	1.6	$4.8 \cdot 10^{-5}$		
Pyridinealdehyde reduced NAD	0.12	$6.4 \cdot 10^{-5}$	0.03	$1.5 \cdot 10^{-5}$
Thionicotinamide reduced NAD	0.57	$2.4 \cdot 10^{-5}$	4.0	$4.0 \cdot 10^{-5}$
Reduced NADP	0.03		<0.1	

[a] Data from Refs. 26, 30, 49.

[b] V_{max} with respect to both substrate and ferricyanide at pH 7.8, 30°, in triethanolamine buffer, except for reduced NADP, which was used at $1.4 \cdot 10^{-4}$ *M* concentration.

slow rate of reduced NADP oxidation is compatible with the rate of decolorization of the enzyme by reduced NADP in stopped-flow experiments and with the rates of appearance of the reduced NADP-induced $g = 1.94$ signal in EPR studies[45].

As expected from the functioning of the corresponding analogues as substrates, the dehydrogenase catalyzes transhydrogenations[26] between reduced NAD and 3-acetylpyridine NAD, thionicotinamide NAD, deamino NAD, 3-pyridine aldehyde NAD, and 3-acetylpyridine deamino NAD. Although the rates of these transhydrogenations are low compared with the rate of the reduced NAD–ferricyanide interaction, they provide an alternate assay of the enzyme in highly purified preparations, which are free from contaminating transhydrogenases[28].

TABLE II

ACCEPTOR SPECIFICITY OF REDUCED NAD DEHYDROGENASE[a]

Electron acceptor	*Relative rate at V_{max}*[b]	
	Beef heart enzyme[c]	*Beef liver enzyme*[d]
Ferricyanide	100	100
DCIP	0.5	~0.5
Cytochrome c	0.02	0.014
Cytochrome b_5		0.009
Menadione	~0.2	0.1
Lipoamide	0.06	0.3
Coenzyme Q_{10}	0	0

[a] Data from Refs. 26, 30, 49.
[b] Each assay was performed at 30° under optimal conditions for the particular electron acceptor[26].
[c] Specific activity = 360, preparation used just prior to gradient centrifugation step[28].
[d] Specific activity = 70.

As seen in Table II, the electron-acceptor specificity of the beef heart enzyme is highly restricted. Besides ferricyanide only 2,6-dichlorophenol-indophenol (DCIP) is reduced by reduced NAD at a significant rate, but even with this oxidant the reaction is very slow and, since the rate of DCIP reduction increases dramatically on fragmentation of the enzyme (*cf.* section 2g, p. 144), DCIP-reductase activity is more a measure of the modification than of the native activity of this flavoprotein[10]. The relatively higher activity of DCIP in certain respiratory-chain preparations is, of course, due to its ability to intercept electrons in the cytochrome c region.

Although the cytochrome c reductase activity of the dehydrogenase is exceedingly small (about 1/6000th of the activity with ferricyanide[26,28]), it is a property of the enzyme itself, rather than of a contaminating protein, since it remains constant during the terminal stages of purification and parallels exactly the distribution of ferricyanide activity in gradient-centrifugation studies. Like DCIP activity, the reduction of cytochrome *c* may increase as much as 100-fold on fragmentation or modification of the protein.

Among other electron carriers of physiological interest vitamin K derivatives, lipoamide, and coenzyme Q homologues should be mentioned. At earlier stages of purification menadione has a slight activity (0.9% of the ferricyanide rate[26]), which declines to an even lower value on further purification (Table II). In view of this and the insensitivity of the enzyme to dicumarol, the postulated role of vitamin K in the reduced NAD–oxidase system at the flavoprotein level[61] is doubtful. The slight lipoyl dehydrogenase activity of crude preparations[62] also decreases to a very low value on further purification (Table II) and even this may represent a trace impurity.

Among coenzyme Q derivatives only the Q_{10} and Q_1 homologues have been tested. The former was found to be inactive (Table II) but is also reported to be inactive with the particulate "reduced NAD–coenzyme Q reductase complex"[63]; the latter reacts with the dehydrogenase at < 0.1% of the rate of ferricyanide, while in the "reduced NAD–coenzyme Q reductase complex" it is about 2% as active[63a] as ferricyanide at V_{max}.

The dehydrogenase also catalyzes the reduction of NAD and of a number of oxidized NAD analogues in the presence of leucomethylviologen as electron donor[16].

Moderately high concentrations of reduced NAD and its reduced analogues inhibit the reduction of ferricyanide. Since the inhibition is competitive with respect to ferricyanide, it has been suggested that at high reduced NAD concentrations the substrate and ferricyanide compete for the same site on the flavoprotein[16]. NAD and its oxidized analogues are competitive inhibitors[16,26] with respect to reduced NAD while the inhibition, by relatively high reduced NADP concentrations, is not purely competitive[64].

The reduced NAD–ferricyanide reaction is insensitive to amytal and rotenone[63a] as is also true of more complex preparations which catalyze the amytal-sensitive reduction of coenzyme Q analogues[16,63]. From experiments of this type it has become clear that the point of action of amytal in the respiratory chain is not on the substrate but on the oxygen side of the flavoprotein, possibly at the coenzyme Q level.

Added FMN and FAD inhibit the dehydrogenase, while dicumarol, cyanide, and *o*-phenanthroline are without effect[26].

The action of —SH combining substances on this enzyme is quite unique. Unlike the reduced NAD–cytochrome reductases derived from this enzyme, which are extensively inhibited at very low concentrations of mercurials[26,65], the unmodified dehydrogenase is not inhibited significantly even at moderately high concentrations of *p*-chloromercuribenzoate or *p*-chloromercuriphenylsulfonate (PCMS) in the cold[26,48], but inhibition develops gradually at higher temperatures. Further, while the inhibition of the derived cytochrome reductases by mercurials is competitive with respect to cytochrome *c*, the inhibition of the dehydrogenase by the same agents is not competitive with respect to electron acceptors.

As shown in Fig. 3, when the dehydrogenase is incubated with a large

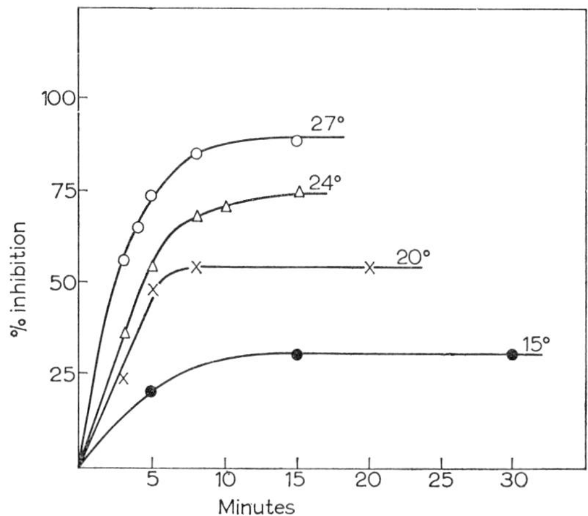

Fig. 3. Effect of *p*-chloromercuriphenylsulfonate (PCMS) on purified reduced NAD dehydrogenase. The enzyme (13.6 mg/ml, spec. act. = 320) was incubated at pH 7.8, 0°, with 0.385 m*M* PCMS for 5 min. Unreacted mercurial was removed at 0° on Sephadex G-25. The enzyme in the excluded fraction assayed immediately (0 time sample) showed no inhibition in the standard ferricyanide assay. Aliquots containing 0.06 *M* triethanolamine buffer, pH 7.8 (at all temperatures), and 1 mg protein/ml were incubated at the temperatures stated and aliquots were cooled to 0° and assayed periodically in order to follow the development of inhibition. A sample maintained at 0° showed no inhibition even after 14 h. Unpublished data of T. Cremona and E. B. Kearney (1962).

excess of PCMS at 0° and uncombined mercurial is removed by gel exclusion at 0°, on subsequent incubation of the derivative at higher temperatures loss of activity develops gradually[66]. Both the rate and the extent of inactivation attained are functions of the temperature of incubation. Similar results have been obtained with *N*-ethylmaleimide (NEM) as inhibitor.

The loss of activity which occurs on incubation of the PCMS- or NEM-derivative at 15–30° is not reversed by cooling or by incubation with thiols and appears to be a conformational change in the protein affecting the catalytically functional non-heme iron moiety[66]. This is apparent from the facts that while PCMS and NEM cause complete loss of activity toward ferricyanide (which involves non-heme iron[45]), transhydrogenase activity, which involves only the flavin, is unaffected[66]. Hence, these —SH groups are not involved in the activation of the substrate.

References p. 194

While thiols do not prevent the loss of ferricyanide activity, they do dissociate the mercurial derivative of the enzyme and thus prevent the loss of activity on subsequent exposure to 15–30°, provided that the thiol is added before the temperature is raised.

Phosphate ions and, under anaerobic conditions, reduced NAD protect the enzyme from inactivation by PCMS and PCMB, but they fail to protect against NEM. The effect of phosphate is quite specific: other anions, including arsenate, do not protect against mercurials. The mechanism of the protective effect has been recently clarified by the finding that phosphate prevents the combination of certain —SH groups with mercurials of the type of PCMS, but once combination has occurred it cannot prevent the loss of activity on raising the temperature. Phosphate is thought to act by combining with an anion-binding site on the enzyme and thereby conferring a net electronegative charge to this site, with consequent repulsion of the negatively charged PCMS and PCMB ions, but not for the neutral NEM molecule[66]. High concentrations of reduced NAD may protect for the same reason.

In addition to these —SH groups, another thiol group appears to play a role in electron transport to coenzyme Q in respiratory-chain preparations[67]. The question whether this type of —SH group is present in the dehydrogenase itself or in another component which links it to coenzyme Q, remains to be resolved.

(ii) Reduced NAD dehydrogenase from liver

The dehydrogenase purified from phospholipase extracts of liver mitochondria is very similar to the heart enzyme with respect to catalytic properties[29,30]. The substrate specificities and Michaelis constants for various reduced pyridine nucleotides are very nearly the same, as are their reactivities with different electron acceptors (Tables I and II) and pH optima. Like the heart enzyme, the dehydrogenase from liver is not inhibited by amytal or dicumarol with ferricyanide as the oxidant, while both NAD and reduced NAD are competitive inhibitors with respect to ferricyanide.

Since, for reasons already discussed, it has not been possible to purify the liver enzyme to a degree comparable to that attained with the dehydrogenase from heart, few of its molecular properties are established. The liver enzyme exhibits nearly the same absorption spectrum as the heart enzyme and similarly shows a high iron: flavin ratio in the most purified preparations. Further, it is also rapidly bleached by reduced NAD and bleaching is most extensive in regions where iron-protein bonds absorb. Thus non-heme iron also seems to be functional in this preparation[29,30]. In view of the inhomogeneity of the preparation, it has not been possible to decide whether the flavin moiety is FMN, as in the heart enzyme.

(*f*) *Paramagnetic resonance*

It has been shown by Beinert and colleagues that the addition of reduced NAD to mitochondria, submitochondrial particles, and particulate complexes of reduced NAD dehydrogenase elicits an asymmetric EPR signal at $g = 1.94$, which is distinct from a similar one produced by succinate[68–70]. The signal has been attributed to a reduced form of protein-bound non-heme iron and on the basis of kinetic studies it has been suggested that this iron functions as an intermediate in electron transport.

Soluble, purified preparations of reduced NAD dehydrogenase from heart[27] show qualitatively the same EPR signals on reduction with reduced NAD as more complex particle preparations[15]. The signal disappears on the addition of ferricyanide or of a NAD analogue of suitable potential, such as acetylpyridine NAD. Thus the non-heme iron seems to be functional in the purified enzyme[15,45]. In contrast, acid-ethanol-heat treated preparations, such as the cytochrome reductases of Mahler *et al.*[32] and of DeBernard[33], and the "reduced NAD–CoQ_6 reductase" of Sanadi *et al.*[71], and thermally degraded preparations[36] do not show the $g = 1.94$ signal on reduction by reduced NAD[72,73], since the catalytically active iron is either lost during extraction by these methods or is rendered inactive. In fact, on controlled thermal degradation of the purified dehydrogenase, activity with ferricyanide and substrate-reducible $g = 1.94$ signal are lost at the same rate[15] (Fig. 1).

Kinetic studies with the rapid-freezing technique[74] have shown a good correlation between the rate of appearance of the reduced iron signal on addition of reduced pyridine nucleotide analogues to the dehydrogenase and the rate of reduction of ferricyanide by these substrates under identical conditions[15,45]. Thus the rates of appearance of the $g = 1.94$ signal in the presence of reduced NAD, reduced NADP and reduced NAD analogues are in satisfactory agreement with the corresponding turnover numbers in the ferricyanide assay. From these studies and from measurements of the $g = 1.94$ signal in the steady state in the presence of both reduced NAD and ferricyanide it appears that the rate-limiting reaction in the catalytic cycle of the enzyme is the substrate–flavoprotein interaction, not the reoxidation of the enzyme by ferricyanide. From the time relations it has been calculated that full development of the $g = 1.94$ signal requires the oxidation of 2 moles of substrate; hence either 2 pairs of iron atoms or one mole of flavin plus a pair of non-heme irons may be reduced under these conditions.

(*g*) *Molecular transformations*

The stability characteristics of mammalian reduced NAD dehydrogenase are rather unusual. The purified enzyme is quite stable in the pH range of 7–8 near

References p. 194

0° and relatively stable even at pH 10 in the cold[26,28], but is labile below pH 7. At temperatures above 30° even at neutral pH it is rapidly fragmented with attendant loss of the characteristic properties of the dehydrogenase. Organic solvents, particularly ethanol, even at very low concentrations bring about the same type of degradation[27,29,31]. In addition to these agents also exposure to bile salts[27] and, in the case of highly purified preparations, freezing and thawing inactivate the enzyme[10].

Modification of the enzyme by exposure to elevated temperatures, organic solvents and acid pH, and a variety of other treatments usually involves breakdown of the original structure to various lower molecular-weight fragments; loss of reactivity with ferricyanide, of substrate-reducible EPR signal at $g = 1.94$, and of non-heme iron; emergence of cytochrome *c* reductase and DCIP reductase activities; changes in the absorption spectrum, substrate specificity, and Michaelis constants; labilization of the flavin; and a marked increase in sensitivity to —SH inhibitors[9,10,31,75].

Although all of these changes are expressions of the loss of the original structure of the enzyme, they do not occur simultaneously, nor are all of them seen with each transforming agent. Consequently, the cytochrome reductases or diaphorases isolated on treatment of mitochondria, submitochondrial particles or of the purified dehydrogenase with various transforming agents may have somewhat different properties, depending on the conditions used for fragmentation and for subsequent isolation of the derived fragment. Hence the number of apparently different reduced NAD–cytochrome reductase or diaphorase preparations which may be produced from a given preparation of the respiratory chain-linked enzyme is theoretically large.

The first type of transformation which was extensively studied[9,31,76] was that produced by the combined action of alcohol, acid pH, and brief exposure to 42–44°, since these were the conditions which had been used in the isolation of several reduced NAD–cytochrome reductase preparations from heart and liver mitochondria[32–35]. It was shown by Watari *et al.*[9,31] that the various reduced NAD–cytochrome reductases isolated from heart are indistinguishable, in terms of a large number of criteria, from each other and from the product arising on exposure of highly purified reduced NAD dehydrogenase to acid-ethanol at 42°. The degradation of reduced NAD dehydrogenase under these conditions involves all of the changes in molecular and catalytic properties listed above. Under the same conditions the reduced NAD dehydrogenase of liver mitochondria is similarly degraded to reduced NAD–cytochrome reductase[29,75].

The remarkable heat lability of reduced NAD dehydrogenase was noted early in the purification of the enzyme: this is why temperatures in excess of 30° were avoided both during its extraction and assay[25]. Thermal degradation of the enzyme was also noted later by Kaniuga and Veeger[76] and by King and Howard[77].

Fig. 4 shows that incubation of the purified enzyme at 37–42° leads to rapid loss of ferricyanide activity and secondary emergence of cytochrome reductase activity. Heat treatment, however, not only creates but also destroys cytochrome reductase activity. The same is true of DCIP reductase (diaphorase) activity[10]. The particle-bound form of the enzyme is somewhat more stable to heat inactivation than soluble preparations but qualitatively

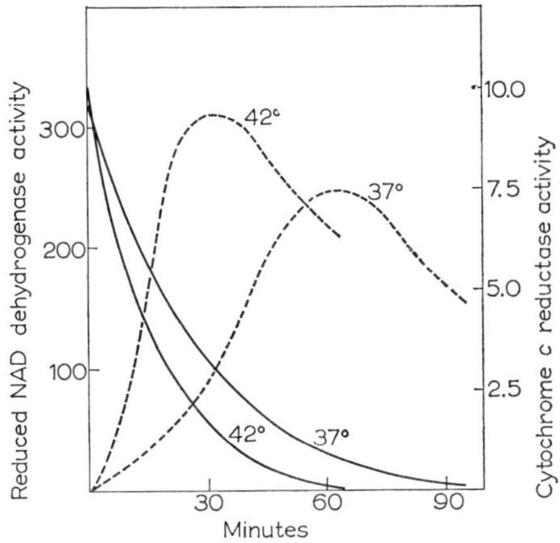

Fig. 4. Time course of degradation of reduced NAD dehydrogenase to cytochrome reductase by heat. Reduced NAD dehydrogenase was dissolved in 0.01 *M* phosphate, adjusted to pH 7.4 at each temperature. Protein concentration, 13.0 mg/ml in 37° experiment, 13.6 mg/ml in 42° experiment. The solid line denotes reduced NAD dehydrogenase activity (ferricyanide assay), the dashed line cytochrome reductase activity. Values on the ordinate are μmoles reduced NAD oxidized per min per mg protein. From Cremona *et al.*[10].

shows the same changes on heat treatment[26]. If the process of thermal inactivation is stopped when cytochrome reductase activity reaches a maximum, the $Fe(CN)_6^{3-}$ – cytochrome *c* activity ratio is found to have declined from the original value of 6000/1 to about 1, the same value as given by acid-ethanol extracted preparations[75]. Comparison of Figs. 1 and 4 further shows that the thermal inactivation is characterized by a very high temperature coefficient.

During thermal inactivation extensive fragmentation of reduced NAD dehydrogenase occurs[10]. Chromatography of the inactivated preparation on hydroxylapatite columns shows two major reduced NAD–cytochrome reductase fragments, in addition to a number of catalytically inactive ones. The preparation of King and Howard[36], which is extracted from Keilin–

Hartree particles by digestion with cobra venom at 37°, gives the same elution pattern. Further, the major component of this preparation, as of heat-degraded reduced NAD dehydrogenase, is not distinguishable from the Mahler enzyme[32] in terms of sedimentation constant, substrate specificity, absorption spectrum, EPR characteristics, response to inhibitors, etc.[10].

Under anaerobic conditions reduced NAD, reduced NADP, NAD and NADP protect the enzyme to varying extents from loss of ferricyanide activity[11] and of EPR signal[45] at 35°, although extensive fragmentation still occurs. Thus substances capable of combining at the substrate-binding site protect the active center without preventing thermal degradation of the enzyme.

The dehydrogenase from liver undergoes thermal fragmentation under the same conditions as the heart enzyme[29,75].

Transformation of reduced NAD dehydrogenase to cytochrome reductase under the influence of proteolytic enzymes was first noted by Lusty[29] with liver preparations and was extensively investigated with the heart enzyme[10,75]. Digestion with crystalline *B. subtilis* proteinase leads to rapid loss of ferricyanide activity, secondary rise in cytochrome *c* and DCIP reductase activities, and a much slower decay of transhydrogenase activity (Fig. 5). The product isolated again appeared to be indistinguishable from

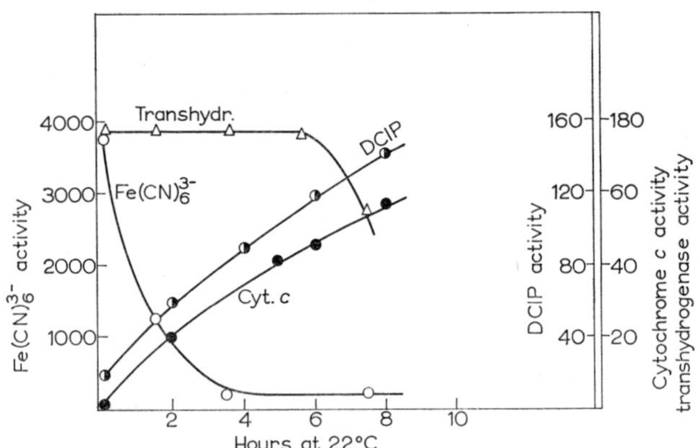

Fig. 5. Time course of degradation of reduced NAD dehydrogenase with bacterial proteinase. 4.0 ml of reduced NAD dehydrogenase (11.8 mg/ml, specific activity = 315) were incubated with 1.18 mg bacterial proteinase in 0.01 *M* phosphate, pH 7.4, at 22°. From Cremona *et al.*[10].

the Mahler enzyme[32] in terms of all criteria applied[10]. In contrast, the cytochrome reductases arising from tryptic hydrolysis, while still in the molecular-weight range of the Mahler enzyme[32] appear to differ from the latter in substrate specificity and kinetic constants[10].

Transformation of the dehydrogenase to cytochrome reductase is also elicited by treatment with urea or thiourea[1,10]. The concentration of urea has a marked effect not only on the rate of inactivation and of fragmentation but also on the nature of the products formed. Although even incubation with 0.1 *M* urea causes a several-fold rise in cytochrome reductase activity[10], the maximal amount of cytochrome reductase activity is far higher with 1–2 *M* urea (Fig. 6) and even higher with 4 *M* urea. At the latter concentration both the formation and the destruction of cytochrome reductase activity

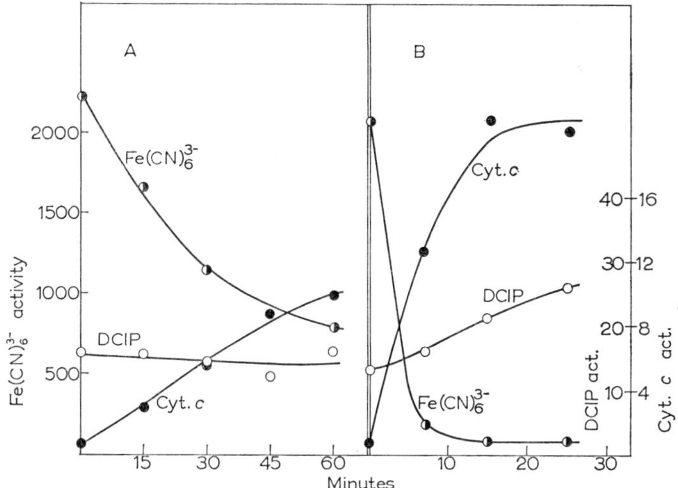

Fig. 6. Time course of degradation of reduced NAD dehydrogenase with urea. The enzyme was incubated at 22° in 0.05 *M* Na arsenate, pH 7.8, containing urea at the indicated concentrations. Protein concentration was 7.5 mg/ml. (A) 1 *M* urea. (B) 2 *M* urea. From Cremona *et al.*[10].

occur within a few minutes. At low and intermediate concentrations loss of ferricyanide activity and formation of cytochrome reductase activity occur *without* the emergence of activity toward DCIP (Fig. 6A). This observation and other data[10] suggest that the pathways of degradation at different urea concentrations are probably not the same. It should be noted that the effect of urea cannot be explained in terms of mere loss of the tertiary structure of the protein, since degradation to low molecular-weight fragments and, at high urea concentrations, extensive liberation of free flavin occur[10].

Treatment of the enzyme with thiourea in the cold leads to cytochrome reductase formation and loss of ferricyanide activity without the formation of DCIP reductase[78], as was also noted on digestion with 1 *M* urea. Thus

References p. 194

the products arising in these cases differ substantially from the fragments produced by acid-ethanol-heat treatment.

Perhaps the most interesting molecular transformation of the dehydrogenase is that induced by the substrate. On incubation with reduced NAD (and, to a lesser extent, reduced NADP) under aerobic conditions even at 0° fairly rapid decay of ferricyanide activity and formation of cytochrome reductase activity are noted[11] (Table III). NAD, NADP, and their constituent nucleotides have no such effect; however, NAD and NADP protect the enzyme from reduced NAD-induced inactivation. Gel filtration on Sephadex G-200 reveals that the inactivated enzyme is fragmented to low molecular-weight units. A number of cytochrome *c* reductases have been separated by chromatography on hydroxylapatite[64], following incubation with reduced NAD, but only one of these resembles the Mahler enzyme. Anaerobic incubation with reduced NAD does not lead to loss of ferricyanide activity or emergence of cytochrome reductase activity (Table III) but the

TABLE III

SUBSTRATE-INDUCED INACTIVATION[a] OF REDUCED NAD DEHYDROGENASE AT 0°

Gas	*Time (min)*	*Control (% of initial activity)*		*1 mM reduced NAD (% of initial activity)*	
		$Fe(CN)_6^{3-}$	*Cyt.*	*$Fe(CN)_6^{3-}$*	*Cyt.*
N_2	60	100		100	
Air	20	100	100	69	104
	40	100	100	46	150
	60	100	100	39	302
	24 h	100	100	30	947

[a] Data from Ref. 64.

TABLE IV

SUBSTRATE-INDUCED FRAGMENTATION WITHOUT INACTIVATION[a,b]

Sephadex G-200 chromatography	*Per cent distribution*		
	$Fe(CN)_6^{3-}$ act.	*Cyt. c act.*	*Protein*
Excluded part	57	58	70
Included part	40	41	27

[a] Data from Ref. 64.
[b] 4 h at 20° with 5 m*M* reduced NAD in N_2. Because of anaerobiosis almost none (less than 8%) of $Fe(CN)_6^{3-}$ activity was lost and no cytochrome reductase was formed.

dehydrogenase is nevertheless fragmented under these conditions (Table IV).

The mechanism of these interesting molecular transformations is poorly understood. A question of particular importance in this regard is whether the reduced NAD–cytochrome reductase fragment can be regarded as the functional unit of reduced NAD dehydrogenase, which is bound to other proteins in a high molecular-weight complex wherein the potential cytochrome reductase and diaphorase activities of the hypothetical subunit were masked. In terms of this hypothesis reduced NAD dehydrogenase would be a multi-enzyme complex, rather than a molecular entity, analogous to the α-ketoglutarate or pyruvate oxidase complexes. The alternate view is that the unmodified dehydrogenase is a discrete molecule and that all the changes in its properties which occur on treatment with transforming agents are manifestations of the loss of the original structure and thus represent stages in degradation. All evidence hitherto obtained favors the latter interpretation[10]. Thus reduced NAD dehydrogenase has the same substrate specificity and turnover number as intact respiratory-chain preparations, contains catalytically functional iron and yields the characteristic EPR signal at $g = 1.94$ on reduction with substrates, all of which properties are lost on conversion to cytochrome reductases: hence the latter are modification products. In contrast, in known multi-enzyme complexes, such as the α-ketoglutarate and pyruvate oxidase systems, the component proteins (*e.g.*, lipoyl dehydrogenase), retain their catalytic properties. Second, although several types of treatment have yielded the same (or very similar) products, with other transforming agents reduced NAD–cytochrome reductases of different properties have been obtained. As noted above, also a single transforming agent (*e.g.*, reduced NAD in aerobic conditions) may yield a whole series of distinct cytochrome reductase fragments. This is as might be expected if cytochrome reductases were merely stages in the fragmentation of the original molecule. Third, the emergence of cytochrome reductase (or DCIP reductase) activity does not parallel the process of fragmentation. During the early stages of tryptic digestion products still possessing a high molecular weight but already endowed with considerable cytochrome reductase activity have been detected[10] and, conversely, on anaerobic incubation with reduced NAD, fragmentation occurs without the emergence of cytochrome reductase activity[64]. Lastly, it has been observed that, after a brief initial exposure to urea, loss of ferricyanide activity and formation of cytochrome reductase activity continue for prolonged periods even after the removal of the transforming agent[10]. Similarly, after brief exposure to pH 5.4 and readjustment to neutral pH, continued formation of cytochrome reductase activity has been noted[10]. This type of "spontaneous" breakdown of the dehydrogenase is more readily reconciled with the view that the appearance of cytochrome reductase activity is only a stage

References p. 194

in a complex process of fragmentation than with the hypothesis that dissociation of a complex into its constituents occurs.

The interpretation which appears to fit best the available data is that the reduced NAD–cytochrome reductases of 80000–100000 molecular weight, which have been isolated after thermal, acid-ethanol or proteolytic degradation, are the only catalytically active fragments of sufficient stability to permit isolation and that they represent only a stage in the fragmentation of the reduced NAD dehydrogenase molecule[9,10].

(*h*) *Mechanism of action*

Owing to the preponderance of absorbance changes attributable to non-heme iron over that attributable to flavin on oxidation–reduction of the enzyme, spectrophotometric studies do not lend themselves to clear-cut measurements of the state of flavin during the catalytic cycle of the dehydrogenase[26]. Purified preparations give only a small and variable free-radical signal on EPR measurements[45]. Consequently, the question whether the flavin shuttles between oxidized and reduced or oxidized and semiquinone states during the normal catalytic cycle remains open.

Participation of at least some of the iron moieties in the catalytic activity is strongly suggested by EPR studies with the purified enzyme and with more complex preparations, as well as by the absorbance changes observed on reduction of the dehydrogenase with reduced NAD. From the parallel loss of ferricyanide activity and of $g = 1.94$ signal on thermal modification (Fig. 1) it seems quite possible that non-heme iron may be the immediate electron donor to ferricyanide. If so, the slow decay of transhydrogenase activity as compared with the rapid loss of ferricyanide activity on fragmentation of the enzyme (Fig. 4) might be interpreted to suggest that the transhydrogenase reaction involves only the flavin component.

(*i*) *Comparison of different preparations*

With respect to FMN content, non-heme iron: flavin ratio, and EPR signals the primary dehydrogenase discussed in the foregoing sections resembles fairly closely the more complex reduced NAD–coenzyme Q reductase preparation of Hatefi *et al.*[63]. The latter, however, contains considerable amounts of lipids, including coenzyme Q. Its turnover number in the ferricyanide assay is reported[63] to be relatively low ($7.1 \cdot 10^4$/mole FMN at 38°) as compared with the dehydrogenase ($8 \cdot 10^5$ at 30°)[28,63]. It should be mentioned, however, that Hatefi *et al.*[63] assayed their preparation at a fixed ferricyanide concentration, which measures only about 11% of the activity[63a], and at an unfavorable temperature: under comparable conditions the turnover numbers of the two preparations are quite similar. The property of the reduced NAD–coenzyme Q reductase complex which has received major emphasis is its ability to catalyze the amytal-sensitive reduction of coenzyme Q_1 and Q_2, although, as already mentioned, the turnover numbers reported for these reactions are quite low ($2 \cdot 10^4$ and $5 \cdot 10^3$/min at 38°, respectively). The difference in the reactivities of the complex and of the primary dehydrogenase with CoQ_1 (reduced NAD–CoQ_1/reduced NAD–$Fe(CN)_6^{3-}$ = 2% for the former and 0.05–0.1% for the latter preparation)[63a] cannot be taken as evidence that the dehydrogenase has undergone preparative modification, however, since (*a*) short-chain coenzyme Q derivatives are not natural electron acceptors for mammalian enzymes, (*b*) coenzyme Q_{10} is not yet established as the obligatory reaction partner of reduced NAD dehydrogenase in the respiratory chain (*cf.* section 1, p. 129), and (*c*) it is not known what factors present in the coenzyme Q reductase complex (such as bound Q_{10}?) may be required for interaction between the flavoprotein and short-chain coenzyme Q homologues.

Recent work by Fleischer *et al.*[78a] and Machinist and Singer[63a,78b] has clarified several aspects of the interaction of reduced NAD dehydrogenase with coenzyme Q derivatives. It has been shown[63a] that the particle-bound form of the dehydrogenase has two reaction sites for external, short-chain CoQ homologues. One is amytal- and rotenone-insensitive, has the same turnover number (per mole of FMN) in ETP, "reduced NAD–coenzyme Q reductase complex" and the purified dehydrogenase and represents a direct reaction of CoQ_1 with the flavoprotein. This reaction does not require the presence of catalytically active non-heme iron nor of lipid and is sterically hindered in the native enzyme. As is the case with cytochrome *c*, thermal or acid-ethanol denaturation greatly increases the reactivity of the dehydrogenase with CoQ_1. The other reaction site, responsible for some 90% of the reduced NAD–CoQ_1 reaction in respiratory-chain preparations[63a], is completely inhibited by amytal and rotenone and requires the presence of phospholipid[78b]. This has been demonstrated by very brief digestion of ETP or ETP_H with a low concentration of purified phospholipase A, which rapidly abolishes amytal-sensitive coenzyme Q reduction. Following removal of the phospholipase, amytal- and rotenone-sensitive CoQ reduction is fully restored by the addition of micellar phospholipids. If the treatment with phospholipase A is continued, irreversible loss of CoQ reductase activity occurs (without solubilization of the dehydrogenase). It has been proposed[78b] that during the second phase an additional lipid factor necessary for the reduction of CoQ_1 is extracted by phospholipase A, which is not readily replaced in a functional form. This factor may be CoQ_{10}: the reduction of CoQ_1 would then proceed by way of internal CoQ_{10}. In terms of this hypothesis[78b] the amytal-sensitive step is the reduction of endogenous CoQ_{10}.

As pointed out in section 2g (p. 144), the various cytochrome and DCIP reducing preparations (with the exception of lipoyl dehydrogenase) extracted by acid-ethanol-heat treatment, digestion with cobra venom at 37°, or with thiourea are modification products of reduced NAD dehydrogenase. Another preparation which may fall in this category is the "reduced NAD–CoQ_6 reductase" described in recent preliminary communications[71,79,80]. In line with the fact that it has been extracted by the acid-ethanol-heat treatment of DeBernard and Mahler, the preparation does not show a substrate-reducible EPR signal[73] and its sedimentation constant ($s_{20} = 5{\cdot}7$)[79] has been reported to be the same as that of the Mahler enzyme[9]. Further, 92–95% of the activities toward ferricyanide, CoQ_1, and CoQ_6 are lost during the extraction of the preparation from ETP_H by means of exposure to acid-ethanol-heat[63a] and a very large increase in reduced NAD–cytochrome reductase activity is created. Comparison of the Mahler enzyme[9] and of Pharo and Sanadi's preparation[80a] in the author's laboratory under identical conditions failed to reveal significant differences in chromatographic properties, "labile" S and non-heme iron content, substrate specificity, reactivity with different electron acceptors, including coenzyme Q_1 and Q_6, and sensitivity to inhibitors[63a,78b]. Both preparations are *partially* inhibited by amytal and rotenone. However, the rotenone inhibition of coenzyme Q_6 reduction by this type of fragment is quite distinct from that observed in intact respiratory-chain preparations, since inhibition of the soluble flavoprotein is observed only in a narrow range of rotenone concentration and disappears when the rotenone concentration is increased[80a]. It appears, therefore, that the "reduced NAD–CoQ_6 reductase" is not a soluble form of Hatefi's preparation[63] but a modified fragment of the dehydrogenase, which is closely related to, or identical with, the Mahler enzyme[9].

3. Succinate dehydrogenase

(a) *Historical*

Since its discovery[81,82] in 1909, succinate dehydrogenase has been one of the most widely and intensively studied enzymes. Until its isolation[83] in 1954 most investigations were concerned with the kinetics of the dehydrogenase, the effect of various drugs, hormones, and inhibitors on the enzyme, its role in metabolic processes, and its interaction with the cytochrome chain. Much information concerning the properties of the dehydrogenase emerged from these early studies, although, with few exceptions, they utilized particle or cell preparations of varying complexity and date back to a period when no reliable assay for the enzyme was available.

The failure of many early efforts to isolate the dehydrogenase may be traced to a large extent to the use of inadequate assay methods, and, in part, to the difficulty of solubilizing the enzyme without major modification (at least from aerobic organisms) and its pronounced instability in purified preparations. When it was discovered that, unlike other artificial electron acceptors tested, *N*-alkylphenazonium compounds, such as phenazine methosulfate, react directly and efficiently with the mammalian enzyme in both soluble and respiratory chain-bound form[83], the enzyme was isolated first from beef heart[83,84], then from pig heart[85,86], and aerobic yeast mitochondria[87]. Highly purified preparations were later obtained from *Micrococcus lactilyticus*[88] and *Propionibacterium pentosaceum*[89].

The catalytic properties of the enzyme have also been studied in a wide variety of vertebrates, invertebrates, plants, and microorganisms in many laboratories in recent years. While isolation of the dehydrogenase in most cases has not been undertaken, or has progressed only to a modest degree, these studies have firmly established the fact that the molecular and catalytic properties of succinate dehydrogenase vary considerably in different organisms and that they appear to have evolved in accord with the physiological needs of the particular type of cell. This problem is discussed in the last part of this Chapter (section 3g, p. 192).

(*b*) *Catalytic assay and chemical determination of succinate dehydrogenase*

The method of choice for the assay of succinate dehydrogenase depends on the source and, hence, the properties of the enzyme. In mitochondria from aerobic organisms the dehydrogenase catalyzes the oxidation of succinate much faster than the reduction of fumarate[89]. In order to measure the full or nearly full activity of the enzyme from such sources, the assay must be based on the oxidative reaction. The only acceptors known to interact rapidly and directly with the dehydrogenase from aerobic cells in both soluble and particulate preparations are phenazine methosulfate and its homologues. (The reactions of the particle-bound enzyme with methylene blue, tetrazolium dyes, indophenol dyes, ferricyanide, and cytochrome *c* are either indirect or involve several reaction sites along respiratory chain and measure only a fraction of the activity, depending on the nature and physiological state of the preparation. In assays involving the complete respiratory chain the activity of the dehydrogenase is also not the limiting factor.)

The phenazine assay, although convenient and reliable in its present form, has undergone many modifications since it was first proposed. In early studies[90] a manometric assay based on a fixed dye concentration was used. It was soon recognized[91–93], however, that the apparent K_m for the dye may vary widely with the source of the enzyme, with the state of purification, and the method of isolation. The true activity of a given sample must, therefore, be based on V_{max} with respect to the dye. Second, it was later found[94,95] that in the manometric assay under certain conditions the reoxidation of the leuco dye may become rate-limiting. The dilemma was circumvented by adapting the method to spectrophotometric use[94] with DCIP or cytochrome *c* as terminal oxidant, as originally suggested by Singer and Kearney[96].

Three additional factors which must be taken into account are the state of activation of the enzyme, permeability limitations to phenazine methosulfate, and the stability of the dehydrogenase from the particular source. As discussed below, the process of activation is an intramolecular change in the dehydrogenase involving a reversible transformation from a form of low (or no) activity to one of full activity on incubation with the substrate or a suitable competitive inhibitor[7]. In well-washed mitochondria or other respiratory-chain preparations from mammalian sources the dehydrogenase may be almost completely in the unactivated form so that in spectrophotometric assays conducted at moderately low temperatures less than 2% of the activity is measurable[96a] (Table V). Activation prior to assay is an

TABLE V

REVERSIBLE ACTIVATION OF SUCCINATE DEHYDROGENASE[a] IN BEEF HEART ETP

Treatment	*Specific activity*[b] *at 15°*	
	Without activation[c] *prior to assay*	*Activated*[c] *prior to assay*
ETP, deactivated[d] by washing 4 times and Sephadex G-25 passage	0.062	0.981
Same after activation for 5 min at 30° with 0.02 *M* succinate under N_2	0.980	0.981
Same after second deactivation	0.042	0.955

[a] Unpublished data of T. Kimura, J. Hauber and T. P. Singer.

[b] Micromoles succinate oxidized/min/mg protein at 15° (V_{max} with respect to phenazine) determined by the spectrophotometric phenazine methosulfate–DCIP assay.

[c] Activation prior to assay was performed by incubating the complete reaction mixture without dyes, but including 0.02 *M* succinate for 7 min at 38°, then cooling the cuvette to 15°; the catalytic reaction was started by addition of phenazine methosulfate and DCIP. The samples assayed without prior activation were maintained at 15° without succinate or dyes; the reaction was started by addition of substrate, DCIP and phenazine methosulfate.

[d] First deactivation was performed by 4 successive centrifugations for 15 min at 144000 × *g* and resuspensions in 0.25 *M* sucrose–3m*M* imidazole, pH 7.6, followed by passage through a Sephadex G-25 column equilibrated with sucrose–imidazole. Activation of the resulting preparation involved incubation with 0.02 *M* succinate in 0.05 *M* imidazole buffer, pH 7.6, for 5 min at 38°, followed by cooling to 0°. In the second deactivation the ETP preparation thus activated was centrifuged as above, resuspended in sucrose–imidazole, passed through Sephadex G-25; the excluded part was again centrifuged for 15 min at 144000 × *g*, resuspended in sucrose–imidazole and maintained at 0° till assay.

absolute requisite, therefore. Full activation is reached by 7 min incubation with 0.02 *M* succinate, in the absence of an electron acceptor, with preparations from mammalian heart and in 5 min at 30° with preparations from yeast mitochondria[46].

It has been known for several years[97] that intact mitochondria show a strong permeability barrier to *N*-alkylphenazonium dyes and related nitrogenous compounds. Damage to the mitochondrial membrane by freeze-thawing, treatment with Ca^{2+}, etc. removes partly, but not entirely, this permeability barrier. For full permeability of the dye to mitochondrial systems and, hence, reliable activity determinations, brief digestion with crude *Naja naja* venom or purified phospholipase A is recommended: this treatment causes no known damage to the flavoprotein[94,98]. The amount of phospholipase A and the period of digestion varies markedly from tissue to tissue and must be standardized for each cell type to be studied. (In yeast mitochondria, no such permeability barrier appears to exist.)

An additional factor which must be taken into account in assays of the dehydrogenase, regardless of the electron acceptor used, is that the dehydrogenase shows marked differences in stability even in the respiratory chain-bound form, in different cells. Thus the flavoprotein from mammalian heart, liver, and brain is relatively thermostable in respiratory-chain preparations and may be conveniently activated and assayed at 38°. In contrast, the dehydrogenase in yeast mitochondria or ETP is rapidly inactivated[46] at 38° and, hence, both activation and assay are conducted at 30°.

The fumarate–$FMNH_2$ assay[99] (reductive reaction) has also been extensively used for the assay of the enzyme from aerobic cells. While this assay is simpler than the phenazine methosulfate reaction in that it is not influenced by activation and appears to involve only the bound flavin component of the enzyme, its disadvantage is that the dehydrogenase–$FMNH_2$ interaction is hindered by steric factors in the native structure of the protein and that on preparative modification of the enzyme a great increase in the turnover number of the fumarate–$FMNH_2$ reaction may occur[12,13]. Thus, compared with heart mitochondria or ETP, such particulate preparations as the succinate–coenzyme Q reductase complex and Keilin–Hartree preparations (isolated at neutral pH), and all soluble preparations described in the literature show a greatly increased turnover number in the $FMNH_2$ assay[13].

Assays based on fumarate reduction are, however, the methods of choice for the determination of the activity of succinate dehydrogenases which catalyze the reductive reaction much faster than the oxidative one. Examples of this type of enzyme are the flavoproteins from the obligate anaerobe *Micrococcus lactilyticus*[88] and the recently discovered cytoplasmic succinate dehydrogenases from yeast[100,101]. The electron donor which functions opti-

References p. 194

mally varies with the source of the enzyme: $FMNH_2$ and leucomethylviologen are among those most commonly used. In the instances quoted (and in the case of succinate dehydrogenases from several facultative anaerobes, which catalyze the oxidative and reductive reactions at approximately equal rates) the "fumarate reductase" assay is quite straightforward: no activation appears to be required and no artifactual increase in the turnover number of the fumarate–$FMNH_2$ reaction has been observed during isolation.

The fact that the flavin group of succinate dehydrogenases from mammalian and yeast mitochondria is covalently bound to the protein provides the means for determining the concentration of the enzyme from these sources by chemical methods. This permits, in turn, the determination of the turnover number at various stages of purification, including tissue homogenates, and offers an unequivocal means of measuring the total dehydrogenase content independently of catalytic activity[13,102,103]. In practice samples are exhaustively extracted with trichloroacetic acid to remove all acid-soluble flavins, digested with trypsin and chymotrypsin (a procedure which renders the flavin peptides originating from succinate dehydrogenase acid-soluble); the flavin is then extracted with trichloroacetic acid, hydrolyzed to the mononucleotide level, and its concentration is determined fluorometrically. FMN shows maximal fluorescence over a wide range of pH; the pure flavin hexapeptide isolated by Kearney[104] from beef heart succinate dehydrogenase has a sharp optimum of fluorescence at pH 3.2 and is virtually non-fluorescent at neutral pH (Fig. 7). Proteolytic digests of acid-extracted mitochondria or Keilin–Hartree preparations from heart[102] manifest the same pH of maximal fluorescence as the pure peptide (Fig. 7), and this pH has been reported[105] to be optimal also for the fluorometric determination of the dehydrogenase in liver and kidney homogenates. As shown in Fig. 7, proteolytic digests of respiratory-chain preparations isolated from aerobic yeast mitochondria exhibit nearly the same pH of optimal fluorescence but less-pronounced tendency toward internal quenching as neutrality is approached[46].

Although the method is simple and unambiguous, it has certain obvious limitations. First, since the pH–fluorescence curve of proteolytic digests of the flavoprotein have so far been determined only for the tissues listed, application of the method to other tissues and species requires prior determination of the pH–fluorescence curve of proteolytic digests. Fluorometric determination of the distribution of succinate dehydrogenase at neutral pH (where flavin peptides show little or no fluorescence) has led to erroneous data in the literature. Second, the fact that succinate dehydrogenase is the only enzyme which contains covalently bound flavin has been established only for heart muscle and, although it is also probably true of yeast mitochondria and rat brain, it is almost certainly not the case for rat or beef liver[101,106]. Also, mitochondria from "petite" mutants of yeast, which are essentially devoid of measurable succinate dehydrogenase activity, nevertheless contain a small but measurable amount of covalently bound flavin with an atypical pH–fluorescence curve (Fig. 7).

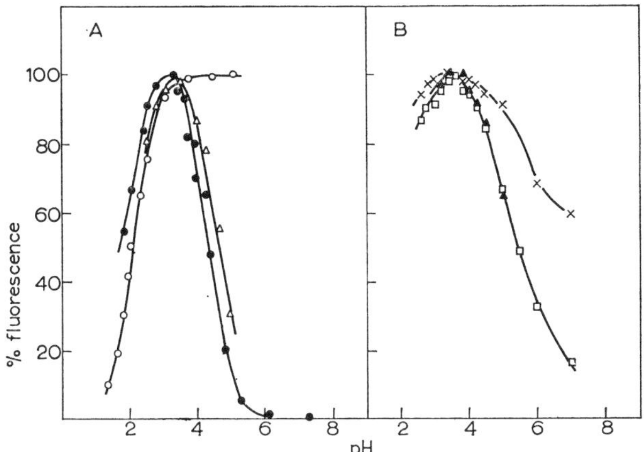

Fig. 7. Comparison of pH–fluorescence curves of FMN and of flavin peptides from heart muscle and yeast. (A) Open circles, FMN; shaded circles, pure flavin peptide from heart succinate dehydrogenase; open triangles, proteolytic digests of beef heart Keilin–Hartree preparation, all determined in 0.03 *M* buffers as follows: below pH 3.6, glycine; pH 3.6–5.1, acetate; 5.1–7.3, phosphate. (B) Squares, beef heart mitochondria; shaded triangles, ETP from baker's yeast; crosses, ETP from "petite" mutants, all determined in buffers made by mixing 0.05 *M* citric acid and 0.1 *M* Na_2HPO_4. The ordinate denotes the relative degree of fluorescence of each sample as compared with that observed at the pH of optimum fluorescence. All preparations were trypsin–chymotrypsin digests, hydrolyzed to the mononucleotide level. Data from Refs. 46, 101, 103, 104.

Lastly, mention may be made of the fact that in recent papers[17,107,108] King stated that (*a*) the spectrophotometric phenazine methosulfate assay is less accurate than the manometric one and entails some 15% error, (*b*) that the measurement of V_{max} in succinate dehydrogenase assays is not necessary, and (*c*) that catalytic assays of the dehydrogenase involving the use of artificial electron acceptors are less reliable than "reconstitution" tests. As to (*a*), the spectrophotometric assay has been found in many laboratories to be superior to the manometric one in ease, reliability, and accuracy: in the hands of a skilled operator and with the precautions mentioned above its accuracy is about 2%. As to (*b*), the need for expressing activities at infinite dye concentrations has been amply documented in the literature and its theoretical basis has been discussed[1,13,91–93]. Point (*c*) will be dealt with in section 3c, *vi* (p. 181).

References p. 194

(c) *Mammalian succinate dehydrogenase*

(i) *Isolation*

Extensively purified preparations were obtained from beef heart mitochondria in 1954[83]. Shortly thereafter the enzyme was isolated in homogeneous form from this source[84,109]. Solubilization was accomplished by extraction of acetone-desiccated mitochondria at mildly alkaline pH and the resulting extract was purified by a series of protamine and ammonium sulfate precipitations, adsorption on calcium phosphate gel, and differential ultracentrifugation. As reported by Singer and Kearney[83] and confirmed by Basford *et al.*[110], the dehydrogenase may also be isolated by alkaline extraction from acetone powders of the particulate "succinate dehydrogenase complex". The dehydrogenase has also been solubilized from a wide variety of mammalian mitochondria[13,90] by this method but isolation from sources other than heart has not been undertaken.

Shortly thereafter Wang and colleagues[85,86] isolated the enzyme by a very similar procedure from pig heart but substituted a Keilin–Hartree preparation for mitochondria and aqueous butanol, as originally proposed by Morton[111], for acetone in the removal of lipids. The two preparations show rather similar properties but, as judged by the analytical values published, the pig heart preparation is not homogeneous. One disadvantage of the method of the Chinese workers is that succinate dehydrogenase is already modified in the starting material (whether or not cyanide is included in its preparation), as judged by the lower turnover number in the phenazine methosulfate assay (10000–12000)[50] compared with mitochondria (15000–18000)[50,111].

The method of Singer *et al.*[109] was later modified[99] by substituting differential extractions for the lengthy fractionation procedure and by the omission of $(NH_4)_2SO_4$ steps, both of which tended to inactivate this labile enzyme. By this method preparations of approximately 50% purity may be obtained in a few hours' time.

Among the many particulate complexes of succinate dehydrogenase in the literature, which are fragments of the respiratory chain of varying complexity, the preparation closest to succinate dehydrogenase is the "succinate–coenzyme Q reductase" complex of Ziegler and Doeg[112]. The flavoprotein appears to be linked to cytochrome *b* in stoichiometric proportion in this complex, but the cytochrome component is reported to be nonfunctional.

(ii) *Molecular properties*

The minimum molecular weight of homogeneous preparations from nonheme iron content is 49000 and from flavin content 200000. Physical measurements[109] support a molecular weight of approximately 200000. This value is also in accord with gel exclusion studies[19] on Sephadex G-200. Thus the enzyme contains 1 mole of flavin and 4 g.atoms of non-heme iron per mole. The somewhat lower molecular weight (140000–160000) reported by Wang *et al.*[86] for their preparation on the basis of iron and flavin content may have been due to the presence of impurities and to incomplete removal of acid-soluble flavin prior to proteolytic digestion or to other technical problems (*cf.* Ref. 13).

The sedimentation velocity of the beef heart enzyme at 10–15 mg protein/ml is 6.5 S and the mobility in free electrophoresis is $2.8 \cdot 10^{-5}$ $cm^2 \cdot volt^{-1} \cdot sec^{-1}$ (Ref. 109).

As first noted by Green and coworkers[113], respiratory-chain preparations do not release their total flavin content in acid-soluble form except after proteolytic digestion. That the acid-insoluble flavin is covalently bound to the apoenzyme of succinate dehydrogenase and occurs in the form of flavin peptides even after exhaustive proteolytic digestion was demonstrated by Kearney[104,114,115] and, independently, by Wang *et al.*[86,116]. Both groups have purified several of the flavin peptides resulting from tryptic–chymotryptic digestion and a pure flavin hexapeptide was isolated by Kearney[104]. The N-terminal amino acid of this peptide is serine, but the amino acid linked to the riboflavin residue and the point of linkage on the isoalloxazine ring are not known. It is established, however, that the point of linkage must be on the isoalloxazine ring system, rather than on the ribityl chain[104]. According to the Chinese workers[117] the peptide chain is linked to position 4 of the isoalloxazine ring, but according to Hemmerich[118] linkage at the 4 position would not confer the spectral and fluorescent properties observed with the pure flavin peptide.

Covalent attachment of the flavin dinucleotide to the protein alters markedly the chemical and biological properties of the flavin[104]: the 375-mμ absorption band is shifted to longer wavelengths; the fluorescence becomes internally quenched above pH 3.2 even at the mononucleotide level (Fig. 7), and the dinucleotide is inactive in D-amino acid oxidase assays and certain microbiological tests for riboflavin.

The iron moieties of the isolated enzyme appear to be in the ferric state[119]. Unless precautions are taken to bind the —SH groups released on denaturation, thermal or acid liberation of the iron is accompanied by reduction to the ferrous form. While in preparations extracted below pH 10 the iron is stable[86,109], in those extracted above pH 10 the iron–protein bonds appear to be more labile[99]. In all preparations tested the iron is relatively unreactive toward iron-chelating agents, but prolonged exposure to organic mercurials or to agents which modify the tertiary structure of the protein (*e.g.*, hydrosulfite) renders the iron moieties rapidly reactive with chelators[120]. Treat-

References p. 194

ment with high concentrations of mercurials also results in a gradual change in the absorption spectrum until it resembles that of flavin peptides. Since the deviations of the absorption spectrum of the dehydrogenase from that of simple flavoproteins has been ascribed to iron–protein bonds, and since the iron moieties are not released in inorganic form at a time when the iron–protein absorption is completely bleached by mercurials, it appears that mercurials change the chelate structure of the iron and thereby increase its reactivity with chelators.

These studies of Massey and the observation that H_2S was released when succinate dehydrogenase was denatured by whatever method were perhaps the first indications of the presence of "labile sulfide" in iron–proteins and suggested an intimate structural relation between iron and sulfur in this group of enzymes. More recent studies in this laboratory[49] with the "succinate–coenzyme Q reductase" complex[112] have shown that a stoichiometric relation exists between non-heme iron and "labile sulfur" in this preparation (and, hence, probably also in the dehydrogenase itself), just as in ferredoxins[59], photosynthetic pyridine nucleotide reductase[60], reduced NAD dehydrogenase[49], and dihydroorotic dehydrogenase[58]. The "succinate–coenzyme Q reductase" complex, which is stated to contain 8 gramatoms of non-heme iron per mole of covalently bound flavin was found to contain also 8.8 gramatoms of labile sulfide per mole of flavin.

The non-heme iron of succinate dehydrogenase is also thought to be responsible for the asymmetric, temperature-sensitive $g = 1.94$ signal which appears on the addition of succinate to suitable preparations of the enzyme. Beinert and colleagues[71,121], who first described this signal and tentatively attributed it to non-heme iron, noted that it accounts for only a fraction of the iron associated with succinate dehydrogenase. A free-radical signal in the EPR spectrum ascribable to flavin semiquinones has also been described by Beinert and Sands[122], the formation of which was noted on the addition of succinate to respiratory-chain preparations or to the purified enzyme. Commoner and Hollocher[123,124] also described a free-radical signal in the same region, which they attributed to the formation of a charge-transfer complex between the dehydrogenase and succinate or fumarate.

Unfortunately, it has not yet been possible to establish a correlation between the kinetics of the formation and decay of these EPR signals and those of the catalytic reaction, as has been done with xanthine oxidase and reduced NAD dehydrogenase, despite considerable efforts. The main reason for this is the phenomenon of activation described below. There is considerable evidence that those dehydrogenase molecules which are activated (and, hence, function catalytically) contain bound substrate. If the activator is succinate, the reduction may have already occurred; if it is a competitive inhibitor, its presence on the enzyme might complicate the initial kinetics, particularly at the high enzyme concentrations required in EPR work. On the other hand, if the activator is removed, extensive or complete deactivation occurs: in this case, on the addition of succinate, activation (a relatively slow process) would precede reduction of the iron–flavoprotein (a rapid process, since the turnover number is 18000 at 38°).

The activation of succinate dehydrogenase is one of the most interesting properties of the enzyme; it is also of great practical importance in assays of the dehydrogenase. Although it has been amply documented[7,125,126] that failure to assure full activation prior to assay may easily lead to erroneous results, in many current papers dealing with this enzyme no provisions are made for activation. To quote Thorn[126] "Table VI shows how misleading

TABLE VI

COMPARISON[a] OF ASSAYS OF ACTIVATED AND UNACTIVATED HEART MUSCLE PREPARATIONS AT 20°

Pretreatment before assay[b]	*Succinate oxidase activity* (Q_{O_2})	
	Manometric[c]	*Spectrophotometric*[d]
Kept at 0°	112	66
Kept at 37° for 20 min	227	226

[a] Abbreviated from Thorn[126].
[b] Incubations prior to assay were in 0.1 *M* phosphate, pH 7.6; at 0° no activation occurs.
[c] O_2 uptake; 2 mg protein (Keilin–Hartree preparation) present in 3 ml volume; assay in Tris–acetate, pH 7.6.
[d] Measurement of fumarate formation at 230 mμ; 0.1 mg protein in 3 ml, in Tris–acetate, pH 7.6.

results for succinate-oxidase activity might be obtained with manometric and spectrophotometric methods ... if the activation phenomenon is ignored. The error involved in ignoring the activation process ... was less in the manometric than in the spectrophotometric method, because partial activation took place during the equilibration period". In fact, even in the spectrophotometric method used by Thorn a relatively long reaction period was used, which allowed some activation to take place. In rapid spectrophotometric (*e.g.*, stopped-flow), polarographic or EPR procedures (*e.g.*, rapid-freezing technique), with well-washed particles the error can be well over 10-fold, particularly at low temperatures.

The phenomenon was first described by Kearney *et al.*[127] in 1955, who noted that succinate dehydrogenase assayed in phosphate-free media showed a considerably lower activity than when preincubated and assayed with phosphate. Other inorganic anions could not replace phosphate; arsenate competitively inhibited the effect of phosphate. Since Slater and Bonner[128,129] had shown that phosphate combines with the active center of the dehydrogenase, activation by substrates and competitive inhibitors was

References p. 194

also tested[7]. Succinate, fumarate, and malonate were found to be even more potent activators; *i.e.*, they produced full activation at much lower concentrations than phosphate, *although all substances known to combine at the active center, including phosphate, produced the same final activation* if sufficient time was allowed for their action[7,125]. This point is specifically illustrated for phosphate and succinate in Fig. 8. At infinite concentration of each activator the extent of activation is identical. The phosphate-activated enzyme cannot be further activated by succinate, nor the succinate-

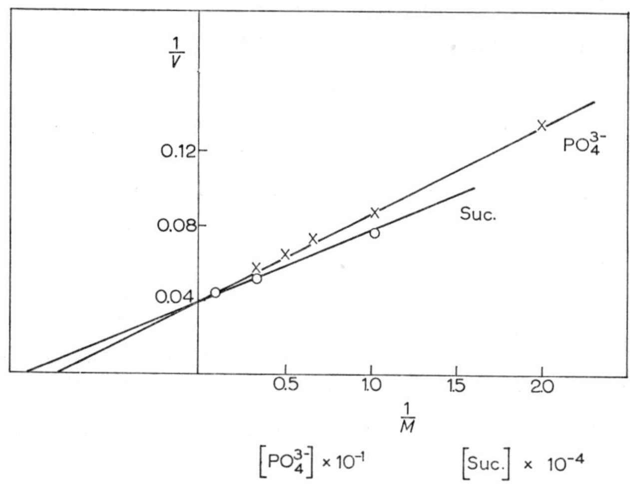

Fig. 8. Comparison of succinate and phosphate as activators. Aliquots of a purified enzyme sample (45% pure) equivalent to 0.52 mg of protein were incubated in 1.5 ml of 0.075 *M* imidazole buffer, pH 7.6, with the amounts of succinate or phosphate indicated on the abscissa for 15 min at 25°. A control sample was similarly treated but without activator present to ascertain the basal activity of the non-activated enzyme. After cooling to 0°, aliquots (0.35 mg of protein) were placed in Warburg vessels held in ice and assayed at 15° by the phenazine methosulfate method. The ordinate represents the reciprocal of the O_2 uptake per 9 min after subtraction of the basal activity. From Kearney[7].

activated enzyme by phosphate; the temperature coefficients for succinate and phosphate activation are identical, and both are competitively inhibited by arsenate. Hence, activations by phosphate and succinate are clearly the same process. This point is emphasized, since considerable confusion has been created by the suggestion of Wang *et al.*[116] that the effect of phosphate is one of removal of heavy metals. Although these workers have confirmed the activation of the enzyme by succinate[86] with their preparation, and found a considerabe degree of activation by phosphate[116], EDTA increased the activity to a similar extent as phosphate. The increased activity elicited by succinate was ascribed by these workers to an activation, the effect of phosphate to the reversal of metal inhibition. In subsequent papers by other workers[17,130] it was repeatedly suggested that the beef heart and pig heart enzymes differ in that one is activated by phosphate, the other not and that the phosphate effect is an artifact but the succinate effect is not.

In this laboratory activation (by phosphate, succinate, malonate) has been observed in all particulate and soluble preparations of the enzyme tested from a variety of animal tissues, and the phenomenon has been confirmed by Thorn[126]. None of these preparations was affected by EDTA, possibly because rigorous care was used to remove trace metals from all reagents which came in contact with the enzyme. On the other hand, it seems likely that the preparation of Wang *et al.*[86] was indeed contaminated with metals. Their failure to observe phosphate activation while confirming the succinate activation may have been due to the experimental conditions used. Kearney[7] has shown that activation is extremely rapid at 38° and negligibly slow at 15°: hence activation was tested by prior preincubation of the enzyme with the activator at an elevated temperature, followed by activity measurements at 15°. In the studies of Wang *et al.*[86,116] preincubation was apparently omitted and assays were carried out at 38° (phenazine assays) where activation by the substrate may mask the effect of phosphate, while in other experiments they used an inefficient acceptor (ferricyanide) and measured ferricyanide disappearance over a 10-min period, under which conditions effects on initial rate would certainly be missed. In this laboratory it has been found that the preparation of Wang *et al.*, following deactivation on Sephadex G-25, is activated by phosphate and succinate exactly as the beef heart enzyme when tested under the conditions used by Kearney[7].

At all temperatures tested activation follows first-order kinetics with an energy of activation of 35600 cal/mole[7]. While the rate of activation is thus markedly temperature-dependent, the maximal extent of activation reached is independent of temperature. In Kearney's original studies reversibility of the activation was tested by dialysis of the malonate-activated enzyme. Although malonate was removed sufficiently by this procedure that its inhibitory effect on succinate oxidation was fully reversed, the enzyme remained in the activated state. From this it was concluded that the activation process may be irreversible[7]. Kimura *et al.*[96a] recently demonstrated, however, that the activation by succinate is nearly fully reversed while malonate activation is partly reversed if more efficient methods are used for removal of the activator (*e.g.*, chromatography on Sephadex). Activation by malonate is accompanied by characteristic changes in the absorption spectrum[7], but on deactivation of the enzyme the spectral changes remain[96a]. It seems likely that the spectral changes represent an enzyme–inhibitor complex[131], the formation of which requires prior activation[96a].

References p. 194

Thorn has noted that a modest degree of activation occurs at elevated temperatures in the absence of added substrates or competitive inhibitors and that this activation is fully reversed on cooling of the enzyme[126]. Activation by phosphate, succinate, etc. is, however, not reversed by lowering the temperature[96a].

The chemical basis of the activation process remains uncertain. The high energy of activation suggests a configurational change in the protein, consequent on initial combination with the substrate[7].

(iii) Catalytic properties

The mammalian enzyme oxidizes succinate, methylsuccinate, ethylsuccinate, and chlorosuccinate but not dialkyl substituted or long-chain monoalkyl derivatives[132–134]. The action of the enzyme is reversible: no separate "fumarate reductase" is thought to occur in higher animals[93]. In the reductive direction fumarate is the only substrate which has been studied.

According to Gawron *et al.*[134] the action of the enzyme is asymmetric since only the L-configuration of methyl- and chlorosuccinate is oxidized appreciably. The dehydrogenation involves a *trans*-directed elimination of hydrogens[135].

At 38° the pH optimum is 7.6 and, provided that the enzyme is fully activated, the activity is independent of the nature of the buffer and of ionic strength[109].

Until relatively recently reliable values for the turnover number of the mammalian enzyme have not been available. The wide range of values reported in the literature is partly the consequence of technical and theoretical difficulties in the determination of the catalytic activity and of the concentration of the enzyme, and partly an expression of the ease with which the enzyme undergoes modification with consequent decline of the turnover number. Since the turnover number is a characteristic constant of an enzyme under a given set of conditions, clearly the assay must be selected so as to assure that the catalytic cycling of the enzyme rather than the efficiency of the electron carrier, is the limiting factor. Hence values based on succinoxidase activity or on the rate of reduction of ferricyanide or cytochrome *c* cannot be considered turnover numbers, since in such assays the activity is always lower than in the phenazine methosulfate assay. Even measurements based on the phenazine assay may yield low values, however, unless provisions are made to overcome permeability barriers and to assure full activation of the enzyme (*cf.* section 3b, p. 154).

As shown in Table VII, essentially the same turnover number has been recently found for fresh mitochondria and tissue homogenates of beef, pig, and rat heart and rat brain (17000–19000 moles succinate oxidized/min/

mole of covalently bound flavin at 38°). The apparent turnover number in liver preparations is considerably lower, however, possibly because of the presence of other enzymes containing covalently bound flavin[106].

Table VII also shows that the value is much lower in some particle-bound and in all soluble preparations from heart than in mitochondria. In view of the impression that the dehydrogenase is quite stable in the particulate form, the decreased turnover number in the succinate–coenzyme Q reduc-

TABLE VII

TURNOVER NUMBERS OF SUCCINATE DEHYDROGENASE FROM DIFFERENT TISSUES

Preparation	*Assay*[a]	*Turnover number*[b]	*Reference*
Beef heart mitochondria[c]	Spectrophotometric	17000 ± 1000	98
Pig heart mitochondria[c]	Spectrophotometric	17000 ± 1000	98
Rat heart homogenate[c]	Manometric	16300 ± 2300	137
Rat brain homogenate[c]	Manometric	18400	137
Beef liver mitochondria[c]	Spectrophotometric	9300	98
Rat liver mitochondria[c]	Spectrophotometric	5200	98
Rat liver homogenate[c]	Manometric	5900 ± 500	137
Beef heart ETP	Spectrophotometric	16000 ± 1500	50
Beef heart Keilin–Hartree preparation	Spectrophotometric	11000 ± 1000	50
Succinate–CoQ reductase from beef heart	Spectrophotometric	11300 ± 600	13,50
Soluble enzyme from beef heart (Wang *et al.* method)	Spectrophotometric	4400	103
Soluble enzyme from beef heart (Singer *et al.* method)	Manometric	3700 ± 400	13,109
Soluble enzyme from beef heart (Bernath and Singer method)	Spectrophotometric	8450 ± 2250	103

[a] V_{max} with respect to phenazine methosulfate, 38°, pH 7.6.
[b] Moles of succinate oxidized/min/mole covalently bound flavin. The low values in liver mitochondria may be due to bound flavin originating from other enzymes.
[c] Determined in the presence of phospholipase A to permit maximal penetration of the dye. Lower values in the literature were obtained with Ca^{2+}, instead of phospholipase A.

tase complex, for example, may seem unexpected but is fully supported by the fact that the turnover number of this preparation in the fumarate–$FMNH_2$ assay is greatly *increased* over that measured in mitochondria[13,103], an unfailing indication that preparative damage to the enzyme has occurred.

The low turnover number of soluble preparations in the succinate–phenazine methosulfate assay is partly due to preparative modification of the enzyme, as judged by increased activity toward $FMNH_2$[13,103], and partly to the loss of one of the two reaction sites of the dye on extraction.

References p. 194

TABLE VIII

KINETIC CONSTANTS OF SUCCINATE DEHYDROGENASES FROM VARIOUS ORGANISMS

Preparation	Succinate oxidation				Fumarate reduction				Ratio of rates of succinate oxidation to fumarate reduction	Reference
	Assay	K_m succ. (mM)	K_I fum. (mM)	K_I malon. (mM)	Assay	K_m fum. (mM)	K_I succ. (mM)	K_I malon. (mM)		
Beef heart mitochondria	38°, pH 7.6, PMS[a]				38°, pH 7.6, $FMNH_2$				62	98
Beef heart, homogeneous enzyme	38°, pH 7.6, PMS[b]	1.3	1.9	0.041	20–23°, pH 7.6, $FMNH_2$	0.50	0.12	0.12	9[c]	93, 109
Aerobic yeast mitochondria	30°, pH 7.6, PMS[a]				30°, pH 7.6, $FMNH_2$				34 ±2	46
Aerobic yeast, purified enzyme	38°, pH 7.8, PMS[b]	1.0	1.03	0.01	38°, pH 7.8, $FMNH_2$				9	87
Pumpkin seeds, purified enzyme	35°, pH 7.8, PMS[d]	1.4	1.5	0.061						138
Proteus vulgaris, aerobically grown, extract	38°, pH 7.6, PMS[b]	1.3	1.8		38°, pH 7.6, LMV[e]				0.11	90, 139
Claviceps purpurea (ergot fungus), purified enzyme	35°, pH 7.7, PMS[d]	3.3	0.93	0.03						140
Mytilus edulis (mussel), purified enzyme	35°, pH 7.4, PMS[b]	2	0.15	0.06						141

TABLE VIII (continued)

Propionibacterium pentosaceum, purified enzyme	30°, pH 7.4, PMS[b]	2.2			30°, pH 5.4, $FMNH_2$	0.7		3	142
Micrococcus lactilyticus, homogeneous enzyme	30°, pH 7.6, PMS[b]	5.3	0.22	0.23	30°, pH 7.6, LMV[e]	<0.3		0.026	88, 143
E. coli, aerobic normal cells[f]	30°, pH 7.5, PMS[h]	0.26			30°, pH 7.5, $FMNH_2$[d]	0.45		25	144
E. coli mutant(S^-) cells[g]	30°, pH 7.5, PMS[h]	1.0			30°, pH 7.5, $FMNH_2$[d]	0.017		1.5	144

[a] Spectrophotometric phenazine assay, V_{max} with respect to dye.
[b] Manometric phenazine assay, V_{max} with respect to dye.
[c] Ratio at 38°.
[d] Assay at fixed dye concentration; values subject to possible revision.
[e] Leucomethylviologen assay.
[f] When grown under these conditions most of the activity is due to the aerobic enzyme.
[g] Contains only the "anaerobic" enzyme.
[h] Phenazine methosulfate (fixed concentration) as immediate electron acceptor; a tetrazolium derivative serves as terminal oxidant; the assay is not known to measure the full activity.

References p. 194

As discussed in section 3c, *iv* (p. 172), in particle-bound preparations phenazine methosulfate has two reaction sites, one of which is cyanide-sensitive, whereas soluble preparations retain only the cyanide-insensitive site[136].

Since it appears that, unless both reaction sites are operative, the phenazine assay cannot keep up with the rate of cycling of the flavoprotein, it is doubtful whether figures for soluble preparations can be considered turnover numbers in the usual sense.

The Michaelis constants of the dehydrogenase for succinate, fumarate, and malonate are listed in Table VIII. As shown in this Table, the mammalian enzyme catalyzes the oxidation of succinate far faster than the reduction of fumarate with the most active electron carriers available used in each assay. These forward/reverse ratios are, of course, not equilibrium constants, since the reactions measured in the two directions of catalysis are not the same, but are merely intended to show that the enzyme from aerobic organisms, such as mammalian or O_2-adapted yeast mitochondria, appears to be geared for the oxidative reaction, while that from anaerobes for the reductive one. The physiological significance of this fact will be discussed later.

It is also apparent that the forward/reverse ratio declines on extraction and purification of the enzyme from mammalian tissues. This is to be expected from the fact just mentioned that one of the two reaction sites of phenazine methosulfate (responsible for about 70% of the activity in the forward direction) is lost on solubilization, while reactivity toward $FMNH_2$ and, hence, fumarate reductase activity is increased under these conditions.

(*iv*) *Inhibitors, inactivating agents*

Since succinate dehydrogenase has been a favorite test system for screening the action of drugs, poisons, and enzyme inhibitors on enzymes for several decades, the relevant literature is too voluminous to be surveyed here. The present discussion will be, therefore, confined to three classes of inhibitors: —SH reagents, competitive inhibitors, and reagents which combine with one of the prosthetic groups.

The presence of —SH groups essential for the activity of the enzyme was first demonstrated by Hopkins and coworkers[145,146], who also showed that the substrate and competitive inhibitors protect the enzyme from the action of —SH inhibitors. The latter observation was interpreted to suggest that the combining site of the substrate is in the immediate vicinity of certain thiol residues, an interpretation which was confirmed and accepted in many subsequent investigations. The hypothesis that reversible inhibition by sulfhydryl reagents affects the initial combination of the enzyme with the substrate is particularly strongly supported by the finding[93] that in highly purified preparations *p*-chloromercuribenzoate elicits identical inhibition of the succinate–phenazine methosulfate and fumarate–$FMNH_2$ activities.

Inhibition of the enzyme by every major type of —SH combining or oxidizing agent has been studied with particle-bound[147–154] and soluble, purified[109] preparations. Although in many of these studies multi-enzyme preparations were used, the effects noted probably reflect inhibition of the dehydrogenase itself, since it is the most sensitive component of the respiratory chain toward —SH inhibitors.

Prolonged contact of the purified enzyme with moderately high concentrations of —SH combining agents leads to irreversible loss of activity, configurational changes in the enzyme which increase the reactivity of the non-heme iron moieties, and eventually to extensive denaturation[120,155].

Besides the —SH groups concerned with catalytic activity, the presence of another type of sulfhydryl group is suggested by the finding that on exposure of particle-bound preparations to alkaline pH values, along with progressive loss of catalytic activity, the reactivity of the flavoprotein with external flavins gradually increases[12,20]. Thus, Keilin–Hartree preparations incubated at pH 9.3–9.4 (as in the preparations of respiratory-chain samples for reconstitution studies[18]) show almost complete loss of succinoxidase and succinate dehydrogenase activity but the fumarate–$FMNH_2$ activity of such preparations is partly preserved, and they show a greatly increased apparent K_m for $FMNH_2$ (Table IX). On brief treatment with glutathione, cysteine, or mercaptoethanol the reactivity of such alkali-treated samples and their K_m for $FMNH_2$ are greatly decreased[20,50]. In contrast, thiols have no effect on the fumarate–$FMNH_2$ activity or the K_m for $FMNH_2$ of untreated samples. Under the same conditions thiols do not influence the succinate–phenazine methosulfate activity of alkali-treated preparations (Table IX). These observations suggest that in the native structure the reaction of the bound flavin with external $FMNH_2$ is hindered but that on alkaline exposure oxidation of certain —SH groups occurs, which increases the reactivity of the enzyme with external flavins. Subsequent reduction of the newly formed disulfides largely reverses this effect. The fact that the reaction with flavins and not with fumarate is affected is shown by the lack of effect of thiols on the fumarate–leucomethylviologen reaction in alkali-treated samples.

These effects may explain the *increased* turnover number of the dehydrogenase in the fumarate–$FMNH_2$ assay in certain particulate preparations and in all soluble ones[13,103]. It appears that in the isolation of these, oxidation of the —SH groups concerned with the $FMNH_2$ reaction may have occurred. It should be noted, however, that the increased reactivity of soluble samples with $FMNH_2$ is not reversed by treatment with reducing agents.

An additional effect of thiols on the dehydrogenase is their influence on the combination of the soluble enzyme with alkali-treated respiratory-

References p. 194

TABLE IX

EFFECT OF GLUTATHIONE ON THE REACTION OF SUCCINATE DEHYDROGENASE WITH $FMNH_2$ IN KEILIN–HARTREE PREPARATIONS[a]

Sample	Fumarate–$FMNH_2$ assay			Succinate–PMS assay		
	V_{max} (µmole/min/mg)	Fraction of original activity (%)	K_m for dye (mM)	V_{max} (µmole/min/mg)	Fraction of original activity (%)	K_m for dye (mM)
Untreated	0.064	(100)	0.15	1.97	(100)	0.22
Same + GSH[b]	0.064	100	0.15	1.69	86	0.19
Alkali-treated[c]	0.028	44	2.3	0.13	7	0.14
Same + GSH[b]	0.011	17	0.33	0.12	6	0.15

[a] Data from Ref. 20.
[b] Glutathione treatment by incubation with 10 m*M* GSH for 10 min at 0°, pH 7.4, followed by reisolation of the particle by repeated centrifugations and passage through Sephadex G-25 in order to remove unreacted GSH.
[c] A 3% suspension of beef heart Keilin–Hartree preparation in 0.05 *M* borate was cautiously adjusted at 0° to pH 9.3, maintained for 120 min at 21°, then cooled to 0° and neutralized[20]. This is the technique used for the isolation of respiratory-chain preparations capable of combining with the soluble dehydrogenase in reconstitution studies.

TABLE X

EFFECT OF THIOLS ON THE RECOMBINATION OF SUCCINATE DEHYDROGENASE WITH ALKALI-TREATED PREPARATION[a]

Component	SD activity (µmoles/min/mg) (phenazine–DCPIP)	Bound flavin content (mµmoles/mg)	Bound flavin incorporation (µmoles/mg)
KH[b], untreated	1.44	0.132	
ATKH[c]	0.23	0.122	
ATKH + GSH-treated[d] SD, reisolated particle	0.66	0.171	0.049
ATKH + untreated SD, reisolated particle (normal value)	1.42	0.210	0.088

[a] Unpublished data of T. Kimura and J. Hauber.
[b] Keilin–Hartree preparation.
[c] Alkali-treated Keilin–Hartree preparation.
[d] Soluble dehydrogenase (Wang *et al.* preparation) was treated for 10 min with 10 m*M* glutathione at 0° and then passed through Sephadex G-25 to remove glutathione.

chain preparations, the dehydrogenase activity of which has been inactivated (reconstitution). As shown in Table X, prior treatment of the soluble enzyme with thiols, followed by removal of unreacted thiols, greatly decreases the ability of the enzyme to combine with alkali-treated preparations and thus restore their catalytic activity[12]. Although not shown in this table, prior incubation of the alkali-treated sample with thiols similarly inhibits the reconstitution.

Competitive inhibition of bacterial succinate dehydrogenase by malonate was discovered[156] in 1928 and has been intensively studied in multi-enzyme preparations and in purified, soluble ones from animal tissues[86,109,157–159]. It was, in fact, from the study of the interaction of malonate with the dehydrogenase that the concept of competitive enzyme inhibition originally emerged. The K_I value of the beef heart enzyme for malonate is given in Table VIII. Other frequently used competitive inhibitors of the enzyme, in decreasing order of effectiveness, are oxaloacetate[90,109,147,159,160], pyrophosphate[161,162], and fumarate[109]. Various other competitive inhibitors have been investigated by Slater and Bonner[128], Stoppani and Brignone[163], and Tietzl and Klotz[164].

As already mentioned, the purified enzyme reacts only slowly and incompletely with even the strongest iron-chelating agents, such as *o*-phenanthroline and pyrocatechol disulfonate, as judged either by loss of catalytic activity or the formation of colored complexes. The loss of activity which develops with time is more properly classified as an inactivation than as an inhibition, since it is accompanied by structural changes in the protein[120,155]. It has been reported, however, that the iron-chelating agent 2-thenoyltrifluoroacetone inhibits the reduction of CoQ, but not of phenazine, in particulate preparations[165]. Inhibition of the enzyme by inorganic iron has been suggested to be due to combination with the flavin moiety[166].

The behavior of the dehydrogenase toward cyanide is interesting and unusual. In 1951, Tsou[167] reported that upon incubation of heart muscle particles with moderately high concentrations of cyanide the succinate–methylene blue reaction was gradually abolished. The inactivation followed first-order kinetics, had a high activation energy, and its rate depended on temperature and cyanide concentration but was said to be pH-independent and irreversible. Reducing agents (succinate, hydrosulfite) prevented the inactivation completely. The phenomenon was further explored by Keilin and King[162] and by Giuditta and Singer[136] with assay methods which intercept electrons at the dehydrogenase level. The latter authors found that, although the soluble enzyme from heart is unaffected by cyanide in the phenazine methosulfate assay, in respiratory-chain preparations, using the manometric method, some 50% inactivation of the succinate–phenazine methosulfate reaction occurred (Fig. 9). Further, at and below pH 7.8 the

References p. 194

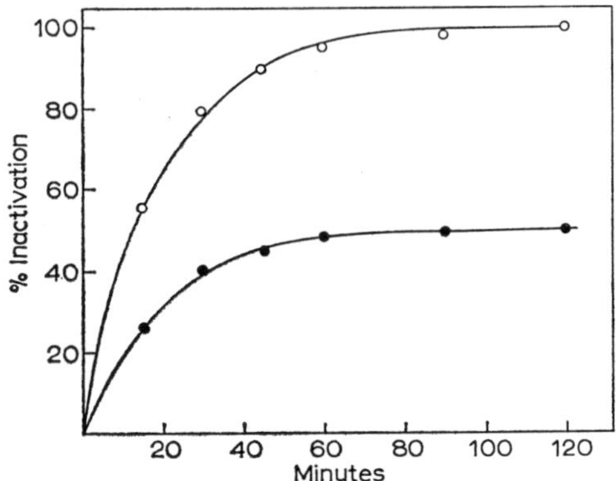

Fig. 9. Time course of the inactivation of succinate dehydrogenase in Keilin–Hartree preparations by 0.02 *M* cyanide at pH 7.85, 30°. Activity determinations were based on V_{max} values with both dyes at 38°. Open circles, methylene blue. Black dots, phenazine. Data from Ref. 136.

loss of activity toward methylene blue and phenazine methosulfate occurred at identical rates. In the spectrophotometric phenazine assay, which is free from the limitations of the manometric method, a value of 65–70% has been found to be the maximal extent of cyanide inactivation of the succinate–phenazine methosulfate reaction[20,168]. Since this inactivation is manifest in all particulate preparations of the heart enzyme, including "succinate–coenzyme Q reductase" (the one closest to the flavoprotein), it has been proposed[136] that phenazine methosulfate accepts electrons at two points in the respiratory chain of heart: the flavoprotein itself (the cyanide-insensitive reaction) and another site in the immediate vicinity of the dehydrogenase (cyanide-sensitive reaction): the latter reaction site is the one lost on extraction of the enzyme in soluble form. This hypothesis is supported by the recent report[20] that on recombination of the soluble enzyme with alkali-treated respiratory-chain preparations the cyanide-sensitive phenazine methosulfate reduction reappears. The finding[169] that $K^{14}CN$ is incorporated into soluble preparations in no way militates against this idea, since there is no reason to believe that the uptake of cyanide observed involves the same functional groups as are responsible for the inactivation of the particle-bound enzyme.

Although Keilin and King (*cf.* p. 175 in Ref. 162) have fully confirmed that part of the activity toward phenazine methosulfate in respiratory-chain preparations is abolished by cyanide, in later writings[108,169], without experimental evidence, King has claimed that the phenazine methosulfate reaction is cyanide-insensitive.

In contrast to an earlier report based on less-satisfactory assays[167], the

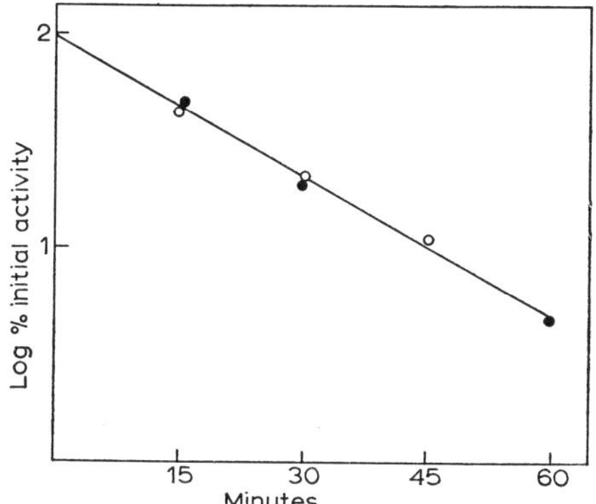

Fig. 10. Reaction order of the inactivation by 0.02 M cyanide at 30°, pH 7.6. In the phenazine methosulfate assay inactivation was calculated on the assumption that only 50% of the initial activity can be abolished by treatment with cyanide. Open circles, methylene blue. Black dots, phenazine.

rate of the cyanide inactivation was found to be highly pH-sensitive[136]. At pH values alkaline to 7.8 the rates of loss of activity toward methylene blue and phenazine methosulfate are quite different: thus the reaction site of methylene blue cannot be identical with the cyanide-sensitive phenazine methosulfate reaction site. Further, it was found that the cyanide inactivation is at least partially reversible: on incubation of cyanide-treated samples with succinate the very large change in K_m for the dye is fully reversed although the activity at V_{max} remains unaltered[136].

Incubation with cyanide also abolishes the reactivity of the dehydrogenase

TABLE XI

MAXIMAL EXTENT OF INACTIVATION OF SUCCINATE DEHYDROGENASE ACTIVITY IN KEILIN–HARTREE PREPARATIONS BY CYANIDE WITH DIFFERENT ELECTRON CARRIERS[a]

Electron carrier[b]	*Reaction measured*	*Inactivation (%)*	*Increase in K_m for electron carrier*
Phenazine methosulfate	Succinate oxidation	65–70[c]	+
Ferricyanide	Succinate oxidation	65–70	+
Methylene blue	Succinate oxidation	100	+
Brilliant cresyl blue	Succinate oxidation	100	+
Cytochrome *c*	Succinate oxidation	100	
Leucomethylviologen	Fumarate reduction	50	0
$FMNH_2$	Fumarate reduction	0	+

[a] Data from Refs. 20 and 136.
[b] V_{max} with respect to dye.
[c] 50% in manometric assay.

References p. 194

with a number of other electron carriers (Table XI). Of particular interest is the fact that while the fumarate–leucomethylviologen reaction is 50% inactivated, the fumarate–$FMNH_2$ reaction is not inactivated, although an increase in K_m for the dye occurs on cyanide treatment. Thus, whatever the functional group affected by cyanide treatment, it does not seem to play a role in the flavin–flavin interaction but is essential for interaction with the other electron carriers listed in Table XI.

The reaction of the dehydrogenase with cyanide has also been studied[169] by following the incorporation of $K^{14}CN$. This method fails to distinguish between cyanide incorporation related to inactivation of the dehydrogenase and unspecific effects, as judged by the fact that while succinate prevents cyanide inactivation of the enzyme, it does not influence the uptake of $K^{14}CN$.

The mechanism of the cyanide inactivation has been interpreted[136] as a multi-step process, probably involving a rapid, reversible combination of the enzyme with CN^- (since the effects on K_m values appear almost immediately on contact with cyanide, while inactivation is a gradual process), followed by secondary, irreversible changes in the enzyme which lead to loss of activity. The site of combination of cyanide is visualized by Giuditta and Singer[136] to be non-heme iron, while Keilin and King[162] favored the interpretation that cyanide cleaves certain disulfide groups in the protein. This interpretation was somewhat revised in a later publication[169].

(v) Mechanism of action

Although much attention has been devoted to the problem in several laboratories, at this writing the reaction mechanism of the dehydrogenase has not been established with any high degree of probability. Since investigations aimed in this direction have been reviewed *in extenso* recently[13], the present section is only intended as a brief summary.

The first direct evidence for the involvement of flavin in the catalytic cycle came from the observations that succinate causes a modest degree of bleaching with a difference spectrum centering around 460 mμ, that malonate inhibits this bleaching, while fumarate causes a rapid recolorization of the reduced enzyme[83,109,170]. Although the bleaching by succinate is more rapid in activated than in unactivated preparations[7], it is still far too slow compared with the catalytic activity. Indeed, one cannot be certain that the flavin shuttles between the oxidized and fully reduced (rather than semiquinoid) forms in the normal catalytic cycle. Flavin free-radical has been detected on treatment of both purified and particle-bound preparations of the enzyme[69,121,122], but it is not known whether its rate of appearance and decay is compatible with the catalytic rate.

Addition of succinate to the oxidized enzyme also causes absorption changes which cannot be ascribed to flavin but have been tentatively identified as being due to the reduction of ferric to ferrous iron[166]. Although Massey's studies[155] failed to provide evidence for the catalytic involvement of non-heme iron in soluble, purified preparations, it appears quite likely that in more nearly intact particulate systems non-heme iron participates in electron transport from flavin to the cytochrome system. This view rests in part on the observations of Beinert and colleagues[69,121,122] that addition of succinate produces an EPR signal at $g = 1.94$ tentatively ascribed to ferrous iron, and in part on the interpretation of the cyanide inactivation[136] discussed above. The inhibition of the succinate–coenzyme Q interaction[165] in particulate preparations by 2-theonyltrifluoroacetone also supports this view although it does not prove that protein-bound iron actually undergoes a valency change in the reaction.

There have been reports[171,172] of the chemical determination of valency changes in non-heme iron during succinate oxidation. As more fully discussed elsewhere[13], the validity of the conclusions hinges on the unresolved question of the reliability of the analytical method used for distinguishing ferrous and ferric iron, and is, at best, a static method which does not lend itself to establishing a correlation between catalytic activity and turnover rate of the iron. As mentioned earlier, kinetic studies concerned with the iron moieties of the enzyme by any method are presently hindered by the vexing problem of the reversible activation of the enzyme.

(vi) Reconstitution experiments and the question of the "nativity" of different preparations

In 1940 Keilin and Hartree[147] reported that treatment of Keilin–Hartree heart muscle preparations at pH 9.0 results in complete loss of succinoxidase and succinate–methylene blue activities, attended by only slight inactivation of cytochrome oxidase. Keilin and Hartree interpreted their results as suggesting that the alkaline treatment inactivates succinate dehydrogenase and that its destruction "may be due to the oxidation of some groupings, the integrity of which is essential for enzyme activity". Several years later it was shown in the same laboratory[18,162] that the addition of soluble succinate dehydrogenase and of cytochrome *c* to such inactivated preparations regenerates their succinoxidase, succinate–methylene blue, and succinate–DCIP activities (Fig. 11) and that the restoration of these activities was due to the uptake of the soluble enzyme by the alkali-treated particles, since the resulting complex could be repeatedly washed by centrifugation without loss of the restored activities. That incorporation of the soluble enzyme occurred was also indicated by the fact that the dehydrogenase was much more stable in the complex than in the soluble form. These important findings have been fully confirmed in the author's laboratory[13,20,50].

Extending these studies, King[108,173] reported that the "reconstitution

References p. 194

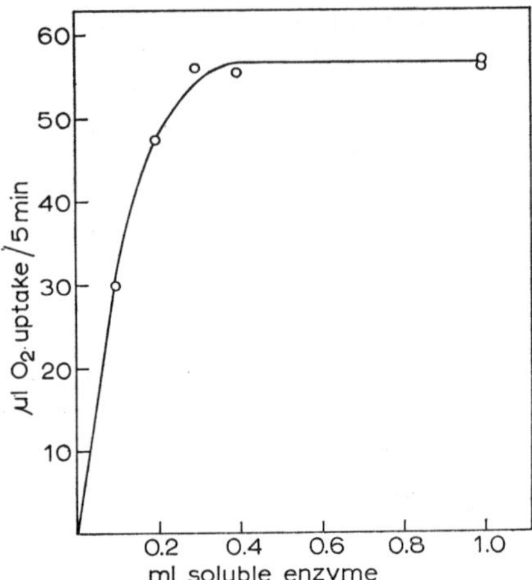

Fig. 11. Regeneration of succinoxidase activity resulting from the recombination of a soluble preparation of succinate dehydrogenase with an alkali-treated heart muscle preparation. Experimental conditions as in Kimura *et al.*[20]; data from Kimura and Hauber[168].

test" involves a reversible cleavage of the dehydrogenase from the respiratory chain in that during the preparation of the alkali-treated sample the dehydrogenase is solubilized and that the added soluble dehydrogenase recombines at the site left vacant by the dissociated (and inactivated) flavoprotein. He further proposed that succinate dehydrogenase is held to the respiratory chain by hydrogen bonds or simple electrostatic attraction, rather than by covalent bonds, as generally believed. Since these conclusions were based entirely on catalytic assays, it was desirable to check their validity by chemical analysis for succinate dehydrogenase during the cycle

TABLE XII

COMPARISON OF BOUND FLAVIN CONTENT OF UNTREATED AND ALKALI-TREATED KEILIN–HARTREE PREPARATIONS[a]

Type of preparation[b]	*Bound flavin content (mμmoles/mg protein)*				
	Preparation				
	1	*2*	*3*	*4*	*5*
Untreated	0.140	0.129	0.112	0.105	0.139
Alkali-treated	0.130	0.115	0.095	0.098	0.129
Alkali-treated and centrifuged at pH 9.4 before neutralization	0.130				0.130

[a] Data from Refs. 13 and 20.

[b] Keilin–Hartree preparations and alkali-treated preparations were made exactly as per Keilin and King[18,162] and King[173]. Although only the values in the reisolated complex are shown, the amounts of flavin in the supernatant and pellet always equalled that present in the original sample.

of alkali inactivation and reactivation. It was found by Singer *et al.*[20,50,103] that under the conditions of the alkali treatment used by Keilin and King for reconstitution (pH 9.3–9.4) only about 10% of the dehydrogenase was rendered soluble, as judged by ultracentrifugal separation, and (Table XII) on readdition of soluble enzyme to the inactivated preparation an additional amount of dehydrogenase was taken up, which was approximately equal to that originally present (Fig. 12). The result is that maximally reactivated preparations contain a double-headed respiratory chain, with 2 moles of succinate dehydrogenase present, as compared with one in untreated preparations[20,103]. While these experiments provided proof for the hypothesis[18] that stoichiometric binding of the dehydrogenase occurs during reconstitution, they contradicted King's interpretation of the reversible dissociation of the dehydrogenase and of the complete identity of reconstituted and untreated preparation[173].

King[108,175] defended his hypothesis by pointing out that at pH 9.95 succinate dehydrogenase is dissociated from the respiratory chain to a considerable extent. While the fact that at sufficiently alkaline reactions succinate dehydrogenase is rapidly and extensively dissociated has been known for many years, the point is not relevant to the argument. The question is not what happens at pH 9.95, where reconstitutively active preparations are not obtained[168] under the conditions of Keilin and King[162], but what happens at pH 9.3–9.4, the experimental conditions used in reconstitution tests[18,162]. As shown in Table XI (last line), under these conditions little or no dissociation takes place. The dehydrogenase still present is then not "first dissociated, in soluble form, then inactivated and denatured, and finally precipitated . . ." as has been argued[108], all the more since the linkages of the dehydrogenase to the respiratory chain are not materially different in normal and in alkali-treated preparations: the same conditions are required to produce equal extraction of the dehydrogenase from either source[168].

The second point advanced in King's recent papers[17,108,173] is that reconstituted preparations are in every respect identical with untreated ones, and that, therefore, the reconstitution test is a physiological phenomenon. As mentioned above, the reconstituted system differs from the original one in having twice the content of succinate dehydrogenase. It has been shown[20,50] that, although in several catalytic tests the two were indistinguishable, the reconstituted system had higher phenazine methosulfate oxidase and fumarate reductase activities than untreated samples. This is to be expected from the facts that (*1*) the dehydrogenase is only inactivated but not extracted during alkali-treatment, (*2*) that the loss of phenazine methosulfate activity is less complete at alkaline pH than of oxidase activity[18,20], and (*3*) that alkali-treatment causes oxidation of —SH groups with a resultant increase in the interaction of the dehydrogenase with

References p. 194

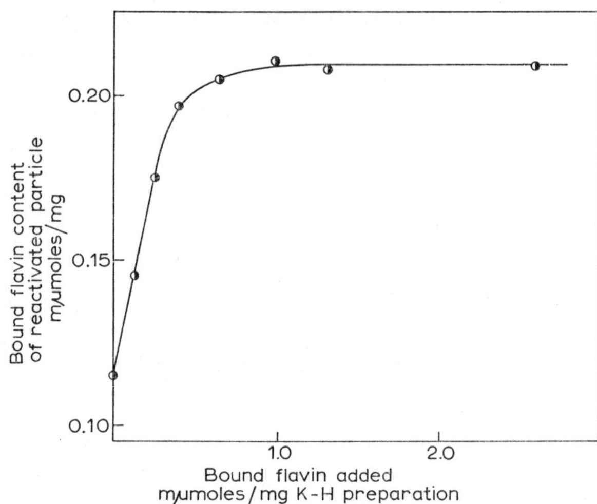

Fig. 12. Relation between added and incorporated succinate dehydrogenase. Aliquots of an alkali-inactivated, neutralized Keilin–Hartree preparation (0.6 ml, containing 18.1 mg protein) were mixed at 0° with varying amounts (0.3–6.0 ml) of soluble succinate dehydrogenase in 0.075 *M* phosphate buffer, pH 7.8, prepared by the method of Wang *et al.* and containing 3.77 mg protein per ml. The mixtures were diluted to 6.6 ml with 0.075 *M* phosphate, pH 7.8, centrifuged for 15 min at 144000 g_{max}; the supernatant solution was discarded and the pellet washed twice with 6.6 ml of the same buffer by centrifugation. Aliquots of the untreated Keilin-Hartree preparation and of the alkali-inactivated one to which no dehydrogenase had been added were similarly centrifuged and washed. Aliquots of the final pellet in each case were assayed for bound flavin, succinate dehydrogenase, and succinoxidase. The values for the original sample were 0.129 mμmoles bound flavin per mg protein and 1.47 and 0.897 μmoles succinate oxidized/min/mg protein in the dehydrogenase and oxidase assays, respectively. The corresponding figures for the alkali-treated samples were 0.115 mμmoles/mg, 0.198 and 0.041 μmoles/min/mg. Data from Kimura *et al.*[20].

$FMNH_2$ (and, hence, of fumarate reductase activity)[12], as predicted by Keilin and Hartree[147] many years ago. As to the physiological nature of this test, although it undoubtedly detects different types or degree of modification than catalytic assays, it is well to recall that both the starting material (Keilin–Hartree preparations) and the soluble enzyme used in reconstitution tests are modified as judged by their turnover numbers (Table VII) and that in preparations considered native by the reconstitution test only a very small fraction of the molecules are capable of combining with alkali-treated preparations (Fig. 12).

The facts that reconstituted samples contain twice the succinate dehydrogenase content of untreated ones but the turnover number in both dehydrogenase and oxidase assays per mole of *newly incorporated* flavin is under suitable conditions the same as in untreated preparations[20], raise the interesting question as to which of the two dehydrogenase molecules, that originally present or that newly incorporated, is functioning in these assays. Kimura and Hauber[19] resolved the problem in an ingenious manner: they added to an alkali-treated ETP preparation, in which the dehydrogenase had been deactivated by repeated washing, a fully activated sample of the soluble dehydrogenase at 17° (Fig. 13). Full succinoxidase activity appeared in less than a minute, the time necessary for combination of the components, while activation at this temperature requires hours. Hence it is the newly acquired molecule of flavoprotein, rather than that originally present, which donates electrons to the respiratory chain. However, reactivation of the flavoprotein originally present may also occur under the conditions of the reconstitution test, since in several reconstituted ETP preparations the turnover number in the *dehydrogenase* assay, per mole of newly incorporated flavin, was significantly higher than in untreated samples[168].

In earlier studies[103] no strict correlation was noted between the uptake of covalently bound flavin and the regeneration of catalytic activity, but in

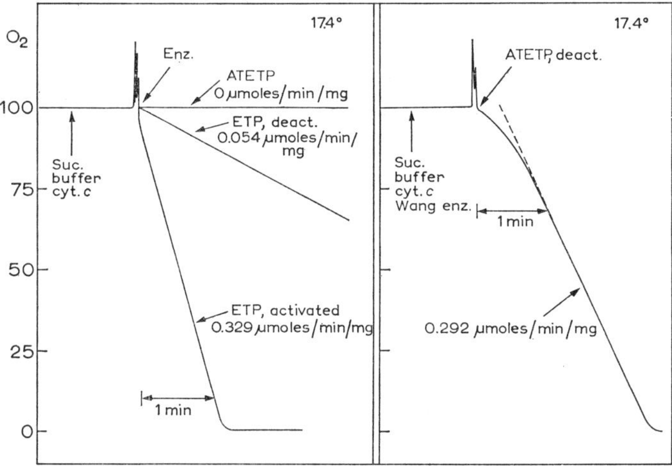

Fig. 13. Demonstration of the functioning of the newly acquired succinate dehydrogenase moiety of reconstituted samples in succinoxidase assay. Polarographic assays of succinoxidase activity at 17°, in the presence of 0.1 *M* phosphate–0.06 *M* succinate. The left side of the figure shows the activities of (*1*) beef heart ETP, deactivated by repeated centrifugation, (*2*) the same after 15 min activation with 80 m*M* succinate in N_2 (control sample for full activity), and (*3*) of an alkali-treated, deactivated ETP, prepared by exposing (*1*) to pH 9.4 for 60 min. Sample (*3*), denoted as ATETP, contains all of its original succinate dehydrogenase content in *de*activated and inactivated form. The right side shows the rapid recombination of this ATETP with a sample of fully activated soluble dehydrogenase. Since nearly the same activity is reached within 1 min as in the untreated, activated control and since activation at 17° is very slow, the flavoprotein in the added soluble enzyme must be functioning in respiration. Data of Kimura and Hauber[168].

References p. 194

later studies in the same laboratory a good correlation was noted[20]. This discrepancy has now been resolved. It has been found that even in strictly fresh preparations of the Wang type[86] only some 10–22% of the succinate dehydrogenase is capable of being bound by the alkali-treated respiratory chain sample[19,20], but even that fraction capable of being bound is heterogeneous[19]. Fractionation of strictly fresh preparations of the soluble enzyme on Sephadex G-100 or G-200 resulted in the partial separation of three forms of the dehydrogenase: one capable of combining but yielding low (or no) dehydrogenase activity on reconstitution, one capable of combining and conferring relatively high dehydrogenase but low oxidase activity (Type I), and one capable of combining and reconstituting all the original activities (Type II) (Table XIII and Fig. 14). The majority of enzyme molecules present belong to a fourth type, which neither combines with alkali-treated preparations nor restores their activities. These types probably differ in the degree of modification of the original structure. Kimura and Hauber[19] have also shown that during reconstitution a competition exists between these various forms for the binding site on the respiratory chain, but the type capable of restoring the oxidase activity is preferentially bound. Thus

TABLE XIII

DIFFERENCES IN THE BEHAVIOR OF SUCCINATE DEHYDROGENASE FRACTIONS SEPARATED ON SEPHADEX COLUMNS IN THE RECONSTITUTION TEST[a]

SD sample[b]	*SD added (mμmoles flavin/mg ATKH)*[c]	*Bound flavin incorporated (mμmoles/mg)*	*Turnover number*[d] *(thousands)*		*Per cent incorporation of bound flavin*
			Phenazine assay	*Oxidase*	
Before column separation	0.22	0.020	11	4	9
	0.44	0.031	12	5	7
Type I	0.15	0.021	5	1	14
	0.30	0.029	7	1	10
Type II	0.24	0.027	12	4	11
	0.48	0.048	13	4	10

[a] Data from Ref. 19.

[b] A sample of soluble enzyme (Wang *et al.* preparation, isolated without cyanide, gel eluate stage) was chromatographed on a Sephadex G-100 column (V_0 = 48 ml, 15 m*M* phosphate–5 m*M* succinate, pH 7.6) and 2.1-ml fractions of the excluded part were collected. Type I contains fractions 4–9; Type II fractions 14–20. For other conditions see Kimura and Hauber[19].

[c] Alkali-treated Keilin–Hartree preparation.

[d] Moles of succinate oxidized/min/mole of newly incorporated bound flavin after titration of ATKH with soluble enzyme and reisolation of the resulting complex. The TN of the untreated Keilin-Hartree preparation was 13000 and 6000, respectively, in the two assays.

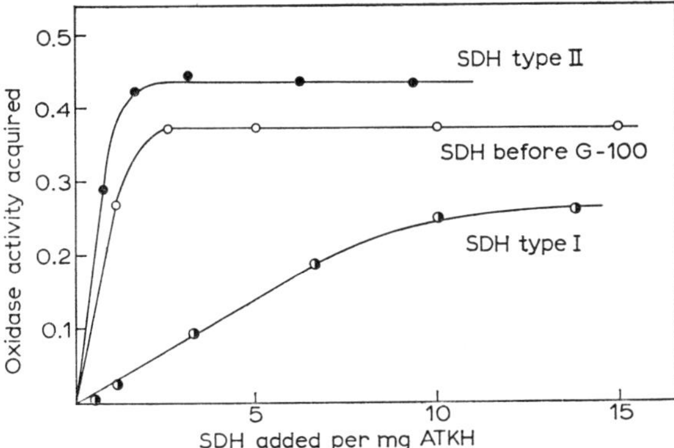

Fig. 14. Reconstitutive activity of different forms of soluble succinate dehydrogenase. The purified enzyme was a preparation of the Wang *et al.*[86] type, as modified by Keilin and King[18]. A limiting amount of alkali-treated Keilin–Hartree preparation (ATKH) was titrated with this unfractionated preparation (SDH before G-100) and with fractions separated on Sephadex G-100 columns (SDH Type I and Type II, *cf.* Table XIII). The abscissa denotes the amount of SDH added per mg ATKH in terms of dehydrogenase activity (μmoles succinate oxidized/min in the phenazine assay); the ordinate gives the succinoxidase activity of the resulting complex. Note that at low levels of added dehydrogenase Type II SDH is much more active than Type I and also yields higher succinoxidase activity when added in excess, although the two have equal combining potential for ATKH (*cf.* Table XIII). Data from Kimura and Hauber[19].

whether or not a correlation is found between uptake of the dehydrogenase and restoration of the various activities depends on the exact composition of the soluble preparation with regard to these various forms of the flavoprotein (Fig. 14).

The present visualization of the events of the reconstitution test is schematically presented in Fig. 15.

Lastly, mention should be made of the point of view advocated by King[17,108,176] that "physiological" tests, such as the reconstitution, rather than activity determinations based on artificial electron carriers should be used for assays of this type of enzyme, since the latter test fails to distinguish artifacts from the naturally occurring forms of enzymes. Although this point of view has been dealt with in section 1, its applicability to succinate dehydrogenase merits further comment, since this view tends to cast doubt on much of the knowledge which has accrued from many laboratories about succinate dehydrogenase.

This point of view is based on two observations[17]: (*1*) that the preparation of Wang *et al.*[86], modified[162] by the omission of cyanide, was active in reconstitution tests, while that of Singer *et al.*[109] was not; (*2*) that on aging of soluble preparations activity toward phenazine methosulfate was lost more slowly than the capacity to restore the succinoxidase activity of alkali-

References p. 194

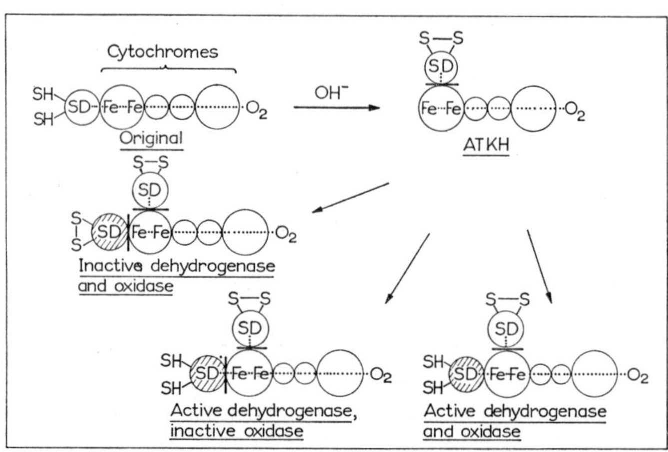

Fig. 15. Schematic representation of the events attending the alkali inactivation of succinoxidase and its reactivation with various forms of soluble succinate dehydrogenase. Alkali inactivation is visualized as resulting in a "displacement" of SD on the respiratory chain, as originally proposed by Keilin and King[18], with loss of dehydrogenase and oxidase activity, and a simultaneous oxidation of certain —SH groups, which increases the reaction of the enzyme with $FMNH_2$. The alkali-treated Keilin–Hartree preparation (ATKH) takes up various forms of succinate dehydrogenase, yielding a double-headed respiratory chain. The newly acquired dehydrogenase is shaded; interruption of electron transport is noted by a solid line. One form of soluble SD present in the preparation of Wang *et al.* combines stoichiometrically but confers no dehydrogenase or oxidase activity on the resulting complex, possibly because its —SH groups are oxidized. Another modified form combines and restores dehydrogenase activity but cannot transfer electrons to the cytochrome system. The third form restores all activities.

treated preparations. As to the first observation, it was later amended[108,177] when it was found that both are active in reconstitution if succinate is present during extraction (a standard step in the Wang *et al.* method, which does not influence catalytic activity, however). As to the second observation, it confirms earlier findings[93,166] that aging, thermal inactivation, and other procedures which tend to modify this labile enzyme often elicit differential inactivations, depending on the assay employed. Actually, modification of the dehydrogenase on aging is readily detected by the phenazine methosulfate assay by an increase in K_m long before catalytic activity is lost[19] (Fig. 16).

The main weaknesses of the contention that the reconstitution test is more reliable than catalytic assays are the underlying assumptions (*a*) that the reconstitution test involves the recombination of only the native form of the enzyme with a respiratory-chain preparation devoid of the dehydrogenase, analogously to the formation of a holoenzyme from its components,(*b*) that the combination restores the original structure in every respect, and

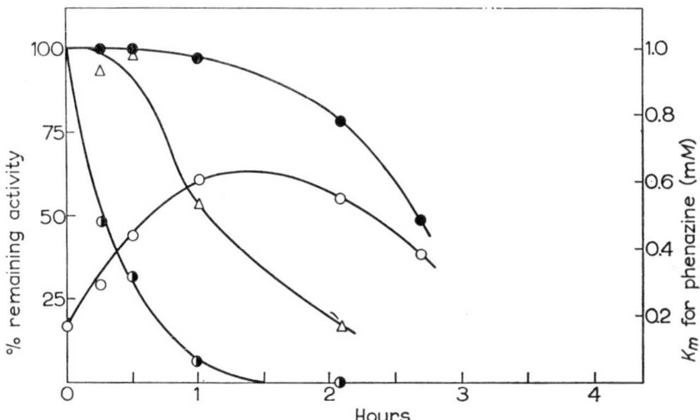

Fig. 16. Differential inactivation of soluble SD. A strictly fresh preparation of succinate dehydrogenase (Wang *et al.*, calcium phosphate gel eluate, 3.9 mg/ml (biuret basis), act. = 9.5 μmoles succ./min/mg in phenazine assay at 38°) was incubated in air at 22° in 75 m*M* PO_4–5 m*M* succinate, pH 7.8. Aliquots were assayed for dehydrogenase activity (spectrophotometric phenazine assay), for oxidase reconstitution by direct addition of 0.14 mg SD preparation/mg ATKH protein directly to Warburg vessels, for flavin peptide (bound flavin) incorporation by adding 0.71 mg SD preparation/mg ATKH and reisolation, washing, and fluorometric analysis of the bound flavin content in the resulting complex[102]. Methods and preparations as per Kimura *et al.*[20]. Data from Kimura and Hauber[19]. ●—● Succinate phenazine assay. ◑—◑ Oxidase reconstitution. △—△ Bound flavin incorporation. ○—○ K_m for phenazine.

(*c*) that measurement of the restored succinoxidase activity is a reliable index of the catalytic activity of the dehydrogenase used for reconstitution. The fact that points (*a*) and (*b*) are not supported by available evidence has been pointed out above. As to (*c*), its fallacy is manifest from the fact that in the oxidase assay the activity of the dehydrogenase is never rate-limiting and, hence, it cannot yield reliable data on the catalytic activity of the enzyme used for recombination.

It is quite apparent that a completely unmodified preparation of the soluble, purified enzyme has not yet been obtained. With the advent of new techniques for detecting such modifications, of which the reconstitution test is one, it has become clear that what appeared at one time to be preparations possessing the same catalytic properties as the particulate starting material are in reality all preparations modified to an appreciable extent and that even the dehydrogenase present in the particulate material is often modified, as compared with mitochondria. The low turnover numbers of Keilin–Hartree preparations and of the "succinate–coenzyme Q reductase" complex in phenazine assays and their increased activity in the fumarate–$FMNH_2$ reaction are examples of this (Table VII, p. 165). That all available soluble preparations of the dehydrogenase are to some degree modified is also clear from the same catalytic criteria. The fact that such soluble preparations

References p. 194

are nevertheless active in the reconstitution test in no way contradicts this argument, since they contain a heterogeneous population of enzyme molecules and on recombination with the respiratory chain those few appear to be selected which most closely resemble the native enzyme[19]. Further, the structural alterations responsible for the lowered turnover number and the behavior of such preparations in reconstitution experiments may be subtle: other catalytic and molecular properties of the mitochondrial enzyme remain unaltered[166].

(*d*) *From yeast*

(*i*) *Mitochondrial succinate dehydrogenase*

Prior to the studies of Slonimski[174], many investigators believed that succinate dehydrogenase is absent from yeast cells. The lack of succinate oxidation by yeast cells was later traced to permeability barriers. Slonimski demonstrated that mitochondria from aerobically grown yeast cells actively catalyze the succinate–methylene blue and succinate–cytochrome *c* reactions.

The dehydrogenase was solubilized and purified from butanol-desiccated mitochondria by a procedure substantially similar to that used for the isolation of the heart enzyme[87]. The dehydrogenase is an iron-flavoprotein, containing 4 atoms of non-heme iron and a mole of covalently bound flavin dinucleotide per 200000 g protein, as in the case of the mammalian enzyme. The flavin is liberated in acid-soluble form only after proteolytic digestion. Contrary to a recent report[175], tryptic digestion does not liberate free FAD, since the pH–fluorescence curve of digests is characteristic of flavin peptides (Fig. 7, p. 157) and since no activity is registered in the D-amino acid oxidase test[46].

In most of its molecular and catalytic properties the yeast enzyme resembles very closely its counterpart in heart muscle[87]. The enzyme catalyzes the oxidation of succinate far faster than the reduction of fumarate and its K_m and K_I values are typical of aerobic succinate dehydrogenases (Table VIII, p. 166). Its turnover number[46] in particle-bound form (12500 ± 1000 in the spectrophotometric phenazine assay at 30°) is nearly the same as that of the heart enzyme, considering the different temperatures of assay. The absorption spectra, inhibition patterns, and sedimentation constants of the heart and yeast enzymes are also nearly identical. The yeast enzyme reacts poorly with electron acceptors other than phenazine methosulfate in particulate preparations and almost not at all in soluble ones[87]. It is highly labile in the soluble form and is more labile in the particulate form than the heart enzyme (*e.g.*, it is rapidly inactivated at 38°)[46].

In earlier studies[87,136], in which the manometric phenazine assay was used, no activation by the substrate or inactivation by cyanide was noted. It has been recently shown, however, that these apparent differences between the yeast and heart enzymes do not exist in reality[46,101]. Thus the enzyme is strongly activated by succinate, phosphate, and malonate in oxidase

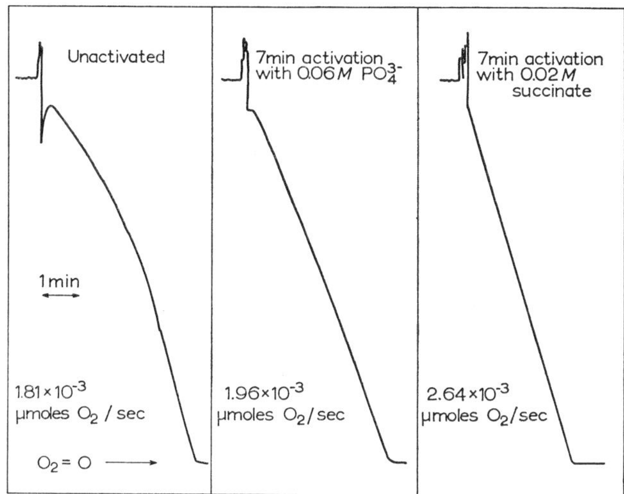

Fig. 17. Activation of succinate oxidase in yeast ETP preparation[175] by phosphate and succinate. The incubation mixture for activation contained in the main compartment of Thunberg tubes 0.15 ml 0.2 *M* phosphate, pH 7.5, and 0.3 ml ETP (6.9 mg protein); the side arm contained 0.05 ml H_2O (phosphate activation) or 0.05 ml 0.4 *M* succinate. The tubes were repeatedly evacuated and filled with N_2 at 0°. After 3 min equilibration at 30°, the contents of the side arm were tipped. The tubes were maintained at 30° for the time indicated, then cooled to 0° and a 25-μl aliquot was immediately added to the assay mixture (already at 30°) containing 0.04 *M* phosphate, pH 7.5, 0.05 *M* succinate, and 0.4 mg horse heart cytochrome *c* in a 2-ml final volume. Assays were performed with an O_2 electrode. The unactivated sample was added directly to the assay mixture without preincubation. The specific activity on full activation was 0.95 μmoles succ./min/mg at 30°. The inactivated sample (left pattern) shows a pronounced lag and a maximal respiration of 1.81 mμmoles O_2/sec. The sample (middle pattern) activated with 0.06 *M* phosphate shows almost no lag and the final rate is 1.96 mμmoles O_2/sec. The succinate activated sample (right pattern) shows no lag and the initial rate is 2.64 mμmoles O_2/sec. Activation by phosphate or succinate was performed at 30° under N_2. Data of Rocca *et al.*[46] (see also Ref. 101).

assays (Fig. 17) and the activation is even more apparent in the spectrophotometric phenazine–DCIP reaction. Activation is so rapid that it is not readily detected in manometric tests. Progressive inactivation of particulate samples by cyanide at pH 8.0–8.2 has also been recently noted with the aid of the phenazine–DCIP assay[46]. The apparent cyanide-insensitivity previously reported[136] remains unexplained.

Slonimski[174] noted that in anaerobically cultured cells as well as "petite"

References p. 194

mutants (which are devoid of a functional respiratory chain), the succinate–methylene blue reaction is absent and he concluded that the dehydrogenase is not synthesized in such cells. Since methylene blue is a poor electron acceptor for succinate dehydrogenase and may not react directly with the flavoprotein, it was desirable to reexamine this question with the phenazine methosulfate assay. The almost complete absence of the enzyme in "petite" mutants has been confirmed[46]; respiratory-chain preparations from "petite" cells also contain virtually no covalently bound flavin; the trace amount present gives an atypical pH–fluorescence curve and might not originate from the dehydrogenase (Fig. 7, p. 157).

The situation with regard to anaerobic, wild-type cells appears to be much more complex. Hebb *et al.*[176] showed that a strain of cells isolated from a commercial yeast (Red Star) contained appreciable succinate dehydrogenase activity when assayed with the manometric phenazine assay and that during the O_2-induced synthesis of the respiratory chain the increase in dehydrogenase activity was relatively modest, compared with the dramatic rise in succinoxidase and succinate–cytochrome *c* activities. The presence of the dehydrogenase in anaerobic yeast mitochondria has been confirmed in two laboratories[177,178].

Recently, however, Linnane[178a] reported that anaerobically grown yeast contains only a trace of succinate dehydrogenase and that high glucose concentration represses the formation of this enzyme in aerobic cells almost completely. These results contradict the report of Schatz[177], who found that neither anaerobiosis nor high glucose concentration prevents the synthesis of the enzyme, although the latter is associated with small particles (regarded as mitochondrial precursors) under these conditions.

With the availability of improved methods for the assay of true succinate dehydrogenase activity and of dehydrogenase *content* (bound flavin) the problem was recently reexamined in the author's laboratory[46,178b]. It was found that in several strains of commercial yeast (including Red Star) the content and activity of succinate dehydrogenase are both trivial in anaerobic cells, compared with aerobic ones. In confirmation of Linnane's findings[178a] high glucose (mannose) was found to repress the synthesis of the dehydrogenase during respiratory adaptation completely. During O_2-induced synthesis of the respiratory chain, succinate and reduced NAD dehydrogenases were formed long before succinoxidase or reduced NAD oxidase activities became maximal. During the early phase of respiratory adaptation and during aerobic growth in galactose the bound flavin content is relatively high, but succinate dehydrogenase activity is low: the consequently low turnover number suggests the occurrence of a possible precursor of the enzyme.

An indication of the interest and complexity of the problem is that aerobic cells, harvested either in the log or stationary phase, when aerated in the absence of nutrients, show a remarkable oscillation of succinate dehydrogenase activity, but the *content* of the enzyme remains constant[178b]. It appears that some sort of metabolic control operates in a cyclic manner in the system.

(ii) Cytoplasmic fumarate reductases

Over 25 years ago Fischer *et al.*[179,180] reported that crude, aged preparations of the "old yellow enzyme" from anaerobic yeast contain a flavoprotein which slowly catalyzes the reduction of fumarate with leucosafranin dyes as electron donors but cannot oxidize succinate in the presence of methylene blue. The activity was reported to be lost on prolonged dialysis and restored by FAD. Apparently no attempt was made to isolate the enzyme from fresh yeast. Fischer and coworkers considered the possibility that the activity measured was due to degraded or altered succinate dehydrogenase (a possibility which cannot be dismissed since the isolation of the "old yellow enzyme" contains many steps which destroy the dehydrogenase and inactivation of the latter is usually much more extensive in the direction of succinate oxidation than of fumarate reduction[93]), they concluded that fumarate reduction in yeast is catalyzed by a separate, unidirectional enzyme.

Subsequently, Massey and Singer[87,93] demonstrated that on isolation of succinate dehydrogenase from yeast the ratio of rates of succinate oxidation (with phenazine methosulfate) to fumarate reduction remained constant from mitochondria to highly purified preparations. Further, a series of inhibitors had identical effects on the forward and reverse reactions. Since the fumarate reductase activity ascribable to the mitochondrial enzyme was several orders of magnitude higher than the activities reported by Fischer *et al.*[179,180], it seemed possible that the German workers were indeed dealing with differentially inactivated succinate dehydrogenase samples, all the more since the methylene blue assay would not reveal any surviving dehydrogenase activity even in fresh samples of the soluble enzyme. On the basis of these studies it was concluded[166] that "while the existence of a separate 'fumaric reductase' is not disproved, the 'reductase' activities of . . . yeast mitochondria may be readily accounted for by the reversible action of succinic dehydrogenase . . ." and it was further suggested "that at present no unequivocal evidence points to the existence of a separate 'fumaric reductase' ". The presumed reversible resolution with respect to flavin[180] remained puzzling, since the flavin of the dehydrogenase is covalently bound, but the possibility could not be precluded[93] that added FAD acted as a non-enzymatic catalyst in the assay system of Fischer *et al.*

The problem was later reopened by Kováč[181], who confirmed the conclusions of Massey and Singer[93] but also called attention to the fact that fumarate reduction in extracts and broken-cell preparation of yeast, partic-

References p. 194

ularly when grown anaerobically, is only partially inhibited by malonate, succinate, and *p*-chloromercuribenzoate, whereas succinate oxidation is completely inhibited by malonate and by mercurials. He suggested, therefore, that the malonate and mercurial-resistant fraction of fumarate reductase activity may be due to a separate enzyme. Evidence of this type was inconclusive, since it has been shown earlier[143] that fumarate reduction by the homogeneous enzyme from *M. lactilyticus* is far less sensitive to inhibition by malonate and *p*-chloromercuribenzoate than succinate oxidation. Furthermore, it has been found that while treatment of respiratory-chain preparations of yeast ("ETP"[182]) with 5 m*M* *N*-ethylmaleimide inhibits some 80% of succinate dehydrogenase activity, the fumarate–$FMNH_2$ reaction remains unaffected[100,101]. Ultimate resolution of the problem clearly called for isolation and identification of the hypothetical fumarate reductase.

Since previous work[87] had definitely established that mitochondria contain only one enzyme, succinate dehydrogenase, capable of reducing fumarate, Rossi *et al.*[100] undertook a systematic search for the enzyme in cytoplasm. They found that cell-free extracts of both aerobic and anaerobic yeast cells, freed from mitochondria by centrifugation at 144000 × *g* for 1 h, followed by clarification with protamine, contained three flavoproteins which catalyze the fumarate–$FMNH_2$ reaction. One of these, present in

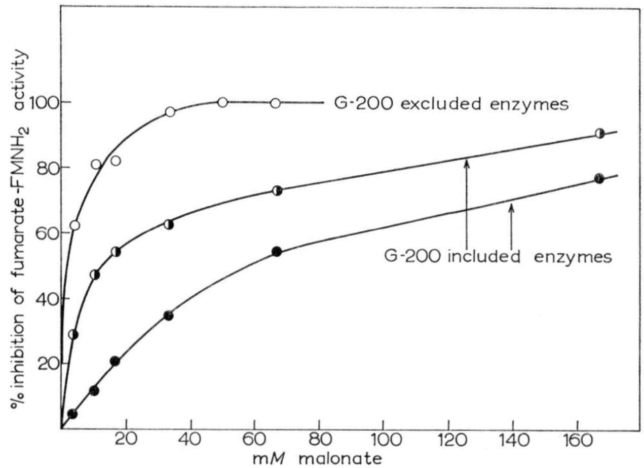

Fig. 18. Malonate sensitivity of three fumarate-reducing enzymes isolated from yeast cytoplasm. The Sephadex-excluded enzyme is probably identical with, or closely related to, mitochondrial succinate dehydrogenase (see text); the two other enzymes are included on Sephadex G-100 and separated from each other on hydroxylapatite columns (see Fig. 19). Activities noted on the abscissa refer to the fumarate–$FMNH_2$ assay at 30°, pH 7.6, in the presence of 2 m*M* fumarate. Data of Rossi *et al.*[100].

very small amounts, was excluded on Sephadex G-200, precipitated at low $(NH_4)_2SO_4$ concentrations, was activated by succinate, and catalyzed the succinate–phenazine methosulfate reaction much faster than fumarate reduction. In these and other properties it was not readily distinguishable from mitochondrial succinate dehydrogenase. Conceivably, in the course of breakage of the yeast cells a small fraction of succinate dehydrogenase may have been detached from the respiratory chain and passed into the soluble phase. The other two flavoproteins, present in substantial quantities, differed markedly from the mitochondrial enzyme in stability, solubility in $(NH_4)_2SO_4$, behavior on Sephadex columns (both are completely included on Sephadex G-100 and G-200), sensitivity to malonate (Fig. 18) and particularly the fact that neither enzyme reduced phenazine methosulfate, DCIP, ferricyanide or cytochrome *c* in the presence of succinate. The two flavoproteins are of relatively low molecular weight, possibly near 50000, since they are partly included on Sephadex G-75. They are separable from each other on hydroxylapatite columns (Fig. 19); rechromatography either of type I or of the type II enzyme on hydroxylapatite yields a single symmetri-

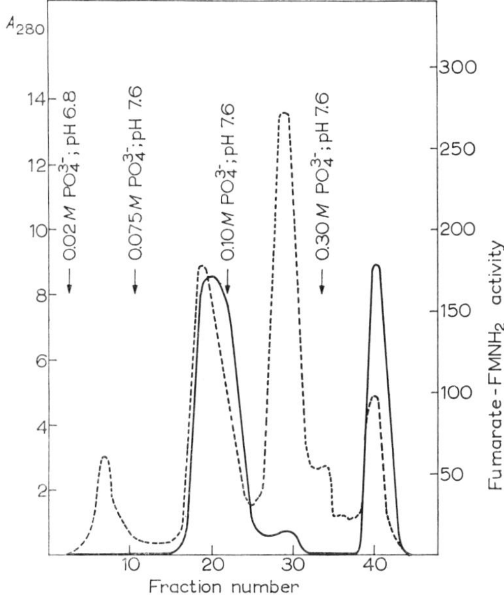

Fig. 19. Separation of the two low molecular-weight fumarate-reducing enzymes present in yeast cytoplasm on hydroxylapatite. Solid line denotes activity in the fumarate–$FMNH_2$ assay, interrupted line absorbancy at 280 mμ. When rechromatographed on another hydroxylapatite column, the type I (0.075 *M* phosphate eluate) and the type II (0.3 *M* phosphate eluate) enzymes gave single, symmetrical peaks. Data of Rossi *et al.*[100].

References p. 194

cal peak. The type I and II enzymes further differ in their solubilities in $(NH_4)_2SO_4$, reactivity with malonate (Fig. 18), and particularly in their relative reaction rates with a series of electron donors ($FMNH_2$, leucomethylviologen, and leucobenzylviologen). All attempts to demonstrate the oxidation of succinate by either protein have hitherto yielded negative results. Neither enzyme contains bound flavin. Type II fumarate reductase has been reversibly resolved with respect to flavin[182a]. Both are present in anaerobic yeast as well as in "petite" mutants in undiminished amounts, in contrast to the mitochondrial dehydrogenase[100]. Oxygen represses their formation but high glucose concentrations stimulate their biosynthesis, in complete contrast to mitochondrial succinate dehydrogenase[182a].

Thus yeast cells indeed contain fumarate reductases distinct from mitochondrial succinate dehydrogenase. In view of their cytoplasmic location, the biological function of these enzymes is of particularly great interest.

(*e*) *From bacteria*

(*i*) *Succinate dehydrogenase in obligate anaerobes*

Peck *et al.*[183] observed that extracts of *M. lactilyticus* catalyze the reduction of fumarate rapidly but oxidize succinate only extremely slowly, even in the presence of phenazine methosulfate. Further, the reduction of fumarate was only slightly inhibited by malonate at concentrations which would completely abolish fumarate reduction in mammalian or yeast mitochondria.

In order to elucidate this remarkable behavior of the *M. lactilyticus* enzyme, Warringa *et al.*[88,143] isolated it in homogeneous form. The dehydrogenase is a freely water-soluble, high molecular-weight protein ($s_{20,w} = 54$ S) containing an unusually large amount of non-heme iron (40 gramatoms/mole FAD/460000 g protein). The flavin (FAD) is readily liberated in the free form by acid treatment and is, therefore, not covalently bound. On the other hand, proteolytic digestion is required to liberate all of the iron in inorganic form. Although the molecular weight is not known, the high sedimentation coefficient suggests that it must be a multiple of 460000 (the minimum molecular weight based on FAD content) and thus the presence of several active centers in each molecule is indicated.

The absorption spectrum is typical of enzymes containing large amounts of non-heme iron. The brown color is discharged by succinate and reappears on the addition of fumarate: this suggests that non-heme iron may be involved in the catalysis.

As in most of its molecular properties, also in regard to kinetic parameters, the *M. lactilyticus* enzyme differs markedly from mammalian succinate dehydrogenase[88,143]. Neither its specificity for electron donors nor for electron acceptors is restricted; it is not activated by the substrate and it catalyzes the reduction of fumarate far faster than the oxidation of succinate (Table VIII, p. 166); at 38° the turnover number in the direction of succinate oxidation is $2.6 \cdot 10^3$, while in the direction of fumarate reduction 10^5. The Michaelis constant for fumarate is much lower and for succinate and malonate higher than in typical aerobic succinate dehydrogenases (Table VIII). These properties and the presence of a selective inhibitor of succinate oxidation (but not of fumarate reduction) in crude extracts explain the observations of Peck *et al.*[183] regarding the virtual absence of succinate dehydrogenase activity in cell-free extracts and the ability of malonate to inhibit succinate oxidation but not fumarate reduction in this organism. As discussed at the end of this Chapter, these properties of the enzyme are also admirably suited to the physiological needs of the organism.

Although various inactivating agents affect fumarate reduction and succinate oxidation by the enzyme to identical extents, as expected from the fact that a single enzyme catalyzes both reactions, —SH combining reagents are much more inhibitory in the direction of succinate oxidation than in the reverse assay. As mentioned above, a similar situation has been observed in yeast mitochondria. It would appear that —SH groups are not directly concerned with the combination of the substrate in these instances.

(*ii*) *Succinate dehydrogenases in facultative anaerobes*

A survey of the kinetic properties of succinate dehydrogenases from facultative anaerobes (*P. vulgaris, P. pentosaceum, E. coli*) reveals that these enzymes fall between the extremes presented by preparations from strict aerobes and obligate anaerobes: the ratio of maximal rates of succinate oxidation to fumarate reduction is an intermediate value and the K_m succinate/K_m fumarate ratio is usually higher than in aerobes but lower than in obligate anaerobes (Table VIII, p. 166). Among these preparations the enzymes from *P. pentosaceum*[142] and from *E. coli*[144] are of particular interest.

Succinate dehydrogenase from *P. pentosaceum* is present in both soluble and particle-bound form in cell-free extracts. Both forms have been purified by Lara[142] and, although they differ in their behavior in fractionation procedures, they show identical composition and catalytic properties. Conceivably, the two preparations might represent different forms of the same protein. Besides non-heme iron a catalytically functional *cytochrome b* is present in both preparations, as in the dehydrogenase from *Corynebacterium diphtheriae*[184].

The apparent absence of flavin from the *P. pentosaceum* enzyme, if confirmed with more highly purified preparations, would represent a unique exception to the rule that succinate dehydrogenases are flavoproteins. Another unusual property of the enzyme (also shown by the dehydrogenase from *M. lactilyticus*[143]) is the occurrence of dual pH optima in the direction of fumarate reduction but only one in succinate oxidation.

Hirsch *et al.*[144] have recently demonstrated that *E. coli* cells contain two succinate dehydrogenases, both of them reversible in their catalytic action. Although no attempt was made to separate them by fractionation procedures, a mutant (S^-) was found to be devoid of one of these enzymes. Extracts of this mutant catalyze the oxidation of succinate about 1.5 times as fast as the reduction of fumarate and the K_m values for succinate and fumarate are typical of anaerobic succinate dehydrogenases (Table VIII, p. 166). Since the activities of the two enzymes vary independently with growth conditions in wild-type cells, the conditions of culture may be adjusted to yield predominantly the aerobic enzyme (aerobic growth in glucose). In such extracts the oxidation of succinate is 25 times faster than the reduction of fumarate and the Michaelis constants for succinate and fumarate resemble the values found in aerobic organisms (Table VIII).

(*f*) *From other sources*

In higher plants, as in animal tissues, the dehydrogenase is a mitochondrial enzyme and catalyzes the oxidation of succinate considerably faster than the reduction of fumarate[185]. The properties of a partially purified preparation from pumpkin seedlings[138] do not differ materially from those of the mammalian enzyme.

Among invertebrate sources succinate dehydrogenases from the mussel *Mytilus edulis*[141] and from the parasitic worm *Ascaris lumbricoides*[186] have been investigated in some detail. The mussel enzyme seems to resemble its counterpart in mammalian heart in many respects but its K_m value for succinate is higher and K_I for fumarate is lower than corresponding values in typical aerobic organisms (Table VIII). This might be an expression of the relatively low O_2 tension in the natural habitat of this organism.

The metabolism of *Ascaris* is adapted to life under essentially anaerobic conditions: fumarate replaces O_2 as a terminal electron acceptor and thus the reduction of fumarate to succinate is an all-important metabolic event[186]. The properties of succinate dehydrogenase from this source are well-adapted to this role: the K_m for fumarate is very low and the K_I for succinate is high; further, the rate of reduction of fumarate greatly exceeds the maximal rate of succinate oxidation.

(*g*) *Conclusions concerning the comparative biochemistry of succinate dehydrogenases*

From the few examples quoted it is apparent that the properties of succinate dehydrogenases are excellently adapted to the physiological needs of the organism. In typical aerobic cells, as a member of the tricarboxylic acid cycle, it catalyzes an oxygen-linked reaction which leads to energy conservation. The dehydrogenase from such cells catalyzes the oxidative reaction almost two orders of magnitude faster than the reductive one. The K_m for succinate is relatively low and the K_I for fumarate moderate; hence fumarate accumulation does not readily arrest the oxidation of succinate. In its tight structural union with the respiratory chain efficient transport to the cytochrome system is assured and loss of energy by auto-oxidation prevented. It is tempting to think that activation by the substrate (which has been detected only in aerobic cells) might serve the same end. It would be easy to visualize a possible control mechanism which operates by activating additional molecules of the dehydrogenase when succinate concentration is high and deactivating the enzyme when the concentration falls below a level compatible with the needs of the cell.

In many typical anaerobic forms of life (*e.g.*, *Ascaris* and *M. lactilyticus*) the cytochrome system is absent and the succinate dehydrogenase–fumarate couple replaces the cytochrome oxidase–O_2 system as terminal electron acceptor. The important metabolic event in these organisms is then the reduction of fumarate. In accord with this the rate of the reductive reaction by far exceeds that of the oxidative one; the K_m for fumarate is very low, the K_I for succinate is high: thus fumarate is efficiently metabolized without interference by the accumulation of succinate.

This correlation between metabolic need and the catalytic properties of succinate dehydrogenases has been recognized for many years[89,139], but the best examples of this adaptation have come to light only recently. It has been known that in facultative anaerobes, such as *Propionibacterium pentosaceum*, the properties of the enzyme are between those of succinate dehydrogenase from aerobic and anaerobic cells; thus they are suited either to the requirements of aerobic life or to anaerobic fermentations[89]. A much more efficient arrangement is that recently demonstrated in *E. coli*[144] and in yeast[100]. Here separate enzymes concerned with aerobic succinate oxidation and anaerobic fumarate reduction exist within the same cell; each enzyme is uniquely adapted to one task and when environmental conditions do not require its presence, it may develop only to a very limited extent or not at all.

References p. 194

REFERENCES

[1] T. P. Singer, in P. Boyer, H. Lardy and K. Myrbäck (Eds.), *The Enzymes*, Vol. 7, 2nd ed., Academic Press, New York, 1963, p. 345.
[2] B. Chance and G. R. Williams, *J. Biol. Chem.*, 217 (1955) 409.
[3] M. Klingenberg and T. Bücher, *Ann. Rev. Biochem.*, 29 (1960) 669.
[4] T. Kimura, T. P. Singer and C. J. Lusty, *Biochim. Biophys. Acta*, 44 (1960) 284.
[5] R. L. Ringler and T. P. Singer, *J. Biol. Chem.*, 234 (1959) 2211.
[6] F. L. Crane and H. Beinert, *J. Biol. Chem.*, 218 (1956) 717.
[7] E. B. Kearney, *J. Biol. Chem.*, 229 (1957) 363.
[8] H. Beinert and F. L. Crane, in W. D. McElroy and B. Glass (Eds.), *Inorganic Nitrogen Metabolism*, Johns Hopkins Press, Baltimore, 1956, p. 601.
[9] H. Watari, E. B. Kearney and T. P. Singer, *J. Biol. Chem.*, 238 (1963) 4063.
[10] T. Cremona, E. B. Kearney, M. Villavicencio and T. P. Singer, *Biochem. Z.*, 338 (1963) 407.
[11] J. Machinist, C. Rossi and T. P. Singer, *Federation Proc.*, 23 (1964) 485.
[12] T. P. Singer and J. Hauber, *Federation Proc.*, 22 (1963) 466.
[13] T. P. Singer and E. B. Kearney, in P. Boyer, H. Lardy and K. Myrbäck (Eds.), *The Enzymes*, Vol. 7, 2nd ed. Academic Press, New York, 1963, p. 383.
[14] Y. Hatefi, A. G. Haavik, L. R. Fowler and D. E. Griffiths, *J. Biol. Chem.*, 237 (1962) 2661.
[15] H. Beinert, G. Palmer, T. Cremona and T. P. Singer, *Biochem. Biophys. Res. Communs.*, 12 (1963) 432.
[16] S. Minakami, R. L. Ringler and T. P. Singer, *J. Biol. Chem.*, 237 (1962) 569.
[17] T. E. King, *Biochim. Biophys. Acta*, 47 (1961) 430.
[18] D. Keilin and T. E. King, *Nature*, 181 (1958) 1520.
[19] T. Kimura and J. Hauber, *Biochem. Biophys. Res. Communs.*, 13 (1963) 169.
[20] T. Kimura, J. Hauber and T. P. Singer, *Nature*, 198 (1963) 362.
[21] H. Beinert, in P. Boyer, H. Lardy and K. Myrbäck (Eds.), *The Enzymes*, Vol. 7, 2nd ed., Academic Press, New York, 1963, p. 467.
[22] T.P. Singer and E. B. Kearney, *J. Biol. Chem.*, 183 (1950) 409.
[23] F. L. Crane, J. L. Glenn and D. E. Green, *Biochim. Biophys. Acta*, 22 (1956) 475.
[24] B. Mackler, in *Biochemical Preparations*, Vol. 9, John Wiley, New York, 1963, p. 40.
[25] R. L. Ringler, S. Minakami and T. P. Singer, *Biochem. Biophys. Res. Communs.*, 3 (1960) 417.
[26] S. Minakami, T. Cremona, R. L. Ringler and T. P. Singer, *J. Biol. Chem.*, 238 (1963) 1549.
[27] R. L. Ringler, S. Minakami and T. P. Singer, *J. Biol. Chem.*, 238 (1963) 801.
[28] T. Cremona and E. B. Kearney, *Nature*, 200 (1963) 542.
[29] C. J. Lusty, *Federation Proc.*, 21 (1962) 47.
[30] C. J. Lusty, *Doctoral Dissertation*, Wayne State University, 1963.
[31] H. Watari, E. B. Kearney, T. P. Singer, D. Basinski, J. Hauber and C. J. Lusty, *J. Biol. Chem.*, 237 (1962) PC 1731.
[32] H. R. Mahler, N. K. Sarkar, L. P. Vernon and R. A. Alberty, *J. Biol. Chem.*, 199 (1952) 585.
[33] B. DeBernard, *Biochim. Biophys. Acta*, 23 (1957) 510.
[34] B. Mackler, *Biochim. Biophys. Acta*, 50 (1961) 141.
[35] I. Raw, O. C. Nogueira and J. B. M. Filho, *Enzymologia*, 23 (1961) 123.
[36] T. E. King and R. L. Howard, *J. Biol. Chem.*, 237 (1962) 1686.
[37] A. G. Chapman and V. Jagannathan, Manuscript circulated by I.E.G. No. 1 of the National Institutes of Health, 1963.
[38] V. Massey, *Biochim. Biophys. Acta*, 37 (1960) 314.
[39] V. Massey, *Biochim. Biophys. Acta*, 38 (1960) 447.
[40] R. L. Searls and D. R. Sanadi, *Proc. Natl. Acad. Sci. (U.S.)*, 45 (1959) 697.
[41] L. Ernster, L. Danielson and M. Ljunggren, *Biochim. Biophys. Acta*, 58 (1962) 171.

42 A. Giuditta and H. J. Strecker, *Biochem. Biophys. Res. Communs.*, 2 (1960) 159.
43 F. Märki and C. Martius, *Biochem. Z.*, 333 (1960) 111.
44 L. Ernster, in T. W. Goodwin and O. Lindberg (Eds.), *Biological Structure and Function*, Vol. 2, Academic Press, New York, 1961, p. 139.
45 H. Beinert, G. Palmer, T. Cremona and T. P. Singer, *J. Biol. Chem.*, 240 (1965) 475.
46 E. Rocca and E. B. Kearney, *Federation Proc.*, 24 (1965) 297.
47 T. Cremona and E. B. Kearney, *J. Biol. Chem.*, 239 (1964) 2328.
48 T. P. Singer, S. Minakami and R. L. Ringler, in E. C. Slater (Ed.), *Fifth International Congress of Biochemistry, Symposium 5, Moscow, 1961*, Pergamon, Oxford, 1963, p. 174.
49 C. J. Lusty, J. Machinist and T. P. Singer, *J. Biol. Chem.*, 240 (1965) 1804.
50 T. P. Singer and T. Cremona, in F. Dickens (Ed.), *Symposium on Oxygen in the Animal Organism*, Pergamon, Oxford, 1964, p. 389.
51 D. M. Ziegler, D. E. Green and K. A. Doeg, *J. Biol. Chem.*, 234 (1959) 1916.
52 V. Massey and B. E. P. Swoboda, *Biochem. Z.*, 338 (1963) 474.
53 A. J. Merola, R. Coleman and R. Hansen, *Federation Proc.*, 22 (1963) 466.
54 F. M. Huennekens, S. P. Felton, N. A. Rao and B. Mackler, *J. Biol. Chem.*, 236 (1961) PC 57.
55 T. Cremona, E. B. Kearney, J. Salach and T. P. Singer, *Nature*, 200 (1963) 958.
56 J. Salach, E. B. Kearney and T. P. Singer, *Nature*, 201 (1964) 1027.
57 M. Dixon, J. M. Maynard and P. F. W. Morrow, *Nature*, 186 (1960) 1032.
58 P. Handler, K. V. Rajagopalan and V. Aleman, *Federation Proc.*, 23, Part I, No. 1 (1964) 30.
59 W. Lovenberg, B. B. Buchanan and J. C. Rabinowitz, *J. Biol. Chem.*, 238 (1963) 3899.
60 K. T. Fry and A. San Pietro, *Biochem. Biophys. Res. Communs.*, 9 (1962) 218.
61 C. Martius, in G. E. W. Wolstenholme and C. M. O'Connor (Eds.), *Ciba Foundation Symposium on the Regulation of Cell Metabolism*, Churchill, London, 1959, p. 194.
62 T. P. Singer, in T. W. Goodwin and O. Lindberg (Eds.), *Biological Structure and Function*, Vol. 2, Academic Press, New York, 1961, p. 103.
63 Y. Hatefi, A. G. Haavik and D. E. Griffiths, *J. Biol. Chem.*, 237 (1962) 1676.
63a J. M. Machinist and T. P. Singer, *Proc. Natl. Acad. Sci., (U.S.)*, 53 (1965) 467.
64 C. Rossi, T. Cremona, J. M. Machinist and T. P. Singer, *J. Biol. Chem.*, 240 (1965) 2364.
65 H. R. Mahler and D. Elowe, *J. Biol. Chem.*, 210 (1954) 165.
66 T. Cremona and E. B. Kearney, *J. Biol. Chem.*, 239 (1964) 2328.
67 S. Minakami, F. J. Schindler and R. W. Estabrook, *J. Biol. Chem.*, 239 (1964) 2042.
68 R. H. Sands and H. Beinert, *Biochem. Biophys. Res. Communs.*, 3 (1960) 47.
69 H. Beinert and W. Lee, *Biochem. Biophys. Res. Communs.*, 5 (1961) 40.
70 H. Beinert, W. Heinen and G. Palmer, *Brookhaven Symp. Biol.*, 15 (1963) 229.
71 D. R. Sanadi, T. E. Andreoli, R. L. Pharo and S. R. Vyas, *Federation Proc.*, 22 (1963) 405.
72 H. Beinert and R. H. Sands, *Biochem. Biophys. Res. Communs.*, 1 (1959) 171.
73 R. Sanadi, Personal communication, 1963.
74 R. C. Bray, *Biochem. J.*, 81 (1961) 189.
75 T. P. Singer and E. B. Kearney, in T. Bücher (Ed.), *Symposium on Redox-function of Cytoplasmic Structures*, Joint meeting of the German Society of Physiological Chemists and the Austrian Biochemical Society, Vienna, Sept., 1962, Preprints, p. 251.
76 Z. Kaniuga and C. Veeger, *Biochim. Biophys. Acta*, 60 (1962) 435.
77 T. E. King and R. L. Howard, *Biochim. Biophys. Acta*, 59 (1962) 489.
78 T. Cremona, E. B. Kearney and G. Valentine, *Nature*, 200 (1963) 673.
78a S. Fleischer, A. Casu and B. Fleischer, *Federation Proc.*, 23 (1964) 486.
78b J. M. Machinist and T. P. Singer, *J. Biol. Chem.*, 240 (1965) 3182.
79 D. R. Sanadi, T. E. Andreoli, R. E. Pharo and S. R. Vyas, in B. Chance (Ed.),

Energy-linked Functions of Mitochondria, Academic Press, New York, 1963, p. 26.
80 R. L. PHARO AND D. R. SANADI, *Federation Proc.*, 23 (1964) 486.
80a R. L. PHARO AND D. R. SANADI, *Biochim. Biophys. Acta*, 85 (1964) 346.
81 T. THUNBERG, *Skand. Arch. Physiol.*, 22 (1909) 430.
82 F. BATTELLI AND L. STERN, *Biochem. Z.*, 30 (1910) 172.
83 T. P. SINGER AND E. B. KEARNEY, *Biochim. Biophys. Acta*, 15 (1954) 151.
84 T. P. SINGER, E. B. KEARNEY AND N. ZASTROW, *Biochim. Biophys. Acta*, 17 (1955) 154.
85 Y. L. WANG, C. L. TSOU AND T. Y. WANG, Results presented at the *Third International Congress of Biochemistry*, Brussels, August, 1955.
86 T. Y. WANG, C. L. TSOU AND Y. L. WANG, *Sci. Sinica (Peking)*, 5 (1956) 73.
87 T. P. SINGER, V. MASSEY AND E. B. KEARNEY, *Arch. Biochem. Biophys.*, 69 (1957) 405.
88 M. G. P. J. WARRINGA, O. H. SMITH, A. GIUDITTA AND T. P. SINGER, *J. Biol. Chem.*, 230 (1958) 97.
89 T. P. SINGER AND F. J. S. LARA, in K. ICHIHARA (Ed.), *Proceedings of the International Symposium on Enzyme Chemistry, Tokyo-Kyoto, 1957*, Academic Press, New York, 1958, p. 330.
90 E. B. KEARNEY AND T. P. SINGER, *J. Biol. Chem.*, 219 (1956) 963.
91 V. MASSEY AND T. P. SINGER, *J. Biol. Chem.*, 229 (1957) 755.
92 A. GIUDITTA AND T. P. SINGER, *J. Biol. Chem.*, 234 (1958) 662.
93 V. MASSEY AND T. P. SINGER, *J. Biol. Chem.*, 228 (1957) 263.
94 O. ARRIGONI AND T. P. SINGER, *Nature*, 193 (1962) 1256.
95 E. R. REDFEARN AND J. M. DIXON, *Biochem. J.*, 81 (1961) 19P.
96 T. P. SINGER AND E. B. KEARNEY, in D. GLICK (Ed.), *Methods of Biochemical Analysis*, 4 (1957) 307.
96a T. KIMURA, J. HAUBER AND T. P. SINGER, *Biochem. Biophys. Res. Communs.*, 11 (1963) 83.
97 T. P. SINGER AND C. J. LUSTY, *Biochem. Biophys. Res. Communs.*, 2 (1960) 276.
98 T. P. SINGER AND J. HAUBER, *J. Biol. Chem.* (submitted).
99 P. BERNATH AND T. P. SINGER, in S. P. COLOWICK AND N. O. KAPLAN (Eds.), *Methods in Enzymology*, Vol. V, Academic Press, New York, 1962, p. 597.
100 C. ROSSI, J. HAUBER AND T. P. SINGER, *Nature*, 204 (1964) 167.
101 T. P. SINGER, in T. E. KING, H. S. MASON AND M. MORRISON (Eds.), *International Symposium on Oxidases*, Vol. 1, John Wiley, New York, Vol. 1, 1965, p. 448.
102 T. P. SINGER, J. HAUBER AND E. B. KEARNEY, *Biochem. Biophys. Res. Communs.*, 9 (1962) 146.
103 T. P. SINGER, J. HAUBER AND O. ARRIGONI, *Biochem. Biophys. Res. Communs.*, 9 (1962) 150.
104 E. B. KEARNEY, *J. Biol. Chem.*, 235 (1960) 865.
105 P. CERLETTI, R. STROM AND M. G. GIORDANO, *Arch. Biochem. Biophys.*, 101 (1963) 423.
106 W. R. FRISELL AND C. G. MACKENZIE, *J. Biol. Chem.*, 237 (1962) 94.
107 T. E. KING, *J. Biol. Chem.*, 238 (1963) 4032.
108 T. E. KING, *J. Biol. Chem.*, 238 (1963) 4037.
109 T. P. SINGER, E. B. KEARNEY AND P. BERNATH, *J. Biol. Chem.*, 223 (1956) 599.
110 R. E. BASFORD, H. D. TISDALE AND S. E. GREEN, *Biochim. Biophys. Acta*, 24 (1957) 490.
111 R. K. MORTON, *Nature*, 166 (1950) 1092.
112 D. M. ZIEGLER AND K. A. DOEG, *Arch. Biochem. Biophys.*, 97 (1962) 41.
113 D. E. GREEN, S. MII AND P. M. KOHOUT, *J. Biol. Chem.*, 217 (1955) 551.
114 E. B. KEARNEY AND T. P. SINGER, *Résumés des Communications, Third International Congress of Biochemistry, Brussels, 1955*, p. 55.
115 T. P. SINGER, E. B. KEARNEY AND V. MASSEY, *Arch. Biochem. Biophys.*, 60 (1955) 255.
116 T. Y. WANG, C. L. TSOU AND Y. L. WANG, *Sci. Sinica (Peking)*, 7 (1958) 65.
117 Y. L. WANG, T. Y. WANG, C. L. TSOU, K. Y. WU AND S. M. CHEN, *Abstracts, Fifth International Congress of Biochemistry, Moscow, 1961*, Pergamon, Oxford, 1961, p. 103.

118 P. HEMMERICH, Personal communication, 1964.
119 V. MASSEY, *J. Biol. Chem.*, 229 (1957) 763.
120 T. P. SINGER AND V. MASSEY, *Record Chem. Progr. (Kresge-Hooker Sci. Lib.)*, 18 (1957) 201.
121 H. BEINERT AND R. H. SANDS, *Biochem. Biophys. Res. Communs.*, 3 (1960) 41.
122 H. BEINERT AND R. H. SANDS, in M. S. BLOIS JR. *et al.* (Eds.), *Free Radicals in Biological Systems*, Academic Press, New York, 1961, p. 17.
123 B. COMMONER AND T. C. HOLLOCHER JR., *Proc. Natl. Acad. Sci. (U.S.)*, 46 (1960) 405.
124 B. COMMONER AND T. C. HOLLOCHER JR., *Proc. Natl. Acad. Sci. (U.S.)*, 46 (1960) 416.
125 E. B. KEARNEY, in K. ICHIHARA (Ed.), *Proceedings of the International Symposium on Enzyme Chemistry, Tokyo-Kyoto, 1957*, Academic Press, New York, 1958, p. 340.
126 M. B. THORN, *Biochem. J.*, 85 (1962) 116.
127 E. B. KEARNEY, T. P. SINGER AND N. ZASTROW, *Arch. Biochem. Biophys.*, 55 (1955) 579.
128 E. C. SLATER AND W. D. BONNER JR., *Biochem. J.*, 52 (1952) 185.
129 E. C. SLATER, *Discussions Faraday Soc.*, 20 (1955) 231.
130 J. K. MCDONALD, J. A. ANDERSON, V. H. CHELDELIN AND T. E. KING, *Biochim. Biophys. Acta*, 73 (1963) 533.
131 D. V. DERVARTANIAN AND C. VEEGER, *Biochem. J.*, 84 (1962) 65P.
132 T. THUNBERG, *Biochem. Z.*, 258 (1933) 48.
133 W. FRANKE AND D. SIEWERDT, *Z. Physiol. Chem.*, 280 (1944) 76.
134 O. GAWRON, A. J. GLAID, T. P. FONDY AND M. M. BECHTOLD, *Nature*, 187 (1961) 1004.
135 T. T. TCHEN AND H. VAN MILLIGAN, *J. Am. Chem. Soc.*, 82 (1960) 4115.
136 A. GIUDITTA AND T. P. SINGER, *J. Biol. Chem.*, 234 (1958) 666.
137 P. CERLETTI, N. STROM, M. G. GIORDANO, F. BALASTERO AND M. A. GIOVENCO, *Biochem. Biophys. Res. Communs.*, 14 (1963) 408.
138 L. KOVAČ, *Collection Czech. Chem. Commun.*, 23 (1958) 1140.
139 T. P. SINGER, *Ann. N. Y. Acad. Sci.*, 72 (1959) 480.
140 T. E. KING, C. A. RYAN, V. H. CHELDELIN AND J. K. MCDONALD, *Biochim. Biophys. Acta*, 45 (1960) 398.
141 C. A. RYAN AND T. E. KING, *Biochim. Biophys. Acta*, 62 (1962) 269.
142 F. J. S. LARA, *Biochim. Biophys. Acta*, 33 (1959) 565.
143 M. G. P. J. WARRINGA AND A. GIUDITTA, *J. Biol. Chem.*, 230 (1958) 111.
144 D. HIRSCH, M. RASMINSKY, B. D. DAVIS AND E. C. C. LIN, *J. Biol. Chem.*, 238 (1963) 3370.
145 F. G. HOPKINS AND E. MORGAN, *Biochem. J.*, 32 (1938) 611.
146 F. G. HOPKINS, E. MORGAN AND C. LUTWAK-MANN, *Biochem. J.*, 32 (1938) 1829.
147 D. KEILIN AND E. F. HARTREE, *Proc. Roy. Soc. (London), Ser. B*, 129 (1940) 277.
148 V. R. POTTER AND K. P. DUBOIS, *J. Gen. Physiol.*, 26 (1943) 39.
149 E. S. G. BARRON AND T. P. SINGER, *J. Biol. Chem.*, 157 (1945) 221.
150 R. A. PETERS AND R. W. WAKELIN, *Biochem. J.*, 40 (1946) 513.
151 E. C. SLATER, *Biochem. J.*, 45 (1949) 130.
152 W. C. STADIE AND N. HAUGAARD, *J. Biol. Chem.*, 161 (1945) 153.
153 E. S. G. BARRON, Z. B. MILLER, G. R. BARTLETT, J. MEYER AND T. P. SINGER, *Biochem. J.*, 41 (1947) 69.
154 E. S. G. BARRON AND G. KALNITSKY, *Biochem. J.*, 41 (1947) 346.
155 V. MASSEY, *Biochim. Biophys. Acta*, 30 (1958) 500.
156 J. H. QUASTEL AND W. R. WOOLDRIDGE, *Biochem. J.*, 22 (1928) 689.
157 M. B. THORN, *Biochem. J.*, 54 (1953) 540.
158 J. H. QUASTEL AND A. H. M. WHEATLEY, *Biochem. J.*, 25 (1931) 117.
159 D. KEILIN AND E. F. HARTREE, *Biochem. J.*, 44 (1949) 205.
160 N. B. DAS, *Biochem. J.*, 31 (1937) 1124.
161 L. F. LELOIR AND M. DIXON, *Enzymology*, 11 (1937) 81.
162 D. KEILIN AND T. E. KING, *Proc. Roy. Soc. (London), Ser. B*, 152 (1960) 163.
163 A. O. M. STOPPANI AND J. A. BRIGNONE, *Arch. Biochem. Biophys.*, 68 (1957) 432.

[164] F. Tietzl and I. M. Klotz, *Arch. Biochem. Biophys.*, 35 (1952) 355.
[165] D. M. Ziegler, in T. W. Goodwin and O. Lindberg (Eds.), *Biological Structure and Function*, Vol. 2, Academic Press, New York, 1961, p. 253.
[166] T. P. Singer, E. B. Kearney and V. Massey, *Advan. Enzymol.*, 18 (1957) 65.
[167] C. C. Tsou, *Biochem. J.*, 49 (1951) 512.
[168] T. Kimura and J. Hauber, Unpublished data, 1963.
[169] C. P. Lee and T. E. King, *Biochim. Biophys. Acta*, 59 (1962) 716.
[170] T. P. Singer, V. Massey and E. B. Kearney, *Biochim. Biophys. Acta*, 19 (1956) 200.
[171] D. E. Green, D. E. Griffith, K. A. Doeg and D. C. Wharton, in *Proceedings of the Fifth International Congress of Biochemistry, Moscow, 1961*, Pergamon, Oxford, 1963, p. 182.
[172] D. M. Ziegler and K. A. Doeg, *Arch. Biochem. Biophys.*, 97 (1962) 41.
[173] T. E. King, *J. Biol. Chem.*, 236 (1961) 2342.
[174] P. Slonimski, *La Formation des Enzymes Respiratoires chez la Levure*, Masson, Paris, 1953.
[175] B. Mackler, P. J. Collipp, H. M. Duncan, N. A. Rao and F. M. Huennekens, *J. Biol. Chem.*, 237 (1962) 2968.
[176] C. R. Hebb, J. Slebodnik, T. P. Singer and P. Bernath, *Arch. Biochem. Biophys.*, 83 (1959) 10.
[177] G. Schatz, *Biochem. Biophys. Res. Communs.*, 12 (1963) 448.
[178] A. W. Linnane, E. Vitols and P. G. Nowland, *J. Cell Biol.*, 13 (1962) 345.
[178a] A. W. Linnane, in T. E. King, H. S. Mason and H. Morrison (Eds.), *International Symposium on Oxidases*, Vol. 2, Wiley, New York, 1965, p. 1102.
[178b] T. P. Singer, E. Rocca and E. B. Kearny, in E. C. Slater (Ed.), *Flavins and Flavoproteins, (BBA Library Vol. 8)*, Elsevier, Amsterdam, 1966, p. 391.
[179] F. G. Fischer and H. Eysenbach, *Ann.*, 530 (1937) 90.
[180] F. G. Fischer, A. Roedig and K. Bauch, *Ann.*, 552 (1942) 203.
[181] L. Kováč, *Enzymologia*, 22 (1960) 27.
[182] H. R. Mahler, B. Mackler, S. Grandchamp and P. P. Slonimski, *Biochemistry*, 3 (1964) 668.
[182a] T. P. Singer and J. Hauber, *Federation Proc.*, 24 (1965) 297.
[183] H. O. Peck Jr., O. H. Smith and H. Gest, *Biochim. Biophys. Acta*, 25 (1957) 142.
[184] A. M. Pappenheimer Jr. and E. D. Hendee, *J. Biol. Chem.*, 180 (1949) 597.
[185] E. M. Martin and R. K. Morton, *Biochem. J.*, 62 (1956) 696.
[186] E. Bueding, in B. Wright (Ed.), *Control Mechanisms in Respiration and Fermentation*, Ronald Press, New York, 1963, p. 167.

Chapter IV

The Functional Complexes of the Mitochondrial Electron-Transfer System

YOUSSEF HATEFI*

Department of Biochemistry, School of Medicine, Pahlavi University, Shiraz (Iran)

1. Introduction

The electron-transfer system of mitochondria is a multicomponent structure composed of protein, lipid and a number of components capable of undergoing cyclic reduction and oxidation. From the standpoint of their chemical structure, these components may be divided into three groups**: (*1*) Quinoid structures (flavins, coenzyme Q), (*2*) Iron-porphyrin chelates (the heme groups of cytochromes $a+a_3$, b, c_1 and c), and (*3*) Transition-metal ions not chelated with porphyrins (non-heme iron, copper).

The function of the electron-transfer system is: (*a*) to oxidize reduced NAD and succinate respectively to NAD and fumarate; (*b*) to transfer the electrons thus liberated to molecular oxygen; and (*c*) to relay the energy obtained from these oxidations to a set of components which will utilize it in the synthesis of ATP from ADP and inorganic phosphate (*cf.* reactions 1–3).

$$\mathrm{NADH} + \mathrm{H^+} + 1/2\ \mathrm{O_2} \rightarrow \mathrm{NAD^+} + \mathrm{H_2O} + \text{energy} \qquad (1)$$

$$\text{Succinate} + 1/2\ \mathrm{O_2} \rightarrow \text{fumarate} + \mathrm{H_2O} + \text{energy} \qquad (2)$$

$$\mathrm{ADP} + \text{phosphate} + \text{energy} \rightarrow \mathrm{ATP} \qquad (3)$$

In the mitochondrion, the electron-transfer components or electron carriers are arranged essentially in accordance with their oxidation–reduction

---

* Present address: Department of Biochemistry, Scripps Clinic and Research Foundation, La Jolla, Calif. (U.S.A.)

** Sulfhydryl groups may also be considered as participants in electron transfer[1].

References p. 229

potentials. The potential span for the succinic oxidase system is about 0.8 V and for the reduced NAD oxidase system is 1.12 V. As a result of the concerted action of the carriers, electrons are rapidly transferred from reduced NAD and succinate to molecular oxygen. Under conditions that the components of the oxidative phosphorylation system are detached from the electron-transfer system, the rate of oxidation of reduced NAD by molecular oxygen is about 5–7 μmoles/min/mg protein of fragmented bovine-heart mitochondria at 38°, and the rate of oxidation of succinate is about 2–3. However, when electron transfer is coupled to the phosphorylation system, the latter reactions restrict the rate of electron flow. Thus in a phosphorylating system both reduced NAD and succinate are oxidized more slowly[2–4].

In the present Chapter the details of the electron-transfer system of mitochondria will be considered. Oxidative phosphorylation and other functional and structural aspects of mitochondria are discussed in other Chapters of this volume.

2. The primary enzyme complexes of the electron-transfer system

Recently it has become possible to divide the electron-transfer system into four discrete enzyme complexes[5–15]. These complexes catalyze reactions 4–7 and are referred to as: (*I*) Reduced NAD–coenzyme Q reductase[5–7]; (*II*) succinic–coenzyme Q reductase[8–11]; (III) reduced coenzyme Q–cytochrome *c* reductase[12]; and (*IV*) cytochrome *c* (or simply cytochrome) oxidase[13–15]. Reduced coenzyme Q is represented as QH_2.

$$\text{NADH} + \text{H}^+ + \text{Q} \rightarrow \text{NAD}^+ + \text{QH}_2 \tag{4}$$

$$\text{Succinate} + \text{Q} \rightarrow \text{fumarate} + \text{QH}_2 \tag{5}$$

$$\text{QH}_2 + 2 \text{ ferricytochrome } c \rightarrow \text{Q} + 2 \text{ ferrocytochrome } c + 2 \text{ H}^+ \tag{6}$$

$$2 \text{ Ferrocytochrome } c + 2 \text{ H}^+ + 1/2 \text{ O}_2 \rightarrow 2 \text{ ferricytochrome } c + \text{H}_2\text{O} \tag{7}$$

As in the case with the α-ketoglutaric and the pyruvic dehydrogenase complexes (*cf.* Chapter II), each primary complex of the electron-transfer system appears to be a functional unit composed of a fixed number of electron carriers. The components of each of the four complexes are firmly bonded together and are not dissociated by mild fractionation procedures. The bonds that hold two unlike complexes together are, on the other hand, relatively weak and can be severed in a reversible manner. As shall be seen in section 8 (p. 223), the four component complexes of the electron-transfer system can be functionally and physically recombined to form a single unit with all the apparent enzymatic properties of the intact electron-transfer system.

3. Fractionation of mitochondria and the isolation of the primary enzyme complexes

The classical procedures such as precipitation with salts and cold polar solvents, chromatography, electrophoresis, etc., which are used for the fractionation and purification of water-soluble proteins, are essentially unsuited for the isolation of particulate enzymes. Mitochondria contain about 30–35% lipid by weight[16,17], and the major portion of the protein associated with the particulate fraction of mitochondria is water-insoluble[18]. When mitochondrial particles are extracted with aqueous acetone, almost all the lipid content of the particles is removed[17,19]. The lipid-free material, which is composed essentially of protein, is still insoluble in water and salt solutions. The non-lipid components of the electron-transfer system (flavoproteins, cytochromes, transition metals) are firmly bound to this protein fraction[17,19]. Electron-transfer activity disappears concomitantly with the extraction of lipids and can be restored to the particles by addition of the extracted lipids*. The behavior of the lipid-free material in aqueous media appears to be due to a water-insoluble protein, which presumably acts as a framework for the spatial arrangement of the enzymes and electron carriers of the respiratory system. This protein has been referred to by Green and coworkers as the *structural protein* (see Chapter VI).

Both physical and chemical methods have been employed for the fractionation of mitochondrial particles[16,20]. Mechanical, osmotic and sonic shock have been used to disrupt and fragment mitochondria. The fragmentation by physical means results in the release of the water-soluble components that are enclosed in the interior of mitochondria. Thus, the particulate membrane material can be separated from the water-soluble fraction by differential centrifugation. The components of the electron-transfer system remain associated with the particulate fraction. This fraction catalyzes the oxidation of both reduced NAD and succinate by molecular oxygen. Therefore, it has been referred to by Green and his collaborators as the *electron-transfer particle* (ETP). The comminution of mitochondria by physical means, is however, very unspecific and very limited: usually a spectrum of particles of varying size is obtained, and the fragmentation is effective only to the extent of converting whole mitochondria to ETP. The latter is not further fragmented into enzymatically active fractions.

The fragmentation of ETP has been achieved by the use of a number of chemical reagents such as organic solvents (both polar and non-polar), venom phospholipases, acids and alkali, thioglycollate, cetyldimethylethylammonium bromide, various salts and a host of ionic and non-ionic

* Succinoxidase activity is restored, but reduced NAD oxidase activity is irreversibly destroyed by solvent treatment (see p. 217).

detergents[20]. With the aid of these reagents the electron-transfer system (as associated with lipid and "structural protein") has been fragmented at various points, and particles of various partial activities of the respiratory chain have been isolated[21].

It is now known that most of the above reagents are either detrimental to the enzymatic properties of the electron-transfer system, or inhibitory at high concentrations. Thus many of the early preparations of submitochondrial particles showed very low electron-transfer activity and, due to the rigors of the isolation procedure, deviated from mitochondria or ETP in enzymatic properties and relative concentration of components. As a result, the properties and the composition of such preparations of submitochondrial particles could not be extrapolated to those of the intact electron-transfer system.

Fractionation of a particulate, multicomponent structure such as the electron-transfer system poses a number of problems, which if not considered could lead to inaccurate conclusions. For example, the indiscriminate use of reagents and conditions for fractionation may lead to:

(*1*) *Partial or complete inactivation of the enzyme preparation.* The inactivation need not involve all the components of the segment isolated since partial or complete inactivation of only one component in a sequence would necessarily reflect upon the overall activity of that system. The loss of activity of a sequence could also occur without inactivation (*i.e.*, as a result of denaturation or breakdown) of a component. Since the efficiency of electron transfer in ETP depends very much on the spatial arrangement of the components in a semi-rigid state, disarrangement of this organization or dislocation of a single component in any segment of ETP could result in diminution of the overall activity of that segment.

(*2*) *Suboptimal ratio of components in the enzyme preparation.* Since the electron-transfer components are not present in ETP in a 1:1 ratio (see Chapter VI, p. 309 and Ref. 22), it is possible to obtain in an isolated segment of ETP a ratio of components different from that in the intact system. A survey of the literature shows that in the various submitochondrial particles isolated by various investigators (usually segments containing two or three complexes in sequence) deviation from the intact system in the relative concentration of components is largely due to change in the ratio of one whole complex to another. In other words, the ratio of components found in each of the four complexes remains fairly constant, but the concentration of one complex relative to another may change drastically as a result of various fractionation procedures. Among examples of this sort, preparations of reduced NAD–cytochrome *c* reductase[23] (low in complex III), reduced NAD oxidase[24] (low in complexes I and III) and QH_2 oxidase[25], (low in complex III) may be mentioned.

(3) *Impurities in the enzyme preparation.* Aside from excess lipid or "structural protein" in a segment isolated from ETP, impurities due to contamination by components of unwanted segments are detected usually in two ways: (*a*) by assay for unwanted activities in the isolated segment, and, (*b*) by assay for unwanted components in the isolated segment.

Obviously, the prerequisites for these detection methods are that in the first case the unwanted activity could be assayed, and in the second case the characteristics of the unwanted components would be known. However, since all the individual reactions of the electron-transfer system are not yet amenable to assay and all the components of the respiratory system are not yet characterized, impurities in the product could easily remain undetected. In the latter case even when the characteristics of all the components occurring in a certain fraction are known, it is not always possible to decide which components in that fraction constitute an impurity. A notable example of this situation is the presence of an irreducible (by substrate) cytochrome *b* in the succinic–coenzyme Q reductase preparations of Ziegler *et al.* (*cf.* section 5, p. 219).

In an attempt to obviate many of the above difficulties, Hatefi *et al.* have devised a fractionation procedure whereby the activities represented by complexes I, II, III and IV are isolated in separate fractions from a single batch of mitochondria. As seen in Fig. 1, reduced NAD–Q reductase, QH_2–cytochrome *c* reductase and cytochrome oxidase are all isolated in a highly purified and active state from the same preparation of mitochondria. Ziegler *et al.* have isolated succinic–Q reductase by a procedure not involving fraction E. However, it is known that nearly all the succinic–Q reductase activity of mitochondria concentrates in this fraction.

It is important to note that the fractionation procedure outlined in Fig. 1 is extremely mild. It depends essentially upon combinations of cholate, deoxycholate and salts (KCl, ammonium acetate, ammonium sulfate.) As much as possible, all the reagents and conditions (such as organic solvents, proteinases, and lipases, extremes of pH, strong detergents, *e.g.* Duponol, Tweens, Triton, etc.) that are deleterious to one or another activity of the electron-transfer system have been avoided. All fractionations were performed in the cold and at a controlled pH*. Bile salts were used sparingly since at high concentrations cholate and deoxycholate diminish electron-transfer activity in mitochondria and derived particles[7]. The "solubilizing" effect of the bile salts at such low concentrations was enhanced by concomitant addition of an ionizable, neutral salt (low ionic strength to avoid protein precipitation) such as KCl. As shall be seen in subsequent sections, com-

* pH 8.0 rather than 7.0 because of the greater solubility of bile salts in the more alkaline pH.

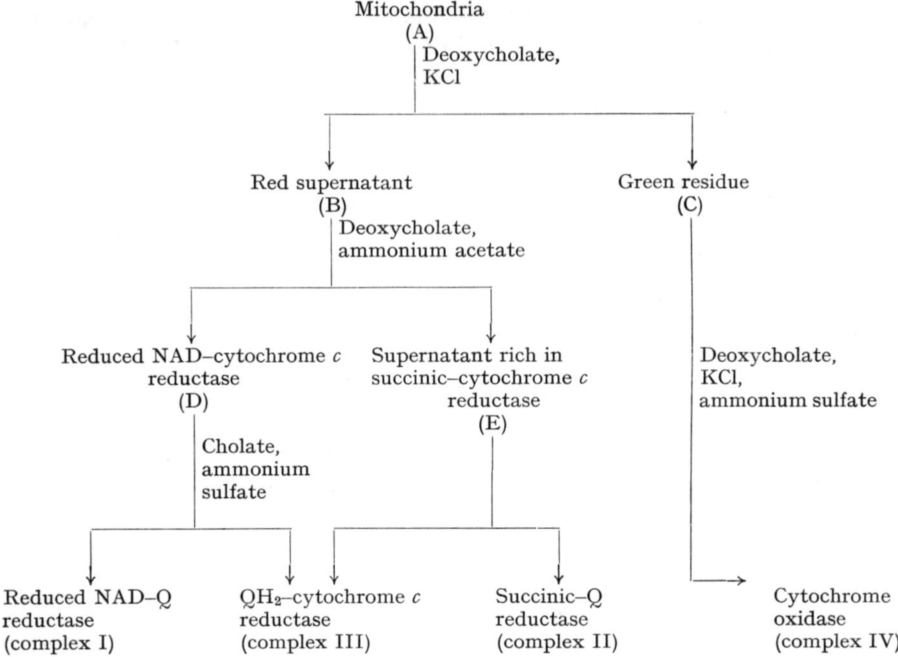

Fig. 1. Profile of the procedure for isolation of the complexes of the electron-transfer system from mitochondria.

plexes II, III and IV catalyze only reactions (5), (6) and (7) respectively. Preparations of complex I exhibit a slight QH_2–cytochrome *c* reductase activity. However, calculations based on the concentration of components of complex III (cytochromes *b* and c_1) in complex I show that the extent of complex III impurity in preparations of complex I is less than 0.8%.

The fractionation procedure described above permits of the following important conclusion. Since the component activities of the electron-transfer system are represented with reasonable recovery of activity units in the four fractions separated from a single batch of mitochondria, and since cross-contamination of activities within the isolated complexes is minimal, it may be safely assumed that the components and activities found in each complex are a reliable estimate of their counterparts in the intact electron-transfer system. Obviously, this conclusion applies best to preparations of reduced NAD–Q reductase, QH_2–cytochrome *c* reductase and cytochrome oxidase.

4. Reduced NAD–coenzyme Q reductase

As seen in Fig. 1, reduced NAD–Q reductase[7] was obtained from preparations of reduced NAD–cytochrome *c* reductase[26–28]. The latter catalyzes the reduction of cytochrome *c* by reduced NAD at a rate of about 60 μmoles/min/mg of protein at 38°. This activity is completely inhibited by amytal (5-ethyl-5-isoamylbarbiturate)[29], antimycin A, 2-hydroxy-3-(2′-methyloctyl)-1,4-naphthoquinone (SN-5949)[30,31], and 2-nonyl-4-hydroxyquinoline-*N*-oxide[32]. The response to these inhibitors is one of the criteria that distinguish the reduced NAD–cytochrome *c* reductase system of the respiratory chain from other enzyme systems of analogous catalytic activity (*cf.* Tables I and III and Ref. 28).

By treatment with potassium cholate and ammonium sulfate, preparations of reduced NAD–cytochrome *c* reductase are resolved into reduced NAD–Q reductase and QH_2–cytochrome *c* reductase[7,12]. The reduced NAD–Q reductase activity is specifically inhibited by amytal[7] and the QH_2–cytochrome *c* reductase activity by antimycin A[12].

Reduced NAD–Q reductase contains, per mg of protein, 1.4–1.5 mμmoles of acid-extractable flavin, 4.2–4.5 mμmoles of coenzyme Q, 26 mμatoms of non-heme iron and about 0.22 mg of lipid[7]. The flavin is the prosthetic group of a flavoprotein enzyme (commonly referred to as the primary reduced NAD dehydrogenase) which initiates electron transfer from reduced NAD into the respiratory system.

(a) *Reduced NAD dehydrogenase flavoprotein*

Several preparations of reduced NAD dehydrogenase have been isolated from mitochondria. The composition and the properties of those preparations derived from the electron-transfer particle are listed in Table I. Since the primary reduced NAD dehydrogenase of the electron-transfer system is a component of reduced NAD–Q reductase, the pertinent characteristics of the latter preparation are also given for comparison.

Recently, Huennekens *et al.*[33,34] (see also Refs. 35 and 87) have established that FMN is the flavin moiety of reduced NAD–Q reductase as well as that of its parent particle, reduced NAD–cytochrome *c* reductase, (fraction D, Fig. 1). The nature of the flavin prosthetic group in dehydrogenases 2–5 (Table I) is also FMN. Cremona and Kearney[36] have recently concurred with the findings of Huennekens *et al.*[33,34] on this point. The former authors have explained that the flavin moiety of their preparation of reduced NAD dehydrogenase (preparation 6, Table I) is also FMN, and that FAD, which in their earlier reports[37] constituted about 30% of the total flavin of their preparation, and riboflavin (also 5′-AMP in amounts equivalent to the molar

References p. 229

TA

REDUCED NAD DEHYDROGENASES DER

Preparation	Nature of flavin	Flavin concentration (mμmoles/mg protein)	Fe concentration (mμatoms/mg protein)
1. Reduced NAD–Q reductase[7]	FMN	1.4–1.5	26
2. Mahler *et al.* dehydrogenase[70]	FMN	13	52
3. DeBernard dehydrogenase[72]	FMN	7	14
4. Mackler dehydrogenase[71]	FMN	9.5	20
5. King and Howard dehydrogenase[91]	FMN	8.3	33
6. Ringler *et al.* dehydrogenase[37]	FMN	0.99	16
7. Ziegler *et al.* dehydrogenase[38]	FAD	14	14–18

[a] This is an amytal–antimycin insensitive cytochrome *c* reduction, and should be distinguished from the particulate reduced NAD–cytochrome *c* reductase system which is inhibited by amytal and antimycin A.

concentration of FMN plus riboflavin) were due to impurities. The dehydrogenase of Ziegler *et al.*[38], however, contains only FAD. Thus the nature of the prosthetic group distinguishes this enzyme from the other dehydrogenases listed in Table I. Green and his associates[39] have suggested recently that the preparation of Ziegler *et al.* is related to lipoyl dehydrogenase[40], and not to the reduced NAD dehydrogenase of the electron-transfer system.

As compared to reduced NAD–Q reductase, preparations 2–6 (Table I), may be divided into two categories:

(*1*) *Preparations 2–5*. Per mg of protein, these preparations have 5–9 times as much flavin as does reduced NAD–Q reductase, and their concentration of non-heme iron relative to flavin is much lower (2–4 times) than it is in reduced NAD–Q reductase (18 times). Preparations 2–5 reduce cytochrome *c* in an amytal–antimycin insensitive manner. This activity is not exhibited by reduced NAD–Q reductase. Similar to reduced NAD–Q reductase, the ferricyanide reductase activity of preparations 2–5 is inhibited by the thiol-binding compound *p*-chloromercuribenzoate (PCMB) (or *p*-chloromercuriphenyl sulfonate, PCMS).

(*2*) *Preparation 6*. This preparation has a lower flavin content (total flavin, *i.e.*, FMN plus FAD and riboflavin impurities, about 50% lower) than reduced NAD–Q reductase. The non-heme iron: flavin ratio of about 16 is approximately the same as the ratio in reduced NAD–Q reductase. Similar to reduced NAD–Q reductase, preparation 6 does not reduce cytochrome *c* but unlike reduced NAD–Q reductase the ferricyanide-reductase activity of preparation 6 is not inhibited by PCMB. The ferricyanide-reductase activity of preparation 6 is, however, considerably higher than that of preparations 2–5, and is more comparable to the ferricyanide-reductase activity of reduced NAD–Q reductase. Similar to the other dehydrogenases listed in Table I, preparation 6 does not reduce coenzyme Q.

THE ELECTRON-TRANSFER SYSTEM

Grams protein per mole of flavin	*Electron acceptor*			*Inhibitor*	
	$K_3Fe(CN)_6$	*Cytochrome c*[a]	*Coenzyme Q*	*PCMS*	*Amytal*
$7 \cdot 10^5$	+	−	+	+	+
$8 \cdot 10^4$	+	+	−	+	−
$1.4 \cdot 10^5$	+	+	−	+	−
$1 \cdot 10^5$	+	+	−	+	−
$1.2 \cdot 10^5$	+	+	−	+	−
$1.1 \cdot 10^6$	+	−	−	−	−
$7.4 \cdot 10^4$	+	−	−	+	−

The characteristics of non-heme iron and absorption spectra of preparations 2–6 are discussed along with those of reduced NAD–Q reductase in sections 4c (p. 210) and 4d (p. 212).

(*b*) *Lipid*

So far as known the general composition of the lipids found in reduced NAD–Q reductase is more or less the same as in ETP. This is also true for complexes II, III, and IV. As pointed out earlier, about 30–35% of the dry weight of ETP is lipid and more than 90% of the latter is phospholipid in nature (see Chapter VI, p. 309). The neutral lipid fraction of mitochondria contains, among other things, carotenoid-like materials[26], coenzyme Q[41] and α-tocopherol[42–45]. Some mitochondrial and bacterial respiratory systems[41] contain vitamin K instead of, or in addition to, coenzyme Q. However, bovine-heart mitochondria appear to be devoid of vitamin K.

Little is known about the involvement of α-tocopherol and the carotenoid-like materials in electron transfer and oxidative phosphorylation. The latter components are not present in the lipid associated with enzyme complexes I, II, III and IV, and may be presumed, therefore, to have no specific function in electron transfer. α-Tocopherol has been implicated, notably by Nason *et al.*[43,44] and Slater *et al.*[42,45], in the reduced NAD oxidase system of mitochondria as well as in oxidative phosphorylation. The lipid extracts of reduced NAD–cytochrome *c* reductase isolated from bovine-heart mitochondria (fraction D, Fig. 1) contain a component which behaves like α-tocopherol[26] by the fluorometric assay procedure of Duggan[46]. The concentration of this component in the non-saponifiable lipids of purified preparations of reduced NAD–cytochrome *c* reductase is about 60% higher than in the total non-saponifiable fraction of mitochondria. However, the increased concentration of this component in reduced NAD–cytochrome *c* reductase does not necessarily prove that α-tocopherol is an integral part of the reduced NAD–cytochrome *c* reductase system: in particles treated with detergent and salt, some lipid redistribution can be expected. The possibility that α-tocopherol serves as a lipid antioxidant has been suggested[47].

Coenzyme Q, or ubiquinone, is a substituted *p*-toluquinone containing two vicinal methoxyl groups and a polyisoprenoid side-chain (I). Depending

(I)

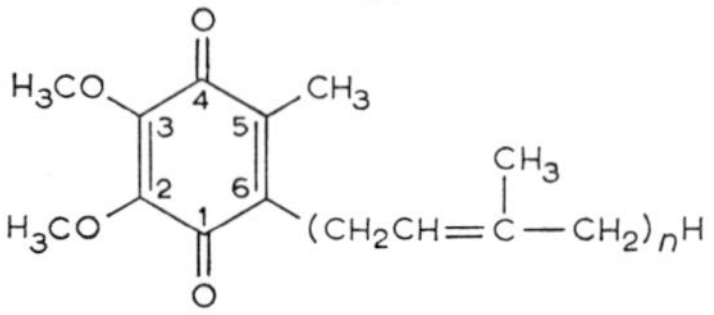

H_3CO, H_3CO, CH_3, $(CH_2CH{=}C(CH_3){-}CH_2)_nH$

Coenzyme Q_{10} $n=10$
Coenzyme Q_9 $n=9$
Coenzyme Q_8 $n=8$
Coenzyme Q_7 $n=7$
Coenzyme Q_6 $n=6$

on the source, the number of isoprenoid units in the terpenyl side-chain may vary from 6 to 10. In man and most other mammals, the predominant form of the quinone is coenzyme Q_{10}, that is, coenzyme Q with ten isoprenoid units in the side-chain. In the rat, the predominant form is coenzyme Q_9.

(II)

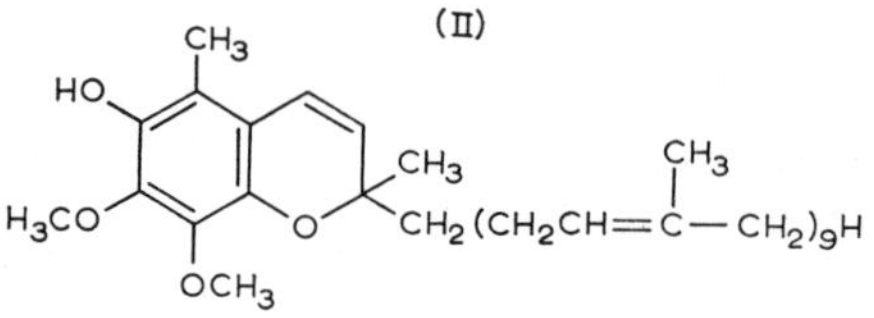

HO, H_3CO, OCH_3, CH_3, $CH_2(CH_2CH{=}C(CH_3){-}CH_2)_9H$

Ubichromenol (50)

(III)

H_3CO, H_3CO, CH_3, $(CH_2{-}CH{=}C(CH_3){-}CH_2)_9{-}CH_2{-}CH_2{-}CH(CH_3){-}CH_3$

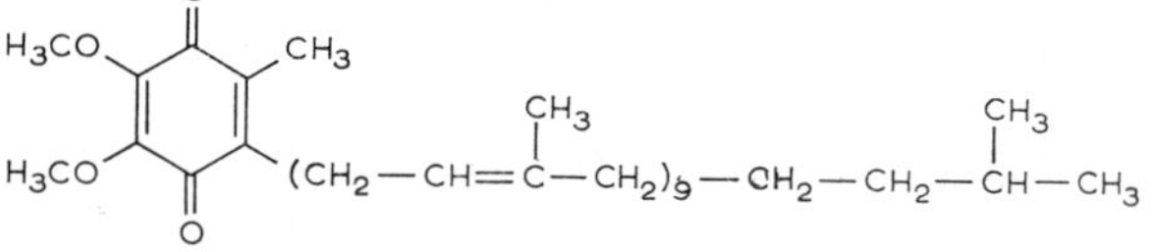

Coenzyme Q_{10} (H—10)

The lower isoprene homologues of coenzyme Q (Q_8, Q_7, Q_6) are mostly found in micro-organisms[41]. In addition to coenzymes Q_6, Q_7, Q_8, Q_9, and Q_{10}, two other derivatives of coenzyme Q have been found in nature. One is the chromenol derivative of coenzyme Q_{10} (ubichromenol(50)) (II)[41,48,49], and the other is a reduced derivative of coenzyme Q_{10}, in which the isoprenoid unit distal to the quinone nucleus is saturated (III)[50]. This compound has been designated coenzyme Q_{10} (H–10). The structural relationship between coenzyme Q and its chromenol derivative is paralleled in nature by other substituted benzoquinones. Thus, α-tocopherol is the chroman derivative of α-tocopherylquinone and solanachromene is the chromene derivative of plastoquinone[41,51–55]. Also, the occurrence of coenzyme Q_{10} and coenzyme Q_{10} (H–10) in biological systems is reminiscent of the natural existence of vitamins K_2 and K_1 (side-chain of K_1 is partially reduced).

In addition to the naturally occurring forms (Q_6 to Q_{10}), all the lower isoprenologues of coenzyme Q (Q_1 to Q_5) have been prepared by unambiguous synthesis. In the vitamin K series, menadione has vitamin K-like activity, and can partially replace vitamin K_1 in the terminal respiratory system of *Mycobacterium phlei*[57–59]. Menadione can restore electron transfer but not phosphorylation[59] to the vitamin K_1-depleted preparations of *M. phlei*. With the coenzyme Q series, however, the terpenyl side-chain (at least one isoprenoid unit as in the case of coenzyme Q_1) is necessary, even under non-phosphorylating conditions, for the proper interaction of coenzyme Q with the appropriate electron-transfer components. Thus, structures which differ from coenzyme Q by possessing a proton or a methyl group (aurantiogliocladin or 2,3-dimethoxy-5,6-dimethyl-1,4-benzoquinone, a naturally occurring compound found in the mold *Gliocladium roseum*) instead of the terpenyl side-chain, cannot substitute for the isoprene homologues of coenzyme Q in the reduced NAD–Q reductase system (*cf.* section 4e, p. 217).

In the oxidized form, all coenzymes Q exhibit a prominent absorption

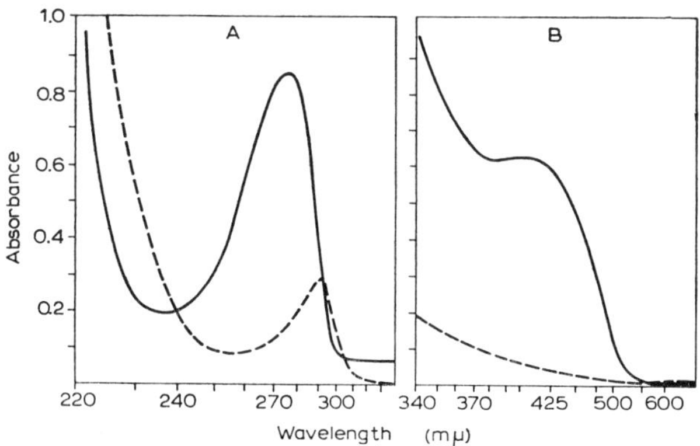

Fig. 2. Absorption spectrum of coenzyme Q in absolute ethanol. Solid line represents oxidized form and the dotted line represents the spectrum obtained after addition of KBH_4. Concentrations used for 1-cm path in mg/ml: ultraviolet range, 0.0425; visible range, 0.75. Data from Crane *et al.* (*Biochim. Biophys. Acta*, 25 (1957) 220).

peak at 275 mμ ($E^{1\%}_{1\,\text{cm}}$ for Q_{10} in ethanol, 165), and a second peak at about 405 mμ ($E^{1\%}_{1\,\text{cm}}$ for Q_{10} in ethanol, 5.9) (Fig. 2). The major peak shifts to 272 mμ when the quinone is dissolved in non-polar solvents such as cyclohexane. The hydroquinone form of coenzymes Q exhibits a single peak at 290 mμ ($E^{1\%}_{1\,\text{cm}}$ for Q_{10} in ethanol, 46.4). During transition from the quinone to the hydroquinone form, the absorption peaks at 275 mμ and 405 mμ disappear and the yellow color of oxidized coenzyme Q fades. The absorbancy change at 275 mμ due to conversion of oxidized to reduced coenzyme Q is equal to 12.26×10^6 cm^2 $\times$ mole^{-1}. Details of chemical and physical properties, distribution in nature, and methods of detection, estimation and isolation of the coenzyme Q group of compounds are reviewed elsewhere[41].

(c) *Non-heme iron*

The electron-transfer particles contain a considerable amount of iron apart from that involved in the heme groups of cytochromes. Green and his associates[60] have referred to this type of iron as non-heme iron. Recent studies have shown that non-heme iron is present in reduced NAD–Q reductase[7], succinic–Q reductase[11], and QH_2–cytochrome *c* reductase[12]. Cytochrome oxidase is the only one of the four enzyme complexes of the electron-transfer system that does not contain non-heme iron[14,15]. The evidence gathered so far is in accord with the possibility that non-heme iron is involved as an electron-transfer component in both the succinic–Q reductase and the reduced NAD–Q reductase systems[61–64].

Preparations of reduced NAD–Q reductase contain about 26 mμatoms of non-heme iron per mg of protein[7]. EPR spectroscopy has shown that a paramagnetic species (g=1.94), believed to be attributable to iron, exists in preparations of reduced NAD–Q reductase. This component is specifically reduced by reduced NAD and is oxidized by coenzyme Q. As estimated from the magnitude of the EPR signal, the concentration of EPR-iron* in preparations of reduced NAD–Q reductase is equivalent to that of flavin. Using the rapid freezing technique of Bray[65,66], Beinert and associates[63,64] have shown by EPR spectroscopy that the rate of appearance of the "iron signal" upon addition of reduced NAD to preparations of reduced NAD–Q reductase is compatible with the overall rate of electron flow in this preparation.

Non-heme iron is also present in the various preparations of reduced NAD dehydrogenase (preparations 2–6, Table I) that are presumably related to the primary dehydrogenase of reduced NAD–Q reductase. The type of non-heme iron present in preparations 2–5 (non-heme iron : flavin ratio = 2–4)

* To be distinguished from other types of non-heme iron which may not exhibit an EPR signal.

does not show an EPR signal, whereas in the preparation of Ringler *et al.* (non-heme iron: flavin ratio = 16) a signal similar to that of reduced NAD–Q reductase has been observed. The dehydrogenase of Ringler *et al.* is converted by incubation at 35–37° (also by acid-ethanol or urea) to a Mahler type enzyme[67–69]. Concomitant with this conversion, the EPR-iron signal is lost. This conversion has been attributed to "thermal breakdown" of the molecule of the Ringler *et al.* dehydrogenase[64,67–69]. Another possibility, however, is that there might actually exist two types of iron in the reduced NAD–Q reductase system. One type of iron might be that which is associated with dehydrogenases of the type 2–5 (Table I). The second type of iron might be that which is present, in addition to the former type, in preparations such as reduced NAD–Q reductase and the Ringler *et al.* dehydrogenase. The minimum molecular weight (per mole of flavin) of preparations 2–5 is about 80–100 · 10^3, and the comparable figures for reduced NAD–Q reductase and the dehydrogenase of Ringler *et al.* are 700 · 10^3 and 1100 · 10^3 respectively. Since the conversion (by heating at 35–37° or other treatments) of the Ringler *et al.* dehydrogenase entails the concomitant loss of a definite amount of iron and protein[69], it is possible that this conversion involves the removal of a ferroprotein of discrete molecular properties. Spectral differences between dehydrogenases 2–5 and reduced NAD–Q reductase (or the Ringler *et al.* dehydrogenase) are in accord with this postulate (see following section).

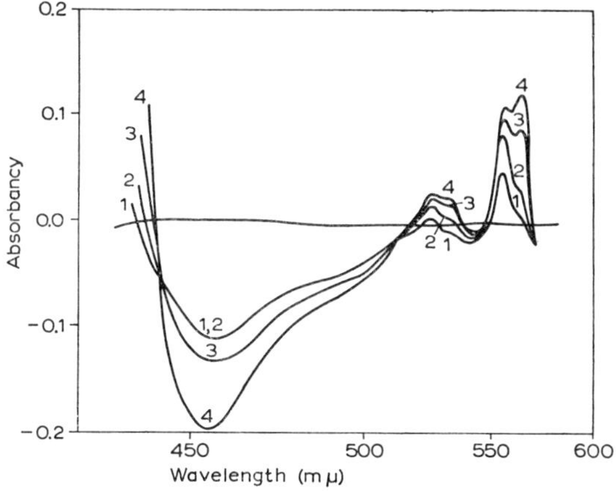

Fig. 3. Difference spectra of reduced NAD–cytochrome *c* reductase reduced with graded amounts of reduced NAD. The solution consisted of 3 mg protein of reduced NAD–cytochrome *c* reductase in 0.66 *M* sucrose and 0.02 *M* K-phosphate, pH 8.0 (total volume, 0.5 ml). The reduction was carried out at 2–4° by adding a total of 29 mμmoles of reduced NAD in the following order: trace 1, 5 mμmoles; trace 2, 10 mμmoles; trace 3, 5 mμmoles; and trace 4, 9 mμmoles. Trace 4 represents complete reduction of reduced NAD–cytochrome *c* reductase. From Hatefi *et al.*[27].

References p. 229

(d) *Possible new components of reduced NAD–Q reductase*

(*1*) In their studies of the reduced NAD–cytochrome *c* reductase system of mitochondria (fraction D of Fig. 1), Hatefi *et al.*[27] concluded in 1961 that the following spectral peculiarities of the enzyme system may be due to an unrecognized component in the preparation:

(*a*) When the reduced NAD–cytochrome *c* reductase preparations were reduced by substrate (*cf.* trace 4 of Fig. 3), the absorbancy change in the vicinity of 460 mμ was twice as great as would have been expected from reduction of the known amount of flavin present (λ_{max}, 450 mμ)*.

(*b*) When preparations of reduced NAD–cytochrome *c* reductase were reduced with graded amounts of reduced NAD, the bleaching at the 460 mμ region** occurred in two different stages: about one-half of the expected change occurred prior to the reduction of cytochromes *b* and c_1, and the other half after the cytochromes were almost completely reduced (Fig. 3).

(*c*) Upon addition of reduced NAD to amytal-treated preparations of reduced NAD–cytochrome *c* reductase, only about one-half of the total expected change at 460 mμ occurred rapidly (Fig. 4). Amytal does not inhibit the reduction of the primary dehydrogenase flavoprotein, but prevents electron transfer beyond this point[7,27].

(*d*) The experiment cited in (*b*) suggests that the excess-absorbancy change at 460 mμ could not be attributed to the reduction of cytochromes *b* and c_1. This point was further confirmed after the isolation of reduced NAD–Q reductase. The latter preparation is essentially free of cytochromes (see p. 204), but its absorbancy change upon reduction at 460 mμ is still twice as much as would be expected from the reduction of its flavin (Fig. 5).

The excess absorbancy in the 460-mμ region is also present in the dehydrogenase preparation of Ringler *et al.*, but not in the dehydrogenases of Mackler[71] and DeBernard[72]. The total absorbancy changes at 450 mμ per unit of flavin are given in Table II for reduced NAD–Q reductase, and for

---

* The extinction coefficient of the flavoprotein was assumed to be equivalent to that of free flavin (ε oxidized minus reduced $= 10.3 \cdot 10^6$ cm$^2 \cdot$ mole^{-1}).

** In reduced preparations of reduced NAD–cytochrome *c* reductase the greatest absorbancy change (bleaching) occurs between 455 mμ and 460 mμ. As seen in Fig. 4 (note especially the difference between trace 1 and trace 3), this change extends from below 420 mμ (*cf.* also spectra of reduced NAD–Q reductase and the dehydrogenase of Ringler *et al.*[37]) to above 500 mμ. For convenience, however, this wide absorbancy change will be identified in the text by its maximum (as it occurs in the spectrum of reduced NAD–cytochrome *c* reductase) at about 460 mμ. In the dehydrogenase of Ringler *et al.*, maximum absorbancy change upon addition of reduced NAD occurs between 420 and 425 mμ. This preparation probably contains the same component that in reduced NAD–cytochrome *c* reductase particles is responsible for the excess absorbancy at 460 mμ. However, the dehydrogenase of Ringler *et al.* does not contain cytochromes; therefore, the bleaching below 450 mμ is not overlapped by the Soret peaks.

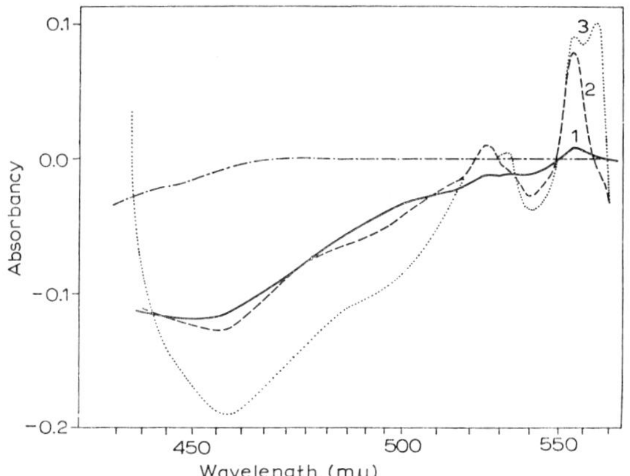

Fig. 4. Difference spectra of reduced NAD–cytochrome *c* reductase. The reference and the experimental cells each contained 3 mg protein of oxidized enzyme in 0.5 ml of a solution of the following composition: sucrose, 0.66 *M*; NaN_3, 2 m*M*; K-phosphate, pH 8.0, 0.02 *M*. Where indicated, 3 m*M* amytal was also present. —·—·—·, oxidized enzyme minus same; ······, reduced NAD-reduced enzyme minus oxidized enzyme; ———, amytal-treated enzyme 10 sec after addition of 60 mμmoles of reduced NAD minus amytal-treated oxidized enzyme; — — — —, same as before 3 min after addition of reduced NAD. The experiments were carried out at 2–4°. From Hatefi *et al.*[27].

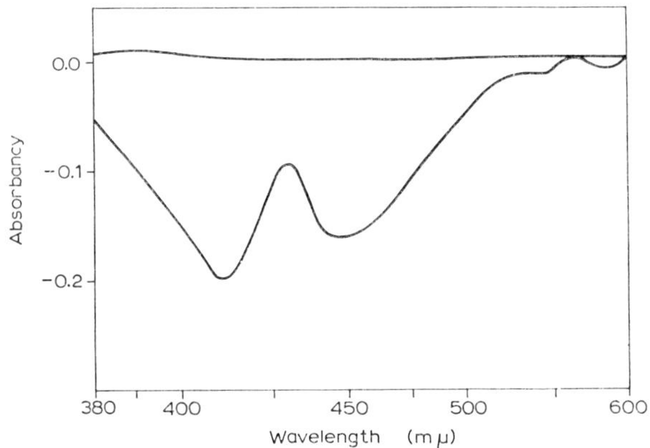

Fig. 5. Difference spectrum of reduced NAD–Q reductase. The reference and the experimental cells each contained 5 mg of oxidized enzyme protein, 20 μmoles of K-phosphate, pH 8.0, and 0.66 *M* sucrose in 1.0 ml. Straight line, oxidized enzyme minus same; curved line, after addition of reduced NAD (0.15 μmole) to the experimental cell. From Hatefi *et al.*[7].

References p. 229

the dehydrogenases of Ringler *et al.*[37], Mackler[71] and DeBernard[72] (preparations 6, 4, 3, Table I, respectively). It is seen that this value is the same for the first two preparations and about half as much for the Mackler and the DeBernard preparations. In the latter preparations, all of the 450-mμ

TABLE II

ABSORBANCY OF REDUCED NAD–COENZYME Q REDUCTASE AND RELATED DEHYDROGENASES AT 450 mμ

Preparation	*Δ450 mμ in absorbancy units (oxidized minus reduced enzyme)*	*Protein concentration (mg/ml)*	*Flavin concentration (mμmoles/mg protein)*	*Δ450 mμ/mμmole flavin/ml (absorbancy units)*
Reduced NAD–Q reductase[7]	−0.17	5	1.4	$24.3 \cdot 10^{-3}$
Ringler *et al.* dehydrogenase[37]	−0.22	9.25	0.99	$24.2 \cdot 10^{-3}$
Mackler dehydrogenase[71]	−0.14	1.3	9.5	$11.4 \cdot 10^{-3}$
DeBernard dehydrogenase[72]	−0.228	2.88	7	$11.3 \cdot 10^{-3}$

Values in columns 2, 3 and 4 were derived for the respective preparations from data of Fig. 5, p. 213, Fig. 4 of Ref. 37, Fig. 3 of Ref. 71, and Fig. 2 of Ref. 72.

change can be attributed to flavin reduction. Such excess absorbancies have been observed also in other iron-containing flavoproteins (xanthine oxidase), and have been assumed to be due to iron–protein complexes[73]. Similar to preparations of reduced NAD–Q reductase, xanthine oxidase and aldehyde oxidase also exhibit EPR signals[74] in the region of $g=1.94$.

Preparations of succinic–Q reductase also exhibit an excess absorbancy in the 460-mμ region. In this case only about 25% of the change (due to reduction with hydrosulfite) at 460 mμ can be attributed to the reduction of flavin (*cf.* Fig. 6). So far as known, non-heme iron is the only component common to both the succinic–Q reductase and reduced NAD–Q reductase preparations. Per mg of protein, the concentration of non-heme iron in succinic–Q reductase (34–38 mμatoms/mg protein) is 1.4 times as much as in reduced NAD–Q reductase. Curiously enough, the ratio of the excess absorbancies in succinic–Q reductase (75%) and reduced NAD–Q reductase (50%) is about the same (75/50=1.5).

There is no definitive proof as yet to indicate the existence of a discrete iron–protein component in, or separable from, reduced NAD–Q and succinic–

Q reductases. However, circumstantial evidence of the nature discussed in this and the preceding sections hints towards this possibility. As pointed out earlier, the conversion of the Ringler *et al.* dehydrogenase (minimal value for $s_{20}=12.6$) to a Mahler-type enzyme involves the loss of non-heme

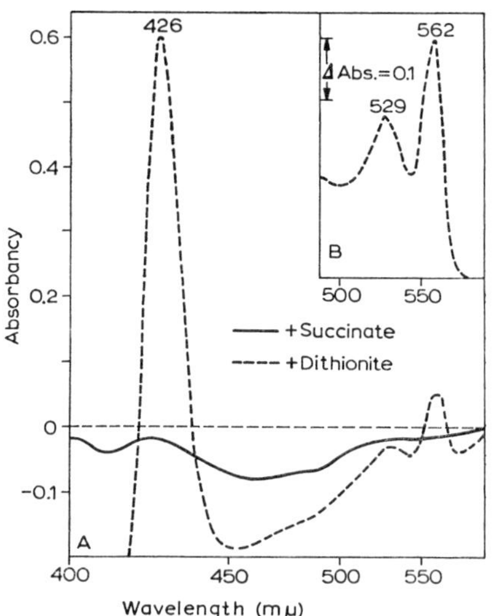

Fig. 6. Difference spectra of succinic–Q reductase (oxidized *vs.* reduced). The enzyme was dissolved in 0.1 *M* phosphate buffer, pH 7.4, at a final concentration of 1.16 mg protein per ml. The enzyme was first reduced with succinate (——) (100 μmoles/ml) and then with dithionite (— — — —). From Ziegler[11].

iron and a substantial diminution in particle size ($s_{20}=5.6$)[69]. The diminution in size is not due to disaggregation of the Ringler *et al.* dehydrogenase; it is rather due to removal of a non-flavoprotein moiety. Therefore, the properties of the subtracted protein, not reported by the authors, might shed considerable light on the possible involvement of a discrete ferroprotein component in the reduced NAD–Q reductase system.

A curious property of dehydrogenases 2–5, not shared by the Ringler *et al.* dehydrogenase, is that these preparations are capable of reducing cytochrome *c* at the expense of reduced NAD. Unlike the cytochrome *c* reductase activity of mitochondria or the particulate reduced NAD–cytochrome *c* reductase, the cytochrome *c* reductase activity of the above flavoproteins is not inhibited by amytal and antimycin A. Although cytochrome *c* reduction by dehydrogenases 2–5 is in all probability a fortuitous, unphysiological reaction, it is not peculiar to these flavoproteins of mitochondrial origin.

References p. 229

Soluble flavoproteins have been isolated from porcine liver[75], yeast[76,77], and *E. coli*[78], which are capable of reducing cytochrome *c* (*cf.* Table III). In addition, the particulate reduced NAD–cytochrome b_5 reductase of microsomes is also capable[79] of reducing cytochrome *c*. Since in the mamma-

TABLE III

FLAVOPROTEINS CAPABLE OF INTERACTING WITH CYTOCHROME *c*

Source	*Substrate*	*Prosthetic groups*	*Reference*
Porcine liver	Reduced NADP	FAD	75
Yeast	Reduced NADP	FMN	76
Yeast	D(—)-Lactate	FAD, Zn	77
E. coli	Reduced NAD	FAD	78

lian system, cytochrome *c* is restricted to mitochondria and is not available to the extramitochondrial medium, the reduction of cytochrome *c* by preparations such as the porcine-liver flavoprotein and the microsomal reduced NAD–cytochrome b_5 reductase also appears to be a chemical possibility of dubious physiological significance. In 1956, Mahler and Glenn[80] pointed out that the cytochrome *c* reductase activity of the Mahler enzyme may be due to the fact that cytochrome *c* simulates a single-electron acceptor which in mitochondria is the natural acceptor for the primary dehydrogenase. If as discussed above, the natural acceptor for dehydrogenases 2–5 turns out to be a ferroprotein, the ability of cytochrome *c* (also other iron-chelates) to replace such an entity is then understandable.

(2) It has been shown by Hatefi *et al.*[26] that electron-transfer activity in preparations of reduced NAD–cytochrome *c* reductase (fraction D of Fig. 1) is inhibited by PCMS. Arsenite at concentrations up to $7 \cdot 10^{-4}$ *M* was not inhibitory. It was later shown that the site of PCMS inhibition resides in the reduced NAD–Q reductase segment of reduced NAD–cytochrome *c* reductase[7]. Reduced NAD–Q reductase activity was strongly inhibited (>90%) at concentrations of PCMS as low as 6 μM. The inhibitory effect of PCMS has been shown also in reduced NAD dehydrogenases (*cf.* Table I) related to the dehydrogenase of reduced NAD–Q reductase. Huennekens, Mackler and their associates have found that the dehydrogenase of Mackler (*cf.* Table I) contains 10–12 titratable thiol groups per molecular weight of 100000 (calculated per mole of flavin). When flavin is removed from the dehydrogenase, the number of titratable sulfhydryl groups is doubled. During titration of the oxidized enzyme with mercurials, dehydrogenase activity declines slowly and is abolished only when about 10–12 equivalents of the inhibitor are added. However, when the enzyme is preincubated with reduced NAD, complete inhibition of activity by PCMB corresponds to inactivation of 1–2 thiol groups. The effect of reduced NAD does not seem

to be due to conversion of a disulfide group to a vicinal dithiol, since arsenite and Cd^{2+} are not effective inhibitors of the dehydrogenase.

(*3*) When mitochondrial particles are treated with venom phospholipase or with organic solvents, reduced NAD oxidase activity is destroyed[81,82]. Similar effects are observed when reduced NAD–Q reductase preparations are subjected to the above reagents[7]. These observations suggest that lipid is necessary for activity of the reduced NAD–Q reductase system. Since organic solvents are not likely to break down lipid molecules contained in preparations of reduced NAD–Q reductase, their deleterious effect might be a consequence of their ability to remove or disarrange the lipids. The role of lipid in reduced NAD–Q reductase might be somewhat similar to the function of phospholipids in the β-hydroxybutyric dehydrogenase system. It has been shown by Jurtshuk *et al.*[83] that lecithin is necessary for the activity of purified preparations of D(–)β-hydroxybutyric dehydrogenase of heart mitochondria. The phospholipid requirement has been interpreted by these authors to be due to the ability of lecithin to provide a hydrophobic area on the enzyme surface at the site of enzyme–substrate interaction. Therefore, since coenzyme Q is water-insoluble, it is possible that in the reduced NAD–Q reductase system, lipid is necessary for solvation and positioning of the quinone. Removal of the lipids from mitochondria by extraction with aqueous acetone also results in the loss of succinic oxidase activity. However, unlike reduced NAD oxidase, succinic oxidase activity can be restored to the particles by addition of the extracted lipids.

(*4*) EPR studies have shown that, in addition to the "iron signal", three other signals also appear and disappear when reduced NAD–Q reductase preparations are reduced and oxidized[7]. One of these signals has been identified as the flavin free radical. The other two originate in components as yet unidentified. Recent *g* value determinations of Beinert and associates have suggested that the unidentified signals cannot be due to free radicals[84].

(*e*) *Enzymatic properties of reduced NAD–Q reductase*

The reactions catalyzed by reduced NAD–Q reductase may be divided into two categories:

(*1*) The reactions that are catalyzed by the reduced NAD dehydrogenase component of the enzyme complex, such as the reduction of ferricyanide, methylene blue, and other oxidoreduction dyes. These reactions are unaffected by amytal, but are inhibited by PCMS (*cf.* Table IV).

(*2*) The reactions that are catalyzed by the entire machinery of the enzyme complex. These reactions are limited to the reduction of the isoprene homologs of coenzyme Q and are inhibited by amytal and PCMS. Thus, preparations of reduced NAD–Q reductase are highly specific for the isoprene homo-

References p. 229

TABLE IV

THE ENZYMATIC PROPERTIES OF REDUCED NAD–COENZYME Q REDUCTASE[d]

Substrate	*Electron acceptor*	*Specific activity*[b]
Reduced NAD	coenzyme Q_1	27.0[c]
Reduced NAD	coenzyme Q_2	7.0
Reduced NAD	coenzyme Q_{10}	< 0.1
Reduced NAD	2,3-dimethoxy-5,6-dimethyl-benzoquinone[a]	< 3.0
Reduced NAD	2,3-dimethoxy-5-methyl-benzoquinone[a]	< 2.6
Reduced NAD	menadione[a]	3.1
Reduced NAD	vitamin K_1	0.0
Reduced NAD	α-tocopherylquinone	0.0
Reduced NAD	$K_3Fe(CN)_6$[a]	200–210
Reduced NADP ($\pm NAD^+$)	coenzyme Q_1	0.0
Reduced NAD	lipoic acid	0.0
Succinate	coenzyme Q_1 or cytochrome *c*	0.0

[a] These reactions are not inhibited by amytal.
[b] Specific activity is expressed as micromoles of electron acceptor (one electron equivalent) reduced per min per mg of protein at 38°.
[c] At infinite concentration of electron acceptor, the Q_1 reductase activity[87] is 50.
[d] Data from Hatefi *et al.*[7].

logues of coenzyme Q. Structures such as vitamin K_1 and α-tocopherylquinone are not reduced by reduced NAD–Q reductase. Also, analogues of coenzyme Q such as 2,3-dimethoxy-5-methylbenzoquinone and 2,3-dimethoxy-5,6-dimethylbenzoquinone are reduced very slowly and their reduction is not inhibited by amytal. The latter compounds, as well as menadione, appear to be reduced by reduced NAD–Q reductase in the same manner as are the electron acceptors of the first category.

As seen in Table IV, coenzyme Q_1 is more rapidly reduced by preparations of reduced NAD–Q reductase than coenzyme Q_2, while coenzyme Q_{10} is not easily reduced. The different reducibility of coenzyme Q isoprenologues by the particulate enzyme system of reduced NAD–Q reductase appears to be in part due to assay difficulties. Coenzyme Q_1 is slightly water-soluble, and coenzyme Q_2 forms a fine suspension in the assay medium. Coenzyme Q_{10}, on the other hand, is utterly insoluble in aqueous media. Moreover, the bulk of the molecule of coenzyme Q_{10} plus the fact that the sites on the enzyme system already contain native coenzyme Q_{10} may further complicate interaction with added Q_{10}. It is important to note, however, that the bound coenzyme Q_{10} of reduced NAD–Q reductase preparations is rapidly reduced by added reduced NAD.

In addition to amytal, demerol (*N*-methyl-4-phenyl-4-carbethoxypiperidine) also inhibits the reduced NAD–Q reductase system. The concentration of amytal required to abolish (> 90%) reduced NAD–Q reductase activity is about 3 m*M*, whereas demerol can inhibit the system to the same extent at about 0.5 m*M* concentration. As pointed out earlier, reduced NAD–Q

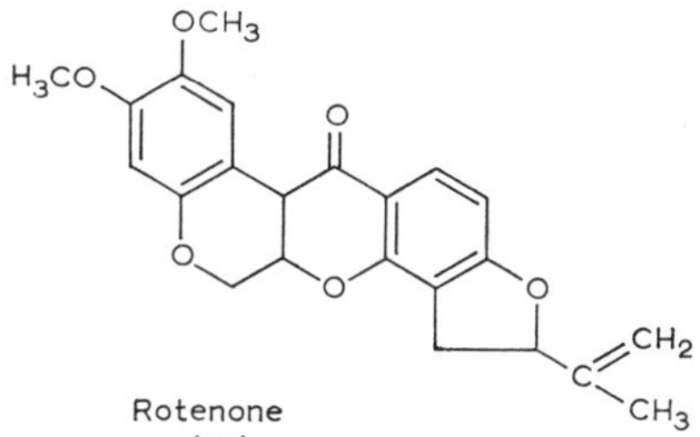

Rotenone
(IV)

reductase activity is also abolished by treating the enzyme preparation with organic solvents (acetone, ethanol, butanol, *tert.*-amyl alcohol), high concentration of detergents (bile salts, Triton) or snake venom (boiled *Naja naja* or *Crotalus* venom). More recently it has been shown that rotenone (IV)[85,86] also inhibits the reduced NAD–Q reductase system[87].

5. Succinic–coenzyme Q reductase

Succinic–Q reductase was isolated from bovine-heart mitochondria by Ziegler *et al.*[8–11]. The enzyme preparation contains 4.2–4.6 mμmoles of flavin, 34–38 mμatoms of non-heme iron and 0.18–0.20 mg of lipid per mg of protein. It also contains 4.4–4.8 mμmoles of cytochrome *b* (λ_{max}, 562 mμ, 529 mμ and 426 mμ) (*cf.* Fig. 6). The flavoprotein moiety of succinic–Q reductase appears to be the same as the succinic dehydrogenase discussed elsewhere in this volume by Singer. Thus, the succinic dehydrogenase activity of succinic–Q reductase, like that of Singer's preparation[88–90], can be measured with phenazine methosulfate as electron acceptor.

The cytochrome *b* in preparations of succinic–Q reductase seems not to participate in electron transfer from succinate to coenzyme Q since it is not reduced and oxidized during the course of the reaction. It has been suggested[11] that this cytochrome may be an entry point into the respiratory chain for electrons derived from extramitochondrial oxidative reactions. In this respect, Ziegler has shown that the dithionite-reduced cytochrome *b* of succinic–Q reductase can be oxidized in the presence of fumarate[11].

References p. 229

Another possibility is that cytochrome *b* is not an integral part of the succinic–Q reductase system, but rather that it is associated with complex II only because of limitations of the particular isolation procedure used by Ziegler *et al.* As discussed in section 3 (p. 201), coisolation of unrelated components of the electron-transfer system is a potential hazard of any fractionation procedure. An example of this type is the occurrence of cytochrome *c* in the reduced NAD dehydrogenase of DeBernard (prep. 3, Table I) isolated from ETP. This preparation is in the same category as the reduced NAD dehydrogenases of Mahler *et al.*[70], King and Howard[91] and Mackler[71]. It differs from these preparations in that it contains a tightly bound cytochrome *c*. That certain mitochondrial proteins are capable of binding cytochromes is demonstrated by Green and associates in their studies of the interaction between preparations of "structural protein" and various hemoproteins (see Chapter VI, p. 309). It is conceivable, therefore, that a certain fractionation procedure would dislodge a cytochrome from one segment of the respiratory chain and thereby allow it to become attached to an unrelated segment.

Although no definite proof is available for the role of iron in the succinic–Q reductase system, several observations suggest an electron-transfer function for this component:

(*1*) The succinic dehydrogenase of Singer *et al.* contains about 4 atoms of iron per mole of flavin and is completely devoid of Q reductase activity[11,88–90]. The preparation of Ziegler *et al.*, on the other hand, contains about 8 atoms of iron per mole of flavin and catalyzes the reduction of coenzyme Q at a rate[11] of about 50 μmoles per min per mg of protein at 38°.

(*2*) Anaerobic dialysis of succinic–Q reductase against ethylenediaminetetraacetate results in the extraction of about one-half of the non-heme iron. This treatment also results in an irreversible loss of Q reductase activity[11].

(*3*) By EPR spectroscopy a paramagnetic species ($g=1.94$) believed to be ferrous iron, has been detected in preparation of succinic–Q reductase[63]. The signal due to this species appears and disappears rapidly when the enzyme preparation is reduced by succinate and oxidized by coenzyme Q or other reagents[63]. Malonate, which inhibits succinate oxidation, also inhibits the appearance of this signal.

(*4*) Succinic–Q reductase, but not succinic–phenazine methosulfate reductase activity is inhibited by 2-thenoyltrifluoroacetone[11]. This compound is capable of chelating iron. It should be pointed out, however, that Beinert *et al.*[63] have shown that 2-thenoyltrifluoroacetone does not inhibit the appearance of the "iron signal" in succinic–Q reductase. It only inhibits the disappearance of the signal when the reduced enzyme preparation is oxidized with coenzyme Q.

6. QH_2–cytochrome *c* reductase

As discussed in sections 4 and 5, reduced NAD–Q reductase and succinic–Q reductase systems reduce coenzyme Q to yield the dihydro form of coenzyme Q, QH_2. The QH_2–cytochrome *c* reductase system then transfers the electrons from reduced coenzyme Q to cytochrome *c*[12]. Preparations of QH_2–cytochrome *c* reductase[12] contain per mg of protein about 8.5 mμmoles of cytochrome *b*, 4.1 mμmoles of cytochrome c_1, 10–12 mμatoms of non-heme iron and about 0.4 mg of lipid. The difference (reduced minus oxidized) spectrum of QH_2–cytochrome *c* reductase is given in Fig. 7.

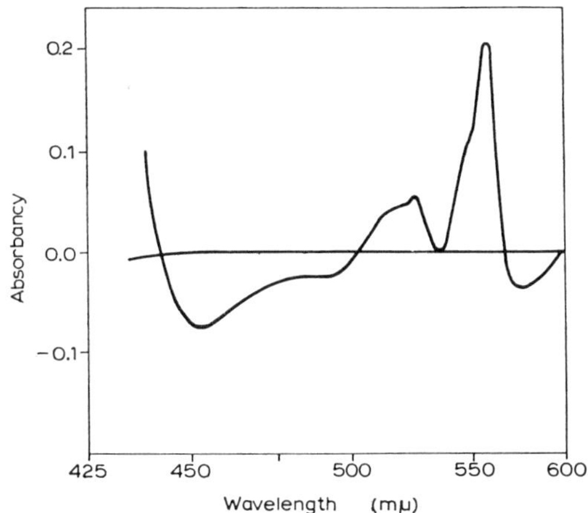

Fig. 7. Difference spectrum of QH_2–cytochrome *c* reductase. The reference and the experimental cells each contained, in a volume of 1 ml, 1.8 mg of oxidized enzyme protein, 20 μmoles of K-phosphate, pH 8.0, and 0.66 *M* sucrose. Straight line, oxidized enzyme minus same; curved line, after addition of $Na_2S_2O_4$ to the experimental cell. From Hatefi *et al.*[5].

When QH_2 is added to preparations of complex III, both cytochromes and non-heme iron are reduced. Cytochrome c_1 is completely reduced by QH_2 but cytochrome *b* is only partially reduced (*ca.* 50% at pH 8.0)[12]. Also reduced cytochrome *b*, but not reduced cytochrome c_1 can be reoxidized by addition of oxidized coenzyme Q. All the reduced components of the enzyme preparation are oxidizable in the presence of catalytic amounts of cytochrome *c* plus cytochrome oxidase. So far as known, cytochrome c_1 is the final electron carrier in the QH_2–cytochrome *c* reductase complex. Reduced cytochrome c_1 reacts directly with cytochrome *c* (*cf.* p. 193 of Ref. 25). Whether or not cytochrome *b* is a requisite intermediate for electron

References p. 229

transfer from QH_2 to cytochrome *c* is not known. Nor is at this time the role of non-heme iron clear. When examined by EPR spectroscopy, reduced preparations of QH_2–cytochrome *c* reductase exhibit a characteristic signal at $g = 1.9$ which is accompanied[92] by a broad peak at about $g = 1.8$. Iron chelators, such as bathophenanthroline sulfonate, 8-hydroxyquinoline, *o*-phenanthroline, phenyl-2-pyridylketoxime and 2,4,6-tripyridyl-*S*-triazine, have no effect on the enzymatic activity of QH_2–cytochrome *c* reductase[12], although this may be due to inaccessibility of the iron.

QH_2–cytochrome *c* reductase has by far the most active enzyme complex in the electron-transfer system. Preparations of the enzyme catalyze the reduction of cytochrome *c* by QH_2 at a rate of about one mmole per min per mg of protein at 38° (corresponding to a Q_{O_2} of more than 320000). This activity is completely inhibited[12] by antimycin A, 2-nonyl-4-hydroxy-quinoline-*N*-oxide, and SN-5949. It has been shown that antimycin A inhibits the reduction of cytochrome c_1 and the oxidation of QH_2 and cytochrome *b*. Therefore, the site of antimycin A inhibition is localized in this segment of the electron-transfer system between coenzyme Q and cytochrome *b* on one side and cytochrome c_1 on the other. Rieske and Zaugg[93] have reported that the splitting of QH_2–cytochrome *c* reductase by ammonium sulfate and high concentrations of bile salts into a cytochrome *b*-rich fraction and a cytochrome c_1-rich fraction is inhibited by addition of antimycin A_3 to the enzyme preparation.

As would be expected, QH_2 can reduce cytochrome *c* in the absence of any added enzyme. However, the rate of this reaction is extremely slow and is not enhanced by addition of purified preparations of cytochrome c_1, cytochrome *b*, or both.

7. Cytochrome *c* oxidase

Cytochrome *c* oxidase is discussed in detail in Chapter V (p. 232). However, as far as the Fowler *et al.*[14] preparation of cytochrome oxidase referred to in Fig. 1 is concerned, its salient features may be summarized here.

The procedure as outlined in Fig. 1 is extremely simple and rapid, and results in a very high yield of cytochrome oxidase. Thus, 1 gram of mitochondrial protein yields approximately 40 mg of purified cytochrome oxidase. The enzyme preparation contains 8.4–8.7 mμmoles of heme *a*, 9.4 mμatoms of copper and about 0.35 mg of lipid* per mg of protein**. The preparation

* Personal communication from Dr. D. C. Wharton.

** The analytical values and specific activities reported here are based on protein determination by the biuret method. As compared to the micro-Kjeldahl procedure, the biuret method overestimates the protein of cytochrome oxidase preparations by about 30% (*cf.* Ref. 14).

is virtually free of cytochromes *b*, c_1 and *c*. The first order velocity constant (k_1) for the oxidation of ferrocytochrome *c* is about 42–45 sec^{-1}/mg oxidase protein/ml, and V_{max} at infinite concentration of ferrocytochrome *c* was calculated by extrapolation (from a plot of velocity *versus* the reciprocal of ferrocytochrome *c* concentration) to be 136 μmoles cytochrome *c* oxidized per min per mg of enzyme protein.

With respect to concentration of components and enzymatic activity, the above preparation of cytochrome oxidase is almost identical to the preparation of Griffiths and Wharton[15], which was isolated essentially according to an earlier procedure devised by Hatefi[13]. The two preparations of cytochrome oxidase also show identical EPR signals due to cupric ions. Since cuprous ion does not have a net magnetic moment, the EPR signal disappears upon treatment of the enzyme preparation with ferrocytochrome *c*. The reduction level of copper (determined concomitantly by EPR spectroscopy and chemical methods) closely parallels the reduction of heme *a* under various conditions.

Cytochrome oxidase prepared according to the procedure outlined in Fig. 1 has one important advantage over the earlier preparations of Griffiths and Wharton, namely, it is better suited for reconstitution with complex III (see below). Since reconstitution requires the physical interaction of two or more daughter particles, surface complementarity of the combining particles is probably an essential factor. It is therefore possible that this feature is better preserved, by the mild procedure of isolation, in the cytochrome oxidase preparation of Fowler *et al.*[14] than in the preparation of Griffiths and Wharton[15].

8. The reconstitution of the electron-transfer system

The isolated and purified enzyme complexes of the electron-transfer system are capable of combining with each other in the expected functional sequence[5,6,28,41,94,95]. For example, when reduced NAD–Q reductase and QH_2–cytochrome *c* reductase are mixed together, a physical and functional union takes place between the respective particles to create a new unit with all the apparent properties of highly active preparations of reduced NAD–cytochrome *c* reductase. Premixing of the daugter particles at high concentration is a necessary preliminary for reconstitution to take place[5,6]. If the two enzyme particles are added without premixing to the assay mixture, their combined activity is not realized.

Reconstitution occurs with a definite ratio between complexes I, II, III, and IV. Thus, titration of a fixed amount of one complex with graded amounts of another gives a typical saturation curve (Fig. 8). Maximum reconstituted activity is achieved at a definite weight ratio between the

References p. 229

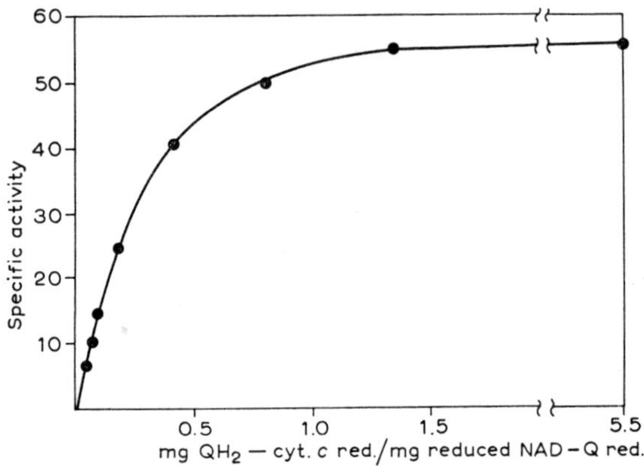

Fig. 8. Specific activity of reconstituted reduced NAD–cytochrome *c* reductase as a function of the relative amounts of the combining particles, QH_2–cytochrome *c* reductase and reduced NAD–Q reductase. For details *cf.* Hatefi *et al.*[6].

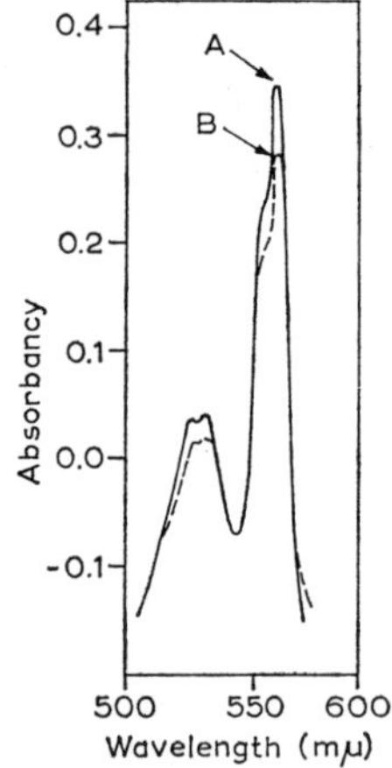

	Activity/mg total protein of mixture	*Activity/mg total protein of the washed pellet*
A	19.7	25.0
B	12.4	22.5

A QH_2–cytochrome *c*/reduced NAD–Q = 1.7
B QH_2–cytochrome *c*/reduced NAD–Q = 3.0

Fig. 9. Reconstitution of reduced NAD–cytochrome *c* reductase in a mixture of reduced NAD–Q reductase (complex I) and excessive amounts of QH_2–cytochrome *c* reductase (complex III). Mixture A contains the correct (approx.) combining ratio of complexes I and III; mixture B contains almost twice as much III as is needed to combine with particles of I present. Before differential centrifugation and removal of excess III, the activity of mixture B per mg protein is considerably lower than that of mixture A. After centrifugation and removal of excess III, which remains in the supernatant layer, the activity of B per mg protein approaches that of A. The absorption spectra of the pellets sedimented from mixtures A and B indicate the near-constancy of the concentrations of cytochromes *b* and c_1 (components of III) in the reconstituted reduced NAD–cytochrome *c* reductase particles. From Hatefi *et al.*[6].

combining complexes. This ratio remains fairly constant from one preparation of the complexes to the next[6,95]. When an excess of one complex is mixed with limiting amounts of another, the newly reconstituted particle can be separated by differential centrifugation from the remainder of the complex that was added in excess (*cf.* Fig. 9)[6]. The reconstituted particles prepared in this manner still contain the same ratio of the combining complexes as determined by titration experiments.

The forces that hold together complexes I, II, and III are very strong, whereas reconstituted systems involving complexes III and IV are somewhat less strong[6,94,95]. A similar pattern is also observed during fractionation of the electron-transfer system. Complex IV can be separated readily from a fraction containing complexes I, II, and III, but the resolution of the latter fraction into the individual complexes is not so easily achieved (*cf.* Fig. 1). Systems reconstituted from complexes I + III, II + III, or I + II + III can be subjected to centrifugation and repeated washing by dispersing the sedimented particles after each centrifugation in buffered sucrose solution. These treatments do not cause dissociation of the reconstituted systems, nor do they diminish the high overall activity that is diagnostic of tight reconstitution. Furthermore, reconstituted preparations can be stored in the frozen state and thawed repeatedly without significant loss of activity[6]. It has been possible, therefore, to reconstruct from enzyme complexes I, II, III, and IV the entire electron-transfer chain as well as all of the possible subunits thereof (*cf.* Table V). All the reconstituted units are functionally indistinguishable from their unfractionated counterparts in mitochondria. As a result of these and other studies, Hatefi *et al.*[5,6] have proposed the functional arrangement of the various components of the electron-transfer system to be as shown in Fig. 10. The first three complexes (reduced NAD–Q reductase, succinic–Q reductase and QH_2–cytochrome *c* reductase) are functionally linked together by way of coenzyme Q, and QH_2–cytochrome *c* reductase and cytochrome oxidase by way of cytochrome *c*. Whereas the flavoproteins, the three non-heme irons and cytochromes $a + a_3$, b, and c_1 are

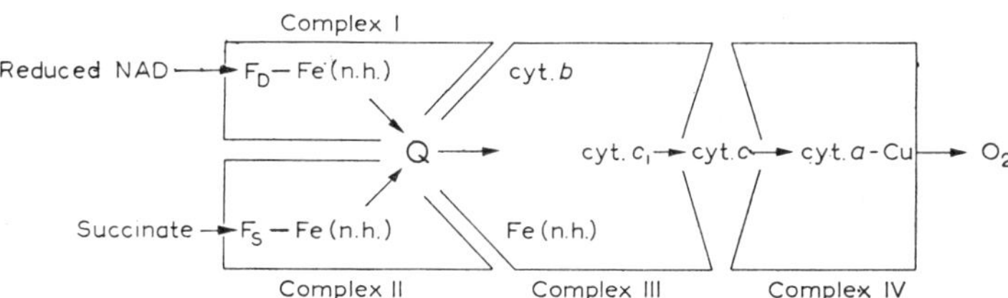

Fig. 10. A schematic representation of the functional complexes and their arrangement in the electron-transfer system. F_D, reduced NAD dehydrogenase flavoprotein; F_S, succinic dehydrogenase flavoprotein; Fe(n.h.), non-heme iron. The Roman numerals refer to the same enzyme complexes as in Fig. 1 and p. 204.

TABLE V

RECONSTITUTION OF THE ELECTRON-TRANSFER SYSTEM[a]

Electron-transfer complex[b]	*Overall activity*[c]	*Inhibitors*
I	Reduced NAD–Q reductase	Amytal
II	Succinic–Q reductase	2-Thenoyltrifluoroacetone (TTFA)
III	QH_2–cytochrome *c* reductase	Antimycin A
IV	Cytochrome *c* oxidase	KCN
I + III	Reduced NAD–cytochrome *c* reductase	Amytal, antimycin A
II + III	Succinic–cytochrome *c* reductase	TTFA, antimycin A
I + II + III	Reduced NAD, succinic–cytochrome *c* reductase	Amytal, TTFA, antimycin A
I + III + IV + cytochrome *c*	Reduced NAD oxidase	Amytal, antimycin A, KCN
II + III + IV + cytochrome *c*	Succinic oxidase	TTFA, antimycin A, KCN
I + II + III + IV + cytochrome *c*	Reduced NAD, succinic oxidase	Amytal, TTFA, antimycin A, KCN

[a] From Hatefi[41].
[b] The Roman numerals refer to the electron-transfer complexes on p. 204 and in Fig. 1.
[c] For the specific activity of the reconstituted systems and other details *cf*. Hatefi *et al.*[6].

fixed components of the four complexes, coenzyme Q and cytochrome *c* are not. Coenzyme Q and cytochrome *c*, which provide the functional links between complexes I, II, III and IV, can be extracted easily from the respiratory particles and readily restored to them[19].

Reconstitution of certain enzymatic activities at the level of apoenzyme plus coenzyme has been known for many years. Recently, Reed and his associates have achieved the resolution and reconstitution of the α-keto acid dehydrogenase complexes, each of which is composed of several enzymes and coenzymes[96–99]. Another excellent example of this phenomenon is the physical reconstitution of tobacco mosaic virus from its nucleic acid core and protein envelope, which has been achieved in the laboratory of Fraenkel-Conrat[100]. The reconstitution of the electron-transfer system from its four multicomponent enzyme complexes shows that this process can occur in nature at a still higher level of complexity.

In recent years, the technique of electron microscopy has enabled histologists to discover a high degree of order in many biological structures. These ordered structures are seen in plasma membrane, the nerve myelin sheath, the mitochondrial particulate fraction, the chloroplast, and the outer segment of retinal photoreceptors[101]. In mitochondria, the ordered structures are concerned with electron transfer from reduced NAD and succinate to molecular oxygen and the capture of the energy liberated in these oxidation reactions. In chloroplasts and the outer segment of retinal photoreceptors, the ordered structures convert light energy into chemical energy. According to Sjostrand[101], all these ordered structures appear to have a basic elementary component which he has termed the "membrane element". The "membrane element" appears to be composed essentially of a sandwich of lipid and protein (see also the discussion of structural protein by D. E. Green in Chapter VI, p. 309). The detailed chemical composition of the "membrane element" is not necessarily the same in different types of structure and varies according to the function of each system.

As seen in Table VI, each complex of the electron-transfer system is

TABLE VI

THE COMPONENTS OF THE FOUR PRIMARY COMPLEXES OF THE ELECTRON-TRANSFER SYSTEM

Enzyme complex	*Components*
I. Reduced NAD–Q reductase	Flavoprotein, transition metal (Fe), lipid
II. Succinic–Q reductase	Flavoprotein, transition metal (Fe), lipid
III. QH_2–cytochrome *c* reductase	Hemoproteins, transition metal (Fe), lipid
IV. Cytochrome *c* oxidase	Hemoproteins, transition metal (Cu), lipid

References p. 229

composed essentially of: (*a*) one or more electron carriers each of which is attached as prosthetic group to a protein molecule; (*b*) a transition metal which appears (at least in complexes I, II, and IV) to participate in electron transfer; and (*c*) lipid. In view of Sjostrand's concept of an elementary structure, this simple pattern which is repeated in the general composition of the four complexes of the electron-transfer system might prove to be more than a mere coincidence.

Another important feature of the complexes of the electron-transfer system is that each complex (specifically complexes I, III and IV) plus its respective substrate appears to comprise the biochemical unit for energy conservation in mitochondria. As seen in reactions 8–11, the primary event for the conservation of oxidative energy as a "high-energy" bond appears to occur as a result of interaction between the complex and its respective substrate[102,103]. Depending on whether the complex is I, III or IV (the potential span of complex II, *i.e.*, succinate to coenzyme Q, does not yield sufficient energy for the formation of a "high-energy" bond), the substrate would be respectively reduced NAD, QH_2 or ferrocytochrome *c*. Once electron transfer from substrate to complex and the formation of a "high-energy" bond occur, the principal act of energy conservation in the cell is accomplished. The subsequent reactions of oxidative phosphorylation (*cf.* reactions 9–11) are merely an iso-energetic transfer of the "high-energy" bond to the final acceptor, ADP. In oxidative phosphorylations involving complexes I and IV, it is known that the "factor" in reactions 9–11 is protein in nature. The work of Boyer suggests that the linkage between phosphate and the protein factor involves the imidazole residues[104].

$$\text{Substrate (reduced)} + \text{complex (oxidized)} \rightarrow \text{substrate (oxidized)} \sim \text{complex (reduced)} \quad (8)$$

$$\text{Substrate (oxidized)} \sim \text{complex (reduced)} + \text{factor} \rightarrow \text{substrate (oxidized)} \sim \text{factor} + \text{complex (reduced)} \quad (9)$$

$$\text{Substrate (oxidized)} \sim \text{factor} + P_i \rightarrow P \sim \text{factor} + \text{substrate (oxidized)} \quad (10)$$

$$P \sim \text{factor} + \text{ADP} \rightarrow \text{ATP} + \text{factor} \quad (11)$$

Much still remains to be learned about the exact details of electron transfer and oxidative phosphorylation. However, the discovery of the complexes as the basic device for electron transfer and energy conservation has considerably simplified the problems that lie ahead.

NOTE ADDED IN PROOF

The reports of Webster *et al.* (see refs. 102, 103, and the discussion above) concerning coupling factors and intermediates for oxidative phosphorylation at the cytochrome *c*–oxygen segment of the electron-transfer system were retracted at the Meeting of the Federation of the American Society for Experimental Biology in April 1965.

REFERENCES

1 N. A. Rao, S. P. Felton, B. Mackler and F. M. Huennekens, in preparation.
2 A. W. Linnane and D. M. Ziegler, *Biochim. Biophys. Acta*, 29 (1958) 630.
3 A. L. Lehninger and C. T. Gregg, *Biochim. Biophys. Acta*, 78 (1963) 12.
4 C. T. Gregg and A. L. Lehninger, *Biochim. Biophys. Acta*, 78 (1963) 27.
5 Y. Hatefi, A. G. Haavik and D. E. Griffiths, *Biochem. Biophys. Res. Communs.*, 4 (1961) 441, 447.
6 Y. Hatefi, A. G. Haavik, L. R. Fowler and D. E. Griffiths, *J. Biol. Chem.*, 237 (1962) 2661.
7 Y. Hatefi, A. G. Haavik and D. E. Griffiths, *J. Biol. Chem.*, 237 (1962) 1676.
8 D. M. Ziegler and K. A. Doeg, *Arch. Biochem. Biophys.*, 85 (1959) 282.
9 D. E. Green, D. M. Ziegler and K. A. Doeg, *Arch. Biochem. Biophys.*, 85 (1959) 280.
10 K. A. Doeg, S. Kreuger and D. M. Ziegler, *Biochim. Biophys. Acta*, 41 (1960) 491.
11 D. M. Ziegler, *I.U.B. Symposium on Biological Structure and Function, Stockholm*, Academic Press, New York, 1960, p. 253.
12 Y. Hatefi, A. G. Haavik and D. E. Griffiths, *J. Biol. Chem.*, 237 (1962) 1681.
13 Y. Hatefi, *Biochim. Biophys. Acta*, 30 (1958) 648.
14 L. R. Fowler, S. H. Richardson and Y. Hatefi, *Biochim. Biophys. Acta*, 64 (1962) 170.
15 D. E. Griffiths and D. C. Wharton, *J. Biol. Chem.*, 236 (1961) 1850.
16 D. E. Green and Y. Hatefi, *Science*, 133 (1961) 13.
17 D. E. Green and S. Fleischer, *Biochim. Biophys. Acta*, 70 (1963) 554.
18 D. E. Green, H. Tisdale, R. S. Criddle and R. M. Bock, *Biochem. Biophys. Res. Communs.*, 5 (1961) 81.
19 R. L. Lester and S. Fleischer, *Biochim. Biophys. Acta*, 47 (1961) 358; *Arch. Biochem. Biophys.*, 80 (1959) 470.
20 D. E. Green, *Plenary Lecture, Vth International Congress of Biochemistry, Moscow, 1961*, Pergamon, Oxford, 1963.
21 D. E. Green, *Advan. Enzymol.*, 21 (1959) 73.
22 D. E. Green and D. C. Wharton, *Biochem. Z.*, 338 (1963) 335.
23 B. Mackler and N. Penn, *Biochim. Biophys. Acta*, 24 (1957) 294.
24 F. L. Crane and J. L. Glenn, *Biochim. Biophys. Acta*, 24 (1957) 100.
25 Y. Hatefi, *Biochim. Biophys. Acta*, 34 (1959) 183.
26 Y. Hatefi, A. G. Haavik and P. Jurtshuk, *Biochim. Biophys. Acta*, 52 (1961) 106.
27 Y. Hatefi, P. Jurtshuk and A. G. Haavik, *Biochim. Biophys. Acta*, 52 (1961) 119.
28 Y. Hatefi, in P. D. Boyer, H. Lardy and K. Myrbäck (Eds.), *The Enzymes*, Vol. 7, Academic Press, New York, 1963, p. 495.
29 L. Ernster, O. Jalling, H. Löw and O. Lindberg, *Exptl. Cell Res.*, 3 (1955) 124.
30 E. G. Ball, C. B. Anfinsen and O. Cooper, *J. Biol. Chem.*, 168 (1947) 257.
31 A. E. Reif and V. R. Potter, *J. Biol. Chem.*, 205 (1953) 279.
32 J. W. Lightbown and F. L. Jackson, *Biochem. J.*, 63 (1956) 130.
33 F. M. Huennekens, S. P. Felton, N. Appaji Rao and B. Mackler, *J. Biol. Chem.*, 236 (1961) PC57.
34 N. Appaji Rao, S. P. Felton, F. M. Huennekens and B. Mackler, *J. Biol. Chem.*, 238 (1963) 449.
35 A. J. Merola, R. Coleman and R. Hansen, *Federation Proc.*, 22 (1963) 466.
36 T. Cremona and E. B. Kearney, *Nature*, 200 (1963) 542.
37 R. L. Ringler, S. Minakami and T. P. Singer, *J. Biol. Chem.*, 238 (1963) 801.
38 D. M. Ziegler, D. E. Green and K. A. Doeg, *J. Biol. Chem.*, 234 (1959) 1916.

39 D. E. Green, R. Coleman and A. J. Merola, *IEG Group 1*, No. 59 (1963).
40 V. Massey, in P. D. Boyer, H. Lardy and K. Myrbäck (Eds.), *The Enzymes*, Vol. 7, Academic Press, New York, 1963, p. 275.
41 Y. Hatefi, *Advan. Enzymol.*, 25 (1963) 275.
42 J. Bouman and E. C. Slater, *Biochim. Biophys. Acta*, 26 (1957) 624.
43 A. Nason and I. R. Lehman, *J. Biol. Chem.*, 222 (1956) 511.
44 A. Nason and F. D. Vasington in D. Rudnick (Ed.), *Cell, Organism and Milieu*, The Ronald Press, New York, 1959, p. 63.
45 E. C. Slater, J. P. Colpa-Boonstra and J. Links, in G. E. W. Wolstenholme and C. M. O'Connor (Eds.), *Ciba Foundation Symposium, Quinones in Electron Transport*, Little Brown, Boston, 1961, p. 161.
46 D. E. Duggan, *Arch. Biochem. Biophys.*, 84 (1959) 116.
47 H. Zalkin and A. L. Tappel, *Arch. Biochem. Biophys.*, 88 (1960) 113.
48 R. A. Morton, *Nature*, 182 (1958) 1764.
49 D. L. Laidman, R. A. Morton, J. Y. F. Paterson and J. F. Pennock, *Chem. Ind. (London)*, (1959) 1019; *Biochem. J.*, 74 (1960) 541.
50 P. H. Gale, N. R. Trenner, B. H. Arison, A. C. Page Jr. and K. Folkers, *Biochem. Biophys. Res. Communs.*, 12 (1963) 414.
51 F. L. Crane, *Plant Physiol.*, 34 (1959) 128.
52 N. R. Trenner, B. H. Arison, R. E. Erickson, C. H. Shunk, D. E. Wolf and K. Folkers, *J. Am. Chem. Soc.*, 81 (1959) 2026.
53 C. N. Planta, E. Billeter and M. Kofler, *Helv. Chim. Acta*, 42 (1959) 1278.
54 M. Kofler, A. Langemann, R. Ruegg, L. H. Chopard-dit-Jean, A. Rayroud and O. Isler, *Helv. Chim. Acta*, 42 (1959) 2252.
55 R. L. Lester and F. L. Crane, *J. Biol. Chem.*, 234 (1959) 2169.
56 A. F. Brodie, M. M. Weber and C. T. Gray, *Biochim. Biophys. Acta*, 25 (1957) 448.
57 A. F. Brodie, *J. Biol. Chem.*, 234 (1959) 398.
58 A. F. Brodie and J. Ballantine, *J. Biol. Chem.*, 235 (1960) 226, 232.
59 P. J. Russell and A. F. Brodie, in G. E. W. Wolstenholme and C. M. O'Connor (Eds.), *Ciba Foundation Symposium, Quinones in Electron Transport*, Little Brown, Boston, 1961, p. 205.
60 D. E. Green, in O. H. Goebler (Ed.), *Enzymes: Units of Biological Structure and Function*, Academic Press, New York, 1956, p. 465.
61 H. Beinert and R. H. Sands, *Biochem. Biophys. Res. Communs.*, 1 (1959) 171; 3 (1960) 41.
62 H. Beinert and W. Lee, *Biochem. Biophys. Res. Communs.*, 5 (1961) 40.
63 H. Beinert, W. Heinen and G. Palmer, Enzyme models and enzyme structure, *Brookhaven Symp. Biol.*, 15 (1962) 229.
64 H. Beinert, G. Palmer, T. Cremona and T. P. Singer, *Biochem. Biophys. Res. Communs.*, 12 (1963) 432.
65 R. C. Bray, *Biochem. J.*, 81 (1961) 189.
66 R. C. Bray and R. Pettersson, *Biochem. J.*, 81 (1961) 194.
67 T. Cremona, E. B. Kearney, M. Villavicencio and T. P. Singer, *Biochem. Z.*, 338 (1963) 407.
68 H. Watari, E. B. Kearney and T. P. Singer, *J. Biol. Chem.*, 238 (1963) 4063.
69 H. Watari, E. B. Kearney, T. P. Singer, D. Basinski, J. Hauber and C. J. Lusty, *J. Biol. Chem.*, 237 (1962) PC 1731.
70 H. R. Mahler, N. K. Sarkar, C. P. Vernon and R. A. Alberty, *J. Biol. Chem.*, 199 (1952) 585.
71 B. Mackler, *Biochim. Biophys. Acta*, 50 (1961) 141.
72 B. DeBernard, *Biochim. Biophys. Acta*, 23 (1957) 510.
73 R. C. Bray, in P. D. Boyer, H. Lardy and K. Myrbäck (Eds.), *The Enzymes*, Vol. 7, Academic Press, New York, 1963, p. 533.
74 K. V. Rajagopalan, V. Aleman, P. Handler, W. Heinen, G. Palmer and H. Beinert, *Biochem. Biophys. Res. Communs.*, 8 (1963) 220.
75 B. L. Horecker, *J. Biol. Chem.*, 183 (1950) 593.
76 E. Haas, B. L. Horecker and T. R. Hogness, *J. Biol. Chem.*, 136 (1940) 747.

[77] A. P. Nygaard, in P. B. Boyer, H. Lardy and K. Myrbäck (Eds.), *The Enzymes*, Vol. 7, Academic Press, New York, 1963, p. 557.
[78] A. F. Brodie, *Methods in Enzymology*, Vol. II, (1955) p. 693.
[79] N. Penn and B. Mackler, *Biochim. Biophys. Acta*, 27 (1958) 539.
[80] H. R. Mahler and J. L. Glenn, in W. D. McElroy and B. Glass (Eds.), *Inorganic Nitrogen Metabolism*, Johns Hopkins, Baltimore, 1956, p. 575.
[81] A. P. Nygaard, *J. Biol. Chem.*, 204 (1953) 655.
[82] F. L. Crane, C. Widmer, R. L. Lester and Y. Hatefi, *Biochim. Biophys. Acta*, 31 (1959) 476.
[83] P. Jurtshuk Jr., I. Sekuzu and D. E. Green, *J. Biol. Chem.*, 238 (1963) 3595.
[84] H. Beinert, Personal communication.
[85] L. Ernster, G. Dallner and G. I. Azzone, *J. Biol. Chem.*, 238 (1963) 1124.
[86] H. Löw and I. Vallin, *Biochim. Biophys. Acta*, 69 (1963) 361.
[87] A. J. Merola, R. Coleman and R. Hansen, *Biochim. Biophys. Acta*, 73 (1963) 638.
[88] T. P. Singer, E. B. Kearney and V. Massey, *Advan. Enzymol.*, 18 (1957) 65.
[89] T. P. Singer, E. B. Kearney and P. Bermath, *J. Biol. Chem.*, 223 (1956) 599.
[90] T. P. Singer and E. B. Kearney, in P. D. Boyer, H. Lardy and K. Myrbäck (Eds.), *The Enzymes*, Vol. VII, Academic Press, New York, 1963, p. 383.
[91] T. E. King and R. L. Howard, *Biochim. Biophys. Acta*, 37 (1960) 557; *J. Biol. Chem.*, 237 (1962) 1686.
[92] H. Beinert, Personal communication.
[93] J. S. Rieske and W. S. Zaugg, *Biochem. Biophys. Res. Communs.*, 8 (1962) 421.
[94] L. R. Fowler and Y. Hatefi, *Biochem. Biophys. Res. Communs.*, 5 (1961) 203.
[95] L. R. Fowler and S. H. Richardson, *J. Biol. Chem.*, 238 (1963) 456.
[96] M. Koike, L. J. Reed and W. R. Carroll, *J. Biol. Chem.*, 235 (1960) 1924.
[97] M. Koike and L. J. Reed, *J. Biol. Chem.*, 235 (1960) 1931.
[98] M. Koike, P. C. Shah and L. J. Reed, *J. Biol. Chem.*, 235 (1960) 1939.
[99] M. Koike, L. J. Reed and W. R. Carroll, *J. Biol. Chem.*, 238 (1963) 30.
[100] H. Fraenkel-Conrat and R. C. Williams, *Proc. Natl. Acad. Sci. (U.S.)*, 41 (1955) 690.
[101] F. S. Sjostrand, *Radiation Res., Suppl. 2* (1960) 349.
[102] G. Webster, *Biochem. Biophys. Res. Communs.*, 13 (1963) 399.
[103] D. E. Green, R. E. Beyer, H. Hansen, A. L. Smith and G. Webster, *Federation Proc.*, 22 (1963) 1460.
[104] P. D. Boyer, *Science*, 141 (1963) 1147.
[105] F. L. Crane, Y. Hatefi, R. L. Lester and C. Widmer, *Biochim. Biophys. Acta*, 25 (1957) 220.

Chapter V

Cytochromes and Cytochrome Oxidase

K. OKUNUKI

Department of Biology, Faculty of Science, Osaka University, Toyonaka, Osaka (Japan)

Histohaematin or myohaematin, which had been discovered by MacMunn[1–3] in muscle tissue, was renamed by Keilin[4] in 1925 as cytochrome. It was widely distributed in the biological kingdom and had physiological functions as a hydrogen (electron) carrier in cellular respiration. At that time, Keilin also assumed the presence of "indophenol oxidase" with the function of oxidizing ferrocytochrome in intact cells. He proposed an interesting hypothesis for the mechanism of cellular respiration, by which oxygen consumption was interpreted as being the result of enzymatic oxidation of ferrocytochrome, which is non-autoxidizable, and reduction by the substrate–dehydrogenase system. Furthermore, he proposed that cytochrome was not a single compound, but consisted of three different components, which were named cytochrome *a*, *b* and *c*, depending on the position of the reduced α band of these components from longer to shorter wavelengths, respectively. Since Yakushiji and Okunuki[5] later discovered a new cytochrome component and named it cytochrome c_1, there are four components of cytochrome in most aerobic cells, and these form a cytochrome system functioning normally in the transfer of electrons released from the substrates of respiration. However, cytochromes can best be defined as those intracellular compounds with haemochromogen-like absorption spectra which appear to function by the transfer of electrons. Electrons are transferred in these cases by virtue of the ability of the haem-bound iron atoms to undergo reversible oxidation and reduction between ferric and ferrous states. The term haemoprotein is used here to imply not only typical iron-porphyrin proteins but also those conjugated proteins whose prosthetic groups are iron chelates of chlorins and other compounds structurally related to porphyrins. If the classification of cytochromes should be made on the basis of the types of haems they contain, regardless of their catalytic functions and physicochemical properties, only four types of haem have so far been known to occur in cytochromes, as shown in Fig. 1. These are haem *a*, protohaem, haem *c* and so-called haem a_2, which are distinguished by the positions of their α bands in the absorption spectrum

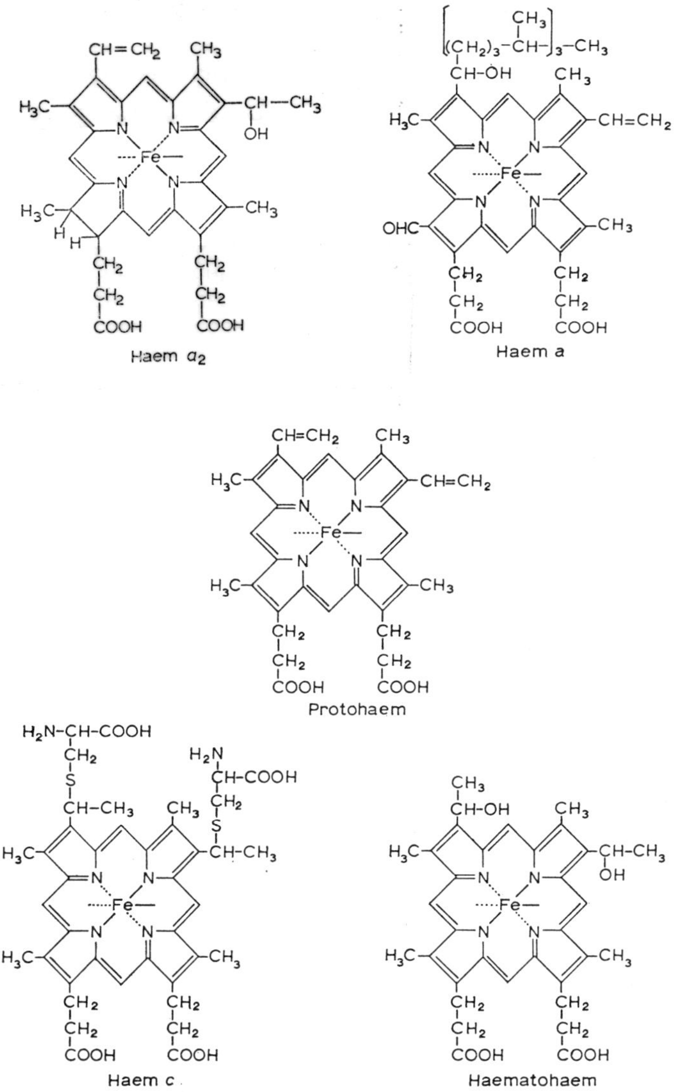

Fig. 1. Chemical structure of the prosthetic groups of cytochromes.

References p. 305

of the pyridine haemochromogens. Thus we can at present distinguish the four groups of cytochromes corresponding to these haems, as indicated in Table I.

TABLE I

HAEMS AND THEIR CYTOCHROME SOURCES

Characteristic haem	*Position of α-band of pyridine haemochromogen (mμ)*	*Cytochrome having these haems*
Haem a_2 (green haem)	613–620	a_2
Haem a (dichroic haem)	585–587	a, a_1
Protohaem (red haem)	557	b, b_1, b_2, b_3, b_5, b_6, b_7, h
Haem c	550	c, c_1, c_2, c_3, c_4, c_5, b_4, f

As is well known, the haem moieties of many haemoproteins are split from their protein moieties by treatment with HCl–acetone, and haem a_2, a and protohaem may then be determined spectroscopically by the pyridine–haemochromogen reaction. On the other hand, the haems of c-type cytochromes are not released by such treatment, since two of the side-chains of haem c have covalent thioether linkages with cysteine residues of the protein. These linkages are broken by Ag_2SO_4 treatment, by which haematohaem is recognized as the prosthetic groups of the c-type cytochromes. Moreover, it is thought to be characteristic that cytochromes a, a_1 and a_2 exhibit affinity towards oxygen and carbon monoxide while the c-type cytochromes are inert in this regard.

Since non-autoxidizable cytochrome c has been isolated in a soluble state from several sources, it is generally believed that the cytochrome components (a, b, c and c_1) in most aerobic cells are not autoxidizable, except the cytochrome a_3 of Keilin and Hartree[8]. Bacterial cells, which lack cytochrome a, contain cytochromes a_1 and a_2 which function as the terminal oxidase of cellular respiration[9–14]. Indeed, it was clearly demonstrated that the presence of cytochrome oxidase (the cytochrome a_3 of Keilin and Hartree[8]) is essential for the oxidation of ferrocytochrome c, even in its crystalline form. However, there were various problems remaining to be solved, including the following: (*1*) What is autoxidizable cytochrome oxidase? (*2*) Are cytochrome components other than cytochrome c non-autoxidizable? (*3*) In what manner are cytochrome components arranged in the electron-transferring system?

With respect to question (*1*), interpretations will be described in another section. In regard to question (*2*), whether the cytochrome components other than cytochrome *c* are non-autoxidizable or not, it is supposed that cytochrome *b* functions as a terminal oxidase in cyanide and carbon monoxide-insensitive respiration since it is an autoxidizable component and does not combine with cyanide and carbon monoxide. Many papers support the proposition that ferrocytochrome *a* is an electron donor for cytochrome a_3, but this is not supported by the evidence described below. As for cytochrome c_1, it was indicated that ferrocytochrome c_1 can readily be oxidized by ferricytochrome *c* and that the haem moiety of insoluble cytochrome c_1 is the same as that of soluble cytochrome *c*, although the protein moiety of the former is acidic, while that of the latter is basic. At present, we are able to establish evidence that ferrocytochrome c_1 is a natural electron donor of cytochrome oxidase, made up of cytochromes *a* and *c*. It is therefore likely that the cytochrome c_1 is the only cytochrome-component performing simple electron transfer, because cytochrome *c* has more complicated functions than hitherto known. Concerning question (*3*), it has been inferred that electrons released from the substrate might be serially transferred along the cytochrome chain based on the E'_0 values of each component in the cytochrome system[15]. However, such a supposition is unreliable without modifications, since as a step towards understanding the mechanism of cellular respiration, cytochromes have been purified and interesting new results are obtained.

A. PREPARATION OF CYTOCHROME COMPONENTS*

1. Isolation, purification and crystallization of cytochrome *a*

The purification procedure was developed from that of Yakushiji and Okunuki[5]. The solubilization of cytochrome *a* from particulate heart-muscle suspensions can be effected in the presence of both cholate and ammonium sulphate, but not by incubation with cholate alone. A concentration of over 2% cholate is required to solubilize the cytochrome, corresponding to 0.75 mg of cholic acid per mg of protein. At this concentration of cholate a clear extract is obtained by addition of 25% saturation of ammonium sulphate. This solubilization procedure for cytochrome *a* can also be applied to insoluble cytochrome components such as cytochromes *b* and c_1. Although the purified cytochrome *a* becomes soluble in non-ionic detergents such as Emasol 1130**, these detergents are not preferred for the extraction of

* In this article the author deals only with the purified components of cytochrome having direct relation with the cytochrome oxidase.

** Emasol 1130, polyoxyethylene–sorbitan–monolaurate, Kas Soap Company Ltd., Tokyo (Japan).

References p. 305

p. 235, footnote 2, Kas Soap Company should read Kao Soap Company.

cytochrome *a* from a particulate preparation in place of cholate or deoxycholate.

Generally speaking, all the cytochrome components bound to mitochondria are first extracted through increase of ionic strength in the presence or absence of cholate, depending on their properties and whether they are insoluble or soluble in water. Then, even in the case of cytochrome *c*, which is soluble in water, it is necessary to elevate the ionic strength up to 0.25–0.4, depending on the source of the material. Naturally, in this case it is extracted in the absence of cholate. Regarding the purification and crystallization of cytochrome *a*, see Okunuki[16]. Concerning the properties of cytochrome *a*, several lines of evidence indicate that cytochrome *a* can function as cytochrome oxidase in collaboration with cytochrome *c*, which will be described in detail below.

2. Isolation, purification and crystallization* of cytochrome *c*

(*a*) *General properties of crystalline cytochrome c's*

The positions of absorption peaks of crystalline baker's yeast cytochrome *c* are as follows: In the oxidized form, 530 mμ, 410 mμ, 358 mμ and 275 mμ; in the reduced form, 550 mμ, 520 mμ, 415 mμ, 316 mμ and 275 mμ, a typical haemochromogen spectrum.

Table II summarizes some properties of crystalline cytochrome *c*'s from various sources. Although the ratio of $A^{\text{red}}_{550\,\text{m}\mu}/A_{280\,\text{m}\mu}$ is applied for estimation of the purity, it is, however, of interest that the ratio and the E_0' value become larger than that reported for native cytochrome *c* when the original conformation of the native protein is somewhat modified or unfolded for some reason. For example, very slightly modified cytochrome *c* prepared by treatment with trichloroacetic acid, is normally able to crystallize in neutral solution, but shows the higher ratio of 1.38, indicating a decrease in extinction at 280 mμ. Moreover, cytochrome *c* sufficiently modified to form the dimer[30] shows a strong affinity for cation exchange resin and has a higher E_0' value[31] of 0.32 V. It was clearly demonstrated by Yamanaka *et al.*[32] that the greater the modification of cytochrome *c*, the more autoxidizable it is. Hence it is necessary with regard to non-autoxidizability of cytochrome *c* to state whether the preparation has the native conformation or the modified one. At any rate, it is established that native cytochrome *c* is non-autoxidizable under physiological conditions. Since it seems certain that the N atoms of tetrapyrrole rings and of two histidine residues from the peptide chain satisfy the six ligands of a haem iron of cytochrome *c*, and the haem is so

* Regarding the preparation of crystalline cytochrome *c*'s see Hagihara *et al.*[17–23] and Okunuki[24].

TABLE II

SUMMARY OF PROPERTIES OF CRYSTALLINE CYTOCHROME *c*'S FROM VARIOUS SOURCES

Sources	$A_\alpha \times 10^{-6}$ (cm²/mole)	$A^{\text{red}}_{550\,\text{m}\mu}/A_{280\,\text{m}\mu}$	E'_0 (at pH 7.0)	Iso-electric point	Mol. wt.
Human heart muscle[25]		1.20[a]			12750 (ref. 26)
Beef heart muscle	28.2 (27.7)	1.25–1.30	+0.255	about 10	12400
Beef kidney muscle		1.26–1.28			
Pig heart muscle		1.28			
Pigeon breast muscle		1.16–1.20			
Tunny heart muscle		1.02–1.05			
Bonito heart muscle		1.02–1.05			
Wheat germ		1.0			
Saccharomyces oviformis, strain M_2		1.28			12700
Pseudomonas cytochrome *c*-551 (ref. 27)	28.3	1.27[b]	+0.286 (at pH 6.5)	4.7	7600–8100
Porphyra cytochrome *c*-553 (ref. 28)	21.7	1.04[c]	+0.335	3.5	13600
Rhodopseudomonas cytochrome-552 (ref. 29)		1.01[d]	+0.33	7.7	15600

[a] The iron content of this electrophoretically pure crystalline preparation is 0.41%, lower than that reported for beef heart (0.45%) and yeast (0.44%) cytochrome *c*'s.
[b] This value shows the ratio of $(A^{\text{red}}_{551\,\text{m}\mu} - A^{\text{red}}_{570\,\text{m}\mu})/A_{280\,\text{m}\mu}$.
[c] $A^{\text{red}}_{553\,\text{m}\mu}/A_{270\,\text{m}\mu}$.
[d] $A^{\text{red}}_{552\,\text{m}\mu}/A_{275\,\text{m}\mu}$.

buried in its protein moiety that the reaction between molecular oxygen and the haem iron does not occur, it seems likely that the electron, being accepted by the ferric haem iron of cytochrome *c* from ferrous cytochrome c_1 and transferred to ferric cytochrome *a*, must be transferred through its protein moiety. This concept regarding the essential role of the protein moiety of cytochromes in relation to electron transfer may also apply to cytochrome c_1, since the conformation of the latter is similar to that of cytochrome *c*. Just how the protein moiety functions must await completion of studies of amino acid sequence of cytochrome *c* and conformation of the protein. Margoliash *et al.*[33,34] have reported the primary structure of cytochrome *c* of horse heart muscle, and now several workers are studying the structure of cytochrome *c* of bovine and human heart muscle and of baker's yeast[35–40]. According to the report of Margoliash and Schejter[34] the amino acid sequence of cyto-

References p. 305

chrome *c* isolated from mammalian heart muscle is summarized as follows.

As can be seen in Fig. 2, it is characteristic of cytochrome *c* that it contains about 20 lysine and only 2 arginine residues per molecule and its basicity is mainly attributed to these basic amino acids, since it is believed that two of three histidine residues might be coordinated to haem iron. By the use of chemically modified cytochrome *c* it was believed that the function of cyto-

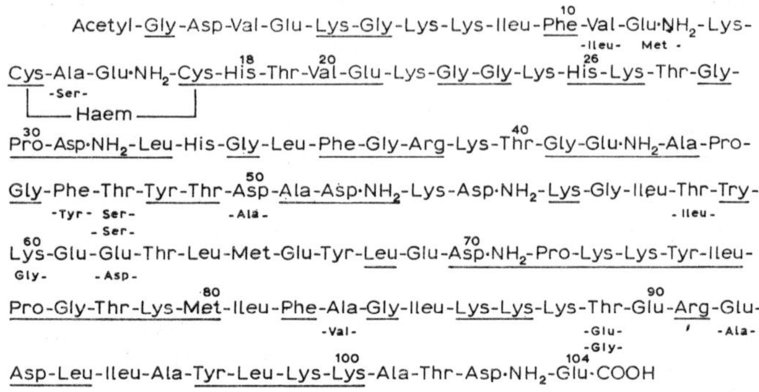

Fig. 2. Amino acid sequence of horse, human, and beef heart cytochrome *c*. Only two amino acid residues of horse cytochrome *c* are replaced by serine and glycine in beef cytochrome *c*, but 12 amino acid residues in the case[33] of human cytochrome *c*. On the other hand, the N-terminal residue of acetylglycine in the mammalian cytochrome *c*'s is replaced by Thr · Glu · Phe · Lys · Ala · Gly in the case of cytochrome *c* of *Saccharomyces oviformis* strain M_2, and the latter is lacking in the $AspNH_2$ residue in position 2 from the C-terminal residue of the molecule. It thus consists of 108 amino acid residues. Even in this case, there are many amino acid residues common to the various cytochrome *c*'s, which are all capable of exhibiting cytochrome oxidase activity in cooperation with beef heart cytochrome *a* (refs. 35–40). These amino acids are underlined.

chrome *c* as an electron-transferring component is lost by the acylation of lysine residues[41]. As discussed later, it seems established that more than four lysine residues which are readily trinitrophenylated (=TNP), and the methionine residue[42,43] at position 80 are necessary for the biological function of cytochrome *c*. Chemically modified forms of cytochrome *c* have been prepared by Takemori and others[30,44–46] in which acetylated, succinylated, trinitrophenylated, guanidinated and trichloroacetic acid modified varieties were made from crystalline beef-heart cytochrome *c* and the pure modified forms of each were isolated.

Since the guanidinated cytochrome *c* is capable of transferring electrons as well as the crystalline native one, and can form with cytochrome *a* a natural complex, exhibiting the normal activity of cytochrome oxidase, it seems likely that this cytochrome *c* has native conformation and a positive charge like the native one.

(*b*) *Conformation change of cytochrome c during oxidation and reduction*[47]

It is well known that native oxidized and reduced cytochrome *c* can be completely separated from each other by chromatography on an Amberlite CG-50 column, since cytochrome *c*, when adsorbed on a cationic resin column, can be more easily eluted in its reduced than in its oxidized form[17–23]. The reduced forms of these compounds have less affinity for the resin than the oxidized forms. This fact indicates that the conformation of the cytochrome *c* molecule is changed very much by a simple change of valence of the iron of its haem moiety. It is very interesting to note that the change in conformation of cytochrome *c* through oxidation or reduction must be attributable to an increase or decrease in some positively charged groups, and to a change in solubility[32,48,49]. Since the reduced form is less soluble in water than the oxidized form, it might be that certain hydrophilic, positively charged groups of cytochrome *c* increase or decrease along with the ferri–ferro interconversion of the haem iron. Moreover, it may be assumed that there are, in the ferrocytochrome *c* molecule, no free lysine and guanidine groups which can conjugate with trypsin, since neither bacterial proteinase nor trypsin can digest native ferrocytochrome *c*, unlike the oxidized form.

With regard to the effect of proteinases on the oxidized and reduced forms of cytochrome *c*, it is interesting to note that there is an appreciable difference in the side-group ionization ratio (SGIR) of the reduced and oxidized forms of cytochrome *c*, which indicates according to Ungar *et al.*[50] that ferrocytochrome *c* is in a more rigid state than is ferricytochrome *c*. It is not known which groups are unmasked in ferricytochrome *c*, but it is reasonable to assume that positively charged groups are unmasked during oxidation, since ferricytochrome *c* has a stronger affinity for cationic exchange resins, is more susceptible to trypsin, has greater solubility, and has a higher electrophoretic mobility toward the cathode in neutral solution than ferrocytochrome *c*. Furthermore, we have recently established chemically that the molecule of ferrocytochrome *c* has a more rigid globular structure than ferricytochrome *c*, because the reactivities of the oxidized and reduced forms with monoiodoacetic acid were found to differ at the 80th methionine residues[42,43]. Therefore, it seems likely that this residue is buried rather inside the protein and becomes more reactive with oxidation of the cytochrome *c*. Since the 80th methionine residue locates at the common region, from the 70th asparagine residue to the 80th methionine residue, the change of state of the methionine residue may occur along with a dynamic change of the common region with oxidation and reduction. In other words, the different reactivity of the 80th methionine residue must reflect a movement of the common region with oxidation and reduction. Together with the haem portion in cytochrome *c*, this region must play an important role for making an

References p. 305

adequate structure to mediate electron flow, either in one protein or between proteins.

3. Cytochrome c_1 isolated from heart muscle*

Properties of purified cytochrome c_1

The preparation of highly purified cytochrome c_1 has absorption maxima at 553 mμ, 523 mμ and 418 mμ in the reduced form and at 523 mμ, 411 mμ and 278 mμ in the oxidized form. The iron content of the highly purified preparation was determined by the *o*-phenanthroline method as 0.15%. Assuming that one atom of iron is present per molecule of cytochrome c_1, the minimum molecular weight of the preparation was calculated to be 36700, but a molecular weight of 1 200 000 was obtained by a physicochemical method. Thus it appears that some kind of polymerization takes place in aqueous medium[54].

The preparation of cytochrome c_1 does not combine with either cyanide or carbon monoxide, indicating that the haem is buried in the protein moiety just as in the case of cytochrome *c*. Although there are some similarities between cytochromes *c* and c_1, such as their absorption spectra, redox potentials, haem species, and the mode of linkage between the haem and protein moieties, it was shown that there are structural and functional differences between them. Since the haems of both cytochromes have been shown to be identical, the structural and functional differences between the cytochromes must be due to the nature of their protein moieties. In fact, cytochrome *c* exhibits cytochrome oxidase activity with cytochrome *a*, while cytochrome c_1 does not do so appreciably. It seems likely that one reason for this can be ascribed to a difference in charge of the components of the cytochromes, since the c_1 component is an acidic protein like cytochrome *a*, whereas the *c* component is basic.

Cytochrome c_1 was rapidly reduced by reducing agents such as $Na_2S_2O_4$, potassium borohydride, ascorbic acid, sodium thioglycolate and cysteine. Reduced cytochrome c_1 showed scarcely any autoxidizability under normal physiological conditions, but it was slowly oxidized by ferricytochrome *a* and rapidly by further addition of a small amount of cytochrome *c*. These results indicate that electron transfer occurs rapidly between cytochromes c_1 and *c*, but slowly between cytochromes c_1 and *a*. Thus, it is reasonable to conclude that cytochrome c_1 is a natural electron donor for cytochrome oxidase, consisting of cytochromes *a* and *c*, because cytochrome c_1 is enzymatically reduced either by the succinate oxidase system, or by a reduced-NAD oxidizing system, both of which are sensitive to antimycin A.

* See Yakushiji and Okunuki[5], Sekuzu *et al.*[51], D. E. Green *et al.*[52,53] and Y. Orii *et al.*[54].

4. *Pseudomonas* cytochrome *c*-551

It has already been demonstrated that *Pseudomonas aeruginosa* contains not only a complicated cytochrome system, but also could convert its respiration system into another type, depending on the cultural conditions. From the cells grown in submerged culture in the presence of nitrate, five respiratory components were isolated in a true water-soluble state without the aid of detergents[55,56]. These components were called *Pseudomonas*(*P*)-cytochrome-554, *P*-cytochrome *c*-551, *P*-blue protein, *P*-cytochrome oxidase[58] and *P*-hydroquinone oxidase[56]. The same microorganism also contains another cytochrome, *P*-cytochrome-560, which is similar to the so-called cytochrome b_1 and which has not yet been solubilized without aid of sodium cholate[55]. From studies on purified respiratory components, cellular fragments and whole cells, it was concluded that in the electron-transferring system of the microorganism, *P*-cytochrome *c*-551 and *P*-blue protein are functional at a site corresponding to cytochrome *c* of animal mitochondria[57,58]. Preliminary studies on the chemical and physical properties of the purified components showed that *P*-cytochrome *c*-551 bears a closer resemblance to a typical cytochrome *c* than it does to *P*-blue protein. From another point of view it seems, however, that the *P*-cytochrome *c*-551 might correspond to the cytochrome c_1 of animal mitochondria, because both *c*-type cytochromes are capable of donating electrons towards the respective cytochrome oxidases *in vivo*.

P-cytochrome *c*-551 has been isolated and crystallized from the microorganism, which was grown in a submerged culture with nitrate as a terminal electron acceptor. The purification involves collection by H-form Duolite CS-101, chromatography on activated aluminium oxide, zone electrophoresis on a starch column and precipitation followed by crystallization from ammonium sulphate solution[58]. Despite the many similarities of *P*-cytochrome *c*-551 to other types of cytochrome *c*, the standard procedure for the purification of the types of cytochrome *c* is inefficient for the purification of *P*-cytochrome *c*-551 (refs. 55, 57). The main reason appears to be the acidic isoelectric point (pH 4.70) of *P*-cytochrome *c*-551 (ref. 24), which decreases the adsorptive power of a weak cationic resin such as Amberlite IRC-50 within its effective pH range. After three recrystallizations, *P*-cytochrome *c*-551 was a homogeneous protein according to electrophoretic and ultracentrifugal criteria. The crystalline *P*-cytochrome *c*-551 shows absorption maxima at 551 mμ, 521 mμ, 416 mμ, 316 mμ, 290 mμ and 280 mμ in the reduced form, and at 530 mμ, 409 mμ, 360 mμ, 290 mμ and 280 mμ in the oxidized form. The molar extinction coefficient at 551 mμ is $28.3 \cdot 10^6$ mole^{-1}cm^2 at pH 7.0. The cytochrome contains 16.2% of nitrogen and 0.69% of iron. The latter figure indicates a minimum molecular weight of 8100. The molecular weight

References p. 305

calculated from the value of the sedimentation constant, diffusion constant and partial specific volume at pH 7.0 (ionic strength, 0.10) is 7600. The cytochrome thus contains one iron atom per molecule and has an E_0-value of +0.286 V at pH 6.50 and 20°.

B. CYTOCHROME OXIDASE

As is well known, Warburg and Negelein[59–64] discovered the oxidase by the absorption spectrum of its CO-complex, established it as a haemprotein, and called it first the respiratory enzyme and later the oxygen-transferring enzyme. Warburg believed that the respiratory enzyme could function as a terminal oxidase in cellular respiration because it had the following properties: (*1*) it had a very high affinity for molecular oxygen and the rate of respiration did not depend on the partial pressure of oxygen, beyond a certain limit; and (*2*) it had heavy metals, and especially iron, in its active centre, because its activity was markedly affected by low concentrations of cyanide and carbon monoxide, and the inhibition caused by the latter was light-sensitive. Although it is generally believed that the respiratory enzyme is identical with Keilin's cytochrome *c* oxidase, which was renamed cytochrome a_3, the identity of the respiratory enzyme has never been thoroughly proved because isolation and purification of the terminal oxidase is very difficult. Based on observations of the particulate preparation of heart muscle, Keilin and Hartree[8] were led to the assumption that the preparation contains two cytochrome components containing haem *a*: "cytochrome *a*"*, which is non-autoxidizable, inert to respiratory inhibitors and mainly contributes to the absorption at 605 mμ; and cytochrome a_3, which is autoxidizable, sensitive to the inhibitors and accounts for most of the absorption at 445 mμ. Since that time many observations have supported this opinion and it has been concluded that the cytochrome a_3 may be the terminal oxidase of cellular respiration and able to oxidize ferrocytochrome *a*.

However, Okunuki and Yakushiji[65] and Wainio[66] have argued against the existence of cytochrome a_3. They studied the spectral properties of their purified cytochrome *a* preparations and were unable to find more than one component. In other words, during purification of cytochrome *a*, cytochrome oxidase activity is found only in the cytochrome *a* fraction, containing equimolar amounts[67] of copper and haem *a*. As described below, it was demonstrated that a highly purified preparation of cytochrome *a*, though it is a polymer, is ultracentrifugally as well as electrophoretically monodispersed[68,69]. It was further established that the oxidase activity of our preparation increases two- or three-fold under appropriate conditions in which the

* In this article the expression "cytochrome *a*" indicates a component with the properties defined by Keilin and Hartree[8].

cytochrome *a* has depolymerized to dimer or monomer[70]. It seems likely therefore that the condition of cytochrome *a*, being an oligopolymer in aqueous medium, may be responsible for some of the disagreement of our concept of purified cytochrome *a* with that of others.

In order to elucidate the oxidation–reduction properties of cytochrome *a* the rate of its reduction was examined by addition of various chemical reductants such as *p*-phenylenediamine, hydroquinone, and ascorbic acid. Only *p*-phenylenediamine reduced cytochrome *a*, while the other reagents tested, except sodium dithionite, had weak reductive activity. It has already been shown that the ferricytochrome *a* is reduced completely under strictly anaerobic condition by addition of *p*-phenylenediamine as well as sodium dithionite, and the ferrocytochrome *a* thus obtained is converted quickly into the so-called oxygenated form when air is introduced. Provisionally we have used the term "oxygenated form" for a complex of ferrocytochrome *a*, which displays an analogous, but clearly different absorption spectrum from that of the ferricytochrome *a* (as shown in Fig. 3) and is converted instantaneously into the oxidized form when a small amount of cytochrome *c* or ferricyanide is added. Hence it seems likely that the oxygenated cytochrome *a* may be ferro-type, but not necessarily analogous with oxygenated haemoglobin.

As shown in Table VI (p. 259), it was established that cytochrome *a* acquires an oxidase activity in conjunction with cytochrome *c* when the oxygen consumption is measured manometrically. However, cytochrome *a* has no oxidase activity in conjunction with chemically modified cytochrome *c*, even though the latter is capable of reducing cytochrome *a* at almost the maximal rate[44–46]. Such a chemically modified cytochrome *c* may be only 20–30% acylated, or contains more than four moles of trinitrophenylated lysine residues per mole of cytochrome *c*. From this evidence it seems probable that cytochrome *a* is not autoxidizable and requires native cytochrome *c*, but not the acylated form, for cytochrome oxidase activity. From the above facts, and the results of Yakushiji and Okunuki[5] showing that electrons are transferred from cytochrome *a* to cytochrome *c* and *vice versa*, the following scheme is proposed to interpret the mechanism of action of cytochrome oxidase:

$$\left[\begin{array}{c} O_2 \cdot \text{Cytochrome } a \\ \upharpoonleft\!\downharpoonright \\ \text{Cytochrome } c \end{array}\right] \leftarrow \text{Cytochrome } c_1 \leftarrow \text{Electron donors}$$

Here the bracket indicates a ternary complex, corresponding to the cytochrome oxidase, while O_2 represents molecular oxygen, though the reaction scheme is not stoichiometric. As to the mode of action of the reconstituted cytochrome oxidase composed of highly purified cytochrome *a* and *c*, it will be described in detail later that the haem of cytochrome *a* functions as an electron acceptor for reduced cytochrome *c* and as an activitor of oxygen in cooperation with cytochrome *c*, whereas cytochrome *c* acts not only as an electron donor but also as an essential constituent of cytochrome oxidase forming an active complex[71,72] with cytochrome *a*. Hence it follows that "cytochrome oxidase" is essentially a complex between cytochrome *a* and *c*.

The oxygenated cytochrome *a* is slowly converted into the oxidized form upon standing aerobically. The rate of this conversion however is greatly accelerated by reduced cytochrome *c*. In the presence of reducing agent and a small amount of cytochrome *c* the ferricytochrome *a* is first converted into ferrocytochrome *a*, followed by the appearance of the oxygenated form. During the course of this latter conversion we can obtain a certain group of absorption spectra having isosbestic points at 420 mμ, 439 mμ and 457 mμ. Therefore, it appears that there is a dynamic equilibrium between reduced and oxygenated cytochrome *a*. On the other hand, during the course of reduction of the ferricytochrome *a* in the presence of a trace of dithionite we can find another type of oxidized form of cytochrome *a* having the isosbestic point at 427 mμ between it and the ferrocytochrome *a*, while the isosbestic points between ferri- and ferrocytochrome *a* must lie at 432 mμ and 465–467 mμ. It seems likely that ferrocytochrome *a* might be in dynamic equilibrium with another type of oxidized cytochrome *a*, but not with the usual ferricytochrome *a*.

Moreover, there is evidence showing that a dynamic equilibrium is brought about between the other type of oxidized form and oxygenated ferrocytochrome *a*, as can be seen in the results shown in Figs. 17–19 (pp. 271–273). It is further demonstrated clearly that the rate of oxygen consumption increases in proportion to the increase in ratio of the amount of cytochrome *c* to that of cytochrome *a*, and that the amount of another type of oxidized form in the dynamic equilibrium state increases in comparison with that of the oxygenated one. Based upon these results it is reasonable to conclude that the cytochrome oxidase consisting of cytochromes *a* and *c* does not function as catalyst indicated by such simple reversible reaction as $Fe^{2+} \rightleftharpoons Fe^{3+} + e^-$, but the oxygenated cytochrome *a* in cooperation with cytochrome *c* does undergo a dynamic equilibrium between another type of oxidized form and the reduced one[72]. Thus, a scheme in dynamic equilibrium could be represented as given below.

As can be seen in this scheme, the oxygenated form of cytochrome *a* participates in the cyclic change of cytochrome *a* in its functional state. Therefore, it is reasonable to assume that the anomalous spectral behaviours might result from a composite of the spectral characteristics of the oxidized, reduced and oxygenated forms of cytochrome *a*. Kinetic analysis described later has

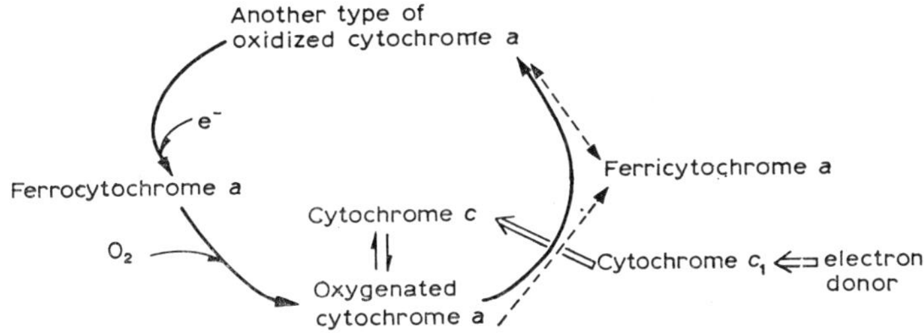

made it possible to interpret anomalous spectral behaviours[73] of cytochrome *a* on the basis of a "Unitarian" concept and has provided answers to the questions raised by Yonetani[74]; why are the α and γ peaks of cytochrome oxidase in difference spectra always reduced to different extents during aerobic steady states and why does the α peak of reduced cytochrome oxidase disappear to a selectively smaller extent than the γ peak on addition of oxygen? We have already indicated that assumptions made on a spectral differentiation of "cytochromes *a*" and a_3 are invalid[75]. In addition, there is no evidence to demonstrate that cytochrome a_3 itself is autoxidizable and also able to oxidize "ferrocytochrome *a*", without the cooperation of cytochrome *c*.

In addition the properties of *P*-cytochrome oxidase involving the so-called cytochrome a_2 and *c*-type cytochrome will be discussed in comparison with the cytochrome oxidase system of heart muscle, since the former is believed to function as a terminal oxidase in the cellular respiration of *P. aeruginosa*.

5. Cytochrome oxidase system of heart muscle

(*a*) *Properties of purified cytochrome a*

(*i*) *Absorption spectra*[76,77]

The absorption spectrum of purified cytochrome *a* shows four distinct peaks at 600 mμ, 424–418 mμ, 340 mμ and 280 mμ in the oxidized form. The former two bands correspond to the α and γ bands, respectively. After reduction with sodium dithionite, the α and γ bands shift to 605 mμ and 444 mμ, as shown in Fig. 3.

No band corresponding to the β band found by Ball and Cooper[78] was observed in our preparation. These results show that all other cytochrome components have been completely removed from the preparation. In Table III are summarized the effects[75,77] of cyanide, carbon monoxide, nitric oxide, and oxygen on cytochrome *a*. As shown in Table III, the absorption peak of the ferrocytochrome *a*–CN complex does not shift from the position

References p. 305

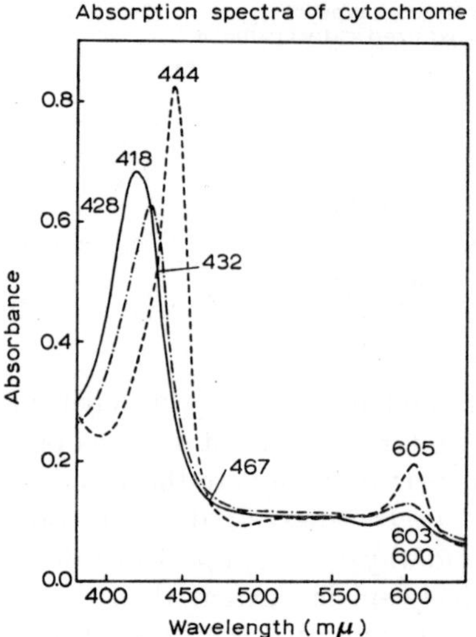

Fig. 3. Absorption spectra of cytochrome *a*. A reaction mixture contained 15.8 mμ-moles of cytochrome *a* in 2.0 ml. ———, oxidized form; -----, reduced form (this spectrum was measured in 0.1 *M* phosphate buffer, pH 7.4, containing 0.5% Emasol 1130 (v/v) and 0.001 *M* EDTA, 10 min after the addition of a small amount of $Na_2S_2O_4$); –·–·–·–, oxygenated form (after the spectrum of the reduced form was recorded, the sample in the cuvette was transferred to a test tube and a fine stream of air was flushed over the surface of the solution).

TABLE III

SUMMARY OF SPECTROSCOPIC OBSERVATIONS OF CYTOCHROME *a*

Treatment	*Position of band (mμ)*	
	α	γ
Oxidized form (Fe^{3+})		
$K_3Fe(CN)_6$	600	424–418
KCN	600	428
Reduced form (Fe^{2+})		
$Na_2S_2O_4$	605	444
100% CO	605	430
50% CO + 50% O_2	603	430
100% O_2	603	426–428
100% NO	603	430
NH_2OH	603	433
$Na_2S_2O_4 \rightarrow KCN$[a]	600 (590)	443
$KCN \rightarrow Na_2S_2O_4$[a]	603	442
KCN + O_2	603	428
Pyridine haemochromogen	585	430

[a] See ref. 75; the bracket indicates a shoulder of α band.

of the reduced form, but the optical density of the γ band at 444 mμ is about 10% less[66,79]. Furthermore, we find a new shoulder in the absorption spectrum of ferrocytochrome *a*–CN complex at about 590 mμ in the presence of cyanide in concentration[75] of 5 m*M*. Thus it seems likely that cyanide can combine, as described by Keilin and Hartree[8], not only with the oxidized form, but also with the reduced form of cytochrome *a*. Contrary to general concepts, the ferricytochrome *a*–CN complex can be reduced by dithionite or ferrocytochrome *c*. Indeed, the absorption spectrum having maxima at 603 mμ and 442 mμ appears if dithionite is added to ferricytochrome *a* previously treated with cyanide (Preparation B), but in this case the unique spectrum having a shoulder at 590 mμ, did not appear. On the contrary, a prominent shoulder appeared at 590 mμ when the cyanide was added to ferrocytochrome *a* solution (Preparation A); it diminished however as the pH of the medium was raised. Although the spectrum of ferrocytochrome *a* was not changed by formaldehyde (*M*/30) under strictly anaerobic conditions, the unique spectrum was diminished instantaneously on addition of formaldehyde and the same spectrum as that of ferrocytochrome *a* was obtained. These results, and the fact that formaldehyde removes cyanide from the medium, clearly indicate that the shoulder was due to cyanhydrin formation and it was deduced that in Preparation A cyanide combined with both haem–iron and the formyl group of ferrocytochrome *a*, while in Preparation B it only combined with haem–iron. The possibility that reactivity of the formyl group was dependent on the redox state of the haem–iron could be deduced from the results reported by Lemberg and Newton[89]. Why was not cyanhydrin formed in Preparation B, while it was in Preparation A, when the haem–iron in both preparations was in the reduced state? The observations indicate that the reactivity of the formyl group in ferrocytochrome *a* might be affected by the bound state of the haem–iron before its reduction. We found that when cytochrome *c* or $NaHSO_3$ was added to ferricytochrome *a*–HCN, a shoulder at 590 mμ appeared slowly after reduction with dithionite and the absorption spectrum in the region of interest approached that of Preparation A (unpublished data).

On the other hand, a configurational change in the protein moiety of cytochrome *c* depending on its redox state has been shown[32,49] and this could be true also for cytochrome *a*. Such a configurational change, which might cause steric effects around the formyl group, should be taken into consideration in interpreting the effect of cytochrome *c* or $NaHSO_3$ and the difference between Preparations A and B. It was suggested, therefore, that the effect of cyanide on cytochrome *a* changes, depending on the electronic structure of haem as well as on the steric effects around a formyl group. Moreover, spectrophotometric analyses on the reaction between ferricytochrome *a* and

References p. 305

cyanide clearly indicate that one molecule of ferricytochrome *a* combines[75] with one molecule of HCN (Table IV). These results do not agree with the view that there are two kinds of haem prosthetic groups in a cytochrome *a* preparation, one of which reacts with cyanide and one which does not.

TABLE IV

DETERMINATION OF THE DISSOCIATION CONSTANT OF FERRICYTOCHROME *a*–HCN[75]

Conc. of KCN (M)	α[a]	*K (M)*	
		$n = 1$	$n = 2$
10^{-5}	0.079	$9.6 \cdot 10^{-5}$	$5 \cdot 10^{-10}$
$5 \cdot 10^{-5}$	0.317	$9.3 \cdot 10^{-5}$	$3 \cdot 10^{-9}$
10^{-4}	0.506	$8.7 \cdot 10^{-5}$	$6.1 \cdot 10^{-9}$
$5 \cdot 10^{-4}$	0.836	$9.4 \cdot 10^{-5}$	$4.2 \cdot 10^{-8}$
10^{-3}	0.915	$9.1 \cdot 10^{-5}$	$8.6 \cdot 10^{-8}$
		Average $9.2 \cdot 10^{-5}$	

(ferricytochrome *a*) + (ferricytochrome *a*–HCN) = $2.15 \cdot 10^{-5}$ *M*, pH 7.4, 20°.
[a] This is the average of the absorbance differences between 430 mμ and 410 mμ.

In the presence of carbon monoxide, the γ band of ferrocytochrome *a* shifts from 444 mμ to 430 mμ. On the other hand, the α band at 605 mμ shows a shoulder in the region of its shorter wavelength, which is confirmed as the α band of the ferrocytochrome *a*–CO complex appearing at about 590 mμ in a difference spectrum. This is in partial agreement with the results of other investigators (Straub[83]; Okunuki and Yakushiji[65]; Dannenberg and Kiese[84]; Smith and Stotz[85]). The shoulder at about 444 mμ noted by most of these investigators tends to disappear with time.

On addition of nitric oxide, the γ peak shifts to 430 mμ with a slight decrease in optical density, but the twinning of the γ peak on treatment with nitric oxide, as reported by Wainio[66], is not observed. In the region of the α band, nitric oxide causes a slight increase in absorbance and shifts the maximum from 605 mμ to 603 mμ. It is generally agreed, especially in the view of the competitive reaction of oxygen and carbon monoxide, that the specific characteristic of cytochrome oxidase is that it can react with oxygen. Accordingly, if the cytochrome *a* preparation is strongly autoxidizable, dithionite-reduced cytochrome *a* should rapidly be oxidized by oxygen, giving the spectrum of the oxidized form. As noted by Yakushiji and Okunuki[86] and Okunuki and Yakushiji[65], however, cytochrome *a* has little autoxidizability. This fact was also observed by them in particulate preparations. On the other hand, ferrocytochrome *a* can react with carbon monoxide as mentioned above, and this disagrees with the fact that cytochrome *a* is not autoxidizable. Therefore, the effect of oxygen on ferrocytochrome *a* was examined.

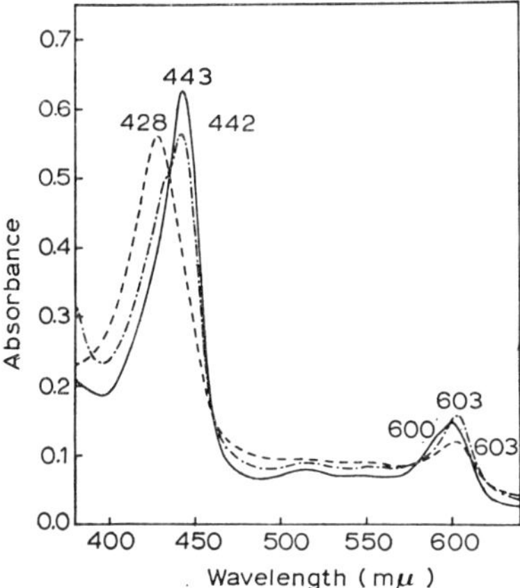

Fig. 4. Relationships among the absorption spectra of cyanide-treated cytochrome *a*'s. A solution of cytochrome *a* which was dissolved in 0.1 *M* phosphate buffer, pH 7.4, containing 0.5% Emasol 1130 (v/v) to a concentration of $7.9 \cdot 10^{-6}$ *M* was employed for the measurement. ———, to 2.95 ml of this solution was added a trace of solid $Na_2S_2O_4$ and after standing for about 20 min to ensure the complete reduction of the cytochrome, 0.05 ml of 0.2 *M* KCN was added. The spectrum obtained is that of ferrocytochrome *a*–CN. -----, after the above spectrum was recorded, the solution was transferred from the cuvette to a test tube and was air-flushed as described in the text. This spectrum is that of ferrocytochrome *a*–(CN,O_2). –·–·–·–, a trace of $Na_2S_2O_4$ was further added to the above solution. This spectrum is that of ferrocytochrome *a*–CN (Preparation B).

When the air is flushed over the surface of the solution of a dithionite-reduced cytochrome *a* preparation with a spray, a new band appears (maxima at 603 mμ and 426–428 mμ) and the spectrum is clearly distinguishable from that of the oxidized form, as shown in Figs. 3 and 20 (p. 275). This new band which appears on oxygenation is in almost the same position in the various preparations. The spectrum changes further to that of the oxidized form on addition of a small amount of potassium ferricyanide or of cytochrome *c* in the presence of air. Moreover, the spectrum can be changed to that of the reduced form by addition of a small amount of borohydride, while the oxidized form is hardly reduced by this reagent. The spectrum of the oxygen–ferrocytochrome *a* complex is very similar to that of the carbon monoxide–cytochrome *a* complex in the region of the γ peak, but differs in the region of the α peak. Thus this new spectrum suggests that oxygenation

References p. 305

of cytochrome *a* occurs in a way similar to that of haemoglobin or myoglobin (see p. 276).

As reported by Yakushiji and Okunuki[5], and Okunuki and Yakushiji[65], cytochrome *a* can react with cytochrome *c*, while there is no oxygen uptake when a chemical reductant such as *p*-phenylenediamine or hydroquinone is added to the preparation in the absence of cytochrome *c*. Therefore, the action of oxygen on ferrocytochrome *a* was also examined in the presence of a small amount of cytochrome *c*. In this case ferrocytochrome *a* is not only rapidly converted to the oxidized form by oxygen, but also takes up oxygen[87,88] as shown in Table VI (p. 259). There is no change in the spectrum on further addition of ferricyanide. These findings will be studied in detail in connection with the mechanism of the cytochrome oxidase reaction[72].

(*ii*) *Ultracentrifugal and electrophoretic analyses*[68,69]

Highly purified cytochrome *a* was dialysed against 0.1 *M* phosphate buffer containing 0.25% Emasol 1130 at pH 7.4 for 12 h. The sedimentation pattern of cytochrome *a* in the presence of the non-ionic detergent, Emasol 1130, showed a single, homogeneous, symmetric and monodispersed component, whereas in the presence of the ionic detergent, sodium cholate, the protein behaved as a polydispersed, aggregate system.

The sedimentation constant was determined at different protein concentrations and found to vary slightly. A corrected value of $s^{\circ}_{20,w}=21.9$ S was obtained. From the results at different protein concentrations, the mean value for the diffusion constant was calculated as $D_{20,w}=3.58 \cdot 10^{-7}$ cm^{2}sec^{-1}. The partial specific volume was found to be 0.72 ml·g^{-1}. Combining these values in the familiar Svedberg equation, a molecular weight was calculated to be 530000. Assuming that cytochrome *a* contains only one haem and one copper atom per molecule, it was estimated to be 100000 from the haem *a* content. Based on these results it is concluded that cytochrome *a* has about 5 moles of haem per mole of protein. Therefore it would be expected provisionally that some kind of polymerization takes place and a monodispersed pentamer of cytochrome *a* exists in the non-ionic detergent solution. At any rate, the frictional ratio f/f_0 was calculated to be 1.12. If the molecule is an unhydrated rotational ellipsoid, the axial ratio would thus be about 3:1 (refs. 68, 69).

Using a highly purified preparation of cytochrome *a* dialysed against the above buffer for 48 h, electrophoresis was carried out by the usual method at different pH values at 20°. Contrary to the result of Connelly *et al.*[90], the protein appeared to be homogeneous at pH 6.4, 7.8 and 8.6. Even at pH 6.4, the boundaries moved slowly toward the anode. No electrophoretic experiment was carried out below pH 6.4, owing to the fact that a large amount of precipitation occurred during dialysis at pH 6.4. From the above results it was established that the isoelectric point of cytochrome *a* lies at an acidic pH, probably in the region of pH 4–5 (ref. 69).

(*iii*) *Analysis of haem*

After the addition of pyridine to the dithionite-reduced cytochrome *a* solution, the pH was adjusted to 10 with 1 *N* NaOH. The α and γ bands then shift to 585 mμ and 430 mμ, respectively. The haem which was separated from the protein moiety with acid acetone (1 ml of 20% HCl plus 100 ml of acetone) and purified by chromatography on an aluminum column, when treated with pyridine at pH 10, shows the same absorption spectrum as cytochrome *a* treated with pyridine. These results indicate that the haem of cytochrome *a* is a dichroic haem or haem *a*.

Lemberg and Falk[91] demonstrated the presence of a formyl group in porphyrin *a* from the effect of aldehyde reagents on its spectral properties. To confirm this, porphyrin *a* was prepared from haemin *a* which had been isolated, as described above, from highly purified cytochrome *a*, by the ferrous acetate–acetic acid method of Warburg and Negelein[9]. To a solution of the porphyrin *a* in pyridine, a few mg of a mixture of equivalent amounts of solid aldehyde reagent and sodium carbonate were added. The solid was dissolved by gentle rotation and the solution allowed to stand for 30 min at room temperature. Porphyrin *a* reacted with the aldehyde reagents resulting in a shift in the absorption bands towards shorter wavelengths. This result is in good agreement with those of Lemberg and Falk[91], Lemberg[92], and Oliver and Rawlinson[93]. It seems likely that the spectral changes in the above reaction are probably due chiefly to the formation of an oxime or hydrazone with the formyl group of porphyrin *a*, because the shift of the absorption bands during oxime or hydrazone formation is typical of formyl-substituted porphyrins such as chlorocruoroporphyrin and porphyrin *a*, but is not given by protoporphyrin[75,94].

(*iv*) *Analysis of the iron and copper content*

Eichel *et al.*[95], Green and Crane[96], and Okunuki *et al.*[97] have reported that their cytochrome oxidase and cytochrome *a* preparations contain high concentrations of copper as well as of haem iron. On the other hand, many investigators[98–100] have observed from dietary experiments that copper-deficient tissues and yeast have a low cytochrome oxidase activity and a decreased cytochrome *a* content. From the above results, it has been considered that the copper in the cytochrome oxidase of a typical cytochrome system plays an important role in the cytochrome oxidase reaction. However, there is no direct evidence to support the above role of copper. In order to determine whether the copper participates in the cytochrome oxidase reaction, the iron and copper contents of various preparations of cytochrome *a* were

References p. 305

first analyzed. From the results thus obtained it was concluded that cytochrome *a* contains equimolar amounts of copper and cytochrome *a* or iron[69]. As illustrated in Table V, the ratio of the cytochrome *a* and copper contents during purification was also one[69]. Secondly, a study was made of whether cytochrome *a* contains a copper porphyrin as its prosthetic group.

From the results of haem *a* analyses using the acid–acetone method, more than 90% of the total iron could be accounted for as haem iron, while more than 90% of the total copper was recovered in the non-haem moiety of the cytochrome *a* preparation[69]. A similar result was obtained by Yonetani[74].

Although the copper is quantitatively liberated as inorganic copper by treatment with trichloroacetic acid, it is not liberated by heat treatment, even at 100° for 30 min. Moreover, very little copper is released from the protein moiety by 48-h dialysis against copper-chelating agents such as potassium cyanide or salicylaldoxime, and the activity, after removing these reagents, was unaffected by this treatment. Therefore, the copper in cytochrome *a*, unlike that of copper enzymes such as laccase[101], seems to be firmly bound to the protein moiety. Thirdly, to check the valency state of the copper in cytochrome *a*, the colour developed by addition of 2,2-diquinolyl or 2,9-dimethyl-1,10-phenanthroline was examined. It was found that the copper of the oxidized cytochrome *a* is in the cupric state, but changed to the cuprous form in the presence of substrates (*e.g.*, lactate, lactic dehydrogenase from baker's yeast, and cytochrome *c*) under anaerobic conditions[69]. None of the spectrophotometric studies done to date has given direct evidence of the involvement of the copper component of cytochrome *a* in the reaction, as specific absorption bands are not known with certainty. The assignment of a band at 830 mμ has still to be considered tentative[102], although it has been reported that the reaction kinetics of this band are closely similar to the 605-mμ band[103]. On the other hand, from the results obtained by electron spin resonance it has been established that the copper component of both the purified cytochrome *a*[104,105] and of phosphorylating particles is able to undergo rapid changes in oxidation and reduction.

(*b*) *Cytochrome oxidase activity of cytochrome a*

(*i*) *Reaction with Emasol*

Although, as is well-known, cholate inhibits cytochrome oxidase[106,107], it was used as a reagent for extraction or solubilization of cytochrome *a* from beef heart muscle[5], because it is not known whether any detergents other than cholate or deoxycholate are effective for extraction of cytochrome *a* from these source materials. Therefore, it is very important to test the inhibition of activity in the cytochrome *a* preparation by cholate and to examine whether the activity lost during purification can be recovered by other types of detergents. It was found that Emasol 4130*, a synthetic non-ionic detergent, reactivated purified cytochrome *a*[108].

As can be seen in Table V, the final preparation retained only a weak activity. However, complete loss of activity of the fraction was not observed and the activity was not recovered in any fraction other than that of cytochrome *a*. The lost activity is not regained by the addition of any other fraction of the cytochrome *a* preparation.

TABLE V

EFFECT OF EMASOL 4130 UPON THE ACTIVITY OF VARIOUS FRACTIONS DURING THE PURIFICATION OF CYTOCHROME *a* FROM BEEF HEART

Fraction[a]	Total volume (ml)	Total cytochrome *a* (10^{-5} mole)	Yield (%)	Purity (10^{-8} mole/mg N)	Turnover number[b]		Copper (10^{-5} atom)	Cu/cytochrome *a*
					− Emasol	+ Emasol		
S_1	1100	1.33	100	1.05	158.3[c]	114.2[c]	1.38	1.04
S_2	200	1.09	82	1.07	203.2	150.0	1.45	1.33
S_3	80	0.56	42	3.75	8.3	42.2	0.71	1.27
S_4	40	0.44	33	5.09	1.2	36.4	0.52	1.19

[a] Regarding the fractionation see ref. 16 or Okunuki *et al.*[76]. S_1, S_2, S_3 and S_4 indicate the order of purification, namely: S_1 is crude extract containing cytochromes *a*, *b*, *c* and c_1; S_2 contains cytochromes *a*, *b* and c_1; S_3 contains cytochrome *a* and a trace of cytochrome *b*; S_4 contains only cytochrome *a*.

[b] O_2 uptake in μmoles per min per μmole of cytochrome *a*.

[c] These values are inaccurate because of inhibition due to ammonium sulphate.

Since the activity diminished as purification proceeded an attempt was made to prevent loss of activity by addition of 10% sucrose and cytochrome *c*. These additions resulted in about 20–30% reactivation in each fraction, but did not maintain the activity at a constant level.

Next the effect of detergents other than cholate was examined, because cholate is an anionic natural detergent and it has been reported by Miyajima[109] that various anions inhibit cytochrome oxidase.

In a similar manner to that of Wainio and Aronoff[110], the effect of various types of synthetic detergents on the activity of purified cytochrome *a* was examined. It was found that Emasol 4130 is the most effective one for reactivation of cytochrome *a*, while ionic detergents, both anionic and cationic, are highly inhibitory[108]. As shown in Table V, the activity of a purified preparation is maintained at one-quarter to one-fifth of that of Fraction S_2 by the addition of 1% Emasol 4130 to the reaction system. As can be seen, however, reactivation by Emasol 4130 does not appear at the earlier stages of purification, but only after removal of cytochrome *b* from the preparation. In the later stages of purification, a rapid decrease in the turnover number is observed with cholate, but this decrease is slow with Emasol 4130. From the

* Emasol 4130, polyoxyethylene–sorbitan–monooleate, Kao Soap Company Ltd., Tokyo (Japan).

References p. 305

above results, it seems that the loss of activity during purification is due to at least two factors. The first is removal from the preparation of a lipid or lipid-like cofactor associated with the cytochrome *b* complex and the second is the inhibition by cholate. With regard to the former, Wainio *et al.*[111] and Hatefi[112] have reported that some lipid or lipoprotein can restore the lost activity. This loss of activity is prevented by addition of Emasol 4130 to the reaction system. Thus the purified preparation, Fraction S_3, retains a turnover number of about 40, corresponding to about one-sixth of that given by Chance[113] for a particulate preparation.

(ii) Substrate specificity

The substrate specificity of a particulate cytochrome oxidase preparation has been reported by Okunuki[114]. Almost similar results are obtained with Fractions S_2 and S_4 in a solution of 0.2% cholate or 1% Emasol 4130. Among the substrates used, hydroquinone and *p*-phenylenediamine are the most suitable, except for reduced cytochrome *c*. Recently, it has been reported that tetrahalogenated hydroquinones are oxidized[115,116] by cytochromes a_3, *a*, *c* and c_1. However, the properties of the oxidation of tetrachlorohydroquinone by beef heart mitochondria are somewhat different from that of cytochrome oxidase, *e.g.* the addition of protamine, which inhibits the cytochrome oxidase[44], is essential for the oxidation of tetrachlorohydroquinone.

At any rate, the natural substrate of cytochrome oxidase must be ferrocytochrome c_1, since the oxidase itself is a complex of cytochromes *a* and *c*.

(iii) Optimum pH (Orii et al.[71]*)*

With regard to the effect of pH on the activity of cytochrome oxidase, it has already been reported that when measured manometrically the pH–activity curve of cytochrome oxidase reaches a maximum between pH 7 and 8, with hydroquinone as an electron donor. However, since cytochrome oxidase is a complex consisting of cytochromes *a* and *c*, it is reasonable to conclude that ferrocytochrome c_1 plays an important role *in vivo* as a natural electron donor for the cytochrome oxidase. So it is necessary to see whether the pH–activity curve with ferrocytochrome c_1 is the same as that with hydroquinone as an electron donor. The oxidation of ferrocytochrome c_1 in the presence of an equimolecular mixture of cytochromes *a* and *c* was followed spectrophotometrically at various pH values. The pH–activity curve obtained had a maximum at about pH 7. On the other hand, it was demonstrated spectrophotometrically that the pH–activity curve for the oxidation of ferrocytochrome *c* in the presence of cytochrome *a* differs greatly from that for ferrocytochrome c_1, that is, the pH optimum was 5.0 in citrate–phosphate buffer, while that in acetate buffer was 4.5. Using ferrocytochrome *c* as an electron donor, Wainio *et al.*[117] investigated spectrophotometrically the effect of the concentration of buffer and the effect of ions on the pH optimum of cytochrome oxidase in detail. They observed that the maximum activity appeared at pH 5.8 when 0.107 *M* Na_2HPO_4–KH_2PO_4 buffer was used. Yonetani[74] also reported that his crystalline cytochrome oxidase preparation has the same optimum pH as that of Wainio *et al.*[117]. Recently we have also obtained almost the same results as those of others[118].

(iv) Inhibitors

(*a*) *Carbon monoxide.* Regarding the effect of carbon monoxide on the activity of various fractions of cytochrome *a*, see Yonetani[108]. Almost the same inhibition is observed in Emasol 4130 with all the preparations except Fraction S_4, in which case the inhibition is twice that observed in the other preparations. It is noteworthy that this inhibition is completely reversed by light irradiation.

(*b*) *Chelating agents.* Regarding the effect of chelating agent on the activity of cytochrome *a* (Fraction S_4 in Emasol 4130), see Sekuzu[77]. The same effect of inhibitors is observed with other fractions and with detergents such as cholate and Emasol 4130. The effect of a copper-chelating agent suggests that the copper in cytochrome *a* also participates in the reaction. However, the problem still remains unsettled as to where copper is situated in the cytochrome oxidase. Since the CO-inhibition of the reconstructed cytochrome oxidase activity is also light-sensitive under the conditions tested, it is certain that the copper is unable to react directly with oxygen.

(*c*) *Aldehyde reagents.* When measured manometrically, the cytochrome oxidase activity in purified cytochromes *a* and *c* was strongly inhibited by aldehyde reagents such as hydrazine, phenylhydrazine, hydroxylamine, and sodium bisulfite. These reagents were effective inhibitors[94] of cytochrome oxidase even at a concentration of 10^{-3} *M*. There are no other strong inhibitors of cytochrome oxidase except cyanide. Other aldehyde reagents, such as semicarbazide, etc., showed no inhibition at a concentration of 10^{-2} *M*. The inhibition was reversible, as indicated by the following experiment. Cytochrome *a* in 0.1 *M* phosphate buffer containing 0.5% Emasol 4130 at pH 7.4 was incubated with the aldehyde reagents (10^{-3} *M*) for 60 min. Then the mixture was dialysed against the same buffer for 20 h to remove the reagents from the preparation. The preparation showed the same activity as in control experiments to which the reagent had not been added. The above results may imply that the inhibition of the cytochrome oxidase reaction is due to the reaction between aldehyde reagents and the formyl group in the prosthetic group of cytochrome *a*. However, there is also a possibility that aldehyde reagents combine with the haem iron before they have a chance to react with the formyl group, because hydroxylamine, which was used as an aldehyde reagent, is a conventional haem-iron binding inhibitor. It is nec-

References p. 305

essary, therefore, to check the possibility that the reagents are able to react with haem iron. For this purpose, catalase was chosen as a haemoprotein without a formyl group. As has been reported by many workers, the catalase activity was completely inhibited by 10^{-4} *M* hydroxylamine. However, other reagents such as hydrazine, phenylhydrazine, and sodium bisulfite at a concentration of 10^{-3}–10^{-4} *M* had no inhibitory effect as judged by assay of the catalase activity by the titration with permanganate. The effect of the reagents at a concentration of 10^{-3} *M* was also examined manometrically and there was no marked inhibition. Therefore, it seems likely that hydroxylamine is capable of inhibiting both the haem iron and the formyl group of the haem, while the other aldehyde reagents have a greater affinity towards the formyl group than they do toward the haem iron.

To clarify the mode of inhibition, the reaction was analyzed by the method of Lineweaver and Burk[119] at two concentrations of aldehyde reagents and five concentrations of cytochrome *c*. The data were plotted by the double reciprocal procedure and the inhibition was found to be both competitive and non-competitive in type. It was clearly shown that with respect to inhibition by phenylhydrazine and hydrazine all curves met at a common intercept when extrapolated to an infinite concentration of cytochrome *c*. Hence it follows that the inhibition is competitive. In contrast to the above reagents, it appears to be more nearly non-competitive than competitive with respect to the inhibition by hydroxylamine and sodium bisulfite[94].

In attempting to understand the mode of action of cytochrome oxidase it is most interesting that phenylhydrazine and hydrazine inhibit the cytochrome oxidase reaction in a competitive way with cytochrome *c*.

(*v*) *Effect of oxygen tension*

As is well-known, the activity is maximal in 5% oxygen in nitrogen gas and is independent of the tension above this level.

(*vi*) *Stability*

Not only fractions S_2 and S_4 but also purified cytochrome *a* dissolved in 1% cholate and 1% Emasol shows scarcely any loss of activity when measured manometrically after storage of preparations for several months at 5°, except that the activity tends to decrease slightly in the early stage of storage.

(*c*) *Reaction of cytochrome a with cytochrome c and c_1*

As mentioned above, a purified preparation of cytochrome *a* is not autoxidizable, but combines with oxygen. In the presence of cytochrome *c*, however, the preparation becomes autoxidizable and shows strong cytochrome oxidase activity. Thus, in a study of the relationship between cytochromes *a* and *c* it is very important to elucidate the mechanism of the ɔytochrome oxidase reaction.

(i) The effect of oxidizing and reducing agents on cytochrome a

Between pH 7 and 8, cytochrome *a* is rapidly oxidized by potassium ferricyanide and reduced by sodium dithionite, like other normal cytochromes. Reduced cytochrome *c* and *p*-phenylenediamine as well as tetrahalogenated hydroquinones[115,116] are also good reductants of cytochrome *a*, while borohydride and substrates of cytochrome oxidase such as hydroquinone and ascorbic acid hardly reduce it in the absence of a small amount of cytochrome *c*. Fig. 5 shows the time course of the reduction of cytochrome *a* with 0.01 *M* *p*-phenylenediamine, hydroquinone, ascorbic acid[87] and Fig. 6, the reduction with some chemically modified ferrocytochrome *c*'s[44].

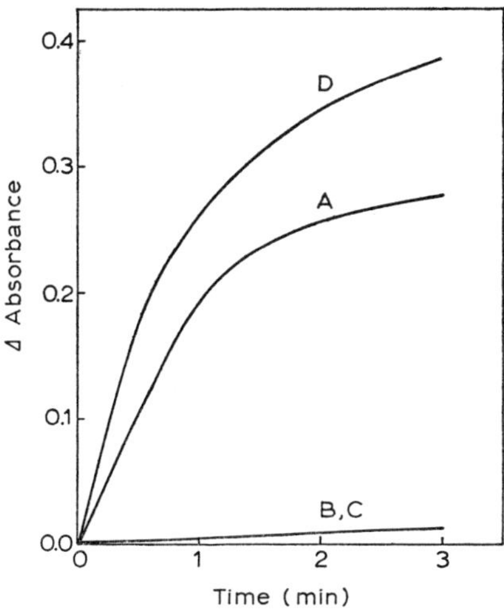

Fig. 5. Reduction of cytochrome *a* by *p*-phenylenediamine, hydroquinone, and ascorbic acid. The sample cuvette contained 2.7 ml of cytochrome *a* solution diluted with 0.1 *M* phosphate buffer containing 1% Emasol 4130 at pH 7.4 ($4.6 \cdot 10^{-5}$ *M* cytochrome *a*). The reaction was initiated by the addition of 0.3 ml of 0.01 *M* solutions of each reagent. The reduction was determined by measuring the increase in absorbance of the α band at 605 mμ or the γ band at 444 mμ in a Cary recording spectrophotometer at 30°. Curves A, B, and C show the time course of the reduction of the α band by *p*-phenylenediamine, hydroquinone, and ascorbic acid, respectively. Curve D shows the reduction of the γ band by *p*-phenylenediamine using a concentration of cytochrome *a* which was one-third of that used for the other curves.

Under the experimental conditions used, *p*-phenylenediamine reduces cytochrome *a* about 50 times more rapidly than the other two reductants. Fig. 6 shows that the greater the modification of the cytochrome *c* the more slowly

References p. 305

does the reduced band of cytochrome *a* appear. Nevertheless, ferrocytochrome *c* containing 20–30% acetylation of the total ε-NH_2 groups of lysine can reduce cytochrome *a* at 80% or more of the rate of that of native ferrocytochrome *c*. However, systems containing the modified cytochrome *c*, in contrast to the native[44], do not consume oxygen (Fig. 7).

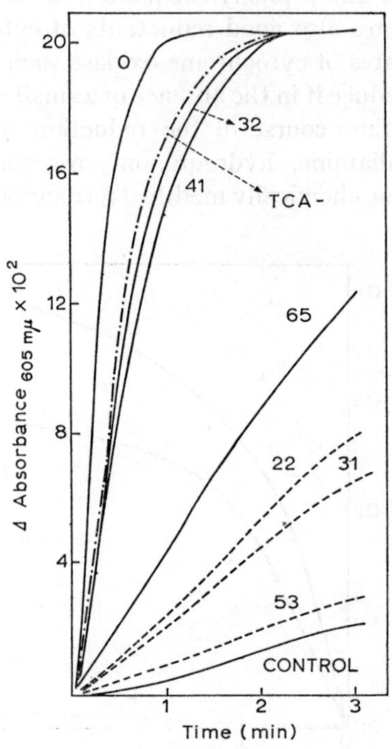

Fig. 6. Effect of chemically modified cytochrome *c* on the reduction of cytochrome *a*. ———, acetylated cytochrome *c*; – – – – –, succinylated cytochrome *c*. The sample cuvette contained $9.1 \cdot 10^{-2}$ *M* phosphate buffer at pH 7.4, 1% Emasol 1130, $3.3 \cdot 10^{-4}$ *M* KCN, $2.5 \cdot 10^{-5}$ *M* cytochrome *a*, $1.0 \cdot 10^{-3}$ *M* hydroquinone, and $4.5 \cdot 10^{-6}$ *M* cytochrome *c* or $4.8 \cdot 10^{-6}$ *M* modified cytochrome *c*. The total volume was 3.0 ml. The reaction was initiated by the addition of the hydroquinone. The reduction was determined by measuring the increase in absorbance of the α band at 605 mμ. The numbers on the curves represent the percent of acetylation or succinylation of free amino groups.

(*ii*) *Non-autoxidizability of cytochrome a*

Since 0.01 *M* *p*-phenylenediamine can completely reduce the α band of cytochrome *a* within a minute, it is judged to be a good reductant of cytochrome *a*, as also reported by Smith[107]. In spite of this, however, *p*-phenylenediamine-reduced cytochrome *a* is not oxidized by oxygen unless a small amount

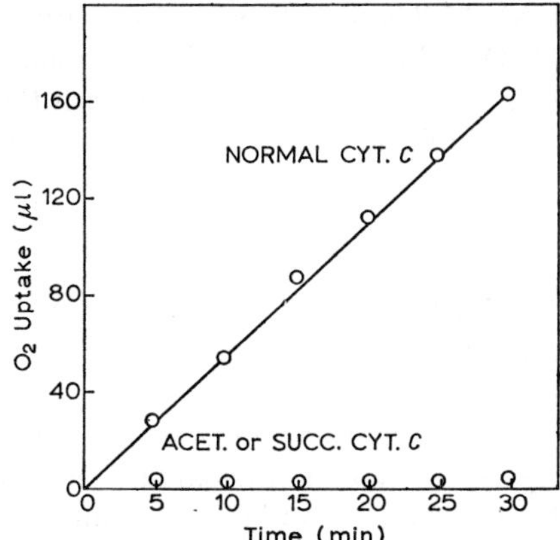

Fig. 7. Effect of chemically modified cytochrome *c* on the cytochrome oxidase activity of cytochrome *a*. The activity was measured manometrically as described in a previous communication[108]. Acet.cyt. *c* was 32% acetylated and succ.cyt. *c* was 22% succinylated.

TABLE VI

EFFECT OF CYTOCHROME *c* ON THE OXIDASE ACTIVITY OF CYTOCHROME *a* AND THE ACTIVITY OF A SUCCINATE OXIDASE SYSTEM CONTAINING NO CYTOCHROME *c*[a]

System	Substrate (10^{-2} *M*)			
	Succinate	*p-Phenylene-diamine*	*Hydro-quinone*	*Ascorbic acid*
Expt. 1				
No addition		4	4	10
Cytochrome *a* ($0.9 \cdot 10^{-5}$ *M*)		6	4	4
Cytochrome *a* + cytochrome *c* ($1.4 \cdot 10^{-5}$ *M*)		104	126	80
Expt. 2				
Ether-treated particulate preparation[b]	5	2		
Same + cytochrome *c* ($0.7 \cdot 10^{-5}$ *M*)	115	137		
Fraction S_2	0	0		
Same + cytochrome *c* ($0.7 \cdot 10^{-5}$ *M*)	61	73		

[a] The oxygen uptake (μl) per 10 min (Expt. 1) and 30 min (Expt. 2) is indicated in the table.

[b] The ether-treated particulate preparation was prepared from an ordinary heart muscle preparation by washing it three times with peroxide-free ether and then three times with 0.1 *M* phosphate buffer, pH 7.4. In this way, cytochrome *c* was completely removed from the preparation, but the x-factor, which may be analogous to antimycin A-sensitive factor, was only partially removed.

References p. 305

of cytochrome *c* is present[87]. These facts were also confirmed manometrically as shown in Table VI. On addition of a sufficient amount of cytochrome *c*, cytochrome *a* consumes a large amount of oxygen with the above reductant.

It has been clearly established that the reduced form of a chemically modified cytochrome *c* can reduce ferricytochrome *a* as well as *p*-phenylenediamine, but there is no oxygen uptake in the absence of intact cytochrome *c*[44]. Based on these facts, it appears that cytochrome *a* does not show any appreciable autoxidizability without cytochrome *c*, as previously reported by Yakushiji and Okunuki[5].

(*iii*) *Stoichiometry between cytochrome a and c in the cytochrome oxidase system*

As proposed already[87,97], a cytochrome oxidase entity is considered to be composed at least of cytochromes *a* and *c*. This complex is necessary for the oxidation of ferrocytochrome c_1 as shown in Fig. 8. Fig. 8 shows the time course of oxidation of natural ferrocytochromes *c* and c_1 with cytochrome *a*. Natural ferrocytochrome *c* is rapidly oxidized by cytochrome *a* forming a

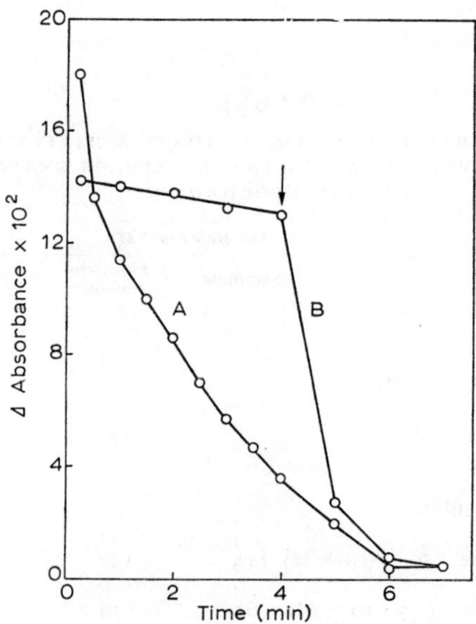

Fig. 8. Oxidation of reduced cytochromes *c* and c_1 by cytochrome *a*. The sample cuvette contained $3.3 \cdot 10^{-2}$ *M* phosphate buffer at pH 7.4, 0.5% cholic acid, $1.4 \cdot 10^{-6}$ *M* cytochrome *a* and reduced cytochrome *c* or c_1. The total volume was 3.0 ml and the temperature was 15°. The oxidation was initiated by the addition of cytochrome *a* and was determined by measuring the decrease in absorbance at 550 mμ for cytochrome *c* and at 553 mμ for cytochrome c_1. Curve A shows the oxidation of $0.9 \cdot 10^{-5}$ *M* cytochrome *c* and curve B shows the oxidation of $1.4 \cdot 10^{-5}$ *M* cytochrome c_1. The arrow shows the time of addition of $2 \cdot 10^{-6}$ *M* cytochrome *c*.

cytochrome oxidase complex, while ferrocytochrome c_1 is scarcely oxidized. On addition of a small amount of natural cytochrome *c* to the latter reaction system, however, ferrocytochrome c_1 is readily oxidized. Using the acylated ferrocytochrome *c* in the place of cytochrome c_1 similar results were obtained[44]. Therefore, it is reasonable to conclude that the small amount of cytochrome *c* which is added forms a cytochrome oxidase complex with cytochrome *a* and thus becomes able to oxidize not only ferrocytochrome c_1 but also acylated ferrocytochrome *c*. Furthermore, it is interesting that neither cytochrome c_1 nor acylated cytochrome *c*'s inhibit the formation of a complex between cytochromes *c* and *a*[44].

If these two components of cytochrome do form the oxidase complex, there may be some stoichiometric relationship between them. Therefore, to obtain information on the ratio of cytochrome *c* to cytochrome *a* when they cooperate most effectively to catalyse the oxidation of reduced cytochrome c_1, a study was done using a fixed amount of cytochrome *a* and varying amounts of cytochrome *c*. The conditions were chosen so that oxidation proceeded linearly with time at the initial stage of the reaction. The oxidation rate of reduced cytochrome c_1 was expressed as the amount of cytochrome c_1 oxidized in the first two minutes. The results are presented in Fig. 9.

The results show that cytochrome oxidase activity is maximal when the ratio of cytochrome *c* to cytochrome *a* is 1.0 and is not increased by more cytochrome *c*. Therefore, cytochrome *a* appears to combine with an equi-

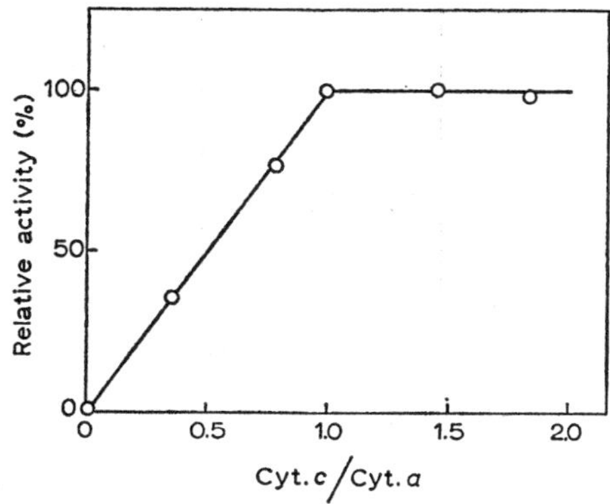

Fig. 9. Oxidation of reduced cytochrome c_1 at various ratios of cytochrome *c* to cytochrome *a*. Initially the reaction mixture contained 82 mμmoles of reduced cytochrome c_1 and 0.84 mμmoles of cytochrome *a* in 0.02 *M* phosphate buffer, pH 7.4. The system also contained 0.17% cholic acid which was added with the cytochrome c_1. The reaction was followed at room temperature (23°) by the decrease in the absorbance at 553 mμ after addition of an appropriate amount of cytochrome *c* to the reaction mixture. The relative activity was calculated from the decrease in absorbance during the initial two minutes, the maximum value in the saturated state being taken as 100.

References p. 305

molar amount of cytochrome *c* to form an active cytochrome oxidase complex[71], and reduced cytochrome c_1 as well as chemically modified ferrocytochrome *c*'s[44] may be oxidized directly by the complex.

(iv) Confirmation by paper chromatography of the formation of a complex between cytochromes a and c

The isoelectric point of cytochrome *a* is at pH 4–5 (ref. 69). Since cytochrome *c* is a basic protein, it is reasonable to assume that the two cytochrome components combine to form a cytochrome oxidase complex. Therefore, the difference in behaviour of cytochrome *a*, cytochrome *c*, and a mixture of the two on paper chromatography was examined[71]. Typical results are illustrated in Fig. 10.

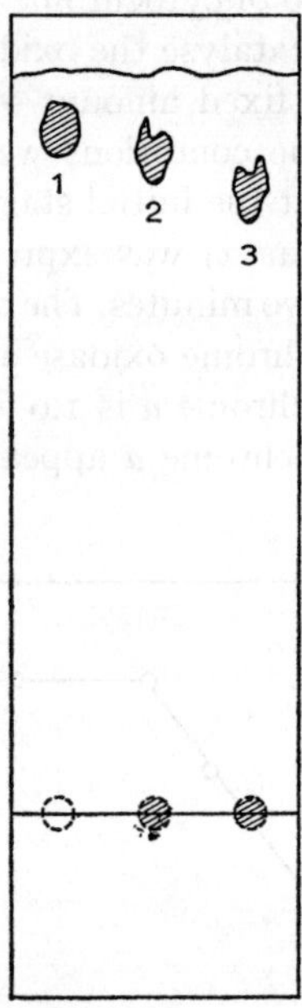

Fig. 10. Paper chromatography of cytochromes *a* and *c*, and a mixture of the two. (1) cytochrome *c*; (2) a mixture of cytochromes *a* and *c*; (3) cytochrome *a*.

As shown, cytochrome *a* has a strong affinity even for detergent-treated paper, so that some remains at the origin, but no tailing is observed in the migrating protein. The R_F values lie between 0.83 and 0.92 for these samples, such that cytochrome *c* moves close to the front and is followed by the mixture of the two cytochrome components. Cytochrome *a* moves rather similarly to the latter. From these results, it is concluded that there is an interaction, suggesting the possibility of combination of cytochromes *a* and *c*.

(v) Separation of cytochrome a–c complex with column chromatography on Sephadex[120,121]

In order to obtain further confirmation of formation of the cytochrome *a–c* complex an attempt was made to separate it using column chromatography on Sephadex (Sephadex G 75), which was washed and decanted with distilled water to remove fine particles, and equilibrated with 0.01 *M* phosphate buffer containing 0.1% Emasol 1130 at pH 7.4. A mixture of cytochromes *a* and *c* was layered on the top of the column. The chromatography was developed with 0.01 *M* phosphate buffer, pH 7.4, containing 0.1% Emasol 1130 at 4–6°. On passing the bed, the red coloured zone was rapidly separated into two main fractions. The fast-moving fraction consisted of cytochromes *a* and *c* and had an R_F value of 0.96. The slow-moving fraction contained cytochrome *c* alone, and appeared at an R_F value of about 0.42. Rechromatography of the fast-moving fraction gave only a single peak. The molar ratio of cytochrome *a* to *c* in the fast-moving fracting was estimated to be about 5:1.

It has been previously reported that cytochrome *a* exists as a monodispersed pentamer in the non-ionic detergent solution and treatment with sodium dodecyl sulphate or urea is necessary to disperse the polymer to subunits[69]. Recently, it was found that the cytochrome oxidase activity of a purified cytochrome *a* is reactivated by treatment with sonic oscillation. Based on these results, a parallel relationship between the degree of dispersion of cytochrome *a* and the ratio of cytochrome *a* to cytochrome *c* in the complex

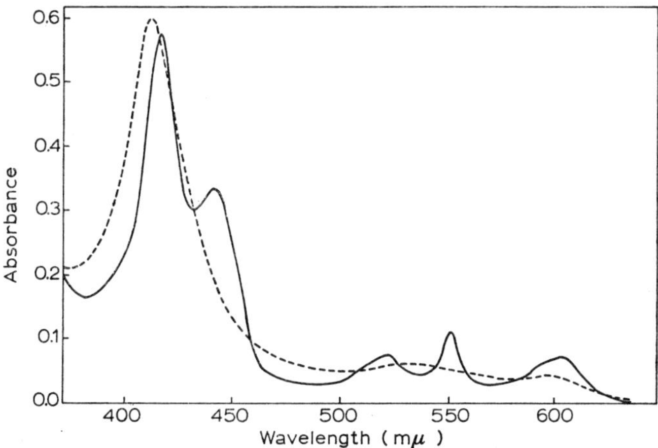

Fig. 11. Absorption spectrum of cytochrome *a–c* complex separated by column chromatography after treatment by sonic oscillation[120]. The preparation was diluted with 0.05 *M* phosphate buffer, pH 7.4, containing 1% Emasol 1130. ----, oxidized form; ——, reduced form. The reduced form was obtained with $Na_2S_2O_4$ in the presence of 0.001 *M* NaN_3. Sodium azide was added to inhibit the cytochrome oxidase activity.

References p. 305

would be anticipated. Accordingly an artificial mixture of cytochromes *a* and *c* was subjected to sonic oscillation in a Raytheon 200-W, 10-kC sonic vibrator at the maximum power output. The absorption spectrum of the cytochrome *a–c* complex obtained by Sephadex column chromatography as described before is given in Fig. 11. The ratio *a*:*c* was found to be 1:1.

In order to determine whether the complex obtained by the above treatment was homogeneous or not, rechromatography was done on the column under the same conditions. Since the sample obtained from the first chromatography was very dilute, it was concentrated with polyvinyl pyrrolidone and then put on another small Sephadex column (0.7×5 cm). A homogeneous single band was obtained when eluted with the same buffer. The components of the cytochrome *a–c* appear to be firmly combined and inseparable by column chromatography on Sephadex. However, the complex was easily split into two components by treatment with a cation exchange resin, Amberlite IRC-50, and the complex formation was not accomplished in a medium of high ionic strength. Thus, it appears established that the cytochrome *a* is capable of combining with cytochrome *c* in a molar ratio of unity both *in vitro* and *in vivo*. The complex exhibits strong cytochrome oxidase activity, and functions as the terminal oxidase of cellular respiration.

(vi) The effect of chemically modified cytochrome c on cytochrome oxidase activity[44–46]

To study the formation of a complex between cytochromes *a* and *c*, chemically modified cytochrome *c* was used in experiments on the cytochrome oxidase activity in place of native cytochrome *c*. As is well known, about 20 lysine residues are present per molecule of cytochrome *c*. About 70% of these groups were readily acylated with acetic or succinic anhydride. In other experiments, more than 90% of these were guanidinated[122] with *O*-methylisourea neutral sulphate and trinitrophenylated to various extents with 2,4,6-trinitrophenylbenzene sulphonate (TNBS), which is believed to be able to mask only free NH_2 groups under the condition used[123]. Using chemically modified ferrocytochrome *c*'s a study was made of whether cytochrome *a* was reduced and whether the cytochrome oxidase activity is exhibited by the formation of the complex between cytochrome *a* and the modified cytochrome *c*'s. The results obtained are summarized in Figs. 6 (p. 258) and 7 (p. 259), and Table VII.

As shown in Fig. 6, the ability of chemically modified ferrocytochrome *c* preparations to reduce ferricytochrome *a* decreases more after succinylation than after acetylation (or trinitrophenylation). The above phenomena might be anticipated from the fact that succinic anhydride replaces a NH_3^+ group by a $—NHCOCH_2 \cdot CH_2 \cdot COO^-$ function, while acetic anhydride

TABLE VII

THE EFFECT OF CHEMICALLY MODIFIED CYTOCHROME *c* PREPARATIONS ON CYTOCHROME OXIDASE ACTIVITY[44]

Sample	*NH_2 groups reacted (%)*	*Relative activity (%)*
Native cytochrome *c*	0	100
Trichloroacetic acid modified cytochrome *c*[30]	0	16
Acetylated cytochrome *c*	32	0
	41	0
	71	0
Succinylated cytochrome *c*	22	0
	31	0
	65	0
Trinitrophenylated cytochrome *c*	2.5[a]	30
	3.6[a]	8
	4.6[a]	0
	5.5[a]	0
Guanidinated cytochrome *c*	49	110
	70	116
	92	123

[a] The numbers indicate moles of the ε-NH_2 groups reacted with trinitrobenzene sulphonate per mole of cytochrome *c*. The assay system (2 ml final volume) contained $9 \cdot 10^{-2}$ *M* phosphate buffer (pH 7.4), 1% Emasol 1130, $3.6 \cdot 10^{-6}$ *M* cytochrome *a* and $1.2 \cdot 10^{-5}$ *M* chemically modified cytochrome *c* or native cytochrome *c*. The activity was measured manometrically at 30° using $1.0 \cdot 10^{-2}$ *M* hydroquinone as substrate.

replaces in contrast the positively charged ammonium group by a non-ionized functional group. To study this further, paper electrophoresis was used to show the change of isoelectric point of chemically modified cytochrome *c* preparations. As can be seen in Fig. 12, acetylated and succinylated cytochrome *c* preparations moved to the anode at pH 6.8, whereas native or TNP–cytochrome *c* preparations moved to the cathode at this pH. The extent of change of electrophoretic mobility increased with the degree of modification. Therefore, it may be suggested that the reducing activities of the chemically modified cytochrome *c* preparations for cytochrome *a* depend on their net charges.

Using TNBS, which binds only with the amino group of proteins, it was observed that the specific binding of TNBS with more than 4 moles of the ε-NH_2 groups of the lysine residues per mole of cytochrome *c* caused loss of the cytochrome oxidase activity, although the ability to reduce ferricytochrome *a* was hardly changed. According to Titani *et al.*[124], the N-terminal amino acid of beef cytochrome *c* is acetylated glycine, indicating that there is no reaction between an α-NH_2 group and TNBS. Hence it may be suggested that some free ε-NH_2 groups of lysine residues in the cytochrome *c* molecule, which can be easily blocked by TNBS, participate in the cytochrome oxidase

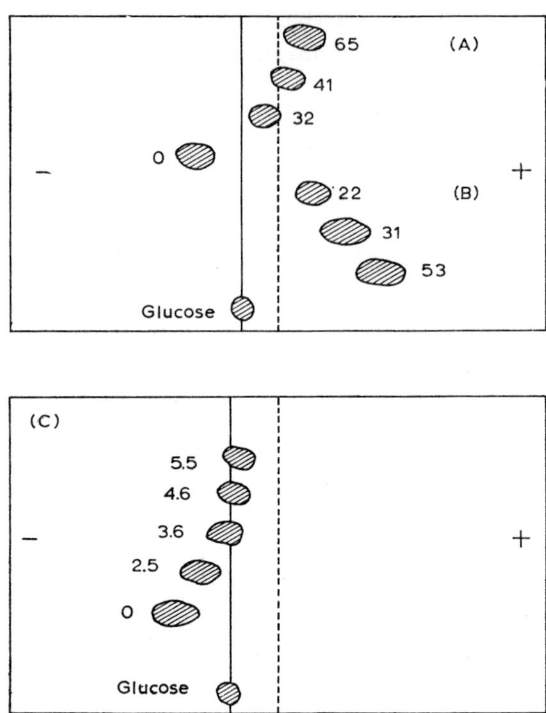

Fig. 12. Paper electrophoresis of chemically modified cytochrome *c* preparations[44]. Paper electrophoresis was carried out under the following conditions: 0.3 mA per cm width, 10 V per cm length, 2.5 h (A and B), 5 h (C), 0°. The buffer used was 0.025 *M* phosphate buffer, pH 6.8. (A) Acetylated cytochrome *c*; (B) succinylated cytochrome *c*. The numbers shown in A and B represent the percentage extent of modification of the free amino groups. (C) TNP–cytochrome *c*. The values shown in C represent the extent of binding of TNBS (moles/mole of cytochrome *c*).

reaction with cytochrome *a*, whereas the other ε-NH_2 groups of the molecule, which can be less readily blocked, function in the reduction of ferricytochrome *a*. Furthermore, studies were made on whether there is any specificity in the chemical modification with TNBS and whether there is any relationship between the specificity of the chemical modification, if any, and the oxidase activity[42,43]. We have recently noted that the lysine residue in position 72 or 73 from the N-terminal residue of the cytochrome *c* molecule is the most readily modified by TNBS and the cytochrome oxidase activity declines upon further action by TNBS. Based on the evidence that the lysine residues 72 and 73 are situated on the common large peptide (from the 70th $AspNH_2$- to the 80th Met-residue[34]) in the various cytochrome *c* molecules which are reactive with beef cytochrome *a*, it is reasonable to assume that these residues are in the second tight turn on the *e*-shaped cytochrome *c*[125], facilitating interaction with the formyl group in haem *a*.

On the other hand, it was demonstrated that the ε-NH_2 groups of lysine in cytochrome *c*, like those of other proteins, were found to be guanidinated by treatment with *O*-methyl-iso-urea. Moreover, the guanidinated cytochrome *c* preparations, which are more basic than naturally occurring cytochrome *c*, were still fully active in the cytochrome oxidase reaction, in contrast to the acylated cytochrome *c* preparations which were shown to possess no activity. In fact, the activity of guanidinated cytochrome *c* preparations appears to be slightly greater than that of native cytochrome *c*.

In addition to these findings it is noteworthy that the acylated cytochrome *c*'s do not seem to inhibit the function of native cytochrome *c* in the cytochrome oxidase reaction, even when large quantities of the acylated cytochrome *c* preparations were added to the reaction mixture containing cytochrome *a* and native cytochrome *c*. Hence it follows that for the maintenance of cytochrome oxidase activity, what is essential is the conservation of the positive charge on the lysine side-chain, and that it does not matter whether these positive charges are on free ε-NH_2 groups or on guanidino groups. In this connection however, the case of trichloroacetic acid–modified cytochrome *c* is of interest. This modified cytochrome *c* differs in biological and physico–chemical properties from native cytochrome *c*, although both of them show close similarities in their absorption spectra. Particularly, trichloroacetic acid–modified cytochrome *c* is not readily eluted from an Amberlite CG-50 column with ordinary buffer, although it is easily eluted with more concentrated buffer. The modified cytochrome *c* is rapidly digested by trypsin and other proteinases, while the native one in its reduced form is scarcely digested. Molecules of the modified cytochrome *c* exist mainly as dimer. From these results, it seems likely that the conformation of the modified cytochrome *c* differs from that of the native one; the former has exposed amino acid residue(s) carrying a positive charge, probably lysine residue(s), available to the functional groups of a cation resin column and of proteinases.

Using the modified cytochrome *c* thus characterized, it was found that, in contrast to the native cytochrome *c*, it does exhibit markedly lower activity in the cytochrome oxidase reaction, while its ability to reduce ferricytochrome *a* does not decrease much. Based on these results, it may be suggested that not only some of the amino acid residue(s) with positive charge, but also the conformation of the cytochrome *c*, are essential for cytochrome oxidase activity.

A similar conclusion was also made from investigations on the effects of basic proteins, synthetic polypeptides and basic amino acids on the cytochrome oxidase activity. As can be seen in Table VIII, protamines were

References p. 305

effective inhibitors of cytochrome oxidase as well as poly-L-lysine, even at a concentration of $3 \cdot 10^{-5}$ *M*. However, lysozyme had less inhibitory effect than the protamines, though it is also a basic protein. To clarify the mode of inhibition, the reaction was analysed by the method of Lineweaver and Burk[119] and the inhibitions were found to be nearly non-competitive with cytochrome *c*. On the contrary, copoly-1:1-(L-glutamic acid, L-lysine) had little inhibitory effect on cytochrome oxidase activity at a concentration of $3 \cdot 10^{-5}$ *M*. This is not unexpected, since the net charge of the copolymer is zero. However, since the basic amino acids, such as DL-lysine and DL-arginine, are not inhibitory, it must be that the inhibitions when obtained depend not on net charge alone but on the conformation of these molecules.

TABLE VIII

THE EFFECT OF BASIC PROTEINS, POLYPEPTIDES AND AMINO ACIDS ON CYTOCHROME OXIDASE ACTIVITY[44]

Sample	*Concentration (M)*	*Inhibition (%)*
Salmine	$3 \cdot 10^{-5}$	83
	$1 \cdot 10^{-5}$	68
	$5 \cdot 10^{-6}$	55
Clupein	$3 \cdot 10^{-5}$	80
	$1 \cdot 10^{-5}$	69
	$5 \cdot 10^{-6}$	54
Lysozyme	$3 \cdot 10^{-5}$	20
Poly-L-lysine	$3 \cdot 10^{-5}$	70
	$1 \cdot 10^{-5}$	63
	$5 \cdot 10^{-6}$	52
Copoly-1:1-(L-glutamic acid, L-lysine)	$3 \cdot 10^{-5}$	17
DL-Lysine	$1 \cdot 10^{-3}$	0
DL-Arginine	$1 \cdot 10^{-3}$	0

The details of the assay procedure are in the legend for Table VII except that various concentrations of the inhibitors were used as indicated.

(*vii*) *Significance of the oxygenated cytochrome a in the cytochrome oxidase function*[72]

From the findings described above, it seems that cytochrome *c* functions not only as an electron-transferring carrier but also as a complementary component for cytochrome oxidase activity. It is not well known, however, how cytochrome *c* changes the function of cytochrome *a*. In order to obtain further knowledge about the function of cytochrome *a*, spectrophotometric investigations were carried out under various conditions.

(*a*) *Relationships among the absorption spectra of the reduced, oxidized and the oxygenated cytochrome a.* Three forms of cytochrome *a* show spectra represented in Fig. 3. If the oxygenated form is a mixture of the reduced and oxidized forms as suggested by Chance[126], it would be reasonable to expect a spectrum during the reduction of ferricytochrome *a* in which the isosbestic points are situated at 432 mμ and 465–467 mμ. Figs. 13 and 14 show the progressive reduction of cytochrome *a* by dithionite, and do not indicate such a spectrum. It should be noticed, however, that the spectra recorded share isosbestic points at 427 and 465 mμ except for one spectrum which was recorded immediately after the addition of a reductant.

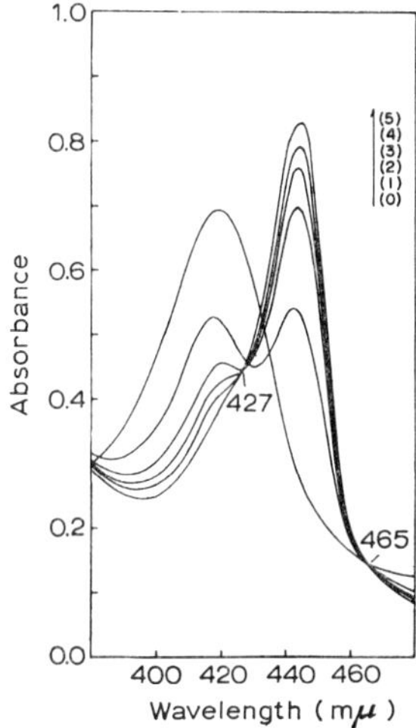

Fig. 13. Time-dependent change of the absorption spectra of ferricytochrome *a* when reduced with $Na_2S_2O_4$. The reaction mixture initially contained 15.8 mμmoles of ferricytochrome *a* in 2.0 ml of the medium. 5 sec after the addition of a small amount of solid $Na_2S_2O_4$, the first run was recorded at a scanning speed of 10 mμ/sec starting from 480 mμ. These recordings were repeated at time intervals of 90 sec. (0), oxidized form; (1), 5 sec; (2), 90 sec; (3), 180 sec; (4) 270 sec; (5), 600 sec.

When a trace of dithionite was added to the oxygenated cytochrome *a*, the spectrum changed as shown in Fig. 15. None of the changing spectra resembles those which were noted during the reduction of ferricytochrome *a*, and it should be stressed that the speed of the deoxygenation was faster than that of ferricytochrome *a* reduction. The process corresponds to the deoxygenation of the oxygenated cytochrome *a* by dithionite.

On the other hand, when the oxygenated cytochrome *a* was placed in air, its absorption spectrum changed gradually in its peak position to a shorter wavelength and the height of the peak became higher and approached that of the oxidized one. A small amount of cytochrome *c* accelerated this process as

References p. 305

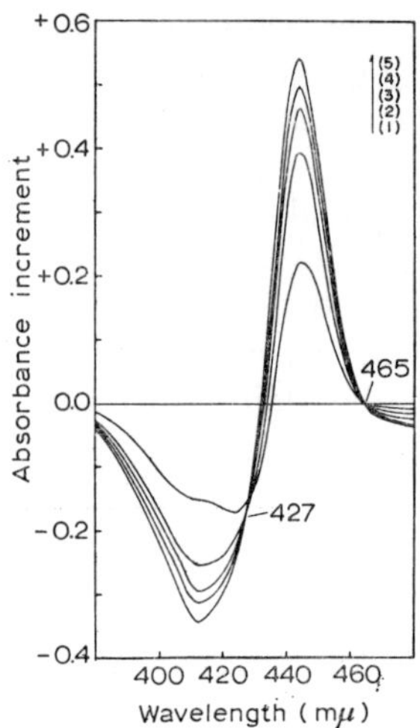

Fig. 14. Time-dependent changes of the difference spectra (reduced minus oxidized) of cytochrome *a* upon addition of $Na_2S_2O_4$. Both sample and reference cuvettes contained 15.4 mμmoles of cytochrome *a* in 2.0 ml of the medium. Reduction was initiated by the addition of solid $Na_2S_2O_4$ to the former. Other techniques were the same as in Fig. 13. (1), 5 sec; (2), 90 sec; (3), 180 sec; (4), 270 sec; (5), 600 sec.

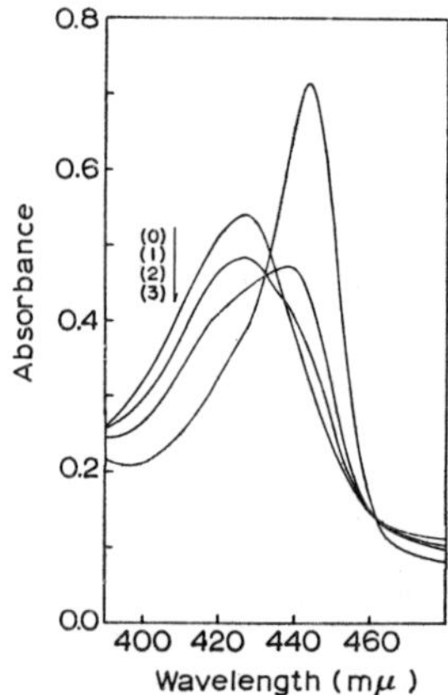

Fig. 15. Conversion of the oxygenated cytochrome *a* to its reduced form. To 1.9 ml of the air-saturated medium, 0.1 ml of a concentrated cytochrome *a* ($1.58 \cdot 10^{-4}$ *M*), which was reduced previously with a small amount of $Na_2S_2O_4$, was added to make a final volume of 2.0 ml. After standing 3 min, the spectrum was recorded as that of the oxygenated form. Then, a small amount of $Na_2S_2O_4$ was added to this solution and repeated scannings were made from 480 mμ to 380 mμ as soon as possible at a scanning speed of 10 mμ/4 sec. (0), oxygenated form; (1), 90 sec after the addition of a reductant; (2), 180 sec; (3), 360 sec.

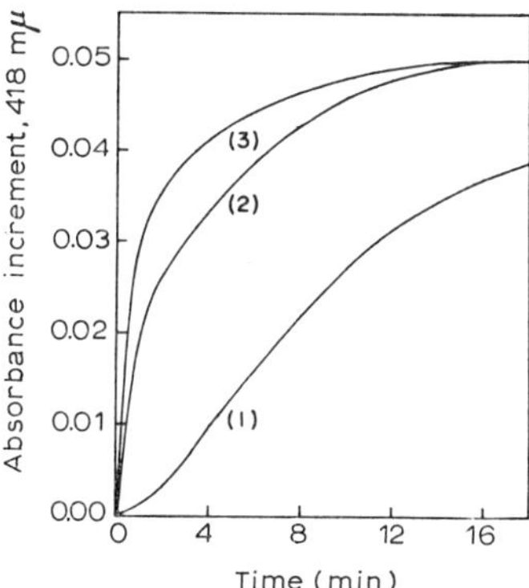

Fig. 16. Time course of the conversion of the oxygenated cytochrome *a* to its oxidized form. The reaction mixture initially contained 15.8 mμmoles of the oxygenated cytochrome *a* in 1.95 ml of the medium. (1), no cytochrome *c* present; (2), 1.69 mμmoles of the ferricytochrome *c* was added; (3), 1.69 mμmoles of the ferrocytochrome *c* was added. For the latter 2 cases, correction was made for the contribution of cytochrome *c* to the absorption at this wavelength by setting the starting line at the settled pen position after the addition of cytochrome *c*.

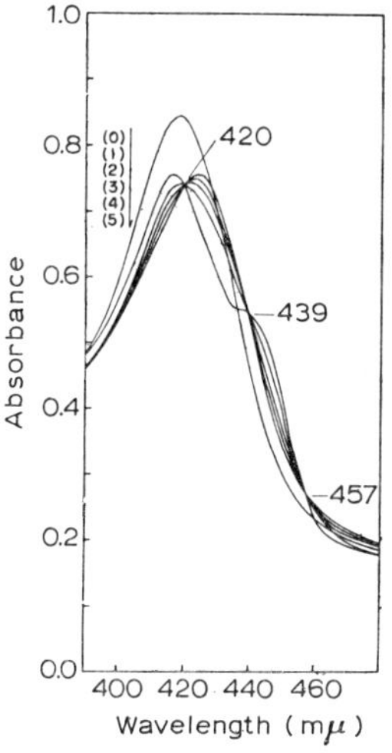

Fig. 17. Change of the absorption spectrum of cytochrome *a* during the transient state in the presence of a small amount of cytochrome *c*. The reaction mixture contained initially 16.9 mμmoles of cytochrome *a* in 1.95 ml of the medium with 1/40 the amount of the oxidized cytochrome *c*. The reaction was started by the addition of 0.05 ml of a reductant containing 5 μmoles of *p*-phenylenediamine and 20 μmoles of ascorbic acid. Scanning was repeated at 2-min interval covering the wavelength range from 480 mμ to 380 mμ. The time of start of scanning at 480 mμ after the addition of a reductant was as follows. (0), oxidized form; (1), 5 sec; (2), 2 min; (3), 4 min; (4), 6 min; (5), 8 and 10 min.

References p. 305

shown in Fig. 16. It should be noticed that the ferrocytochrome *c* as well as the ferri form was effective in promoting this reaction.

(*b*) *Dynamic equilibrium among three forms of cytochrome a in its functional state.* The changes in the absorption spectrum of cytochrome *a* in the presence of a small amount of cytochrome *c* were recorded after the addition of a mixture of ascorbic acid and *p*-phenylenediamine as shown in Figs. 17 and 18. Fig. 18 clearly shows that all spectra recorded cross at isosbestic points at 420, 439 and 457 mμ and inspections of these results suggest that the possible dynamic equilibrium between the oxygenated, another type of the oxidized, and the reduced forms, which are specified by the absorption around 426 mμ, 418 mμ and 444 mμ, respectively, is established when cytochrome *a* functions in the presence of cytochrome *c*.

When the concentration of cytochrome *c* in the reaction system was changed, the results shown in Fig. 19 were obtained. These results clearly indicate that in the dynamic equilibrium state, an increase of cytochrome *c* in the system results in a relative increase of the other type of the oxidized form of cytochrome *a* as opposed to the oxygenated one. However, when equimolar amounts of cytochrome *c* and cytochrome *a* were present, the rapid reduction of both cytochromes was apparent. As the concentration of cytochrome *c* was increased, the rate of oxygen uptake by the system was accel-

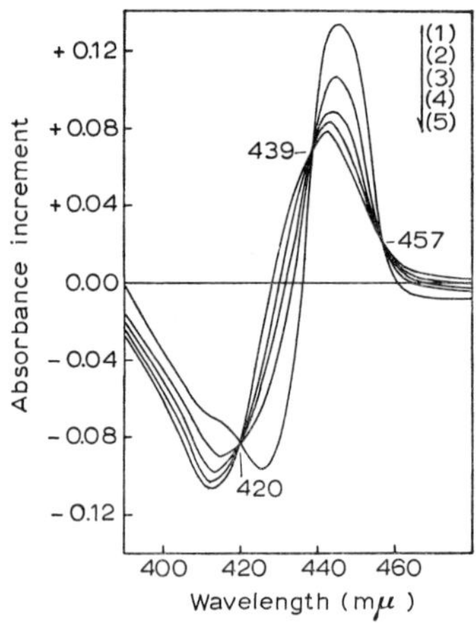

Fig. 18. Change of the difference spectrum of cytochrome *a* during the transient state in the presence of a small amount of cytochrome *c*. The reaction mixture prepared contained initially 50.7 mμmoles of cytochrome *a* and 1/40 the amount of the ferricytochrome *c* in 6.0 ml of the medium. Each 1.95 ml of this mixture was pipetted into both the sample and reference cuvettes and the reaction was started by adding 0.05 ml of a reductant as described in Fig. 17, while to the reference cuvette the same volume of water was added. The time of start of scanning at 480 mμ after the addition of a reductant was as follows. (1), 5 sec; (2), 2 min; (3), 4 min; (4), 6 min; (5), 8 and 10 min.

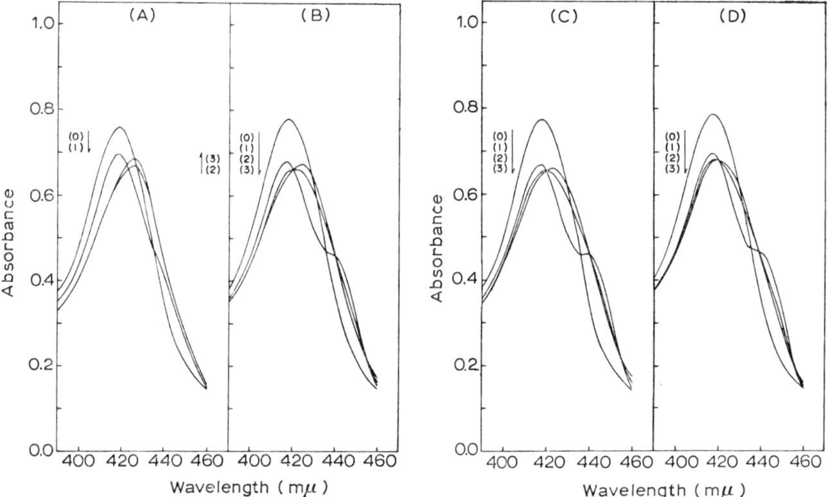

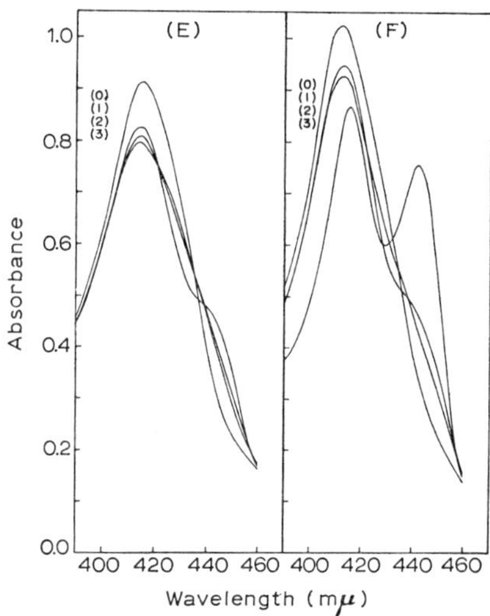

Fig. 19. Effect of cytochrome *c* on the dynamic equilibrium state of cytochrome *a* in its functional state. The experimental conditions were the same as described in Fig. 17, but the amount of cytochrome *c* was changed as indicated in each experiment. The time of start of scanning after the addition of a reductant was as follows. (0), oxidized form; (1), 5 sec; (2), 5 min; (3), 10 min. The ratios of cytochrome *c* to cytochrome *a* were as follows. (A), cytochrome *c* being absent; (B), 1:40; (C), 1:20; (D), 1:10; (E), 4:10; (F), 1:1.

References p. 305

erated. Under these conditions and in the steady state, cytochrome *a* appears like a mixture of the oxidized and reduced forms, but the transient occurrence of cytochrome $a\text{–}O_2$ complex should not be ignored. That is, in the presence of cytochrome *c* the oxygenated form would not be detected spectrophotometrically by the usual techniques.

From these considerations, the following interpretations would be reasonable for the behaviour of cytochrome *a* in its functional state and for the role of cytochrome *c* in the cytochrome oxidase system. When an appropriate reductant is used, the reduction of cytochrome *a* is observed even in the absence of cytochrome *c*, but its rate is clearly enhanced by the latter. Thus one of the functions of cytochrome *c* would rest in this stage and be due to the electron-transferring ability of cytochrome *c*. Once the reduced form is formed, most of it is rapidly converted to the oxygenated form by combining with molecular oxygen. This rate is so rapid that the absorption due only to the reduced form is only observed immediately after the addition of a reductant.

The oxygen-consuming reaction of cytochrome *a* would require the oxygenated form both in the presence and absence of cytochrome *c*, but cytochrome *c* greatly enhances the conversion of the oxygenated to the oxidized form of cytochrome *a* (see Fig. 16). In this latter action both ferri- and ferrocytochrome *c* are effective, hence the action must be attributed to more than the electron-transferring ability of cytochrome *c*, a subject under further investigation. In summary, the scheme depicted on p. 245 illustrates the cyclic role of cytochrome *a*.

(*viii*) *Interpretation of the anomalous spectral behaviour of cytochrome a*[73]

From the observations that the α (605 mμ) and γ (444 mμ) bands of cytochrome *a* or cytochrome oxidase behave differently in the functional state, it has been believed by many investigators that there are two cytochrome components containing haem *a*: "cytochrome *a*", which contributes mainly to the absorption at 605 mμ and cytochrome a_3, which accounts for most of the absorption at 445 mμ. Indeed, these anomalous spectral behaviours of the oxidase component were thought to be difficult to interpret in terms of a single component, but it is also possible that the anomalous spectral behaviour might result from a composite of the spectral characteristics of the oxidized, reduced and oxygenated forms of cytochrome *a* in its various functional states.

(*a*) *Determination of the absorption spectrum of oxygenated cytochrome a.* Absorbance differences between the oxidized and reduced forms at 605 and 444 mμ can be determined at a definite time after addition of a reducing agent to cytochrome *a*. Proportions of the oxidized, reduced and oxygenated forms of cytochrome *a* can be calculated using ratios of the molar extinction coefficients of the oxygenated and reduced forms to that of the oxidized form. These ratios are represented by $K_{\lambda,\text{oxy}}$ and $K_{\lambda,\text{red}}$, respectively, where λ indicates the band position. To calculate these indices exactly, the spectral properties of the oxidized and reduced forms are defined by absorption after ferricyanide or sodium dithionite treatment.

On the other hand, the actual spectrum of the oxygenated form is not easily obtained, since the uncontrolled aeration of the dithionite-reduced cytochrome *a* converts a portion of the oxygenated form once formed to the oxidized one. Therefore, after the complete reduction of cytochrome *a* by dithionite, formaldehyde at a final concentration of 10 m*M* was added to trap the excess reagent and the air was introduced to effect the oxygenation. By this treatment a rapid decrease in absorbance was recorded at 444 mμ, followed by a very slow decrease. Further agitation of the solution had no effect on the absorbance change. Since the result was reproducible in repeated experiments with a single preparation, the absorbance obtained immediately after the introduction of air was considered due to the oxygenated form. The results at various wavelengths result in the spectrum shown in Fig. 20. This spectrum resembles that of the oxygenated form reported previously[137], but the absorption of the α-band is higher.

The calculated values of $K_{\lambda,\text{oxy}}$ and $K_{\lambda,\text{red}}$ are summarized in Table IX.

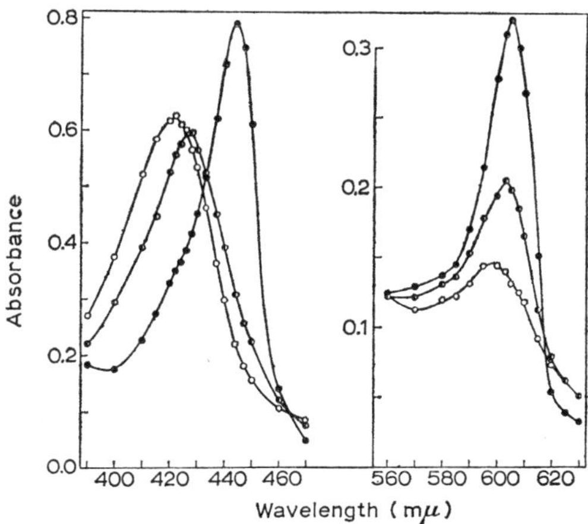

Fig. 20. Absorption spectra of cytochrome *a*. The concentration of cytochrome *a* was $1.74 \cdot 10^{-5}$ *M* in the range of 560–630 mμ and $0.86 \cdot 10^{-5}$ *M* in the range of 390–470 mμ. Each cuvette contained cytochrome *a* in 2.00 ml of medium. The absorbance of the oxidized form was recorded after ferricyanide treatment. The absorbance of the reduced form was obtained on another sample with the same composition after reduction with dithionite. The absorbance of the oxygenated form was recorded by treating the reduced sample with formaldehyde and then aerating it, as described in the text. —○—, oxidized form; —●—, reduced form; —◐—, oxygenated form.

TABLE IX

VALUES[a] OF $K_{\lambda,\text{oxy}}$ AND $K_{\lambda,\text{red}}$ OF CYTOCHROME *a*

	K_{oxy}	K_{red}
α (605 mμ)	1.52	2.42
γ (444 mμ)	1.40	3.60

[a] These values should be determined on each lot of a cytochrome *a* preparation, because they varied slightly depending on samples used. (ref. 73)

(*b*) *Relative changes in the oxidized, reduced and oxygenated forms of cytochrome a on addition of reductants*

(α) *Effect of ascorbate.* The rate of oxygen consumption by a system composed of ascorbate and cytochrome *a* is negligible because cytochrome *c* is omitted. However, cytochrome *a* seems to be partially reduced, according to the report by Smith[107], and in this case, too, a cyclic change of cytochrome *a* is suggested to be occurring. Based on records of the absorbance change of cytochrome *a* on addition of ascorbate, we calculated the extents of absorbance changes at 605 mμ and 444 mμ at appropriate time intervals as depicted in Fig. 21-1, and, correspondingly, the changes in the proportions of the

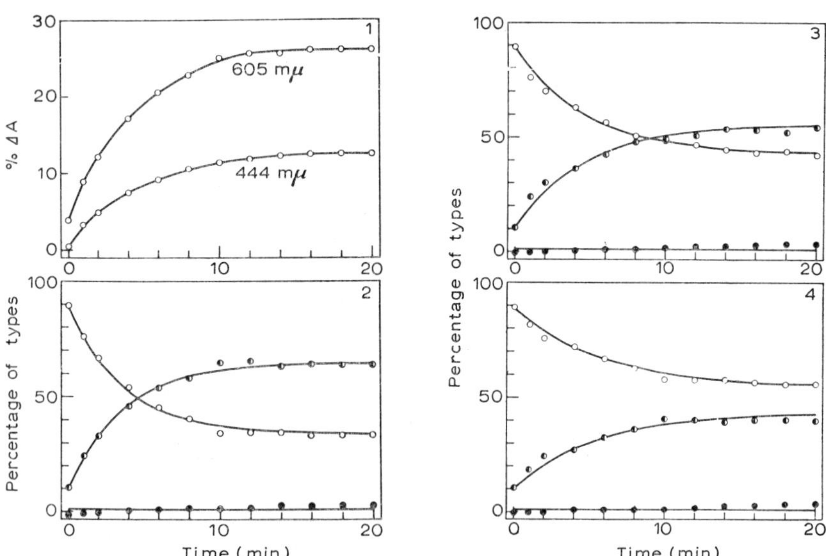

Fig. 21. Variation in the amounts of the reduced, oxidized and oxygenated forms of cytochrome *a* as a function of time. To samples of 34.8 mμmoles of cytochrome *a* preparation in 2.00 ml of medium were added 0.05 ml of ascorbate solutions of the following concentrations. (1) and (2), 0.5 *M*; (3), 0.25 *M*; (4), 0.125 *M*. —○—, oxidized form; —●—, reduced form; —◐—, oxygenated form.

three forms of cytochrome *a* are calculated to give the result shown in Fig. 21-2. The effect of the concentration of ascorbate is shown in Fig. 21-3, 4.

(*β*) *Kinetic analysis.* Attempts were made to interpret the above results on the basis of the reaction scheme[72] for cytochrome *a*. In the present case, however, another type of oxidized form, which was postulated previously, was assumed to have the same absorbance indices as the oxidized form at 605 and 444 mμ, and, for simplicity, the former was replaced by the latter. The simplified scheme we used is shown below[73]. In this scheme x, y and z

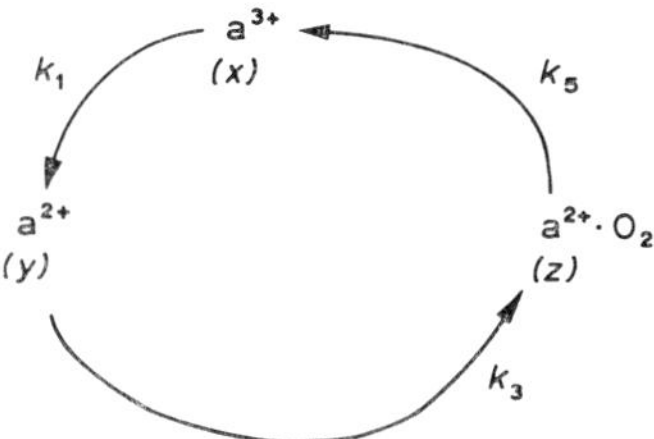

represent the concentration fractions of the oxidized, reduced and oxygenated forms of cytochrome *a* and k_1, k_3 and k_5 indicate the apparent first-order velocity constants. By assuming that k_3 is very large as compared with k_1 and solving the kinetic equations derived from the scheme by a steady-state method, the following equations are obtained.

$$x = \left[\frac{k_1(1 - y_0)}{(k_1 + k_5)} - z_0\right] \exp\{-(k_1 + k_5)t\} + \frac{k_5(1 - y_0)}{(k_1 + k_5)} \quad (1)$$

$$y = y_0 \quad (2)$$

$$z = \left[z_0 - \frac{k_1(1 - y_0)}{(k_1 + k_5)}\right] \exp\{-(k_1 + k_5)t\} + \frac{k_1(1 - y_0)}{(k_1 + k_5)} \quad (3)$$

where y_0 corresponds to the amount of the reduced form in the steady state and z_0 represents the portion of the oxygenated form present in the cytochrome *a* sample as prepared. By introducing the values for (k_1+k_5), $k_1(1-y_0)/(k_1+k_5)$ and $k_5(1-y_0)/(k_1+k_5)$, which were calculated from the experimental results and are summarized in the left-hand columns of Table X, into eqns. (1)–(3), we obtained the theoretical curves shown in Fig. 21-2, 3, 4. These curves fitted well with experimental results and, therefore, it is probable that the anomalous spectral behaviours could result from a composite of spectra of the three forms of cytochrome *a*. Furthermore, calculated values of k_1 and k_5 shown in the right-hand columns of Table X indicate that k_5 is independent of the ascorbate concentration while k_1 increases in proportion to the root of the ascorbate concentration. From these data it is con-

References p. 305

TABLE X

VALUES FOR KINETIC PARAMETERS[73]

Expts.	$k_1 + k_5$	$\frac{k_1(1 - y_0)}{k_1 + k_5}$	$\frac{k_5(1 - y_0)}{k_1 + k_5}$	z_0	*Ascorbate final conc. (M)*	k_1 (min^{-1})	k_5 (min^{-1})
5-2	0.28	0.65	0.34	0.10	0.0125	0.18	0.1
5-3	0.22	0.56	0.43	0.10	0.0063	0.12	0.1
5-4	0.18	0.44	0.55	0.10	0.0032	0.08	0.1

cluded that ascorbate was only effective in reducing cytochrome *a* and was ineffective in the conversion of the oxygenated form, where cytochrome *c* was effective.

(γ) *Effect of cytochrome c.* On adding ascorbate to a mixture of cytochrome *a* and a catalytic amount of cytochrome *c* under aerobic conditions, the absorbances at 605 and 444 mμ due to cytochrome *a* increased rapidly and reached a steady state. On exhausting the dissolved oxygen in the medium, the absorbances at both wavelengths increased to maxima reflecting the complete reduction of the pigment. These changes were consistent with that reported by Yonetani[81]. Calculations showed that during the steady state the relative amounts of the 3 forms of cytochrome *a* were independent of the concentration of cytochrome *c* present in the reaction system, as indicated in Table XI. These results and consideration of the scheme led us to the conclusion that both k_1 and k_5 are functions of the concentration of cytochrome *c*.

TABLE XI

AMOUNTS OF THE OXIDIZED, REDUCED AND OXYGENATED FORMS OF CYTOCHROME *a* SUPPLEMENTED WITH CYTOCHROME *c* IN THE AEROBIC STEADY STATE[73]

cyt. c/cyt. a	a^{3+}	a^{2+}	a^{2+}–O_2
1/20	0.57	0.03	0.41
1/40	0.55	0.03	0.42
1/200	0.59	0.03	0.38
1/400	0.53	0.03	0.44

(δ) *Effect of p-phenylenediamine and hydroquinone.* In place of cytochrome *c*, *p*-phenylenediamine and hydroquinone were employed. The absorbance changes of cytochrome *a* after the addition of ascorbate to the mixture were also investigated. It is apparent from the results that the rate of the absorbance change was slightly greater than when ascorbate was employed and that the change was followed by a gradual decrease. The percentage changes of the 3 forms after the addition of ascorbate and *p*-phenylenediamine are shown in Fig. 22.

It is suggested that the absorbance changes are due to the behaviour of the oxygenated form. The behaviour of the oxygenated form in a system com-

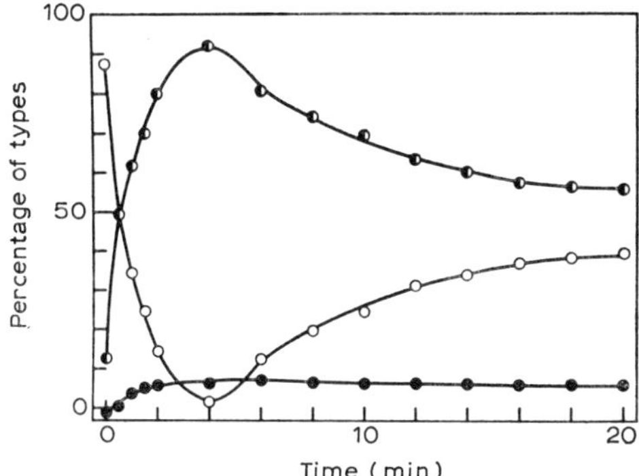

Fig. 22. Changes in the amounts of the reduced, oxidized and oxygenated forms of cytochrome *a* after the addition of ascorbate and *p*-phenylenediamine. To 34.8 mμmoles of cytochrome *a* in 2.00 ml of medium was added 0.05 ml of a solution containing 2.5 μmoles of ascorbate and 0.44 μmoles of *p*-phenylenediamine. —○—, oxidized form; —●—, reduced form; —◐—, oxygenated form.

posed of ascorbate, *p*-phenylenediamine, cytochrome *a* and molecular oxygen, as shown in Fig. 22, can readily be interpreted on the basis of a reaction scheme which postulates one more intermediate, but this is not further explored here. It is interesting that *p*-phenylenediamine simulates the function of cytochrome *c* in an active oxidase complex. Considering the fact that tetramethyl-*p*-phenylenediamine is a good initiator of the oxidase reaction even in the absence of cytochrome *c* (unpublished result), compounds having this kind of structure might take the place of cytochrome *c* in the oxidase system.

From kinetic results, it was apparent that in the steady state the reaction system consisted essentially of the oxygenated and oxidized forms of cytochrome *a*. These results are consistent with the fact that the absorption spectrum of cytochrome *a* after addition of ascorbate under aerobic conditions, or on addition of *p*-phenylenediamine, appeared to be due to the oxygenated form[72,127]. The reduced form was present in small amount, which is consistent with the view that the reaction rate of the reduced form with oxygen was so rapid as to make the accumulation of the reduced form by the action of a poor reductant improbable.

Our investigations so far have made it possible to interpret anomalous spec-

References p. 305

TABLE XII

COMPARISON OF CYTOCHROME OXIDASE ACTIVITY OF VARIOUS PREPARATIONS[118]

Investigator	Conditions for activity assay						Specific activity
	Purity	*Conc. of cyt. c (μM)*	*Conc. of oxidase (μg protein/ml)*	*Assay medium*	*pH*	*Temp. (°C)*	*(sec⁻¹/mg protein/cuvette)*
Yonetani[74]	7.23 mμmoles Fe/mg protein	15	6.6	0.025 *M* citric acid –0.05 *M* Na_2HPO_4–1% Emasol 4130	5.8	25	3.0[a]
				0.05 *M* KH_2PO_4–K_2HPO_4–1% Emasol 4130	5.8	25	2.5[a]
Wharton and Griffiths[172]	8.1–9.2 mμ-moles haem *a*/mg protein	18	0.55–0.62	0.067 *M* KH_2PO_4–K_2HPO_4 + 1 mg "Asolectin"	7.0	38	2.7[b]
Horie and Morrison[173]	[e]	24	1.22	[e]	[e]	25	4.05[c]
Wainio[174]	11.5 mμmoles haem *a*/mg protein	[e]	[e]	0.1 *M* phosphate buffer + lecithin	6.0	25	7.8
Orii and Okunuki[118]	10.8 mμmoles haem *a*/mg protein	15	1.41	0.02 *M* citric acid –0.04 *M* Na_2HPO_4	5.62	25	5.64
		15	1.81	0.075 *M* NaH_2PO_4–Na_2HPO_4	5.95	25	5.20
		15	2.26	0.075 *M* NaH_2PO_4–Na_2HPO_4	5.95	25	17.1[d]

[a] These values were taken from Fig. 5 in ref. 74. The maximum value reported was 4.5.
[b] Calculated from date given in ref. 172.
[c] The maximum value reported was 4.7.
[d] Cytochrome *a* was treated with 0.5 *M* guanidine hydrochloride.
[e] Experimental details were not found in the papers.

tral behaviours of cytochrome *a* without the introduction of any unidentifiable component other than cytochrome *a* and have provided answers to the questions raised by Yonetani[74]. Moreover, we observed cyanhydrin formation with ferrocytochrome *a* as well as haem–iron binding by cyanide under strictly anaerobic conditions. Based on these observations we have already indicated that assumptions made on a spectral differentiation of "cytochrome *a*" and cytochrome a_3 are invalid[75].

(ix) The effect of polymerization and depolymerization on cytochrome oxidase activity

Using the most advanced techniques in protein chemistry, cytochrome a_3 has never been separated in an unmodified form from "cytochrome *a*". Typical purified preparations of cytochrome oxidase presently available show nearly the same properties whether they are claimed to be composed of "cytochromes *a*" and a_3 or of a single component, cytochrome *a*, which aggregates as 4 or 6 molecules in aqueous solution. For example, specific activities of various preparations of cytochrome oxidase are comparable, as shown in Table XII. It seems likely that the variations recorded in Table XII can be ascribed to differences in the assay methods.

(a) Ratio of "cytochrome a" to a_3 in the preparation. Recently Morrison and Horie[128–130] have reported that in the presence of KCN a minor portion of haem *a* in cytochrome oxidase is reduced with borohydride treatment, and the reduced haem *a* is thus removed from the other major portion of haemoprotein which does not exhibit reactivity toward CO and CN^-. They described further that the carbonyl of the prosthetic group of cytochrome a_3 is converted to the alcohol group under conditions in which the prosthetic group of "cytochrome *a*" is unaffected. In other words, cytochrome a_3 could be selectively destroyed leaving a preparation which fills the spectral definition of "cytochrome *a*". Hence it follows that the amount of "cytochrome *a*" in a purified preparation of pig heart cytochrome oxidase corresponds to that of the haem *a* remaining after borohydride treatment. Thus they could determine the individual amounts of "cytochrome *a*" and a_3 present in the cytochrome oxidase preparation.

They have further reported that in the preparation, reduced and saturated with CO, the amounts of "cytochrome *a*" and a_3 can be separately determined, since ferricyanide is able to oxidize only "cytochrome *a*" but not the CO-bound cytochrome a_3 remaining in the reduced state under these conditions. Based on the data obtained from experiments along these lines it was determined that the molar ratio of "cytochrome *a*"/a_3 equals 4 or 5 in their preparation purified from pig heart muscle.

According to the cytochrome a_3 hypothesis, the amount of CO bound per mole of haem is a measure of the "cytochrome *a*" to a_3 ratio, since only

References p. 305

cytochrome a_3 will react with CO. Thus to determine the ratio a method based on the titration of a cytochrome oxidase preparation with CO was employed. In this procedure, varying amounts of CO are added to a preparation of cytochrome oxidase and the changes in spectrum are recorded. The results of this procedure indicate that the ratio[131,132] "cytochrome *a*" to a_3 is between 3 and 4. On the other hand, based on the results of magnetic susceptibility studies, Ehrenberg and Yonetani[133] suggested that their data would be compatible with an "*a*" to a_3 ratio of 2 to 1. Gibson and Greenwood[134,135], studying the reaction of purified heart muscle cytochrome oxidase with CO, made a more direct measurement of this ratio and came to the same conclusion. Furthermore, Slater *et al.*[136] have suggested on the basis of data obtained from another method that the ratio is one. Assuming that the relative contributions of "cytochromes *a*" and a_3 to the γ peak as proposed by Yonetani[80] are about the same, it appears that the ratio should be one.

Finally, new studies concerned with the ratio of "cytochrome *a*" to a_3 were reported by us[137], dealing with highly purified cytochrome oxidase from *Saccharomyces oviformis*, strain M_2. As reported previously[138], this oxidase is a typical cytochrome *a* and has activity of 22–30 μmoles cytochrome *c* oxidized per min per mg protein at 20° and at the concentration of approx. 30 μM cytochrome *c*. Thus this cytochrome oxidase preparation is almost 3 times more active than that of Yonetani or of Horie and Morrison obtained from mammalian heart muscle. In order to measure the amount of so-called cytochrome a_3 in the cytochrome oxidase of *Saccharomyces oviformis* by the method of Yonetani[80] or of Horie and Morrison, the effects of cyanide and carbon monoxide on the spectrum of yeast cytochrome oxidase have been examined. The effects are almost identical with those on mammalian cytochrome *a*, but only 9.7% of the absorbance of the α peak is accounted for by a_3 and the ratio of γ peak to α peak of cytochrome a_3 is calculated to be 26. Furthermore, it is noteworthy that the γ peak of the absorption spectrum of "ferrocytochrome *a*"–CO complex has its maximum at 437 mμ, showing no shoulder in the 443-mμ region, and the α and γ peaks in the difference spectrum of (reduced–CO)—(reduced) are found at 592 mμ and 429 mμ, respectively. Based on these results, it may be assumed that the ratio of "*a*" to a_3 in yeast cytochrome oxidase is very high, despite its high oxidase activity.

Our question is why the ratio of "*a*" to a_3 in such simple enzyme systems is not constant. Even in the case of the mammalian heart muscle preparation, the values obtained by many investigators differ greatly. In the case of yeast cytochrome oxidase, it would further be necessary to account for the relation between the high content of "cytochrome *a*" and high oxidase activity.

Although there are numerical inconsistencies as to the ratio of "cytochrome *a*" and a_3, these results agree on the whole with those of Gibson and Greenwood[134], except that the values of Morrison and Horie and those on yeast cytochrome oxidase give a larger number of haem groups required to bind each mole of CO. A number of possible reasons for this disagreement can be suggested, but the differences between the results of Gibson and Greenwood and those reported by Morrison and Horie may simply reflect the differences in the preparations employed. At any rate, it seems certain that from the viewpoint of reactivity with oxygen, CO, HCN etc. there are two kinds of cytochrome *a*, one reactive and the other inert, in the purified cytochrome oxidase preparation. The question remains whether they actually belong to different molecular species or not.

(*b*) *Cytochrome a polymer.* On the basis of studies of cytochrome *a* in Emasol, we[69] have tentatively concluded that our purified preparation is a monodispersed pentamer, and assume that in the polymerized cytochrome *a* only a fraction, corresponding to so-called cytochrome a_3, is able to react with various reagents such as oxygen, CO, cyanide or borohydride, etc., because the oxidase activity of our preparation rises two- or three-fold under appropriate conditions in which the cytochrome *a* has depolymerized to a dimer or monomer[70]. In other words, it appears that depolymerized cytochrome *a* is reactive, but, except for a minor fraction it will become inactive toward various reagents when polymerized. It is not surprising that such differences in reactivity result from polymerization and depolymerization.

The "cytochrome *a*" polymer which is isolated from cytochrome oxidase preparations by borohydride treatment, is insensitive to CO, does not react with oxygen, as reported by Horie and Morrison[129], and exhibits absorption spectra different from the original cytochrome oxidase. However, the protein to haem *a* ratio in these preparations suggests that during the isolation of "cytochrome *a*" polymer, the haem *a* attributable to so-called cytochrome a_3, might be detached from the protein moiety and then removed[139]. Therefore, it seems likely that the isolated "cytochrome *a*" polymer is a mixture of polymerized "cytochrome *a*" and apoprotein of so-called cytochrome a_3. If this is the case, it is natural that the interaction between "cytochrome *a*" polymer and so-called cytochrome a_3 should remain unchanged even after the "cytochrome *a*" polymer has lost a minor fraction of prosthetic groups by the borohydride treatment. Therefore, it would be anticipated that the isolated "cytochrome *a*" polymer would not exhibit the oxidase activity until the haem *a* is incorporated into the apoprotein of so-called cytochrome a_3.

Indeed, the evidence that the cytochrome oxidase activity could be reconstituted by introduction of haem *a* into the "cytochrome *a*" polymer isolated according to the method of Horie and Morrison[129] has been reported by Kuboyama and King[139]. Hence it follows that the isolation of "cytochrome *a*" polymer free of cytochrome a_3 and the reconstitution of cyto-

References p. 305

chrome oxidase activity does not establish the presence of two cytochromes "a" and a_3 in the cytochrome oxidase.

Chemical evidence for distinction of the cytochromes should indicate that the depolymerized cytochrome a or its monomer is unable to react with oxygen, etc., even in the presence of cytochrome c. Unfortunately it has never been reported that the cytochrome a monomer is inert or that the cytochrome a polymer is free of cytochrome a_3. Thus, it might be very difficult to establish the proposal, since a certain depolymerized fraction is more reactive than the intact original cytochrome a polymer, as can be seen in Table XII and Fig. 23. During the investigations on the activity of cytochrome a treated with various detergents, we have found that the activity rises two- or three-fold under appropriate conditions.

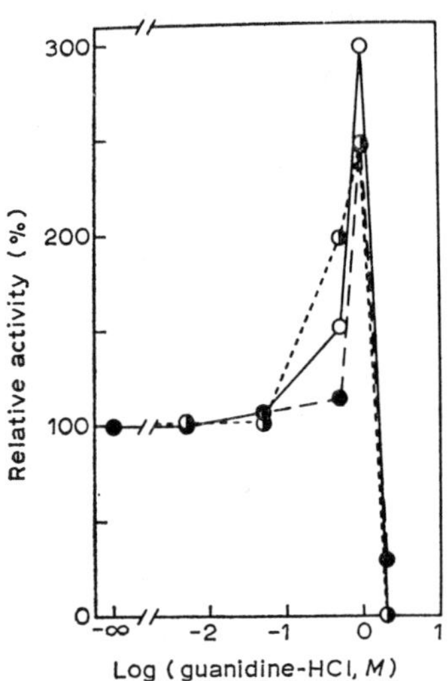

Fig. 23. Effect of guanidine hydrochloride treatment on activity. Cytochrome a was incubated with an appropriate amount of guanidine hydrochloride in 0.05 M Na_2HPO_4–KH_2PO_4, pH 7.4, containing 0.25% (v/v) Emasol 1130 at 20° for 30 min. After diluting the above mixture, if necessary, with the phosphate buffer–Emasol medium, 0.025 ml was added to 2.0 ml of a reaction mixture containing 15 μM ferrocytochrome c in 0.075 M Na_2HPO_4–KH_2PO_4, pH 6.0. The concentration of cytochrome a in the incubation mixture and the dilution factor are as follows. ---●---, cyt. a, $1.01 \cdot 10^{-4}$ M, 41-fold dilution;—○—, cyt. a, $1.01 \cdot 10^{-5}$ M, 5-fold dilution; ---◑---, cyt. a, $1.01 \cdot 10^{-6}$ M, no dilution.

As shown in Fig. 23, the cytochrome oxidase activities of cytochrome a polymer increase rapidly by pretreatment with approximately 1.0 M guanidine hydrochloride, beyond which the oxidase activity decreases undoubtedly due to denaturation[70].

In the case of sodium dodecylsulphate pretreatment, as shown in Fig. 24, the cytochrome oxidase activity increases slowly with increases in detergent concentration, but higher concentrations cause a decrease in activity, as in the case of guanidine treatment.

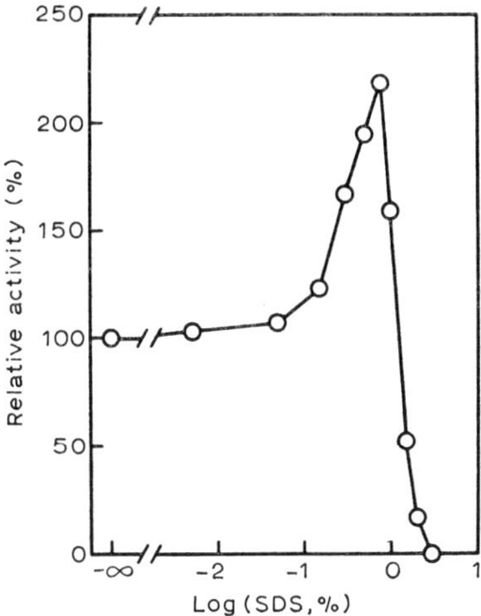

Fig. 24. Effect of sodium dodecylsulphate (SDS) treatment on activity. Cytochrome *a* at a concentration of $0.86 \cdot 10^{-4}$ *M* was incubated with an appropriate amount of SDS in 0.05 *M* Na_2HPO_4–NaH_2PO_4, pH 7.4, containing 0.25% (v/v) Emasol 1130 and 0.002 *M* EDTA at 20° for 30 min. After diluting the incubation mixture 101-fold with the phosphate buffer–Emasol medium, 0.025 ml was added to 2.0 ml of a reaction mixture containing 15 μM ferrocytochrome *c* in 0.075 *M* Na_2HPO_4–NaH_2PO_4, pH 6.0, and 0.002 *M* EDTA.

From the results of ultracentrifugal analyses we have found that the depolymerization of the cytochrome *a* polymer proceeds in parallel with the increase in oxidase activity. For example, in the case of pretreatment with guanidine–HCl, it is indicated clearly that there occurs mainly the dimer of cytochrome *a*, while the oxidase activity increases two- or three-fold[70]. Thus, it could be inferred that only a molecule of cytochrome *a* polymer which is composed of the same molecular species, is reactive toward oxygen, etc., whereas the other ones are inert through interactions occurring among the polymerized molecules.

This inference might be supported by results obtained from studies on the relationship between the midpoint potential (E_{mid}) and activity of cytochrome *a* in the presence and absence of *c*-type cytochrome. Horio *et al.*[140] have recently reported that the cytochrome oxidase activity is shown by cytochrome *a* in the presence of adequate *c*-type cytochrome, and that the

References p. 305

observed E_{mid} values are unchanged whether the assays are based on the α or γ absorption peaks of cytochrome *a*, even if the E_{mid} values of cytochrome *a* vary with the *c*-type cytochromes used. They have concluded that most of the data available may be rationalized by the assumption that oxidase activity can be elicited from cytochrome *a* with any of its haem groups present acting as binding sites for the oxygen, but only when adequate *c*-type cytochromes are combined with the protein to produce the proper complex system.

(x) Photochemical action spectra of CO inhibition of cytochrome oxidase[63,141,142]

In 1929, Warburg and Negelein[63] measured the action spectrum of the photoreversible inhibition of respiration by CO. The photochemical action spectra obtained with whole cells of *Torula utilis* exhibited absorption maxima at 280, 430, 545 and 590 mμ. Since these spectra resembled those obtained with haem compounds, they assumed that the respiratory enzyme involved, which reacts directly with molecular oxygen and forms a photodissociable compound with CO, was a haemoprotein. Afterwards, using a new device and sensitive method for the accurate determination of relative photochemical action spectra, Castor and Chance[141], and more recently, Yonetani and Kidder[142], showed that the action spectrum of baker's yeast and of the reconstituted cytochrome oxidase system prepared from beef heart muscle also had the same maxima. Although it is the typical spectrum expected from a haemoprotein, this spectrum is definitely different from the absorption spectrum of the CO-treated preparation of reduced cytochrome oxidase. The observed difference indicates that only a portion of the cytochrome oxidase preparation corresponds to the respiratory enzyme as defined by Warburg, in agreement with Keilin and Hartree[8]. This was one of the major reasons why Keilin and Hartree introduced the concept of cytochrome a_3. As shown previously[80,143], an absorption spectrum identical with the action spectrum was obtained only after subtracting the absorption of the CO-insensitive component, "cytochrome *a*", from that of cytochrome oxidase. Since then, the discrepancy between absorption and action spectra of cytochrome oxidase has been considered evidence for the separate existence of cytochromes "*a*" and a_3. If only a portion of cytochrome *a* aggregating in aqueous solution is reactive and the remaining portion is inert toward oxygen, CO, CN^-, etc., the same discrepancy would also result.

(d) Studies on the protein chemistry of cytochrome a

There have been many investigations of the reaction mechanism of cytochrome oxidase (EC 1.9.3.1) but some problems still remain to be solved. Yonetani[144] has recently summarized the studies which have been made on cytochrome oxidases and pointed out various problems, including the functions of lipids and copper and theories on the enzymatic action of mammalian cytochrome oxidase. As to the last, we have postulated a hypothesis which supports only one component, cytochrome *a*, being a polymer, instead of two components, cytochromes "*a*" and a_3.

There has been little information available on the protein component of cytochrome *a*. Since the preparation of cytochrome *a* used in our laboratory shows a high degree of purity both ultracentrifugally and electrophoretically, it seemed worth studying the protein part of the enzyme, particularly to help solve the various problems mentioned above. The amino acid composition of cytochrome *a* from beef heart was determined with two different preparations, and the results were similar. This suggests that the preparations obtained in our laboratory are reproducible and worth studying of amino acid composition.

The composition of the preparations studied by Matsubara *et al.*[145] was as follows: Lys_{39}, His_{29-30}, Arg_{30-31}, Try_{30}, Asp_{58-61}, Thr_{52-53}, Ser_{53-55}, Glu_{59-60}, Pro_{46}, Gly_{58-59}, Ala_{60-64}, CyS_7, Val_{49-52}, Met_{35}, $Ileu_{43}$, Leu_{86-88}, Tyr_{32-33}, Phe_{46-47}, $(NH_3)_{56}$.

The minimum molecular weight of cytochrome *a* was calculated from the content of haem *a* and of protein to be 92000, assuming that one molecule of cytochrome *a* contains one molecule of haem *a*, while it is calculated to be around 93000 based on 7 half-cystine residues. The total number of residues of the protein was about 820. The contribution of lipids to the molecular weight has so far been ignored in this case, but more recent studies[70] indicate that the minimum molecular weight of cytochrome *a* may be more nearly 130000. If this value is correct, it seems likely that the molecular weight of cytochrome *a* of 530000 may represent a tetramer molecule consisting of the same 4 haemoprotein species.

There are 3 distinctive features in the composition of the preparations, namely: (*1*) The leucine content was found to be very high, 86–88 per 820; (*2*) The half-cystine content was fairly low as shown above and this suggests that at least one residue must be in the reduced state. (The sulphydryl group(s) of cytochrome *a* will be described later.); (*3*) The most striking result concerned the amide content of cytochrome *a*. Usually cytochrome *a* from beef heart muscle shows a very low isoelectric point[16], pH 4–5, whereas a comparison of the contents of basic groups (lysine plus arginine) and acidic groups (aspartic acid plus glutamic acid) revealed a slight excess (8–11 residues) of basic groups[145]. Two explanations for this result may be considered. One is that some of the basic groups are buried deeply inside the protein and are inactive. Another is that the lipids are bound to a specific area, and cover basic groups. There is approximately 10–20% lipid in the preparation[146]. It is interesting to speculate that the lipids function by supplying a better environment for the reaction of cytochrome *a* with mammalian cytochrome *c*, a basic protein. Thus, cytochrome *a*, itself a neutral or slightly basic protein, gains acidic properties on combination with lipids, and a higher reactivity with the basic protein, cytochrome *c*.

The following facts may be explained on this basis. (*a*) When lipids are removed from the preparation the activity of the cytochrome oxidase decreased and on adding various lipids to a preparation from which the lipids had been removed, the activity increased to some extent[147]. (*b*) Some preparations of cytochrome oxidase were activated by certain lipids[148]. (*c*) Some basic proteins such as protamine inhibited the oxidase activity[44].

Investigations on the amino acid composition of cytochrome *a* showed that 7 moles of cysteic acid were derived[145] from one mole of cytochrome *a* of molecular weight 93000. Because of the rather low content of sulphydryl groups, this result prompted us to investigate the mode of existence of these sulphydryl groups and their role in the function[149] of cytochrome *a*. 4 of the 7 sulphydryl groups were detected amperometrically using Ag^+ as a titrant. It appears that small ions such as Ag^+ are readily accessible to these 4 groups. However, only 2 of the 4 groups can combine with *p*-chloromercuribenzoate (PCMB), which is a more bulky molecule than Ag^+ ion. The remaining 3 groups can combine with Ag^+ only after treatment of cytochrome *a* with 0.5% sodium dodecylsulphate (SDS) but PCMB does not block the sulphydryl groups completely even under these conditions.

Therefore, it is suggested that the first 2 sulphydryl groups described above are fully reactive, the second 2 less reactive and the remaining 3 are inactive. The latter 3 are probably situated in the interior of the molecule or, considering the polymeric nature of cytochrome *a*, within the aggregate. Moreover, it seems likely that even 0.5% SDS does not transform the molecular species into the fully unfolded state. However, the sulphydryl content of cytochrome *a* in the presence and absence of cytochrome *c* was found to be the same and 4 sulphydryl groups are usually detected amperometrically whether cytochrome *c* is present or not[149].

Using a purified cytochrome *a* preparation, Cooperstein[150] studied the inhibition of cytochrome oxidase activity on incubating cytochrome *a* with reagents such as GSH and BAL and the reversal of the inhibition by disulphide compounds. These results led him to suggest that cytochrome *a* contained one or more disulphide bonds which were necessary for the maintenance of the integrity of the cytochrome *a* molecule. Our results, however, apparently contradict his suggestion. The results obtained from the effects of PCMB and *N*-ethylmaleimide on cytochrome *a* clearly showed that no sulphydryl groups are essential for the activity and that the secondary effect of structural modifications is responsible for the apparent inhibition by these reagents.

6. *Pseudomonas* cytochrome oxidase

Yaoi and Tamiya[156] found that when *Escherichia coli* and *Shigella dysenteriae* were grown aerobically they exhibited an absorption band which differed from those of previously described cytochromes in that it lay within the red region of the spectrum. Keilin[157] attributed this band to a cytochrome component, designated "a_2". Warburg and Negelein[10], Warburg *et al.*[11], and Negelein and Gerischer[12], Tamiya and Yamagutchi[13], and Fujita and Kodama[14] independently found spectroscopically that cytochrome a_2 was autoxidizable and could combine with carbon monoxide and cyanide. Fujita and Kodama[14] also showed that this cytochrome was widely distributed in other bacteria, *e.g. Azotobacter chroococcum, Proteus vulgaris, Acetobacter pasteurianum, Eberthella typhosa, Salmonella paratyphi.* The oxidized form in whole cells showed an atypical band at 645 mμ.

Mainly from spectroscopic examination of cytochrome a_2 in whole cells, it is generally assumed that in these organisms cytochrome a_2 functions as a cytochrome oxidase[158]. Recently, Barrett[159] has extracted and purified a green haemin from *Aerobacter aerogenes* and several other bacteria, all of which contain cytochrome a_2. He has designated this as "haemin a_2".

In 1958, Horio[55,57] extracted and partially purified 4 different kinds of soluble respiratory components from *Pseudomonas aeruginosa* without the use of any detergent or organic solvent. Among the purified components there was a greenish brown fraction which possessed a complex absorption that appeared to contain both a so-called cytochrome a_2 and a *c*-type cytochrome. Even after extensive purification, the *P*-cytochrome oxidase preparation showed absorption bands of both the *c*-type cytochrome and the so-called cytochrome a_2. This indicated either that two different kinds of haem moieties were present in one molecule of *P*-cytochrome oxidase, or that the oxidase was a tightly bound complex of two different haemoproteins. *P*-cytochrome oxidase rapidly oxidized cytochrome *c*-551 and *P*-blue protein but oxidized *P*-cytochrome *c*-554 very slowly[55,57,58]. In addition, a preparation of this oxidase, though it has been crystallized, acts as a nitrite reductase[165]. Thus it is very likely that the enzyme is responsible for the nitrite-reducing activity of the organism.

As is well known, cytochromes a_2 and a_1 are found to be present in the cells of *Pseudomonas aeruginosa* grown under a variety of conditions. However, the former is induced only in the presence of nitrate, whereas the latter is repressed by the presence of glucose in the medium[160,161]. Both cytochromes a_2 and a_1, functioning as cytochrome oxidase, are characterized by a strong absorption at about 630 mμ and 590 mμ, respectively. As described below, it was found that the *P*-cytochrome oxidase involving cytochrome a_2 is characterized by having a complex absorption spectrum and is able to reduce molec-

References p. 305

ular oxygen as well as nitrite; it is thus designated as *P*-cytochrome *c*-551 : nitrite, O_2 oxidoreductase.

On the other hand, a partially purified cytochrome a_1, a particulate preparation, has been recently obtained from cell extracts of a strain of *P. aeruginosa* grown aerobically[161]. Although this oxidase is not active with hydroquinone and ascorbate, it oxidizes ferrocytochrome *c* of beef heart ($K_m = 1.5 \cdot 10^{-4}\,M$ and pH optimum of 8–8.5) and is sensitive to the respiratory inhibitors such as CN^-, CO, N_3^- and NH_2OH. This will then be designated as cytochrome *c* oxidase (EC 1.9.3.1).

(a) *Crystallization of P-cytochrome oxidase*[163]

For the purification of *P*-cytochrome oxidase from *P. aeruginosa,* see Horio *et al.*[162] and Yamanaka *et al.*[163]

(b) *Properties of P-cytochrome oxidase*

(i) *Absorption spectra*

The crystalline preparation of *P*-cytochrome oxidase shows a complicated absorption spectrum (Fig. 25). There are absorption peaks at 280 mμ, 412 mμ, 525 mμ and 635 mμ and shoulders at 362 mμ and 562 mμ, in the oxidized form. In the reduced form, there are peaks at 420 mμ, 523 mμ, 549 mμ and 554 mμ, a shoulder at 460 mμ, and a plateau between 620 mμ and 660 mμ.

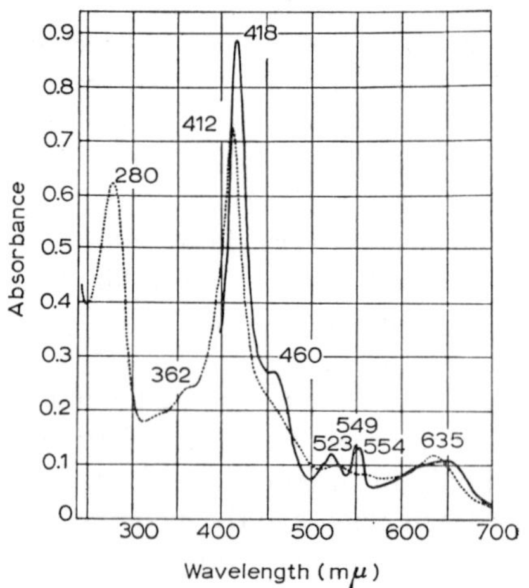

Fig. 25. Absorption spectrum of the crystalline preparation of *P*-cytochrome oxidase[163]. Crystals were dissolved in 0.2 *M* phosphate buffer of pH 6.5. ———, reduced with $Na_2S_2O_4$; - - - - - - -, oxidized form.

p. 290, line 2 from bottom, 420 mμ should read 418 mμ.

In the present preparation, the ratio of $A_{412m\mu}/A_{280m\mu}$ is 1.2. Upon reduction a shoulder appeared at 460 mμ, which may be the γ band due to haem a_2.

From the results obtained with protohaemoproteins, it appears to be a general rule that the rise and fall of the α band of the haemoproteins run parallel with those of the γ band. However, it appeared to us that the rule is not inviolate, since we have found an exception[164]. In the crystalline preparation of *P*-cytochrome oxidase, the α band due to haem a_2 varied in both absorbance and position with pH when the enzyme was reduced with sodium dithionite. Thus, it appeared at 655 mμ, 629 mμ and 652 mμ, and 625 mμ at pH 7.6, 7.0 and 5.6, respectively. In contrast, the corresponding γ band was invariably at 460 mμ. However, when the enzyme was reduced with ascorbate, the α band did not show dependence on pH. The γ band due to haem a_2 was very low in absorbance compared with the corresponding α band.

In the presence of CN^-, a peak appeared at 627 mμ when the enzyme was reduced with dithionite or ascorbate. In this case, a peak appeared at 443 mμ and a shoulder around 472 mμ. These spectral properties are quite similar to those observed in the crude preparation of the enzyme in the absence of CN^-. The activity of *P*-cytochrome oxidase was strongly inhibited by CN^-. The difference spectrum in the presence of CN^- showed 2 peaks at 443 mμ and 472 mμ. Therefore, it seemed very likely that the γ band of the normal enzyme at 460 mμ was split into two parts (Fig. 26).

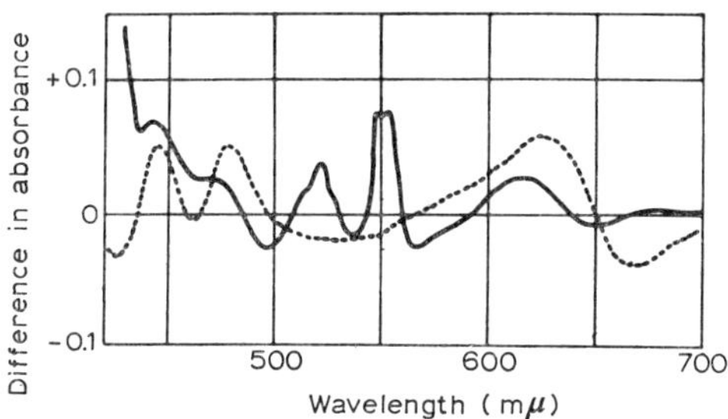

Fig. 26. The difference spectrum of *P*-cytochrome oxidase in the presence of CN^-. The concentrations of *P*-cytochrome oxidase and KCN were $7.3 \cdot 10^{-6}$ *M* and $1.2 \cdot 10^{-3}$ *M*, respectively. Spectrophotometric determinations were carried out in 0.18 *M* phosphate buffer at pH 7.0, in air. ——, difference, (with CN^- and $Na_2S_2O_4$) minus (with oxidized); ----, difference, (with CN^- and $Na_2S_2O_4$) minus (with $Na_2S_2O_4$).

The presence of CO considerably depressed the absorbance of the reduced enzyme in the red region of the spectrum, and the peak of the normal enzyme at 460 mμ disappeared. In this case, it is very probable that as the α band due to haem a_2 was depressed, the corresponding γ band was also depressed. However, it is very curious that when an enzyme solution which

References p. 305

had been in contact with CO was evacuated and then air was introduced, the γ band disappeared, whereas the α band was scarcely depressed. In the presence of NO, a peak at 665 mμ appeared and the corresponding γ band disappeared as in the presence of CO. The facts described above show that the relation between the α band and the γ band is very complicated, although it seems certain that the two bands are due to haem a_2.

(ii) Physico-chemical properties

The isoelectric point of *P*-cytochrome oxidase, pH 5.8, was determined by extrapolation to zero mobility, since a concentrated solution of *P*-cytochrome oxidase became turbid below pH 5.9 (ref. 162).

Coefficients of sedimentation and diffusion and the apparent partial specific volume were determined to be as follows:

$$s_{20,w} = 5.8\ \text{S};\ D_{20,w} = 5.8 \cdot 10^{-7}\ \text{cm}^2\text{sec}^{-1};\ \bar{V} = 0.73\ \text{ml} \cdot \text{g}^{-1}$$

From these values, the molecular weight was calculated to be approx. 90000.

(iii) Iron, copper and nitrogen contents

1 gramatom of iron was detected in each 46900 g of the *P*-cytochrome oxidase sample, but copper was not found, in contrast to the muscle cytochrome *a* preparation. The nitrogen content was 16.3%. Since the molecular weight calculated from the values for $s_{20,w}$, $D_{20,w}$ and $\bar{V}$ was 90000, it was calculated from the iron analysis that 2 iron atoms were present per molecule of *P*-cytochrome oxidase of molecular weight 94000. This conclusion is thought to be tenable since it was shown that 2 kinds of haem, *i.e.* haem a_2 and haem *c*, are present in a molecule of *P*-cytochrome oxidase.

(c) *Properties of the haem moieties of P-cytochrome oxidase*

(i) Haem a_2

To 1 volume of *P*-cytochrome oxidase solution which had been completely dialysed against water were added 4 volumes of cold acetone containing 0.5 *N* HCl. The mixture was allowed to stand for a few minutes in an ice bath and was then centrifuged. The supernatant fluid was bright green, and the precipitate brownish red. The precipitate was washed with a small volume of a mixture of 1 volume of water and 4 volumes of HCl–acetone. The washings were combined with the first supernatant and the mixture was adjusted to pH 8 with 5 *N* NaOH, and then studied spectrophotometrically (Table XIII).

It was apparent that the linkage(s) between the haem a_2 moiety and its protein was very acid-labile, so that without using organic solvents, haemin a_2 could be split from its protein below pH 5. On lowering the pH, increasing amounts of haemin a_2 were liberated.

TABLE XIII

SUMMARY OF THE POSITION OF THE ABSORPTION BANDS OF HAEM a_2[164]

Compound	*Solvent*	λ_{max} *α band*	λ_{max} *γ band*	ε_α *(mole^{-1} cm^{-1})*	A_γ/A_α[a]
Haemin a_2	acetone	—	432	—	—
Haematin a_2	water[b]	684	405	$2.7 \cdot 10^3$	3.5
Haem a_2	water	626	453	$14 \cdot 10^3$	3.0
Pyridine–haem a_2	water	620	432	$24 \cdot 10^3$	1.8
Pyridine–haem a_2[c]	water	613	—	—	—
CN^-–haem a_2	water	632	449; 480	$20 \cdot 10^3$	1.7
CN^-–haem a_2[c]	water	618	—	—	—
NO–haematin a_2	water	645	407	$13 \cdot 10^3$	2.8
NO–haem a_2	water	625	408; 436	$20 \cdot 10^3$	2.0
CO–haem a_2	water	644	413; 440	$20 \cdot 10^3$	2.0
Pyridine–haem a_2	acetone	615	421	$32 \cdot 10^3$	1.9
CN^-–haem a_2	water	635	414; 450; 480	$18 \cdot 10^3$	1.9

[a] Highest peak was selected when 2 or more peaks existed.
[b] Haematin a_2 is insoluble in acetone.
[c] Cited from Barrett[159]. Strictly speaking, haem a_2 of *P. aeruginosa* is not identical with that of *Aerobacter aerogenes*.

The green HCl–acetone extract of *P*-cytochrome oxidase was adjusted to about pH 10 with 1 *N* NaOH, and a green layer at the bottom of the solution was thus formed. A few drops of pyridine were then added and the mixture vigorously stirred for 5 min. The pyridine-haemochromogen separated as a green layer at the bottom of the solution, and was removed from the supernatant layer. The pyridine-haemochromogen readily dissolved in water, thus differing from other kinds of pyridine-haemochromogens. After dilution to an appropriate concentration with water, it was assayed spectrophotometrically. The cyanide-haemochromogen of haem a_2 was prepared in a manner similar to that used in making the pyridine-haemochromogen. In contrast with haemin a_2 extracted with HCl–acetone, pyridine-haemochromogen was fairly stable when reduced anaerobically; however, when reduced in air, its colour faded rapidly from green to pale yellow.

(ii) c-Type haemin

The brownish red precipitate formed after HCl–acetone treatment was fairly readily soluble in water. When 1 *N* NaOH was gradually added to the solution, turbidity developed around pH 6.0. Further addition of alkali clarified the solution completely and greatly increased the solubility of the precipitate. The pH was adjusted to 8, and the resulting red solution was sufficiently stable for spectrophotometric assay. Its absorption spectrum was very similar to that seen with a typical *c*-type cytochrome, except that the α-absorption maximum of its dithionite-reduced form differed from that

References p. 305

p. 293, Table XIII, last line, water should read acetone.

of *P*-cytochrome oxidase which exhibited a distinct trough (Fig. 25). The extinction ratio of the α and β peaks was 1.1, which was notably different from that of typical cytochrome *c*. However, the haem bound to the protein moiety and resistant to HCl–acetone treatment was cleaved from the protein by Ag_2SO_4 treatment, and shown to be haematohaem. Thus it appears that the haem moiety might belong to the haem *c* group. Further, if this protein moiety, carrying a *c*-type haem, was treated with acetone containing a higher concentration of acid, the colour of the protein changed from reddish brown to white, the *c*-type absorption spectrum was lost, and almost all the iron was found in the supernatant and not in the protein.

(iii) Reconstitution of P-cytochrome oxidase from haematin a_2 and its protein moiety[165,166]

As described above, the haem a_2 of the oxidase could easily be separated from the protein moiety by treatment with HCl–acetone, and the protein moiety could be precipitated with the haem *c*. The protein moiety was not soluble at neutral pH, even in the presence of salt. The haem a_2 extracted by the acetone was easily recovered by converting to haematin a_2 which is not soluble in the acetone.

When haematin a_2 and a suspension of the protein moiety were mixed at

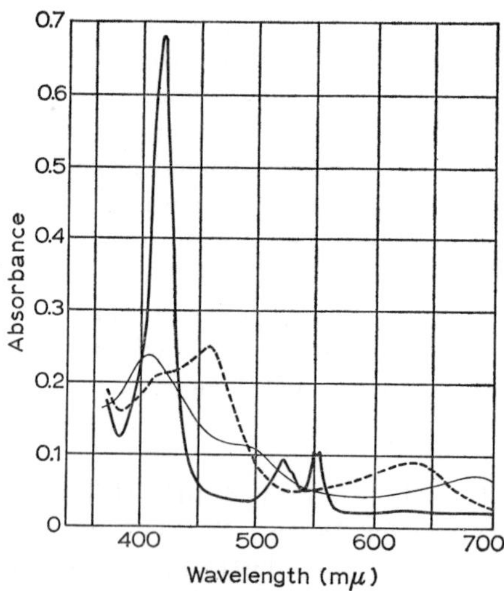

Fig. 27. The absorption spectra of haematin a_2, haem a_2 and the protein moiety having haem *c*. Haematin a_2 was dissolved in 0.2 *M* Na_2HPO_4 and the pH was adjusted to about 11. The haem a_2 was made by addition of $Na_2S_2O_4$ to this haematin a_2 solution. The protein moiety was suspended in 0.2 *M* Na_2HPO_4 and the pH was adjusted to 9.0 with NaOH. Thick solid line: protein moiety reduced with $Na_2S_2O_4$; thin solid line: haematin a_2; broken line: haem a_2.

p. 294, line 4 from bottom, presence should read absence.

approx. pH 9, the mixture became transparent, and on subsequent neutralization of the solution no precipitate appeared. The colour of the solution gradually changed from red to green at 0°. When the green solution was 90% saturated with ammonium sulphate, a green precipitate appeared, which was collected after centrifugation at 2000 × *g* for 10 min. The precipitate was dissolved in 0.2 *M* phosphate buffer at pH 7.0, and some insoluble matter obtained by centrifugation at 2000 × *g* for 10 min was discarded. The resulting supernatant was green, showing that the haematin a_2 had combined with the protein moiety. In Fig. 27, the spectra of haematin a_2, haem a_2 and the protein moiety having haem *c* are shown. The absorption spectrum of the newly formed cytochrome made from haematin a_2 and the protein moiety is shown in Fig. 28.

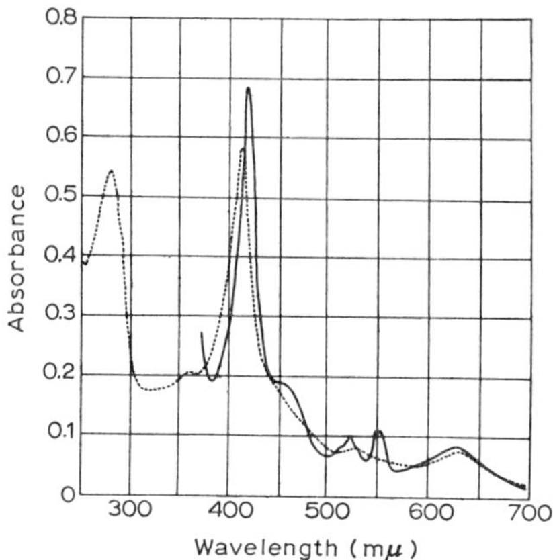

Fig. 28. The absorption spectrum of the reconstituted *P*-cytochrome oxidase. The preparation was dissolved in 0.2 *M* phosphate buffer at pH 7.0. ———, reduced with $Na_2S_2O_4$; ----, oxidized.

The haematin a_2 had its α band at 684 mμ whereas the reconstituted cytochrome had an absorption maximum at 635 mμ in its oxidized form. This together with the fact that the compound was precipitated by ammonium sulphate proved that haematin a_2 had combined with the protein moiety having the haem *c*.

The reconstituted cytochrome functioned both as a cytochrome oxidase and a nitrite reductase. Their turnover numbers were 37% and 54% of those of the original enzyme under aerobic and anaerobic conditions, respectively, although the preparation of the reconstituted cytochrome oxidase was not sufficiently purified. When various haems are used in place of haem a_2, various enzyme models can be constituted[166]. The facts that the Fe–chlorophyllin enzyme is very active and the haem a_2-derivative* enzyme is much less active than the reconstituted enzyme, show that the protein moiety of *Pseudomonas* cytochrome oxidase requires the chlorin derivative for its function. It seems likely that the vinyl group at position 2 is essential for enzymatic activity since the protohaem enzyme is more active than the haematohaem enzyme.

(*d*) *Physiological properties of P-cytochrome oxidase*

(i) Oxidation of reduced P-cytochrome c-551, reduced P-blue protein and hydroquinone by crystalline P-cytochrome oxidase

The pH optimum for oxidation of reduced *P*-cytochrome *c*-551 and reduced *P*-blue protein was 5.1 and for oxidation of hydroquinone it was 6.4. The K_m was determined as $1.9 \cdot 10^{-5}$ *M* for the oxidation of reduced *P*-cytochrome *c*-551, $3.9 \cdot 10^{-5}$ *M* for that of reduced *P*-blue protein, and $4.2 \cdot 10^{-2}$ *M* for hydroquinone oxidation. The turnover number was calculated to be 96 (moles/mole of *P*-cytochrome oxidase/min) at pH 5.1 and at 18° for *P*-cytochrome *c*-551, 100 at pH 5.1 and at 18° for *P*-blue protein, and 54 at pH 6.4 and at 30° for hydroquinone (oxygen uptake in moles for hydroquinone).

On the other hand, *P*-cytochrome oxidase has a strict biological specificity, *e.g.* it oxidizes *P*-ferrocytochrome *c*-551 but scarcely acts on mammalian ferrocytochrome *c*. These properties of the enzyme were used to detect slight differences between *c*-type cytochromes, as shown in Table XIV.

TABLE XIV

THE OXIDATION OF VARIOUS *c*-TYPE CYTOCHROMES BY *P*-CYTOCHROME OXIDASE AND BEEF CYTOCHROME *a*[164]

Sources of c-type cytochromes	*Turnover number (moles/mole of enzyme/min)*	
	P-cytochrome oxidase	*Beef cytochrome a*
Pseudomonas aeruginosa	154 (16°)	0 (15°)
Thallus of *Porphyra tenera*	4.1 (18°)	trace
Plasmodium of *Physarum polycephalum*	0.66 (18°)	3.8 (18°)
Saccharomyces oviformis, strain M_2	6.8 (15°)	50.3 (16°)
Wheat germ	1.2 (18°)	13.2 (18°)
Tunny heart muscle	4.8 (16°)	21.7 (18°)
Pigeon breast muscle	0.68 (18°)	35.3 (18°)
Beef heart muscle	0.81 (18°)	13.2 (18°)

The numbers in parentheses represent the temperatures at which the experiments were carried out.

* A haem derived from haem a_2 by removing extra hydrogen atoms at positions 7 and 8.

p. 296, Table XIV, last line, 13.2 should read 20.0.

Recently, Yamanaka *et al.*[167] have demonstrated another important difference in addition to the above. The rate of oxidation of ascorbate and hydroquinone catalysed by purified *P*-cytochrome oxidase decreased rapidly during the reaction period. On addition of catalase, this decrease in rate was prevented and oxygen consumption was accelerated. It was concluded that *P*-cytochrome oxidase is inactivated during the reaction by hydrogen peroxide formed as a direct reaction product. When reduced *P*-cytochrome *c*-551 was used as an electron donor, however, no activating effect of catalase was observed. Therefore, the activating effect of catalase on *P*-cytochrome oxidase may not be significant biologically. However, the fact that hydrogen peroxide was produced during the oxidation of ascorbate and hydroquinone but not during the oxidation of reduced *P*-cytochrome *c*-551 indicates that the reaction mechanism differs with different electron donors. On the basis of this result it is inferred that at least in the oxidation reaction catalysed by *P*-cytochrome oxidase, 3 components, oxygen, an electron donor, and the enzyme, should react simultaneously.

(ii) Reduction of nitrite by P-cytochrome oxidase

The crystalline *P*-cytochrome oxidase can reduce nitrite, but not nitrate, to nitric oxide in the presence of substances such as reduced *P*-cytochrome *c*-551, reduced pyocyanine and reduced phenazine methosulphate (Yamanaka *et al.*[168–171]). As is well known, reduced pyocyanine and reduced phenazine methosulphate are autoxidizable, but cannot reduce nitrite under anaerobic conditions in the absence of the *P*-cytochrome oxidase. Therefore, this reduction of nitrite by the electron donors mentioned above must be an enzymatically catalysed reaction. If the reduction results from some func-

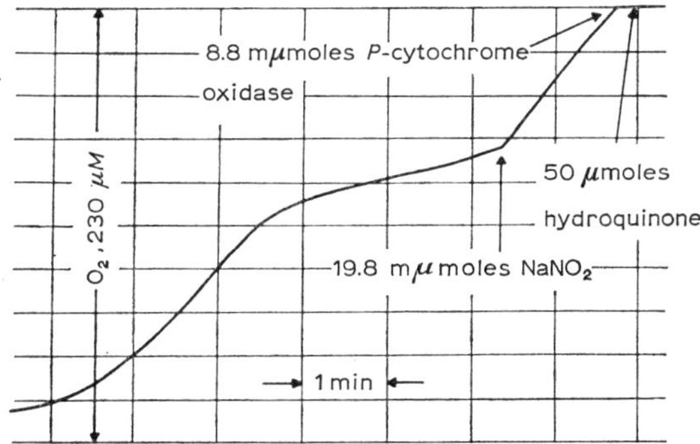

Fig. 29. Effect of nitrite on oxygen consumption catalysed by *P*-cytochrome oxidase. Oxygen consumption was measured with an oxygen electrode. As the electrode is disturbed by hydroquinone, the zero level for the oxygen concentration does not coincide with the zero line presented in the figures.

References p. 305

tion of *P*-cytochrome oxidase, the enzyme may be appropriately called a "reductase" (*e.g.*, *P*-ferrocytochrome *c*-551–nitrite or pyocyanine–nitrite oxidoreductase). Moreover, *P*-cytochrome oxidase can appropriately be named "*P*-ferrocytochrome *c*-551–oxygen oxidoreductase", because this enzyme can reduce molecular oxygen in the presence of appropriate electron donors. As can be seen in Fig. 29, this concept has been confirmed, since nitrite can compete with oxygen in accepting electrons from the *P*-cytochrome oxidase system[168–171].

C. DISCUSSION

The identity of cytochrome oxidase is still under controversy. One view originated with Keilin and Hartree[8] who claimed identity of cytochrome a_3 and cytochrome oxidase, and the separate existence of cytochrome *a* was based on the anomalous spectral behaviour of the *a*-type component in the heart muscle preparation toward respiratory inhibitors. Since then it has been the view that cytochrome *a* functions only to transfer electrons to cytochrome a_3, and the latter is responsible for donating electrons to oxygen. The other view is presented in this chapter, namely that cytochrome *a* is an entity, and that an active oxidase complex of cytochromes *a* and *c* fulfills the requirement for the cytochrome oxidase reaction[16].

It is generally accepted that cytochrome *c* is the most effective activator in the cytochrome oxidase system consisting of an electron donor, cytochrome oxidase and molecular oxygen.

However, we have proposed that cytochrome *c* also forms an active oxidase complex with an equimolar amount of cytochrome *a* to activate molecular oxygen.

From the kinetic analysis of the oxidation of ferrocytochrome c_1 with cytochromes *a* and *c*, we have confirmed the formation of an active complex between the latter cytochromes in a molar ratio of 1, and further presented an experimental result which suggests that the complex formation is due to an electrostatic interaction[71]. Recently Kuboyama, Takemori and King[120] succeeded in isolating the complex of cytochrome *a* and cytochrome *c*, in which the molar ratio of haem *a* and cytochrome *c* is 1. They demonstrated the pronounced activity of the complex. These facts can most simply be interpreted in our opinion that the *a* component is *one* component, and that oxidase function is manifested by the interaction of cytochromes *a* and *c*.

The function of cytochrome *a* in the cytochrome oxidase mechanism should also be made clear, especially its role as a constituent of the active complex. Ever since we have postulated the existence of the oxygenated form of cytochrome *a* from the inspection of spectral behaviours[72,79,151,152], our experimental results have become gradually recognized by other groups[153,154]. Evidence was provided[72] against the possibility that the spectrum of the oxygenated form might be a composite of the spectra of the oxidized and reduced forms of cytochrome *a*, or that the spectrum could be due to a hydrogen peroxide–cytochrome *a* complex[151]. It was established that cytochromes *a* and *c* form an active complex, and that cytochrome *c* is required for a rapid conversion of the oxygenated form of cytochrome *a* to the oxidized form. Based on these findings, we proposed the scheme representing the cyclic change of cytochrome *a* during its function through the oxidized, reduced, oxygenated and then to the oxidized form (see p. 245).

This idea may be extended to account for the anomalous spectral behaviour of the *a* component. Hence the classical experimental findings reported by Keilin as well as the definition conferred[8] on cytochrome a_3 would deserve further examination.

The observations which led Keilin and Hartree to postulate the existence of cytochrome a_3 were as follows:

"According to the effects which they (respiratory inhibitors) produce on cytochrome these substances can be grouped into three categories: (*1*) CO which affects the bands $a\alpha$, $a\gamma$ and $b\gamma$ and modifies them in a similar manner whether the reaction takes place anaerobically or in presence of a small concentration of oxygen. (*2*) KCN which affects the bands $a\alpha$ and $a\gamma$ but only under strictly anaerobic conditions. (*3*) KCN, ... which markedly affect only the band $a\gamma$ under aerobic conditions; the presence of oxygen being essential for this reaction."

".......... it is difficult to understand why the formation of a compound between *a* and KCN .... requires the presence of oxygen and affects only the band $a\gamma$, while the band $a\alpha$, being unchanged, clearly shows that component *a* remains still in the reduced state."

"We can hardly ascribe these changes to the combination of *a* with KCN without postulating the formation of a peculiar compound, one portion of which, responsible for band $a\alpha$, is reduced, while the other, responsible for band $a\gamma$, is oxidized."

"The existence of such a compound is, moreover, difficult to reconcile with the formation of another KCN compound which only takes place under strictly anaerobic conditions. Finally it is difficult to explain how CO can affect simultaneously both α and γ bands of one component (*a*) and only the γ band of another component (*b*)."

"The only satisfactory explanation of these changes which takes into account the results of all our experiments consists in postulating the existence of a new component, ... We shall designate this new component as a_3 ...."

As evidence for the identity of a_3 and oxidase, Keilin summarized the comparisons of the defined properties of cytochrome a_3 with the physiological functions of cytochrome oxidase. One of these is that

"the two bands of its compound with CO ($a_3 \cdot CO$) namely, α 590 mμ and γ 432 mμ, occupy approximately the same positions as the corresponding bands in the photochemical absorption spectrum obtained by Warburg ...."

From these quotations[8], it is clear that the anomalous spectral behaviour of the *a* band induced by KCN under aerobic conditions was difficult to reconcile with reasonable interpretations of the phenomenon in terms of a single component. This difficulty arose from Keilin's consideration that the disappearance of the $a\gamma$ band and its replacement by a weak band at 452 mμ is due to the oxidation of the component responsible for $a\gamma$ band.

There is however an alternative explanation, namely that there is an oxygen-sensitive interaction between cyanide and the cytochrome component in addition to the cyanide–haem binding, thus not requiring the postulate of another component. As is well known, the prosthetic group of cytochrome *a*, haem *a*, has a formyl group conjugated with the porphyrin nucleus. This group reacts with carbonyl reagents[155]. Thus it was natural to expect the formation of a cyanhydrin with cyanide but no evidence was found until we confirmed the formation of porphyrin *a*–cyanhydrin[75]. A possibility of cyanhydrin formation with ferrocytochrome *a* under strictly anaerobic conditions was also presented. By assuming the instability of this compound under aerobic conditions, therefore, we interpreted the spectral behaviours without introducing an unidentifiable component[75] other than cytochrome *a*.

Another support for the cytochrome a_3 hypothesis has come from the interpretation of the unparalleled changes in the α and γ bands of cytochrome oxidase when it was reduced or oxidized[144]. These phenomena can also be explained on our scheme of the cyclic change of cytochrome *a* involving the oxygenated form of cytochrome *a*, as presented recently[73].

As described in the text, Yonetani and Kidder[142] measured the relative photochemical action spectra for the relief of CO inhibition of the reconstituted systems and concluded that the spectra can be interpreted only by the cytochromes "*a*" and a_3 hypothesis. Indeed, it has been known that absorption peaks of mammalian and yeast cytochrome oxidase exhibit peculiar behaviour during its enzymatic reactions and on the addition of respiratory inhibitors such as cyanide and CO, but these peculiarities may also be interpreted as due to polymerized cytochrome *a* which becomes more reactive when depolymerized. Although they reported that the presence of cytochrome *c*, "cytochrome *a*", and flavocytochrome b_2, all even in a large excess, does not interfere with the measurement, it may be difficult to evaluate the data obtained by the photochemical action spectrum method, since for example the unique CO-spectrum of cytochrome oxidase–cytochrome *c* complex specified[121] with a band at 415 mμ is not detected by the method. As King *et al.*[121] suggested, conformational changes of either cytochrome *a* or *c* may result in the development of new properties. This consideration is compatible with our concept of the allosteric effect of cytochrome *c*. In this connection, it should be noticed that the action spectra of cytochrome *a* so far reported were obtained with the system containing cytochrome *c* in addition to cytochrome *a*. To clarify these situations it would be useful to examine the properties of cytochrome *a* as affected by cytochrome *c*.

As described previously, cytochrome *a* can be reduced by *p*-phenylenediamine or chemically modified cytochrome *c*'s even in the absence of native cytochrome *c*. In the absence of native cytochrome *c* however, such systems are unable to consume molecular oxygen. From this it has been concluded that cytochrome oxidase is nothing else but a complex of cytochromes *a* and *c*. Furthermore, it is reasonable to conclude that in the absence of cytochrome *c* an electron is not transferred from reduced cytochrome *a* to oxygen bound to the 6th ligand of haem *a*, since the formyl group of the haem *a*, having electron-attracting properties, can maintain an equilibrium of the electron distribution in the haem *a* moiety, but the electron will be transferred from haem *a* iron to the bound oxygen molecule when the equilibrium of electron density in the haem *a* moiety is lost by the interaction between cytochromes *a* and *c*. According to this viewpoint, we could also account for the evidence that in the presence of protamine or of polylysine, tetrahalogenated hydroquinones (=THQ) are oxidized by cytochrome *a* even in the absence of cytochrome *c*, assuming that the addition of THQ to the protamine produces a model cytochrome *c*, *i.e.* a protamine–THQ complex, in which the basic protein moiety of cytochrome *c* is replaced by protamine or polylysine and the haem group is replaced by THQ[115,116].

Hence it seems likely that such a substance, having properties capable of altering the electron density of cytochrome *a*, could exhibit oxidase activity with cytochrome *a* even in the absence of cytochrome *c*. The oxidation of a substance such as THQ by cytochrome *a*, itself without autoxidizability but with ability to react with CO or cyanide, can hardly be attributed to contamination of the preparation with autoxidizable cytochrome a_3.

Another problem is the elucidation of the properties of polymerized cytochrome *a*. As described in the foregoing section, cytochrome *a* is isolated in aqueous solution as a monodispersed polymer being composed of the same 4 or 6 molecular species. In the case of polymer, it would be very probable that only one molecular species or a minor portion in it exhibits the activity, and the remaining ones are inactive through the interaction occurring among the same aggregating molecular species. If this is the case, the former might correspond to "cytochrome a_3" and the latter to inert "cytochrome *a*". Thus in order to determine the nature of cytochrome oxidase it is necessary

References p. 305

to know whether cytochrome a_3 and "cytochrome *a*" have the same fundamental structure.

According to the method of Morrison and Horie[128–131] a "cytochrome *a*" preparation free of cytochrome a_3 is prepared from a purified cytochrome oxidase preparation by borohydride treatment. This preparation appears to have the properties of "cytochrome *a*" since it is insensitive to CO and does not react with oxygen, and exhibits absorption spectra different from the original cytochrome oxidase. However, it seems likely that the preparation free of "cytochrome a_3" is composed of a mixture of "cytochrome *a*" polymer and apoprotein of cytochrome a_3, since it acquires cytochrome oxidase activity when haem *a* alone is added to the preparation. If the apoprotein remains aggregated with the "cytochrome *a*" polymer, it is reasonable to conclude that the interaction occurring among the aggregating protein molecules should remain unchanged even after the cytochrome oxidase has lost the activity in consequence of releasing the prosthetic group, haem *a*. Therefore, it has never been established that the cytochrome *a* monomer as well as its polymer is inert to oxygen or CO. Hence it would be necessary to demonstrate whether the active depolymerized cytochrome *a* can be prepared from the preparation of "cytochrome *a*" free of cytochrome a_3 or not. Based on the

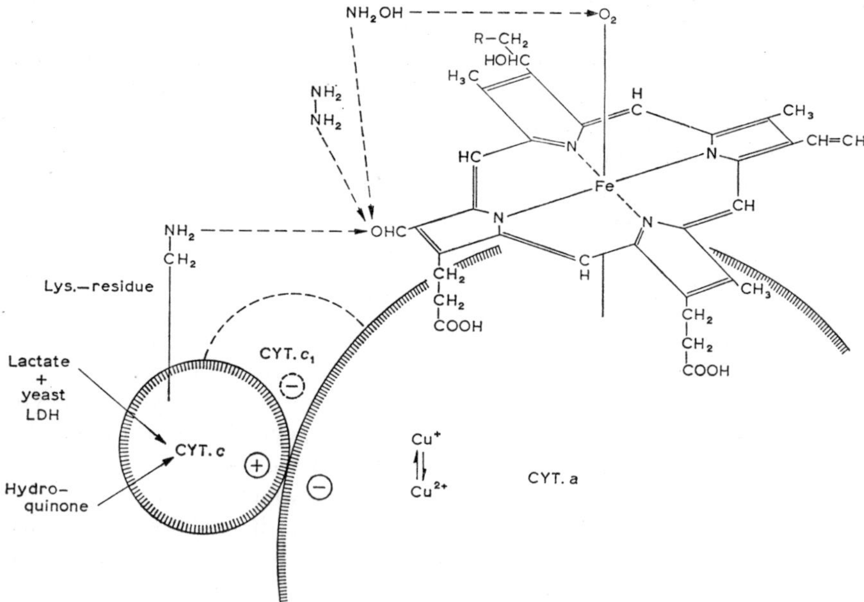

Fig. 30. Scheme representing the interaction between cytochromes *a* and *c* at a molecular level.

results we have obtained it is implied that depolymerized cytochrome *a* is more reactive than its polymer.

From the results described in the foregoing sections, the cytochrome oxidase system in heart muscle may be schematically represented at a molecular level as shown in Fig. 30. It was demonstrated that a dynamic equilibrium is brought about between the ferrocytochrome *a* and oxygenated ferrocytochrome *a*, between the ferrocytochrome *a* and another type of oxidized form, and between the oxygenated form and the other oxidized form. The oxidase function is not the simple reversible reaction ferrocytochrome $a \rightleftharpoons$ ferricytochrome $a + e^-$, but the oxygenated ferrocytochrome *a* in cooperation with cytochrome *c* brings about the cyclic interconversion among the various forms. The anomalous spectral behaviour of cytochrome *a* has been interpreted[73] in terms of the various components in dynamic equilibrium without postulating a separate cytochrome a_3.

Comparing the cytochrome oxidase of *P. aeruginosa*, which has cytochromes a_1 and a_2 in place of cytochrome *a*, with that of heart muscle, it is interesting to find that both contain not only *a*-type but also *c*-type haem, though the cytochrome a_2 of the former has not yet been successfully separated from the *c*-type cytochrome in the preparation. Therefore, there is the possibility either that the *P*-cytochrome oxidase consists of one protein molecule having two kinds of haem or that it consists of two kinds of cytochromes. At any rate, it seems likely, as in the case of the cytochrome oxidase of heart muscle, that the *a*-type haem or cytochrome a_2 may participate in binding molecular oxygen and its reduction in cooperation with *c*-type haem or cytochrome.

It has been clearly demonstrated that *P*-cytochrome oxidase, unlike the cytochrome oxidase of heart muscle, can reduce nitrite as well as oxygen, possibly at the same active site of the enzyme, and also that reduced *P*-cytochrome *c*-551 is required as an electron donor for the reduction of oxygen and nitrite. In this case there is no evidence that hydrogen peroxide is formed during the oxidation of *P*-cytochrome *c*-551, whereas hydrogen peroxide was definitely detected when either hydroquinone or ascorbic acid was added to the *P*-cytochrome oxidase as an electron donor. Therefore, the reaction mechanism may differ with different electron donors. If so, it seems unlikely that the electrons liberated from the electron donor are accepted by the *c*-type cytochrome in *P*-cytochrome oxidase, and then transferred to the oxygen molecule through the cytochrome a_2 which is able to bind molecular oxygen. It seems more reasonable to assume that *P*-cytochrome oxidase, consisting of cytochrome a_2 and *c*-type cytochrome, oxidizes the electron donor such as *P*-cytochrome *c*-551, hydroquinone, and ascorbic acid directly. In other words, it is inferred that during the oxidation–reduction catalysed by *P*- cytochrome oxidase, oxygen, an electron donor, and the enzyme react

References p. 305

simultaneously forming a ternary complex corresponding to the E·S complex, as in the case of cytochrome oxidase of heart muscle.

In short, it is reasonable to conclude that the cytochrome oxidase reaction might perform the reduction of molecular oxygen, resulting from the formation of a ternary complex, which is capable of coupling with phosphorylation, although the latter is not yet established.

REFERENCES

1 C. A. MacMunn, *Phil. Trans. Roy. Soc. (London), Ser. B*, 177 (1886) 267.
2 C. A. MacMunn, *J. Physiol. (London)*, 8 (1886) 57.
3 C. A. MacMunn, *Z. Physiol. Chem.*, 13 (1889) 497.
4 D. Keilin, *Proc. Roy. Soc. (London), Ser. B*, 98 (1925) 312.
5 E. Yakushiji and K. Okunuki, *Proc. Imp. Acad. (Tokyo)*, 16 (1940) 229.
6 D. B. Morell, J. Barrett and P. S. Clezy, *Biochem. J.*, 78 (1961) 793.
7 M. Grassl, U. Coy, R. Seyffert and F. Lynen, *Biochem. Z.*, 338 (1963) 771.
8 D. Keilin and E. F. Hartree, *Proc. Roy. Soc. (London), Ser. B*, 127 (1939) 167.
9 O. Warburg and E. Negelein, *Biochem. Z.*, 244 (1932) 9.
10 O. Warburg and E. Negelein, *Biochem. Z.*, 262 (1933) 237.
11 O. Warburg, E. Negelein and E. Haas, *Biochem. Z.*, 266 (1933) 1.
12 E. Negelein and W. Gerischer, *Biochem. Z.*, 268 (1934) 1.
13 H. Tamiya and S. Yamagutchi, *Acta Phytochim. (Japan)*, 7 (1933) 233.
14 A. Fujita and T. Kodama, *Biochem. Z.*, 273 (1934) 186.
15 E. G. Ball, *Biochem. Z.*, 295 (1938) 262.
16 K. Okunuki, in O. Hayaishi (Ed.), *Oxygenases*, Academic Press, New York, 1962, p. 409.
17 B. Hagihara, T. Horio, J. Yamashita, M. Nozaki and K. Okunuki, *Nature*, 178 (1956) 629.
18 B. Hagihara, I. Morikawa, I. Sekuzu, T. Horio and K. Okunuki, *Nature*, 178 (1956) 630.
19 B. Hagihara, I. Morikawa, I. Sekuzu and K. Okunuki, *J. Biochem. (Tokyo)*, 45 (1958) 551.
20 B. Hagihara, M. Yoneda, K. Tagawa, I. Morikawa and K. Okunuki, *J. Biochem. (Tokyo)*, 45 (1958) 565.
21 B. Hagihara, K. Tagawa, I. Morikawa, M. Shin and K. Okunuki, *J. Biochem. (Tokyo)*, 45 (1958) 725.
22 B. Hagihara, K. Tagawa, I. Sekuzu, I. Morikawa and K. Okunuki, *J. Biochem. (Tokyo)*, 46 (1959) 11.
23 B. Hagihara, K. Tagawa, I. Morikawa, M. Shin and K. Okunuki, *J. Biochem. (Tokyo)*, 46 (1959) 321.
24 K. Okunuki, in P. Alexander and R. J. Bock (Eds.), *Laboratory Manual of Analytical Methods in Protein Chemistry*, Pergamon, London, 1959, p. 31.
25 H. Matsubara and K. T. Yasunobu, *J. Biol. Chem.*, 236 (1961) 1701.
26 S. Paléus, *Arch. Biochem. Biophys.*, 96 (1962) 60.
27 T. Horio, T. Higashi, M. Sasagawa, K. Kusai, M. Nakai and K. Okunuki, *Biochem. J.*, 77 (1960) 194.
28 S. Katoh, *Nature*, 186 (1960) 138; *Plant Cell Physiol. (Tokyo)*, 1 (1960) 29, 91.
29 S. Morita, *J. Biochem. (Tokyo)*, 48 (1960) 870.
30 M. Nozaki, *J. Biochem. (Tokyo)*, 47 (1960) 592.
31 R. W. Henderson and W. A. Rawlinson, *Biochem. J.*, 62 (1956) 21.
32 T. Yamanaka, H. Mizushima, M. Nozaki, T. Horio and K. Okunuki, *J. Biochem. (Tokyo)*, 46 (1958) 121.
33 E. Margoliash, E. L. Smith, G. Kreil and H. Tuppy, *Nature*, 192 (1961) 1121.
34 E. Margoliash and A. Schejter, *Advan. Protein Chem.*, 21 (1966) in the press.
35 K. Narita, K. Titani, Y. Yaoi and H. Murakami, *Biochim. Biophys. Acta*, 77 (1963) 688.
36 K. Narita, H. Murakami and K. Titani, *J. Biochem. (Tokyo)*, 56 (1964) 216.
37 Y. Yaoi, K. Titani and K. Narita, *J. Biochem. (Tokyo)*, 56 (1964) 222.
38 K. Titani, M. Kimura, J. Vaněčeck, H. Murakami and K. Narita, *J. Biochem. (Tokyo)*, 56 (1964) 230.
39 K. Titani and K. Narita, *J. Biochem. (Tokyo)*, 56 (1964) 241.
40 K. Narita and K. Titani, *J. Biochem. (Tokyo)*, 56 (1964) 257.
41 S. Minakami, K. Titani and H. Ishikura, *J. Biochem. (Tokyo)*, 45 (1958) 341.
42 K. Ando, H. Matsubara and K. Okunuki, *Proc. Japan Acad.*, 41 (1965) 79.
43 H. Matsubara, K. Ando and K. Okunuki, *Proc. Japan Acad.*, 41 (1965) 408.

p. 305, ref. 34, in the press should read 113.

44 S. Takemori, K. Wada, K. Ando, M. Hosokawa, I. Sekuzu and K. Okunuki, *J. Biochem. (Tokyo)*, 52 (1962) 28.
45 K. Okunuki, K. Wada, H. Matsubara and S. Takemori, in T. E. King *et al.* (Eds.), *Oxidases and Related Redox Systems*, Wiley, New York, 1965, p. 549.
46 K. Wada, *Ann. Rept. Sci. Works, Fac. Sci., Osaka Univ.*, 12 (1964) 19.
47 K. Okunuki, *Advan. Enzymol.*, 23 (1961) 30.
48 M. Nozaki, T. Yamanaka, T. Horio and K. Okunuki, *J. Biochem. (Tokyo)*, 44 (1957) 453.
49 M. Nozaki, H. Mizushima, T. Horio and K. Okunuki, *J. Biochem. (Tokyo)*, 45 (1958) 815.
50 G. Ungar, E. Aschheim, S. Psychoyos and D. V. Romano, *J. Gen. Physiol.*, 40 (1957) 635.
51 I. Sekuzu, Y. Orii and K. Okunuki, *J. Biochem. (Tokyo)*, 48 (1960) 214.
52 D. E. Green, J. Järnefelt and H. D. Tisdale, *Biochim. Biophys. Acta*, 31 (1959) 34.
53 R. Bomstein, R. Goldberger and H. Tisdale, *Biochim. Biophys. Acta*, 50 (1961) 527.
54 Y. Orii and K. Okunuki, *Seikagaku (J. Japan. Biochem. Soc.)*, 33 (1963) 481 (in Japanese).
55 T. Horio, *J. Biochem. (Tokyo)*, 45 (1958) 195.
56 T. Higashi, *J. Biochem. (Tokyo)*, 47 (1960) 327.
57 T. Horio, *J. Biochem. (Tokyo)*, 45 (1958) 267.
58 T. Horio, T. Higashi, H. Matsubara, K. Kusai, M. Nakai and K. Okunuki, *Biochim. Biophys. Acta*, 29 (1958) 297.
59 O. Warburg and E. Negelein, *Biochem. Z.*, 193 (1928) 339.
60 O. Warburg and E. Negelein, *Biochem. Z.*, 200 (1928) 414.
61 O. Warburg and E. Negelein, *Biochem. Z.*, 202 (1928) 202.
62 O. Warburg and E. Negelein, *Biochem. Z.*, 214 (1929) 26.
63 O. Warburg and E. Negelein, *Biochem. Z.*, 214 (1929) 64.
64 O. Warburg, *Angew. Chem.*, 45 (1932) 1.
65 K. Okunuki and E. Yakushiji, *Proc. Japan Acad.*, 24 (10) (1948) 12.
66 W. W. Wainio, *J. Biol. Chem.*, 212 (1955) 723.
67 S. Takemori, *J. Biochem. (Tokyo)*, 47 (1960) 382.
68 S. Takemori, I. Sekuzu and K. Okunuki, *Nature*, 188 (1960) 593.
69 S. Takemori, I. Sekuzu and K. Okunuki, *Biochim. Biophys. Acta*, 51 (1961) 464.
70 Y. Orii and K. Okunuki, *Symp. Protein Struct.*, 16 (1965) 30.
71 Y. Orii, I. Sekuzu and K. Okunuki, *J. Biochem. (Tokyo)*, 51 (1962) 204.
72 Y. Orii and K. Okunuki, *J. Biochem. (Tokyo)*, 53 (1963) 489.
73 Y. Orii and K. Okunuki, *J. Biochem. (Tokyo)*, 57 (1965) 45.
74 T. Yonetani, *J. Biol. Chem.*, 236 (1961) 1680.
75 Y. Orii and K. Okunuki, *J. Biochem. (Tokyo)*, 55 (1964) 37.
76 K. Okunuki, I. Sekuzu, T. Yonetani and S. Takemori, *J. Biochem. (Tokyo)*, 45 (1958) 847.
77 I. Sekuzu, *Ann. Rept. Sci. Works, Fac. Sci., Osaka Univ.*, 7 (1959) 147.
78 E. G. Ball and O. Cooper, *J. Biol. Chem.*, 226 (1957) 757.
79 I. Sekuzu, S. Takemori, T. Yonetani and K. Okunuki, *J. Biochem. (Tokyo)*, 46 (1959) 43.
80 T. Yonetani, *J. Biol. Chem.*, 235 (1960) 845.
81 T. Yonetani, *J. Biol. Chem.*, 235 (1960) 3138.
82 T. Yonetani, *Biochem. Biophys. Res. Commun.*, 3 (1960) 549.
83 F. B. Straub, *Z. Physiol. Chem.*, 268 (1941) 227.
84 H. Dannenberg and M. Kiese, *Biochem. Z.*, 322 (1952) 395.
85 L. Smith and E. Stotz, *J. Biol. Chem.*, 209 (1954) 819.
86 E. Yakushiji and K. Okunuki, *Proc. Imp. Acad. (Tokyo)*, 17 (1941) 38.
87 I. Sekuzu, S. Takemori, Y. Orii and K. Okunuki, *Biochim. Biophys. Acta*, 37 (1960) 64.
88 A. P. Martin, D. E. Doyle and E. Stotz, *J. Biol. Chem.*, 240 (1965) 1402.
89 R. Lemberg and N. Newton, *Proc. Roy. Soc. (London)*, *Ser. B*, 155 (1961) 364.

90 J. L. Connelly, M. Morrison and E. Stotz, *Biochim. Biophys. Acta*, 32 (1959) 543.
91 R. Lemberg and J. E. Falk, *Biochem. J.*, 49 (1951) 674.
92 R. Lemberg, *Nature*, 172 (1953) 619.
93 I. T. Oliver and W. A. Rawlinson, *Biochem. J.*, 49 (1951) 157.
94 S. Takemori, I. Sekuzu and K. Okunuki, *J. Biochem. (Tokyo)*, 48 (1960) 569.
95 B. Eichel, W. W. Wainio, P. Person and S. J. Cooperstein, *J. Biol. Chem.*, 183 (1950) 89.
96 D. E. Green and F. L. Crane, *Proc. Intern. Symp. Enzyme Chem., Tokyo Kyoto*, (1957) 275.
97 K. Okunuki, B. Hagihara, I. Sekuzu and T. Horrio, *Proc. Intern. Symp. Enzyme Chem., Tokyo Kyoto*, (1957) 264
98 E. Cohen and C. A. Elvehjem, *J. Biol. Chem.*, 107 (1934) 97.
99 H. Yoshikawa, *J. Biochem. (Tokyo)*, 25 (1937) 625.
100 C. H. Gallagher, J. H. Judah and K. R. Rees, *Proc. Roy. Soc. (London), Ser. B*, 145 (1956) 134.
101 T. Nakamura, *Biochim. Biophys. Acta*, 30 (1958) 538.
102 D. C. Wharton and A. Tzagoloff, *J. Biol. Chem.*, 239 (1964) 2036.
103 Q. H. Gibson and C. Greenwood, *J. Biol. Chem.*, 239 (1964) 586, 240 (1965) 2694.
104 H. Beinert, D. E. Griffiths, D. C. Wharton and R. H. Sands, *J. Biol. Chem.*, 237 (1962) 2337.
105 H. Beinert and G. Palmer, *J. Biol. Chem.*, 239 (1964) 1221; in T. E. King *et al.* (Eds.), *Oxidases and Related Redox Systems*, Wiley, New York, 1965, p. 567.
106 W. W. Wainio, S. J. Cooperstein, S. Koller and B. Eichel, *J. Biol. Chem.*, 173 (1948) 145.
107 L. Smith, *J. Biol. Chem.*, 215 (1955) 833.
108 T. Yonetani, *J. Biochem. (Tokyo)*, 46 (1959) 917.
109 S. Miyajima, *Seikagaku (J. Japan. Biochem. Soc.)*, 28 (1956) 342 (in Japanese).
110 W. W. Wainio and M. Aronoff, *Arch. Biochem. Biophys.*, 57 (1955) 115.
111 W. W. Wainio and J. Greenlees, *Science*, 128 (1958) 87.
112 Y. Hatefi, *Biochim. Biophys. Acta*, 30 (1958) 648.
113 B. Chance, in W. D. McElroy and B. Glass (Eds.), *Mechanism of Enzyme Action*, Johns Hopkins, Baltimore, 1953, p. 399.
114 K. Okunuki, *Acta Phytochim. (Japan)*, 12 (1941) 1.
115 J. M. Machinist, F. L. Crane and E. E. Jacobs, *J. Biol. Chem.*, 240 (1965) 1788.
116 E. E. Jacobs, E. C. Andrews and F. L. Crane, in T. E. King *et al.* (Eds.), *Oxidases and Related Redox Systems*, Wiley, New York, 1965, p. 784.
117 W. W. Wainio, B. Eichel and A. Gould, *J. Biol. Chem.*, 235 (1960) 1521.
118 Y. Orii and K. Okunuki, *J. Biochem. (Tokyo)*, 58 (1965) 561.
119 H. Lineweaver and D. Burk, *J. Am. Chem. Soc.*, 56 (1934) 658.
120 M. Kuboyama, S. Takemori and T. E. King, *Biochem. Biophys. Res. Commun.*, 9 (1962) 534, 540.
121 T. E. King, M. Kuboyama and S. Takemori, in T. E. King *et al.* (Eds.), *Oxidases and Related Redox Systems*, Wiley, New York, 1965, p. 707.
122 K. Takahashi, K. Titani, K. Furuno, H. Ishikura and S. Minakami, *J. Biochem. (Tokyo)*, 45 (1958) 375.
123 T. Okuyama and K. Satake, *J. Biochem. (Tokyo)*, 47 (1960) 454.
124 K. Titani, K. Narita and K. Okunuki, *J. Biochem. (Tokyo)*, 51 (1962) 350.
125 O. Levin, *Arch. Biochem. Biophys.*, Suppl. 1 (1962) 301.
126 B. Chance, *Proc. Intern. Symp. Enzyme Chem., Tokyo Kyoto*, (1957) 271.
127 W. W. Wainio, in T. E. King *et al.* (Eds.), *Oxidases and Related Redox Systems*, Wiley, New York, 1965, p. 622.
128 M. Morrison and S. Horie, *Biochem. Biophys. Res. Commun.*, 10 (1963) 160; *J. Biol. Chem.*, 239 (1964) 1432.
129 S. Horie and M. Morrison, *J. Biol. Chem.*, 239 (1964) 1438.
130 M. Morrison and S. Horie, *J. Biol. Chem.*, 240 (1965) 1359.
131 M. Morrison, in T. E. King *et al.* (Eds.), *Oxidases and Related Redox Systems*, Wiley, New York, 1965, p. 639.
132 A. Tzagoloff and D. C. Wharton, *J. Biol. Chem.*, 240 (1965) 2628.

p. 307, ref. 97, T. Horrio should read T. Horio.

133 A. EHRENBERG AND T. YONETANI, *Acta Chem. Scand.*, 15 (1961) 1071.
134 Q. H. GIBSON AND C. GREENWOOD, *Biochem. J.*, 86 (1963) 541.
135 Q. H. GIBSON, C. GREENWOOD, D. C. WHARTON AND G. PALMER, in T. E. KING *et al.* (Eds.), *Oxidases and Related Redox Systems*, Wiley, New York, 1965, p. 591.
136 E. C. SLATER, B. F. VAN GELDER AND K. MINNAERT, in T. E. KING *et al.* (Eds.), *Oxidases and Related Redox Systems*, Wiley, New York, 1965, p. 667.
137 I. SEKUZU, H. MIZUSHIMA AND K. OKUNUKI, *Symp. Enzyme Chem. (Tokyo)*, 16 (1964) 87.
138 I. SEKUZU, H. MIZUSHIMA AND K. OKUNUKI, *Biochim. Biophys. Acta*, 85 (1964) 516.
139 M. KUBOYAMA AND T. E. KING, *Biochim. Biophys. Acta*, 92 (1964) 618.
140 T. HORIO, R. NISHIDA AND J. YAMASHITA, *IEG. #1, Sci. Memo #281*, (1965).
141 L. N. CASTOR AND B. CHANCE, *J. Biol. Chem.*, 217 (1955) 453.
142 T. YONETANI AND G. W. KIDDER III, *J. Biol. Chem.*, 238 (1963) 386.
143 B. CHANCE, *J. Biol. Chem.*, 202 (1953) 383, 397, 407.
144 T. YONETANI, in P. D. BOYER, H. LARDY AND K. MYRBÄCK (Eds.), *The Enzymes*, Vol. 8, 2nd ed., Academic Press, New York, 1963, p. 41.
145 H. MATSUBARA, Y. ORII AND K. OKUNUKI, *Biochim. Biophys. Acta*, 97 (1965) 61.
146 D. E. GRIFFITHS AND D. C. WHARTON, *J. Biol. Chem.*, 236 (1961) 1850.
147 R. P. IGO, B. MACKLER, H. DUNCAN, J. N. A. RIDYARD AND J. HANAHAN, *Biochim. Biophys. Acta*, 42 (1960) 55.
148 M. COHEN AND W. W. WAINIO, *J. Biol. Chem.*, 238 (1963) 879.
149 Y. ORII, T. TSUDZUKI AND K. OKUNUKI, *J. Biochem. (Tokyo)*, 58 (1965) 373.
150 S. J. COOPERSTEIN, *J. Biol. Chem.*, 238 (1963) 3606; *Biochim. Biophys. Acta*, 73 (1963) 343.
151 Y. ORII AND K. OKUNUKI, *J. Biochem. (Tokyo)*, 54 (1963) 207.
152 K. OKUNUKI AND I. SEKUZU, *Seitai No Kagaku*, 5 (1964) 265; K. OKUNUKI, *Seikagaku (J. Japan. Biochem. Soc.)*, 27 (1956) 611 (in Japanese).
153 A. J. DAVISON AND W. W. WAINIO, *Federation Proc.*, 23 (1964) 323.
154 M. MORRISON AND S. HORIE, *Arch. Biochem. Biophys.*, 105 (1964) 213.
155 R. LEMBERG, *Advan. Enzymol.*, 23 (1961) 265.
156 H. YAOI AND H. TAMIYA, *Proc. Imp. Acad. (Tokyo)*, 4 (1928) 436.
157 D. KEILIN, *Nature*, 132 (1933) 783.
158 L. SMITH, *Bacteriol. Rev.*, 18 (1954) 106.
159 J. BARRETT, *Biochem. J.*, 64 (1956) 626.
160 E. AZOULAY, *Biochim. Biophys. Acta*, 92 (1964) 485.
161 E. AZOULAY AND P. COUCHOUD-BEAUMONT, *Biochim. Biophys. Acta*, 110 (1965) 301.
162 T. HORIO, T. HIGASHI, T. YAMANAKA, H. MATSUBARA AND K. OKUNUKI, *J. Biol. Chem.*, 236 (1961) 944.
163 T. YAMANAKA, S. KIJIMOTO, K. OKUNUKI AND K. KUSAI, *Nature*, 194 (1962) 759.
164 T. YAMANAKA AND K. OKUNUKI, *Biochim. Biophys. Acta*, 67 (1963) 379, 394, 407.
165 T. YAMANAKA AND K. OKUNUKI, *Biochim. Biophys. Acta*, 59 (1962) 755.
166 T. YAMANAKA AND K. OKUNUKI, *Biochem. Z.*, 338 (1963) 62.
167 T. YAMANAKA, A. OTA AND K. OKUNUKI, *J. Biochem. (Tokyo)*, 49 (1961) 414.
168 T. YAMANAKA, A. OTA AND K. OKUNUKI, *Biochim. Biophys. Acta*, 44 (1960) 397.
169 T. YAMANAKA, A. OTA AND K. OKUNUKI, *Biochim. Biophys. Acta*, 53 (1961) 294.
170 T. YAMANAKA, *Nature*, 204 (1964) 253.
171 T. YAMANAKA, *Ann. Rept. Scient. Works, Fac. Sci. Osaka Univ.*, 11 (1963) 77.
172 D. C. WHARTON AND D. E. GRIFFITHS, *Arch. Biochem. Biophys.*, 96 (1962) 103.
173 S. HORIE AND M. MORRISON, *J. Biol. Chem.*, 238 (1963) 1855.
174 W. W. WAINIO, *J. Biol. Chem.*, 239 (1964) 1402.

Chapter VI

The Mitochondrial Electron-Transfer System

D. E. GREEN

Institute for Enzyme Research, University of Wisconsin, Madison, Wis. (U.S.A.)

1. Function of the mitochondrion

The mitochondrion is a structured device, found in the cells of all aerobic organisms, that couples the oxidation of various metabolites by molecular oxygen either to the synthesis of ATP or to the translocation of solute molecules or ions (active transfer of molecules from outside to inside the mitochondrion). In general, the coupled oxidative reactions catalyzed by the mitochondrion are part of the citric acid cycle. Each of the five oxidative steps in the oxidation of pyruvic acid to CO_2 and H_2O can be coupled to the synthesis of ATP or to the translocation of solutes. But oxidative reactions other than those of the citric acid cycle can also participate in the coupling process, *e.g.*, the oxidation of fatty acids[1], α-glycerophosphate[2], β-hydroxybutyrate[3,3a], proline[4,5] and choline[6]. Some mitochondria like those of beef heart muscle depend almost exclusively on citric cycle oxidations while others like that of the skeletal muscle of insects depend to a much smaller degree on citric cycle oxidations. The oxidation of α-glycerophosphate occupies a predominant position in some mitochondria[2]. If one thinks of the mitochondrion as an energy-transducing apparatus in which electron flow is coupled to the synthesis of ATP or to translocation of solutes then the origin of the electrons is immaterial as long as their energy is adequate to drive the coupling process. The electrons can be derived from citric cycle substrates or from any of a considerable list of oxidizable substrates that play no part in the cycle.

The conversion of oxidative energy to the bond energy of ATP and the conversion of oxidative energy to osmotic energy both involve the same basic mechanism but the terminal details of the respective transductions are not identical. In both cases electron flow leads to the formation of high-energy

References p. 325

intermediates that can be utilized either in the synthesis of ATP by the interaction of ADP and inorganic phosphate or in the translocation of solute molecules. One or the other end-result can be achieved but the same initial high-energy intermediates power both processes.

2. Membrane layer systems of the mitochondria

The mitochondrion appears to be built up of two membrane systems which closely interlock (Fig. 1) — an outer membrane system that encloses the mitochondrion and a system of inner membranes that radiate into the interior from the periphery[7]. In the intact mitochondrion the two tubular systems are fused and the space within the tubules of one system is continuous with the space in the tubules of the other. In all essential respects the two membrane systems are entirely different. They contain different sets of enzymes, different subunits and fulfill different functions. But the two membrane systems also have several properties in common. They are both lipoprotein systems — the lipid content and composition being virtually the same[8]. Structural protein is found in both membrane systems in about the same amount[9].

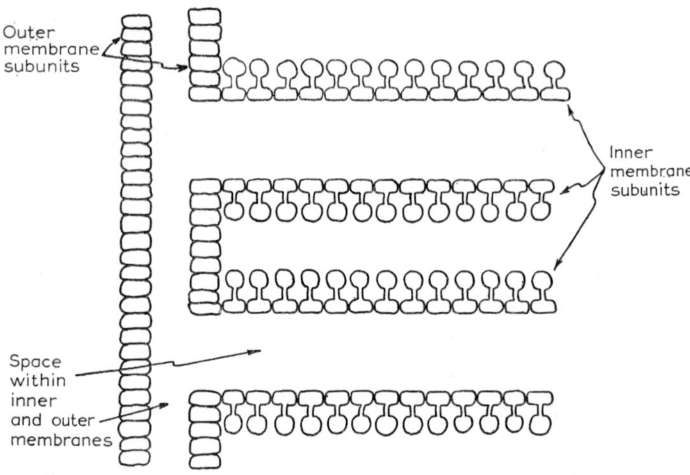

Fig. 1. Diagrammatic representation of the subunit structure of the outer and inner mitochondrial membranes and the relation of the two membranes.

The outer membrane accounts for 10–20% of the total protein (or lipid) of the mitochondrion while the inner membrane makes up the rest[9]. In other words the two membrane systems account for essentially all the protein of the mitochondrion. There appears to be little if any mitochondrial protein that is not membrane-bound.

The outer membrane contains all the enzymes of the citric cycle (other than the succinic dehydrogenase), the enzymes that carry out β-oxidation of fatty acids and the synthesis of long fatty acids from shorter chain fatty acids, and finally a set of the enzymes that are involved in the synthesis of phospholipids[9]. This is by no means the complete roster of enzymes found in the outer membrane. The β-hydroxybutyric dehydrogenase[10] and the enzymes that catalyze the phosphorylation[11] accompanying oxidation of α-ketoglutarate (substrate-level phosphorylation) are some of the additional members of the outer membrane family[9].

The enzymes of the outer membrane fall into two categories: those which are readily detachable from the membrane and which are of relatively small molecular weight and those which appear to be intrinsic elements of the membrane and of relatively high molecular weight[9]. In the former category are enzymes like isocitric dehydrogenase[12] and aconitase[13]; in the latter category are the organized complexes like the pyruvic[14,15] and α-ketoglutaric[16,17] dehydrogenase complexes. The available evidence suggests that the outer membrane is composed of multiple subunits and that each subunit is built up of two parts, a membrane-forming basepiece and a unit which is attached to the basepiece. The latter is the detachable part. The organized enzymatic complexes are localized in the basepieces while the individual enzymes plus associated protein are localized in the units which are attached to the basepieces[9].

The inner membrane contains the complete electron-transfer chain and all the systems required for the coupling of electron flow to synthesis of ATP or to ion translocation. Here again the membrane is made up of subunits which can be resolved into a membrane-forming basepiece and a detachable knob[18,19]. The electron-transfer chain is localized exclusively in the basepieces. There is insufficient knowledge to specify exactly what is localized in the detachable parts of the subunits of the inner membrane. Again, there is good evidence for more than one subunit in the inner membrane layer. The individual basepieces are of insufficient size to accommodate a complete electron-transfer chain.

The separation of outer and inner membrane can be achieved by exposing mitochondria to sonic irradiation and to bile salts. Such a separation at the same time leads to the partial removal of the detachable moieties of each membrane[9].

3. Stepwise degradation of the mitochondrion

Methods are available for the stepwise (probably reversible) fragmentation of the mitochondrion into its component building stones and units. We shall consider here only a few of the general principles that underlie the fragmen-

References p. 325

tation process. The various stages in the comminution of mitochondria may be listed as follows: (*1*) perforation of the external membrane as by freezing and thawing; (*2*) fragmentation of the external envelope and internal cristae into smaller segments; (*3*) resolution of the outer membrane into a particulate fraction containing the pyruvic and α-ketoglutaric dehydrogenase complexes as well as other integrated enzyme complexes and into a "soluble" fraction containing individual enzymes[9]; (*4*) resolution of the inner membrane into a particulate fraction containing the electron-transfer chain[20] and a "soluble" fraction containing enzymes required in the coupling process[21]; (*5*) resolution of the particles with electron-transfer activity into equal parts of two particulate fractions, a colorless structural protein fraction and an intensely colored fraction containing the electron-transfer chain[22]; (*6*) resolution of the electron-transfer chain into four component complexes[23–26].

Mitochondria that have sustained damage to their external membranes sediment more slowly than do intact mitochondria and are often referred to as light mitochondria[27]. When mitochondria are exposed to sonic irradiation they are comminuted to the electron-transfer particles[28] that are essentially fragments of the inner membrane which are partly stripped of their complement of detachable units and also of outer membrane subunits[18]. In general sonication breaks off the detachable units from both the outer and inner membrane[19], and in addition facilitates the separation of outer membrane fragments from inner membrane fragments[9].

Physical methods are insufficient however to resolve the electron-transfer chain into its four component complexes or to resolve the electron-transfer particle into the chain and structural protein. For such resolutions a combination of bile acids (cholate and deoxycholate) and salt is required[23–26]. The resolution of a complex into its component proteins demands even more rigorous conditions such as elevated temperatures in combination with bile acids and salts[29].

4. The elementary particle

The discovery of the smallest, complete functional unit of the mitochondrion *viz.* the elementary particle, had to await the perfection of high-resolution electron microscopy, and the development of more adequate techniques, such as fixation by phosphotungstic acid, for staining mitochondrial preparations exposed to the electron beam. Fernández-Morán[30] was one of the first to achieve this high resolution and to develop techniques for fixing and mounting specimens that could take full advantage of this increased resolution. When mitochondria and sub-mitochondrial particles are examined under proper conditions, regular arrays of many hundreds of elementary particles in cristae or fragments thereof are clearly seen in electron micrographs (Fig. 2). The most definitive pictures of the shape and dimensions of these particles are obtained by the electron-microscopic examination of preparations of sub-mitochondrial particles that contain fragments of cristae. In such preparations the tubular cristae are found to be studded with arrays

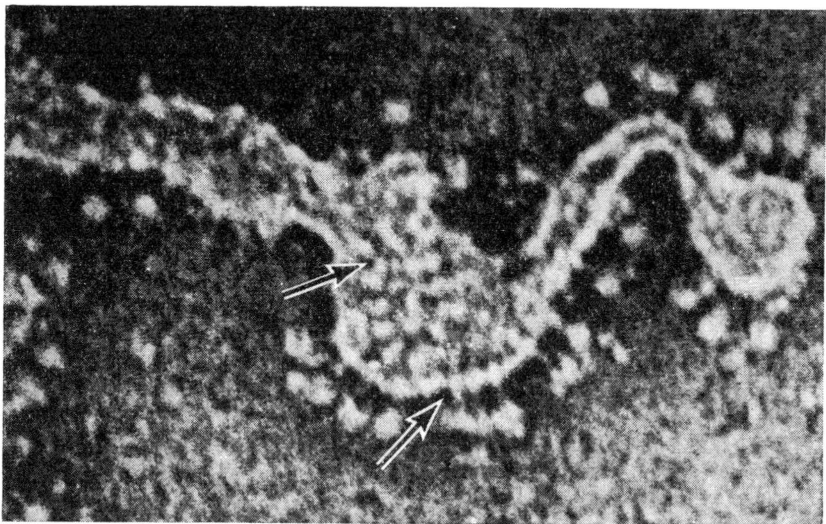

Fig. 2. Arrays of tripartite elementary particles in a crista of beef heart mitochondria. Specimen stained with phosphotungstate. Taken from Fernández-Morán *et al.*[7]. (510000 ×)

of particles which have been named the elementary particles[7]. These particles can exist either in the tripartite form (basepiece, headpiece and stalk) or in a compressed form (a single spherical unit 150 Å in diameter)[31]. The transition from tripartite to compressed form is induced by addition of ATP or substrate to the preparation before exposure to phosphotungstate[32]. The molecular weight of each elementary particle is estimated[7] to be about $1.3 \cdot 10^6$. Sonic irradiation or exposure to bile salts strips the headpiece and stalk from the inner membrane which now consists exclusively of basepieces[18,20]. The electron-transfer chain can be isolated in the form of vesicular structures made up entirely of stripped elementary particles or basepieces. This observation is the experimental basis for localizing the electron-transfer chain exclusively in the basepieces. One complete electron-transfer chain (with a full complement of structural protein) has a molecular weight[20] of about $3 \cdot 10^6$ whereas each basepiece at most can contain a unit of $0.5 \cdot 10^6$ in molecular weight[7]. From this disparity in size it has been deduced that a basepiece can accommodate only a single complex of the chain. Furthermore,

References p. 325

since the electron-transfer chain is separable from structural protein[22] it would follow that structural protein is contained in approximately half the total number of basepieces. The exact interrelationship between subunits containing complexes of the chain and subunits containing structural protein has yet to be determined.

The subunits of the outer membrane are manifestly different in size and shape from the subunits of the inner membrane[32]. As yet, the shape and size characteristic of the subunits of the outer membrane have not been defined.

5. The electron-transfer chain

The electron-transfer chain of the elementary particle consists of a linear array of eleven oxidation–reduction components that transfer electrons from succinate and reduced NAD to oxygen.

Succinate ——
 \> ——→ O_2
reduced NAD ——

This chain consists of two flavoprotein enzymes (succinic and reduced NAD dehydrogenases), five cytochromes (a, a_3, b, c_1 and c), non-heme iron (three separate species), coenzyme Q and copper. The positions of the various oxidation–reduction components and their relative molecular proportions are shown below[33].

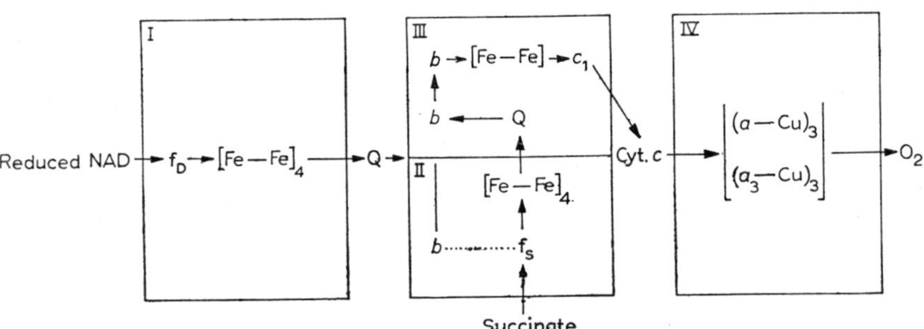

Electrons flow from left to right. The symbols used are: f_S for succinic dehydrogenase, f_D for the reduced NAD dehydrogenase, the letters a, a_3, b, c_1 and c for the five cytochromes, [Fe–Fe] for non-heme iron, Q for coenzyme Q (ubiquinone), and Cu for the copper associated with cytochrome a. The lines between components denote structural and functional links. It is to be noted that cytochrome b is present in two locations. The cytochrome b associated with $f_S(Fe)_8$ is a different molecular species and has entirely different properties from the pair of b cytochromes located beyond coenzyme Q[34].

6. Complexes of the electron-transfer chain

Until recently the point of fusion of the succinic and reduced NAD spurs of the chain was not localized. The presently available evidence suggests that coenzyme Q is the intersection at which the main chain meets the two respective spurs[35]. Depending on conditions either the succinic dehydrogenase or the reduced NAD dehydrogenase can be detached from the chain. Thus, a chain with only one of the two dehydrogenases can be isolated. It was this circumstance that, in fact, led to the view (no longer held) that there are two separate chains, one for the oxidation of succinate and the other for the oxidation of reduced NAD.

In the electron-transfer chain there are three sites[36,37] where non-heme iron is localized: (*1*) between f_S and Q; (*2*) between f_D and Q; and (*3*) between[38] cytochrome *b* and c_1. These three species of non-heme iron have characteristic electron-spin resonance spectra by which one can be distinguished from the others[36,38]. Furthermore, their oxidoreduction is specifically inhibited by different reagents. Thenoyltrifluoroacetone[39] specifically affects the reduction of the non-heme iron associated with f_S; amytal affects the reduction of the non-heme iron associated with f_D; whereas antimycin A inhibits the oxidation of the reduced non-heme iron associated with cytochromes *b* and c_1. The non-heme iron appears to be a polymeric array of iron atoms. Thus, there are eight atoms of iron in the non-heme iron clusters associated with f_S and f_D, and two in the cluster associated with cytochromes *b* and c_1 (Ref. 33). Not all the iron atoms in these clusters are necessarily involved in oxidoreductions. In fact, the calculations of Beinert and Lee suggest that only one iron atom in each cluster is responsible for the electron-spin resonance spectrum[36,37]. The rest of the iron atoms may serve merely in a structural capacity.

Cytochrome *a* is intimately associated with copper; here again both the cytochrome and the metal occur in a cluster of six[40]. There are some experimental grounds for the view that copper and the heme group of cytochrome *a* form a single resonating system. The exact role in the chain of the three species of non-heme iron and of copper has yet to be elucidated.

Coenzyme Q is a tetrasubstituted benzoquinone (Formula 1)[41–48]; it is of interest to point out that chloroplasts contain an analogous quinone (plastoquinone)[49,50] with one unoccupied position in the ring (Formula 2). Plastoquinone occupies a position in the electron-transfer chain of chloroplasts comparable to that of coenzyme Q in the mitochondrial electron-transfer chain[49,51–56]. In Nature the isoprenoid side-chain of coenzyme Q is found[57] with as many as ten isoprenoid units (CoQ_{10}) or with as few as six units (CoQ_6). In animal tissue CoQ_{10} and CoQ_9 are the rule whereas in microorganisms the variation covers the range of six to ten isoprenoid units.

References p. 325

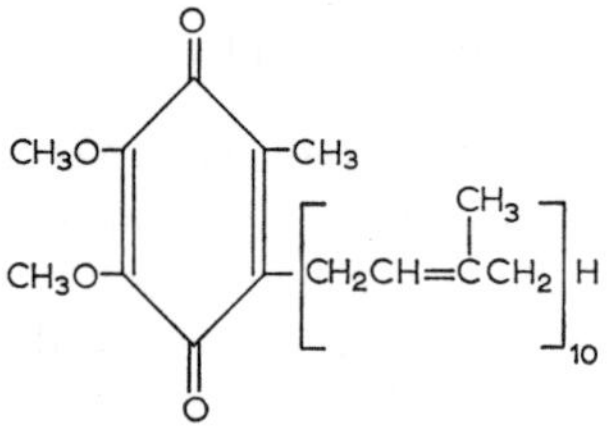

I
COENZYME Q_{10}–UBIQUINONE$_{50}$

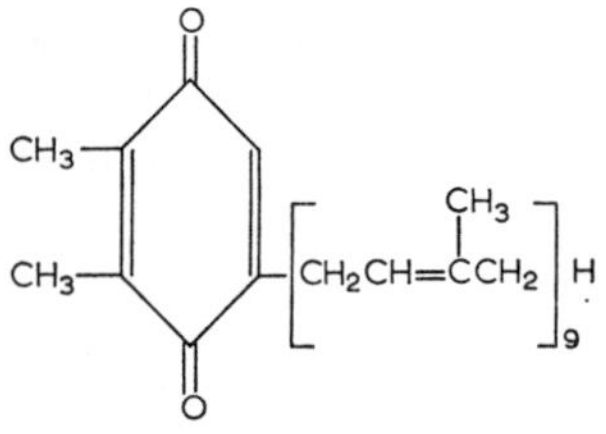

II
PLASTOQUINONE

There has been considerable speculation whether vitamin K is present in mitochondria of animal tissues[58]. At present there is no direct experimental ground for including vitamin K in the chain. It is not detectable as such in any of the particles that contain a complete electron-transfer chain and that are also capable of oxidative phosphorylation.

There is still open the possibility that the reduced NAD dehydrogenase may contain some oxidation–reduction group (part of the chain) that intervenes between reduced NAD and the flavin group. Some observations of Huennekens and Mackler point to the participation of a sulfhydryl group in just such a capacity[59].

TABLE I

THE FOUR COMPLEXES OF THE ELECTRON-TRANSFER CHAIN

Complex	*Designation*	*Reaction catalyzed*	*Composition*
I	Reduced NAD–Q reductase	Reduced NAD → Q	$f_D(Fe)_8$
II	Succinate–Q reductase	Succinate → Q	$f_S(Fe)_8b$
III	QH_2–c reductase	QH_2 → cytochrome c	$(b)_2(Fe)_2(c_1)$
IV	Cytochrome oxidase	Reduced cytochrome c → O_2	$(a\text{-}Cu)_6$

The elementary particle can be resolved into four component complexes which together make up the electron-transfer chain. Each of these complexes has a molecular weight of about 500 000 and contains two or more oxidation–reduction components. These complexes are listed in Table I; they nest together to form the electron-transfer chain of the elementary particles (Fig. 3).

I
 > III – IV
II

The lines between complexes denote the cohesive forces that hold the complexes together. The four complexes reassemble spontaneously to form a particle indistinguishable from the elementary particle in size, shape and

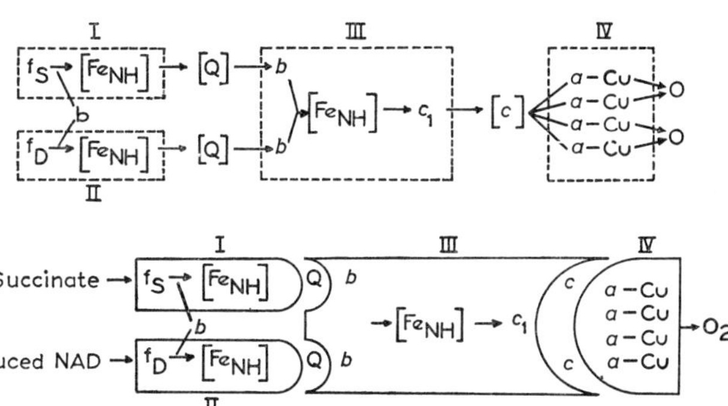

Fig. 3. Diagrammatic representation of the arrangement of the four complexes of the electron-transfer chain. The mobile coenzymes, Q and cytochrome *c*, are located in the region between complexes.

enzymatic properties[60,61]. Recombination of two, three or four complexes has been achieved.

I – III	I – III – IV	I ⟩ III – IV
II – III	II – III – IV	II ⟩

Under optimal conditions a 1:1 molecular stoichiometry of the four component complexes can be approached[61] and in such a reconstituted unit the molecular proportions of the oxidation–reduction groups are similar to those in the chain of the elementary particle.

The interaction of the individual complexes leading to reconstitution is interfered with or retarded in the presence of bile salts and inorganic salts in the medium[61]. The concentration of the interfering salts has to be reduced below a critical minimum in order to effect rapid recombination. The lag period usually observed in recombination studies is related to the interfering action of salts present in the preparations of the individual complexes[61].

The driving force in the recombination of complexes (and the determinant of specificity) is probably the complementarity of the surfaces of the reacting complexes. When the right fit is achieved the complexes nest together in a unique fashion and, presumably, maximal stability is reached at the point of optimal fit. It should be pointed out that the theoretical 1:1:1 stoichiometry of the combining complexes can be achieved under limiting conditions when complexes I, II and III interact. However, as yet perfect stoichiometry involving complex IV has not been reached. The separation of IV from the other three complexes proceeds with great ease whereas the separation of I, II and III, one from the other, is difficult of attainment. Apparently, the bonds between IV and the other three complexes are not as strong as those between complexes I, II and III.

References p. 325

The links between complexes are the mobile coenzymes, coenzyme Q and cytochrome *c*, that can shuttle electrons from one complex to the next[62]. These mobile coenzymes are the only oxidation–reduction components in the chain (other than succinate, reduced NAD and O_2) that are not fixed in position within a complex.

7. Structural protein

In beef-heart mitochondria one special protein alone accounts for about 70% of the total mitochondrial protein. This protein is known as the structural protein[63]. The structural protein is of a relatively small size (mol.wt. of 22000) and is a spherical molecule. It shows a considerable number of unusual properties[63]: (*1*) a tendency to polymerize at neutral pH into a water-insoluble aggregate; (*2*) a high density of both hydrophobic and charged groups which are segregated into well-defined regions covering the protein surface; (*3*) an unusually basic character (isoelectric point pH 9.5–10.5). The interactions of the structural protein (SP) can be classified into three categories:

(*1*) interaction between molecules of SP (leading to polymerization)[63,64]

```
SP—SP—SP—SP
|   |   |   |
SP—SP—SP—SP
```

(*2*) interactions between molecules of SP and other mitochondrial proteins (leading to soluble compounds)[63]

SP—cyt. *a*
SP—cyt. *b*
SP—myoglobin
SP—cyt. *c*
cyt. *a*—SP—cyt. c_1

(*3*) interaction with phospholipid leading to a structural protein–lipid subunit which readily polymerizes with other such subunits[63].

The bonds which are involved both in the polymerization process and in the interaction with lipid are predominantly hydrophobic. The bonds which lead to the formation of soluble compounds of structural protein with one of the various cytochromes are probably predominantly electrostatic in nature.

It is to be noted that cytochromes *a*, *b* and *c*, have properties very similar to those of the structural protein and this parallelism of properties is probably the basis of the specific interactions that take place between these molecules.

8. Lipid

The ratio of lipid to protein in the mitochondrion is about 0.4:1 by weight[65]. Over 90% of the mitochondrial lipid is phospholipid which is made up of phosphatidyl choline, phosphatidyl ethanolamine, cardiolipin and phosphatidyl inositol in the following order of relative abundance (41, 33, 15 and 8% respectively in beef-heart mitochondria)[65]. The fatty acids of these phospholipids are highly unsaturated (on the average about 1.7 double bonds per fatty acid residue); thus they are unusually sensitive to peroxidation by oxygen[66].

Lipid appears to be evenly distributed between outer and inner membrane and the lipid composition of the respective membranes is virtually identical except in respect to components such as coenzyme Q which is localized exclusively in the lipid of the inner membrane[67]. In the separation of either membrane into the detachable fraction and the membrane-forming fraction the distribution of lipid is not equal but is rather concentrated in the membrane-forming faction.

The ratio of lipid to protein in the inner membrane and in the elementary particle is roughly the same, *i.e.*, about 0.4:1 on a weight basis.

When the phospholipids in the elementary particle or in the component complexes are extracted with acetone (90% acetone, 10% H_2O) electron-transfer activity is lost; this lost activity can be restored by adding back mitochondrial phospholipids in solubilized form[68–70]. There appears to be no specificity for individual phospholipids although these differ one from the other in respect to the kinetics of binding to the extracted particle. The absolute essentiality of phospholipids for the electron-transfer process has been interpreted in terms of the lipid providing a non-aqueous medium for the linking of electron flow to the synthesis of ATP.

The β-hydroxybutyric dehydrogenase of the mitochondrion (one of the primary dehydrogenase complexes) has been isolated and shown[10,71] to have an absolute requirement for lecithin in the oxidation of its substrate by NAD^+. The apodehydrogenase combines with lecithin to form an active

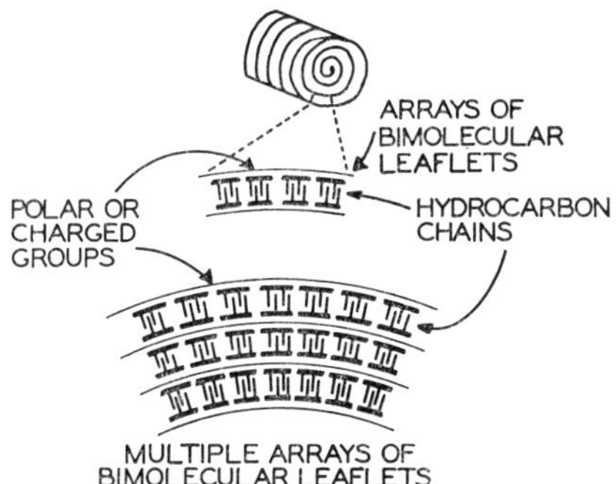

Fig. 4. Diagrammatic representation of the arrangement of phospholipid molecules within regular arrays or micelles. The three-dimensional arrangement is based on the results of electron-microscopic examination of "solutions" of such micelles.

References p. 325

complex. Lecithin has to be in the form of a soluble micellar dispersion (solubilized lecithin) in order to interact effectively with the apodehydrogenase[10,72] (Fig. 4).

The β-hydroxybutyric dehydrogenase is not unique in respect to the essentiality of lipid. The integrated enzyme activity of the electron-transfer chain shows an absolute requirement for the presence of lipid[68]. This requirement probably applies to all the integrated activities of the mitochondrion. The tendency of the membrane-forming segments of the subunits of the inner membrane to form vesicular structures (*i.e.* membranes) is completely lost when lipid is removed, but is restored when lipid is reintroduced into the extracted particles[73].

9. Role of structural protein in mitochondrial structure

The structural protein accounts for at least 50% of the total mitochondrial protein and the upper limit[63] could be as high as 70%. Clearly this protein must fulfill a most significant role in mitochondrial structure and function. The first and obvious question is whether there is more than one species of structural protein. The available evidence provides no support for more than one species. This evidence is derived from finger print studies[74], end-group analysis[75], ultracentrifuge patterns[63] and the binding constant for the structural protein–cytochrome *c* compound[75]. Structural protein is found in both the outer and inner membranes and makes a substantial contribution to the total protein in each membrane[9].

The basepieces of the inner membrane contain both the electron-transfer chain and structural protein. The hydrophobic links between the chain and structural protein are exceedingly stable but under appropriate conditions the two entities can be cleanly resolved[22]. This separability suggests that at least in the basepieces structural protein and chain exist in separate subunits. If structural protein and chain were linked at the molecular level rather than at the level of subunits such a clean separation would be virtually impossible. Under the conditions required to separate structural protein from the chain integrated enzymatic activity is lost in large measure but the loss is not complete. Cytochrome oxidase activity appears to be the least sensitive to this resolution. Whether the two resolved entities can recombine with restoration of the lost enzymatic activity is still an undecided question.

The other forms in which structural protein is present within the two membrane systems of the mitochondrion are still undefined. There is clear evidence that structural protein is intimately associated with the detachable proteins probably of the outer membrane[9]. There is presumptive evidence that structural protein may also be present *within* the complexes of the chain *after* the separation of the chain from the subunits of structural protein.

When structural protein contains its full complement of lipid (about 26% by weight) it readily forms vesicular structures comparable to those formed by the complexes of the electron-transfer chain which have been stripped of structural protein[18]. From such electron-micrographic evidence it is presumed that structural protein constitutes one of the membrane-forming subunits of the inner membrane.

The structural protein combines tightly with inorganic phosphate, ATP or ADP, and cytochrome *c*. These binding reactions may be relevant to mitochondrial function[76].

Exactly how lipid is fitted into the proteins of the two membranes is still not understood. It is of interest that mitochondria from which lipid has been extracted (up to 95% of the normal complement) still show normal morphology in electron micrographs[68]. There are grounds for assuming that lipid plays a key role in the determination of the conformation of mitochondrial proteins; exact conformation is critical for the exercise of catalytic function. The bonds between the complexes of the chain appear to depend upon lipid since the reagents which separate one complex from another readily rupture lipid–protein bonds but not protein–protein bonds.

10. Oxidative phosphorylation

In the oxidation of reduced NAD by molecular oxygen in the elementary particle, three molecules of inorganic phosphate interact with three molecules of ADP to form three molecules of ATP. It can now be demonstrated that each of the three complexes of the chain that participates in the oxidation of reduced NAD (I, III and IV) is responsible for the synthesis of one of the three molecules of ATP (Fig. 5). In other words, the individual complex is the unit of oxidative phosphorylation; and thus, a P/O ratio of three represents the participation of three different complexes, each with equivalent coupling capacity.

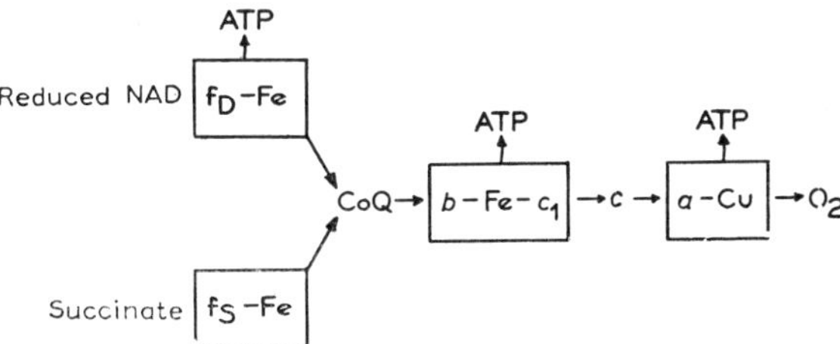

Fig. 5. Diagrammatic representation of the concept of the individual complex as the unit of oxidative phosphorylation. One molecule of ATP is synthesized in each complex as a pair of electrons traverses the chain of that complex.

References p. 325

A specific protein factor provides the means for coupling electron flow to the synthesis of ATP. Each of the three complexes is associated with its own coupling factor; on the basis of available evidence there appears to be no interchangeability among these factors[77,78].

The complex is the unit not only for coupling electron flow to synthesis of ATP but also for coupling electron flow either to translocation of ions[79] or to transhydrogenation[80] from reduced NAD to NADP. In other words each of three complexes (I, II–III and IV) contains all the essential systems required for the several coupling possibilities and this equipment is duplicated (not shared) at each site.

When electrons flow through the chain at each of the three coupling sites a high-energy bond can be formed. Either a special system additional to the chain or a unique state of the chain is needed for the formation of the high-energy bond. There is some evidence for postulating that electron flow leads to a wave of conformational change in the complex and this change results in the formation of a high-energy bond. In other words a conformational change may provide the link between the electron-transfer process and the generation of a high-energy bond. The question now reduces to the nature of the particular molecules that are partners in the high-energy bond at each site.

There is considerable evidence that the reductant for each of the three coupling sites is one of the molecules that eventually forms the high-energy bond (reduced NAD at site I, reduced coenzyme Q at site II and reduced cytochrome *c* at site III)[81]. The respective reductants transfer electrons to the complex and are in the oxidized form when the bond is formed. Thus each of the high-energy intermediates can be represented as NAD$\sim$I, Coenzyme Q$\sim$II and cytochrome *c*$\sim$III where the Roman numerals refer to the complexes at each of the three sites. The second molecule in each of these high-energy bonds is still unknown though ADP is a possibility.

The reactions involved in the transformation of NAD$\sim$I, Coenzyme Q$\sim$II and cytochrome *c*$\sim$III to ATP or to the intermediates required for ion translocation are still undefined. The coupling proteins or synthetases play a role in ATP synthesis but the nature of the systems that convert the first high-energy intermediate to the forms required to drive ion translocation or transhydrogenation is unknown.

11. The mitochondrion and osmotic work

As mentioned previously the mitochondrion carries out two transductions: (*1*) the conversion of oxidative energy to the bond energy of ATP; and (*2*) the conversion of oxidative energy to osmotic energy, *i.e.*, the concentration of solutes against a gradient. Mitochondria can bind Mg^{2+} and phosphate ions in concentrations as high as 1 μmole/mg of protein. This binding is coupled to electron flow but is not dependent on the synthesis of ATP. For example, in presence of oligomycin, phosphate and Mg^{2+} are bound but synthesis of ATP is completely suppressed[82].

The mitochondrion can be conceived of as an organelle into which solutes cannot penetrate freely. The movement into the interior of the mitochondrion is controlled by an active process (electron flow and the generation of a high-energy bond). The binding of Mg and phosphate appears to be intimately related to this active process. These studies have led us to the concept of the elementary particle as the entry port for solutes into the mitochondrion in the sense that the elementary particle controls the penetration of soluble molecules by coupling this penetration to the operation of the electron-transfer process[82]. This concept may have broad significance for cell membranes generally.

In view of this relation between the elementary particle and the process of ion transfer through the mitochondrial membrane, the study of the precise relation between the elementary particle and the membrane system of the external envelope is of prime importance.

12. The complex as the unit of electron transfer and oxidative phosphorylation

The complex is the smallest common denominator of mitochondrial function. Each complex represents a tight association of proteins, some of which carry oxidation–reduction groups. These oxidation–reduction groups are aligned

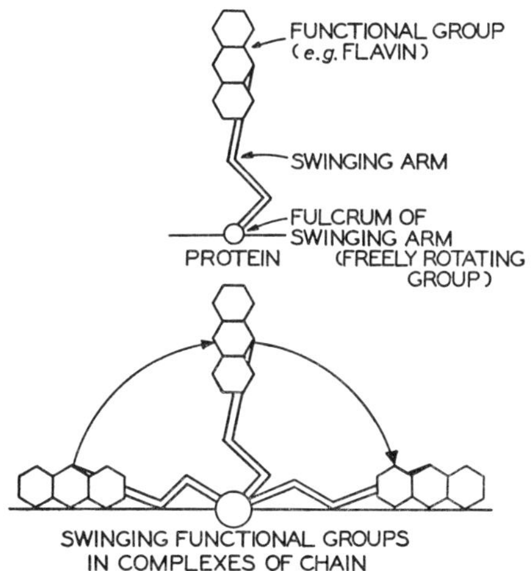

Fig. 6. The swinging arm hypothesis for the mechanism of electron transfer within the four complexes of the electron-transfer chain.

References p. 325

within the complex sufficiently close one to the next that electron transfer can proceed without any relative movement of the bearer proteins. That is to say the protein components of the complex are fixed in position whereas the functional oxidation–reduction groups are the mobile elements. This mobility is probably achieved by the tactic of the flexible arm (Fig. 6). Some group, *e.g.*, the aminobutyl group of a lysine residue provides the structural link between the functional group and the protein and is capable of rotation or fluctuation around the bond that connects it to the protein[83]. This fluctuation, in effect, establishes electronic continuity between neighboring oxidation–reduction groups within the complex. Since each of the 4 complexes has a molecular weight of about 500000 and is roughly spherical in shape the overall diameter of the complex is about 100 Å. A series of oxidation–reduction groups, each attached to the protein by a flexible arm some 5–10 Å in length, would then be in sufficiently close molecular proximity to satisfy the requirements for electronic continuity.

The complex appears to be a device for hybridizing a set of oxidation–reduction systems. The difference in potential between one pair of this set would be insufficient for the formation of one high-energy bond. However, the total difference in potential between the initial reductant and the final oxidant of each complex is adequate for this purpose. At least five oxidation–reduction systems are implicated in the overall process within a given complex (Fig. 7).

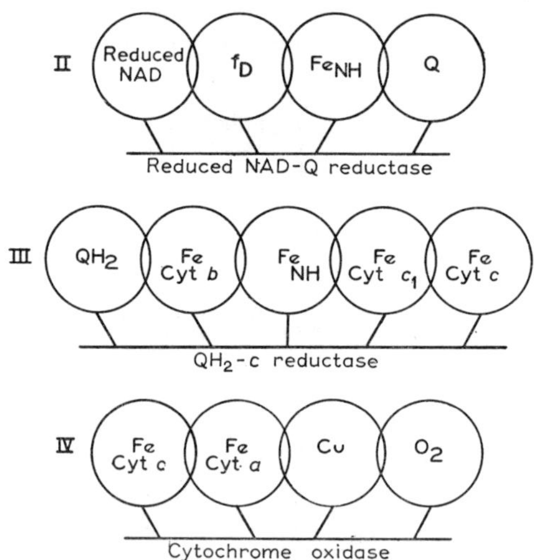

Fig. 7. The multiplicity of oxidation–reduction components that have to be accommodated within the precincts of a single complex.

REFERENCES

1 R. B. Johnson and H. A. Lardy, *J. Biol. Chem.*, 184 (1950) 235.
2 B. Sacktor and D. G. Cochran, *Arch. Biochem. Biophys.*, 74 (1958) 266.
3 R. J. Cross, J. V. Taggart, G. A. Covo and D. E. Green, *J. Biol. Chem.*, 177 (1949) 655.
3a T. M. Devlin and A. L. Lehninger, *J. Biol. Chem.*, 233 (1958) 1586.
4 H. A. Lardy and H. Wellman, *J. Biol. Chem.*, 195 (1952) 215.
5 A. B. Johnson and H. J. Strecker, *J. Biol. Chem.*, 237 (1962) 1876.
6 H. A. Rothschild, O. Cori and E. S. G. Barron, *J. Biol. Chem.*, 208 (1954) 41.
7 H. Fernández-Morán, T. Oda, P. V. Blair and D. E. Green, *J. Cell Biol.*, 22 (1964) 63.
8 S. Fleischer and B. Fleischer, unpublished observations.
9 E. Bachmann, D. Allmann and D. E. Green, unpublished observations.
10 I. Sekuzu, P. Jurtshuk Jr. and D. E. Green, *J. Biol. Chem.*, 238 (1963) 975.
11 D. R. Sanadi, D. M. Gibson, P. Ayengar and M. Jacob, *J. Biol. Chem.*, 218 (1956) 505.
12 A. L. Grafflin and S. Ochoa, *Biochim. Biophys. Acta*, 4 (1950) 205.
13 Sherman, R. Dickman and A. A. Cloutier, *J. Biol. Chem.*, 188 (1951) 379.
14 R. S. Schweet, B. Katchman, R. M. Bock and V. Jagannathan, *J. Biol. Chem.*, 196 (1952) 563.
15 V. Jagannathan and R. S. Schweet, *J. Biol. Chem.*, 196 (1952) 551.
16 D. R. Sanadi and J. W. Littlefield, *J. Biol. Chem.*, 197 (1952) 851.
17 L. J. Reed, *Physiol. Rev.*, 33 (1953) 544.
18 D. E. Green, H. Tisdale, D. McConnell, D. MacLennan and H. Tzagoloff, unpublished observations.
19 J. T. Stasny and F. L. Crane, *J. Cell Biol.*, 22 (1964) 49.
20 P. Blair, T. Oda, D. E. Green and H. Fernández-Morán, *Biochemistry*, 2 (1963) 766.
21 A. L. Smith and M. Hansen, *Biochem. Biophys. Res. Communs.*, 8 (1962) 136.
22 D. E. Green, K. Kopaczyk and H. Tisdale, unpublished observations.
23 D. M. Ziegler and K. A. Doeg, *Arch. Biochem. Biophys.*, 97 (1962) 41.
24 Y. Hatefi, A. G. Haavik and D. E. Griffiths, *J. Biol. Chem.*, 237 (1962) 1681.
25 D. E. Griffiths and D. C. Wharton, *J. Biol. Chem.*, 236 (1961) 1850.
26 Y. Hatefi, A. G. Haavik and D. E. Griffiths, *J. Biol. Chem.*, 237 (1962) 1676.
27 Y. Hatefi and R. L. Lester, *Biochim. Biophys. Acta*, 27 (1958) 83.
28 F. L. Crane, J. L. Glenn and D. E. Green, *Biochim. Biophys. Acta*, 22 (1956) 475.
29 J. S. Rieske and W. S. Zaugg, *Biochem. Biophys. Res. Communs.*, 8 (1962) 421.
30 H. Fernández-Morán, in Tercentenary of the Microscope in Living Biology, *Roy. Microscop. Soc. J.*, 83 (1964) 183.
31 T. Oda, *Symp. Soc. Cellular Chem.*, 13 (1963) 11.
32 H. Fernández-Morán, unpublished observations.
33 D. C. Wharton and D. E. Green, *Biochem. Z.*, 338 (1963) 335.
34 H. D. Tisdale, D. C. Wharton and D. E. Green, *Arch. Biochem. Biophys.*, 102 (1963) 114.
35 D. E. Green and Y. Hatefi, *Science*, 133 (1961) 3445.
36 H. Beinert and W. Lee, *Biochem. Biophys. Res. Communs.*, 5 (1961) 40.
37 H. Beinert and R. H. Sands, *Biochem. Biophys. Res. Communs.*, 3 (1960) 41.
38 J. S. Rieske, W. S. Zaugg and R. E. Hansen, *J. Biol. Chem.*, 239 (1964) 3023.
39 D. Ziegler in T. W. Goodwin and O. Lindberg (Eds.), *Biological Structure and Function*, Proc. of the First IUB/IUBS International Symposium in Stockholm, Vol. II, Academic Press, New York, 1961.
40 S. Takemori, I. Sekuzu and K. Okunuki, *Nature*, 188 (1960) 593.
41 D. E. Wolf, C. H. Hoffman, N. R. Trenner, B. H. Arison, C. H. Shunk, B. O. Linn, J. F. McPherson and K. Folkers, *J. Am. Chem. Soc.*, 80 (1958) 4752.
42 F. L. Crane, Y. Hatefi, R. L. Lester and C. Widmer, *Biochim. Biophys. Acta*, 25 (1957) 220.
43 K. Folkers in G. E. W. Wolstenholme (Ed.), *Quinones in Electron Transport*, Ciba Symposium, Churchill, London, 1961, p. 100.
44 D. E. Green in G. E. W. Wolstenholme (Ed.), *Quinones in Electron Transport*, Ciba Symposium, Churchill, London, 1961, p. 130.

[45] R. A. Morton, U. Gloor, O. Schindler, G. M. Wilson, L. H. Chopard-dit-Jean, F. W. Hemming, O. Isler, W. M. F. Leat, J. F. Pennock, R. Rüegg, U. Schwieter and O. Wiss, *Helv. Chim. Acta*, 41 (1958) 2343.
[46] R. A. Morton, G. M. Wilson, J. S. Lowe and W. M. F. Leat, *Chem. Ind. (London)*, (1957) 1649.
[47] R. A. Morton in G. E. W. Wolstenholme (Ed.). *Quinones in Electron Transport*, Ciba Symposium, Churchill, London, 1961, p. 5.
[48] O. Isler, R. Rüegg, A. Langemann, P. Schudell and G. Rysser in G. E. W. Wolstenholme (Ed.), *Quinones in Electron Transport*, Ciba Symposium, Churchill, London, 1961, p. 79.
[49] F. L. Crane in G. E. W. Wolstenholme (Ed.), *Quinones in Electron Transport*, Ciba Symposium, Churchill, London, 1961, p. 36.
[50] M. Kofler, A. Langemann, R. Rüegg, L. H. Chopard-dit-Jean, A. Rayroud and O. Isler, *Helv. Chim. Acta*, 42 (1959) 1283.
[51] N. I. Bishop, *Proc. Natl. Acad. Sci. U.S.*, 12 (1959) 1696.
[52] D. W. Krogman, *Biochem. Biophys. Res. Communs.*, 4 (1961) 275.
[53] R. L. Lester and S. Fleischer, *Arch. Biochem. Biophys.*, 80 (1959) 470.
[54] D. E. Green in G. E. W. Wolstenholme (Ed.), *Quinones in Electron Transport*, Ciba Symposium, Churchill, London, 1961, p. 130.
[55] D. E. Green, Y. Hatefi and W. F. Fechner, *Biochem. Biophys. Res. Communs.*, 1 (1959) 45.
[56] D. E. Green and R. L. Lester, *Federation Proc.*, 18 (1959) 987.
[57] R. L. Lester, Y. Hatefi, C. Widmer and F. L. Crane, *Biochim. Biophys. Acta*, 33 (1959) 169.
[58] C. Martius in G. E. W. Wolstenholme (Ed.), *Quinones in Electron Transport*, Ciba Symposium, Churchill, London, 1961, p. 312.
[59] F. M. Huenenkens and B. Mackler, unpublished studies.
[60] Y. Hatefi, A. G. Haavik, I. R. Fowler and D. E. Griffiths, *J. Biol. Chem.*, 237 (1962) 2661.
[61] L. R. Fowler and S. H. Richardson, *J. Biol. Chem.*, 238 (1963) 456.
[62] D. E. Green, *Vth International Congress of Biochemistry, Plenary Lecture*, Preprint No. 176, Moscow, 1961.
[63] R. S. Criddle, R. M. Bock, D. E. Green and H. Tisdale, *Biochemistry*, 1 (1962) 827.
[64] D. E. Green, H. Tisdale, R. S. Criddle, P. Y. Chen and R. M. Bock, *Biochem. Biophys. Res. Communs.*, 5 (1961) 109.
[65] S. Fleischer, H. Klouwen and G. Brierley, *J. Biol. Chem.*, 236 (1961) 2936.
[66] R. T. Holman and C. Widmer, *J. Biol. Chem.*, 234 (1959) 9.
[67] S. Fleischer, unpublished observations.
[68] S. Fleischer, G. Brierley, H. Klouwen and D. B. Slautterback, *J. Biol. Chem.*, 237 (1962) 3264.
[69] G. P. Brierley, A. J. Merola and S. Fleischer, *Biochim. Biophys. Acta*, 64 (1964) 218.
[70] G. P. Brierley and A. J. Merola, *Biochim. Biophys. Acta*, 64 (1964) 205.
[71] P. Jurtshuk Jr., I. Sezuku and D. E. Green, *J. Biol. Chem.*, 238 (1963) 3595.
[72] S. Fleischer and H. Klouwen, *Biochem. Biophys. Res. Communs.*, 5 (1961) 378.
[73] D. McConnell, A. Tzagoloff and D. MacLennan, unpublished observations.
[74] K. Takayama, unpublished observations.
[75] R. S. Criddle, unpublished observations.
[76] H. O. Hultin and S. H. Richardson, *Arch. Biochem. Biophys.*, 105 (1964) 288.
[77] R. E. Beyer, *Biochem. Biophys. Res. Communs.*, 16 (1964) 460.
[78] A. L. Smith and M. Hansen, *Biochem. Biophys. Res. Communs.*, 8 (1962) 136.
[79] G. B. Brierley and E. Murer, *Biochem. Biophys. Res. Communs.*, 14 (1959) 437.
[80] L. Ernster and C. P. Lee, *Ann. Rev. Biochem.*, 33 (1964) 729.
[81] G. Webster and D. E. Green, *Proc. Natl. Acad. Sci. U.S.*, 52 (1964) 1170.
[82] G. P. Brierley, E. Bachmann and D. E. Green, *Proc. Natl. Acad. Sci. U.S.*, 48 (1962) 1928.
[83] D. E. Green and T. Oda, *J. Biochem.*, 49 (1961) 742.

Chapter VII

Oxidative Phosphorylation

E. C. SLATER

Laboratory of Biochemistry, University of Amsterdam (The Netherlands)

1. Introduction

By the term oxidative phosphorylation we mean a phosphorylation linked with an oxidation reaction. In all cases studied the phosphorylation reaction is, or can be, linked to the phosphorylation of ADP by inorganic phosphate (P_i). Formally, the oxidative phosphorylation reaction is given by Eqn. 1.1

$$AH_2 + B + \text{ADP} + P_i \rightleftharpoons A + BH_2 + \text{ATP} + H_2O \qquad (1.1)$$

which is the sum of two essentially irreversible reactions

$$AH_2 + B \rightarrow A + BH_2 \qquad (1.2)$$

$$\text{ADP} + P_i \leftarrow \text{ATP} + H_2O \qquad (1.3)$$

The reaction shown in Eqn. 1.2 must deliver sufficient energy to drive Eqn. 1.3 to the right.

Oxidative phosphorylation is (or contains) the mechanism by which the cell utilizes the energy made available by biological oxidations. Despite its fundamental importance, it is not yet possible to describe this mechanism in any detail in chemical terms. The emphasis in this Chapter will be on the way in which the present body of knowledge on oxidative phosphorylation has accumulated, rather than on the most recent theories, which, at the present stage of development of the subject, are liable quickly to be overtaken by the facts, perhaps before the book has been published.

Our first knowledge of oxidative phosphorylation came from the study of the conversion of glucose to alcohol by yeast and to lactic acid by muscle. The stoichiometric requirement for phosphate for fermentation by yeast juice was shown by Harden and Young[1] in 1906, and Young[2] identified the

References p. 388

compound as fructose diphosphate. This enabled Harden and Young[3] to propose Eqn. 1.4 for the sum reaction.

$$2 \text{ glucose} + 2 \text{ P}_i \rightarrow 2 \text{ ethanol} + 2 \text{ CO}_2 + 1 \text{ fructose diphosphate} + 2 \text{ H}_2\text{O} \quad (1.4)$$

In other words, one molecule of glucose is phosphorylated by inorganic phosphate to fructose diphosphate, while a second molecule is split to ethanol and CO_2.

The studies of Neuberg, Embden, Parnas, Meyerhof, Needham and Warburg in the second and third decades of this century led to the discovery that the energy necessary for the phosphorylation reaction is made available by the oxidative reaction of fermentation and glycolysis, the oxidation of phosphoglyceraldehyde by pyruvate or acetaldehyde (Eqn. 1.5),

$$\text{phosphoglyceraldehyde} + \text{pyruvate (or acetaldehyde)} + \text{H}_2\text{O} \rightarrow \text{phosphoglycerate} + \text{lactate (or ethanol)} \quad (1.5)$$

and that the energy of the latter reaction is conserved in the form of high-energy phosphate compounds. In 1939, Warburg and Christian[4] and Negelein and Brömel[5] showed that the first high-energy phosphate compound formed is 1,3-diphosphoglycerate, which, in the presence of a specific enzyme, reacts with ADP to form ATP. Eqn. 1.5 could now be described as the sum of Eqns. 1.6–1.8.

$$\text{phosphoglyceraldehyde} + \text{NAD}^+ + \text{P}_i \rightleftharpoons \text{1,3-diphosphoglycerate} + \text{NADH} + \text{H}^+ \quad (1.6)$$

$$\text{1,3-diphosphoglycerate} + \text{ADP} \rightleftharpoons \text{3-phosphoglycerate} + \text{ATP} \quad (1.7)$$

$$\text{NADH} + \text{H}^+ + \text{pyruvate (or acetaldehyde)} \rightarrow \text{NAD}^+ + \text{lactate (or ethanol)} \quad (1.8)$$

ATP, discovered by Lohmann[6], occupies a central position in cell metabolism, since its terminal phosphate group can be removed in such a way that the free energy which would be dissipated by the hydrolysis of ATP is conserved. We owe much to Lipmann[7] for the development of the concept of this role of high-energy phosphate compounds.

That respiration could also supply the energy for the synthesis of ATP was foreshadowed by Meyerhof's[8] discovery in 1920 that the oxygen consumed during the recovery period after muscular contraction is sufficient to account for only about one-fifth of the lactic acid produced during contraction, and that the energy of this process can be used to resynthesize the remaining four-fifths to glycogen. Eggleton and Eggleton[9] and Fiske and SubbaRow[10] showed that creatine phosphate is rapidly resynthesized during recovery in oxygen.

The first demonstration of the synthesis of ATP coupled to respiration was made by Engelhardt[11] in 1930 during a comparative study of the phosphorus metabolism of erythrocytes. Rabbit erythrocytes, which are nonnucleated and do not respire, were found to form inorganic phosphate when the glycolysis was inhibited by fluoride, whereas the respiratory inhibitor cyanide had no effect. Pigeon erythrocytes, on the other hand, rapidly formed phosphate when respiratory inhibitors (cyanide, urethane or CO) were added. The amount of P_i formed agreed closely with the disappearance of "7-min P" (ATP). After removing the cyanide by washing, a resynthesis of acid-labile P could be demonstrated. Engelhardt concluded that the splitting of ATP occurs both in the absence and in the presence of respiratory inhibitors, but that in their absence the splitting is compensated by a resynthesis of ATP.

Engelhardt's work appears to have had relatively little impact when it was published, and interest in "oxidative phosphorylation", as the process came to be called, stems from the work of Kalckar[12,13] in 1937–1939 with cell-free homogenates of kidney and other tissues. Kalckar showed that phosphorylation of glucose, glycerol or AMP took place when these homogenates catalysed the oxidation of citrate, glutamate, fumarate or malate. No reaction took place under anaerobic conditions, and no phosphoglycerate was formed. At about the same time, Lipmann[14] showed that the oxidation of pyruvate by *Bacterium delbruckii* is coupled with phosphorylation.

Harden and Young[1] in their first studies on the role of phosphate in fermentation established that the extra quantity of CO_2 evolved when phosphate was added to yeast juice was equimolar with the phosphate added. The rate of CO_2 evolution sharply declined when all the phosphate was esterified, and a second addition of phosphate restored the fermentation. By these experiments, as well as demonstrating for the first time the control of metabolism by phosphate, they established the stoichiometry of the phosphorylation associated with glycolysis and fermentation. The stoichiometry of the phosphorylation associated with respiration proved more difficult to establish.

In 1939–1940, two groups of workers — Ochoa[15,16] in Peters' laboratory in Oxford and Belitzer and Tsibakowa[17] in Engelhardt's laboratory in Leningrad — made the very imporant observation that more than one atom of P was esterified for every atom of oxygen (*i.e.* two oxidizing equivalents) consumed by respiring preparations under conditions in which there was no glycolysis. Both groups drew the conclusion that phosphorylation must occur not only when the substrate is dehydrogenated — as in the oxidation reaction of glycolysis or fermentation — but also during the further passage of the hydrogen atoms (or electrons) along the respiratory chain to oxygen. Thus, these workers were the first to postulate what is now known as respiratory-chain phosphorylation. It was not immediately apparent, however, that the newly discovered phosphorylation was different in kind from that involved in glycolysis, since Szent–Gyorgyi's[18] hypothesis — that the

References p. 388

succinate–fumarate and the malate–oxaloacetate couples are involved in the respiratory chain — was then much in vogue. The recognition that the NADH formed by the dehydrogenation of most substrates is oxidized by a respiratory chain consisting of flavoprotein and the cytochrome system[19–22], but free of components of small molecular weight, brought the realization that the nicotinamide–adenine nucleotides, flavins or haems must be concerned more intimately with the phosphorylation process.

2. P:O Ratios and number of phosphorylation steps

It now became important to establish the stoichiometry more closely, *i.e.* to determine exactly how many atoms of phosphorus are esterified for each molecule of substrate oxidized. Ochoa's[23] first attempt to do this — in 1943 — opened up a controversial chapter in this field.

The source of the controversy lies in technical difficulties. The problem is to measure n in the reaction

$$SH_2 + \frac{1}{2}O_2 + n\,\text{ADP} + n\,\text{P}_i \rightarrow S + n\,\text{ATP} + (n+1)\,\text{H}_2\text{O} \qquad (2.1)$$

The enzyme preparations used by the early workers contained hexokinase (EC 2.7.1.1) and phosphofructokinase (EC 2.7.1.11) which catalysed the phosphorylation by the ATP of glucose or fructose included in the reaction mixture, *e.g.*

$$n\,\text{ATP} + n\,\text{glucose} \rightarrow n\,\text{ADP} + n\,\text{glucose 6-phosphate} \qquad (2.2)$$

In the sum reaction,

$$SH_2 + \text{O} + n\,\text{glucose} + n\,\text{P}_i \rightarrow S + n\,\text{HMP} + (n+1)\,\text{H}_2\text{O} \qquad (2.3)$$

where HMP stands for hexose monosphosphate, usually the equilibrium mixture of glucose 6-phosphate and fructose 6-phosphate formed by glucose phosphate isomerase (EC 5.3.1.9) present, the adenine nucleotides no longer appear, *i.e.* they are catalysts in the overall reaction studied. However, the enzyme preparations used also contained ATPases which caused the esterified phosphate to be returned as inorganic phosphate to the reaction medium.

$$n\,\text{ATP} + n\,\text{H}_2\text{O} \rightarrow n\,\text{ADP} + n\,\text{P}_i \qquad (2.4)$$

As a consequence, the measured disappearance of P_i does not always accurately reflect the value of n in Eqn. 2.1. In fact,

$$n = \frac{v_2 + v_4}{v_2} \cdot (\text{P}:\text{O})_{\text{obs.}} = f \cdot (\text{P}:\text{O})_{\text{obs.}}$$

where v_2 and v_4 equal the rates of reactions given by Eqns. 2.2 and 2.4, respectively.

Ochoa[23] recognized this difficulty and estimated the value of f by measuring the P:lactate ratio of the glycolytic phosphorylation reaction, which was allowed to proceed under the same conditions as the oxidative phosphorylation reaction. He assumed that ATP formed by glycolysis would be partitioned by Reactions 2.2 and 2.4 in the same way as the ATP formed by respiratory-chain phosphorylation. In this way, he calculated that the true P : O ratio ($=n$) for the oxidation of pyruvate by heart or brain homogenates is 3. Although this conclusion encountered considerable opposition at the time, it was an elegant and objective attempt to overcome a real difficulty and gave results close to those now generally accepted.

In 1948–9 two improvements were made in the experimental technique which greatly decreased the significance of this source of error. The first[24–26] was the addition to the reaction mixture of a large excess of purified yeast hexokinase, then available thanks to the work of Cori[27]. This so favoured reaction of ATP with glucose that losses by Reaction 2.4 became negligible. The second[28–30] was the introduction of "washed tissue particles", largely composed of mitochondria[28,31], in place of a crude homogenate as the enzyme system catalysing oxidative phosphorylation. This removed some of the ATPases from the preparation, and further improvements in the technique of isolating mitochondria introduced by Schneider and Hogeboom[32], Kielley and Kielley[33] and Lardy and Wellman[34] led to the virtual removal of the hydrolysis of ATP as a source of error in measurements of the P:O ratio.

Nevertheless, the danger of such losses continued to weigh heavily on the minds of many workers in this field. The general experience that the greater the care taken in the preparation of the mitochondria (in particular in the removal of the "fluffy layer" from the sediment of mitochondria in the centrifuge tube) the higher the P:O ratio led to the convention that only the "best" (*i.e.* the highest) ratios were of significance. This is a fundamentally dangerous convention for inexperienced workers since it can lead to some loss of objectivity and to the non-critical acceptance of experimental procedures which appear to give high P:O ratios. As a consequence too of the general climate of opinion at that time an unfortunate "mystique" became wrapped around the method of preparation of rat-liver mitochondria. In fact, Schneider and Hogeboom's[32] procedure, especially as later modified by Hogeboom[35], requires no special skill and has consistently given good results in the writer's laboratory.

The determination of the P:O ratio involves two measurements — the amount of P_i esterified and the amount of substrate oxidized. The latter is usually determined by measuring manometrically the amount of O_2 taken up. When, however, S is not further metabolized, the disappearance of SH_2 (*e.g.* the disappearance of α-ketoglutarate when malonate is added to prevent the removal of succinate[36,37]) or the formation of S (*e.g.* the measurement of acetoacetate formed by the oxidation of β-hydroxybutyrate by rat-liver mitochondria[38]) may be determined.

References p. 388

The amount of phosphate esterified may be determined either by measuring the amount of P_i disappearing or the amount of esterified phosphate formed. Owing to its simplicity, the former method is mostly used, but it is inaccurate when small amounts of P_i disappear, and suffers from the disadvantage that the concentration of P_i in the reaction mixture is fixed mainly for reasons of analytical convenience.

In 1950, Slater[39,40] developed a highly sensitive and specific spectrophotometric procedure for measuring the esterified phosphate, based on Racker's[41] method of determining hexokinase and phosphohexokinase activity. The method depends upon the reaction

$$\text{HMP} + {\sim}\text{P} + 2\ \text{NADH} + 2\ \text{H}^+ \rightarrow 2\ \text{glycerol phosphate} + 2\ \text{NAD}^+ \quad (2.5)$$

(where ${\sim}$P indicates the two terminal phosphate groups of ATP, and the terminal group of ADP), catalysed by enzymes present in rabbit-muscle extracts. When excess ${\sim}$P is added, the oxidation of NADH (measured spectrophotometrically at 340 mμ) is a measure of the amount of HMP present; when excess HMP is added the amount of NADH oxidized is a measure of the ${\sim}$P present.

HMP may also be measured by reduction of $NADP^+$ catalysed by glucose 6-phosphate dehydrogenase (EC 1.1.1.49)[42]. Since NADPH is not oxidized by intact mitochondria, this procedure has been proposed as a method of following oxidative phosphorylation continuously[43].

Ernster *et al.*[44] and Nielsen and Lehninger[45] measure the amount of esterified P by determining the amount of $^{32}P_i$ incorporated into HMP in the presence of hexokinase and glucose, a convenient and sensitive method. Krebs *et al.*[46] introduced a similar method, but did not add hexokinase or glucose and measured the incorporation of $^{32}P_i$ into the ATP. However, since $^{32}P_i$ can be incorporated into ATP by an exchange reaction[47], the measured rate of incorporation can greatly exceed the rate of *net* synthesis of ATP. The method used by Lehninger and by Lindberg and Ernster does not suffer from this disadvantage, since in the presence of sufficient hexokinase the steady-state concentration of ATP is kept so low that this exchange reaction is negligible.

In 1955, Chance and Williams[48] introduced another method of measuring the P:O ratio, based on the fact, discovered by Engelhardt[49] and Lardy[50], that, in the absence of enzymes hydrolysing ATP, Reaction 2.1 will come to a stop when all the ADP is phosphorylated. Since oxidative phosphorylation has a very high affinity for ADP (see later), there will be a sharp "cut-off" in the rate of O_2 uptake at this point, just as the high affinity of cytochrome oxidase for O_2 means that there is a sharp cut-off when the solution approaches anaerobiosis (Fig. 1). By means of an O_2 polarograph, Chance and Williams[48] measured the amount of O_2 necessary to phosphorylate a

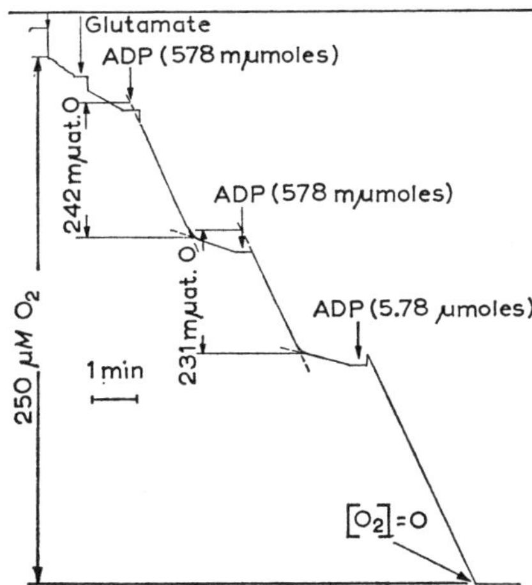

Fig. 1. Determination of the P:O ratio by the method of Chance and Williams. At the first arrow, 0.05 ml rat-liver mitochondria (1.5 mg protein) in 0.25 *M* sucrose were added to 1.75 ml of a reaction mixture containing 60 μmoles phosphate buffer (pH 7.3), 30 μmoles KCl, 2 μmoles EDTA, 100 μmoles Tris–HCl buffer (pH 7.3) and 10 μmoles $MgCl_2$. 0.02 ml L-glutamate (10 μmoles) were added at the second arrow followed by 0.06 ml of ADP (0.578 μmole) at the third arrow. A further addition of 0.06 ml of ADP (0.578 μmole) was made as shown. Finally 0.06 ml of a more concentrated solution of ADP was added to allow the suspension to go anaerobic ([O_2] = 0). The P : O ratios calculated from the two experiments are 0.578/0.242 = 2.39 and 0.578/0.232 = 2.50, respectively. (The short horizontal traces during the additions were caused by the fact that the polarograph was turned off during this period.)

known amount of ADP. This is an ingenious and simple procedure, free of many of the errors of other methods, but is has some disadvantages. First, it is difficult to combine this method with measurement of the disappearance of substrate or appearance of product, which is necessary for the establishment of the stoichiometry of the reaction being studied. Secondly, the accurate measurement of the O_2 consumed presents some difficulties (see Ref. 51), and finally the composition of the ADP used (commercial ADP contains considerable amounts of ATP and AMP) requires to be carefully standardized.

The experimentally found P:O ratios for a number of oxidation reactions catalysed by isolated mitochondria are assembled in Table I. The average values found usually differ significantly from a whole number, which shows that side-reactions in addition to the reaction summarized by Eqn. 2.1 are taking place. As already discussed, the addition of hexokinase can eliminate the ATPase as a source of error. The side-reactions are probably due to "uncoupled" reactions caused by a non-phosphorylytic reaction of high-energy intermediates of Reaction 2.1. Some "uncoupled" reactions may be due to mechanical damage to the mitochondria during isolation or to conta-

TABLE I

P:O RATIOS OF OXIDATIONS CATALYSED BY ISOLATED MITOCHONDRIA

Reaction	*Observed*[a] *P:O ratio*
α-Ketoglutarate + $\frac{1}{2}$ O_2→ succinate + CO_2	3–4
β-Hydroxybutyrate + $\frac{1}{2}$ O_2→ acetoacetate + H_2O	2–3
Succinate + $\frac{1}{2}$ O_2→ fumarate + H_2O	1–2
α-Glycerolphosphate + $\frac{1}{2}$ O_2→ dihydroxyacetone phosphate + H_2O	1–2
Pyruvate + $2\frac{1}{2}$ O_2→ 3 CO_2 + 2 H_2O	2–3
[b] Glutamate + $1\frac{1}{2}$ O_2→ aspartate + CO_2	2–3

[a] The concept of "theoretical" P:O ratios (4, 3 and 2 with α-ketoglutarate, β-hydroxybutyrate and succinate, respectively), which is found frequently in the current literature, introduces an unnecessary and very real difficulty for the beginner. If he is cautious and self-critical, as he should be, he is likely to obtain considerably lower P:O ratios than the "theoretical". Since a "theoretical" P:O ratio has become a "status symbol", he is immediately placed in a disadvantage compared with those who, having obtained P:O ratios approaching the "theoretical" either by selecting their "best" results or by choosing uncritically the procedure giving the highest ratios, can shelter behind the tacit assumption that their technique for the preparation of the mitochondria was superior.

[b] This is the predominate reaction when glutamate is used as substrate with isolated mitochondria[52]. In many studies of oxidative phosphorylation using this substrate, it was assumed that the reaction was largely glutamate + $\frac{1}{2}$ O_2→ α-ketoglutarate + NH_3.

mination with uncoupling agents (*e.g.* unsaturated fatty acids[53–55]). Others may represent physiological reactions, utilizing the energy of high-energy intermediates to maintain the structure and ionic composition of the mitochondria (see p. 380). Although it is theoretically possible to prepare mitochondria without damage and free from uncoupling agents, it is probably not possible completely to eliminate the second type of "uncoupled" reaction. P:O ratios differing from whole numbers are, then, to be expected.

If it is assumed that two hydrogen atoms (or two electrons) are transferred simultaneously through the chain, the conclusion may be drawn from the data in Table I that there are at least 4, 3 and 2 phosphorylation steps in the oxidation of α-ketoglutarate, β-hydroxybutyrate and succinate, respectively*.

* This controversial chapter is not yet closed. Recently, reports have appeared in which it is claimed that P:O ratios greatly exceeding those generally accepted may be obtained. Smith and Hansen[56] reported values of 4.4–5.7 with pyruvate, 4–5 with glutamate and 2.7–3.9 with succinate, using beef-heart mitochondria. Haslam[57], Lenaz and Beyer[58] and Brierley[59] have shown that these high ratios are artefacts, caused by faulty use of the manometric procedure of measuring the oxygen uptake. Gurban and Cristea[60,61] reported P:O ratios of up to 5 with succinate and up to 6.8 with glutamate, in short-time experiments with rat-liver mitochondria. Koivusalo and co-workers[62,63] have shown that the high ratio with glutamate is due to under-estimation of the oxygen uptake in the first few minutes after adding mitochondria to the reaction mixture. Lynn and Brown[64] have also reported very high ratios (more than 7 for α-ketoglutarate, more than 6 for malate and more than 4 for succinate) under special conditions. These high ratios remain to be explained.

3. Specificity and kinetics of oxidative phosphorylation

The kinetics of oxidative phosphorylation were first studied by Slater and Holton[65]. When oxidative phosphorylation is measured by coupling Reaction 2.1 with Reaction 2.2 (the sum is given by Eqn. 2.3) an initial lag in the formation of HMP is found (Fig. 2). When, however, Reaction 1 is followed, in the absence of hexokinase, by measuring the increase of ~P, there is no

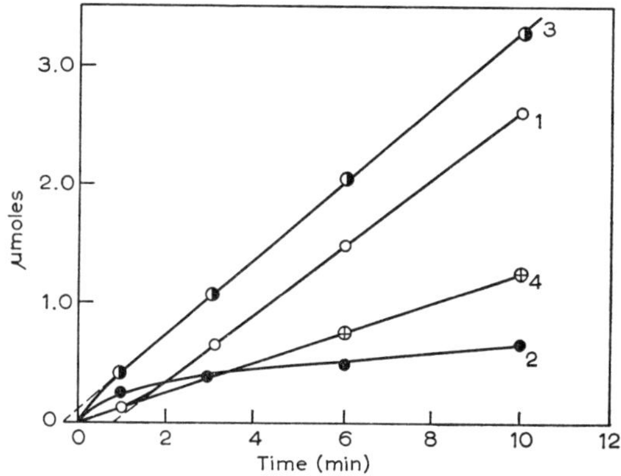

Fig. 2. Kinetics of the early stages of oxidative phosphorylation using small amounts of hexokinase. Rat-heart sarcosomes oxidizing α-ketoglutarate in the presence of malonate and fluoride. Curve 1, ΔHMP; Curve 2, Δ~P; Curve 3, ΔHMP + Δ~P; Curve 4, Δα-ketoglutarate. Reproduced from Ref. 65 with kind permission of the publishers.

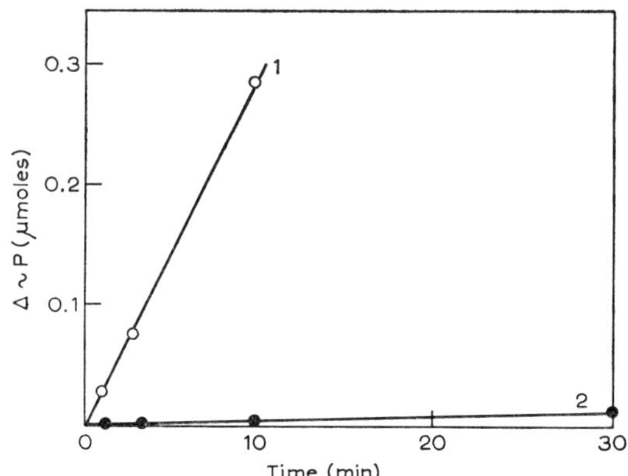

Fig. 3. Kinetics of the early stages of oxidative phosphorylation, measured by increase in ~P. Cat-heart sarcosomes oxidizing α-ketoglutarate in the presence of malonate and fluoride, and absence of hexokinase. Curve 1, ADP; Curve 2, AMP. Reproduced from Ref. 65 with kind permission of the publishers.

lag (Fig. 3). The lag in Fig. 2 is due to the building up of a steady-state concentration of ATP, determined by the relative activities of the systems catalysing Reactions 2.1 and 2.2, and represents the pre-steady state.

Fig. 3 also illustrates that ADP is phosphorylated much more rapidly than AMP. In much of the earlier work on oxidative phosphorylation (*e.g.* Refs. 26, 30, 38, 66) the more readily available AMP was used, but since the discovery[67] of adenylate myokinase (EC 2.7.4.3) in 1943, it was realized that ADP, formed by reaction of endogenous ATP with the added AMP, might be the preferred acceptor. A strong indication that this is the case came from the discovery by Barkulis and Lehninger[68] that the inhibition of oxidative phosphorylation by fluoride, when AMP is used as the acceptor, is due to inhibition of myokinase. The experiment illustrated in Fig. 3 was carried out with cat-heart sarcosomes, which have little myokinase, in the presence of a high concentration of fluoride to inhibit the slight myokinase activity.

Using the same preparation, Slater and Holton[65] were able to show that oxidative phosphorylation has a high affinity for ADP, with a K_m less than

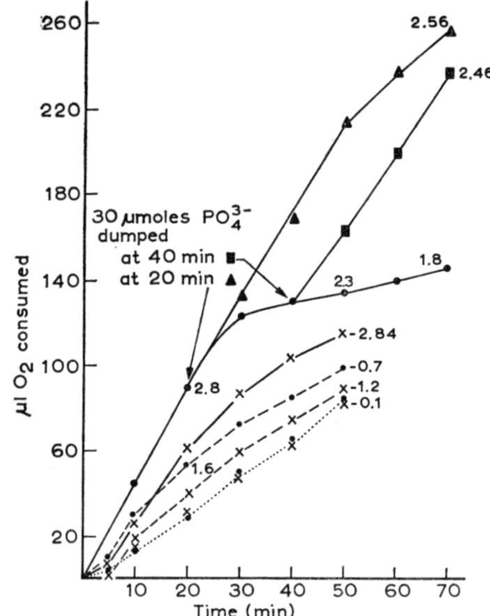

Fig. 4. Effect of inorganic phosphate on oxidation of α-ketoglutarate by rat-liver mitochondria. ——, hexokinase and glucose added as phosphate acceptor; – – –, creatine kinase and creatine added as phosphate acceptor; . . . . ., no acceptor; ×, plus 0.01 *M* fluoride. The numbers in the figure refer to P:O ratio for flasks removed at various time intervals. Reproduced from Ref. 50 with kind permission of the author and publishers.

50 μM. Using their polarographic method already discussed, Chance and Williams[48] found a K_m of 20–30 μM for rat-liver mitochondria. These mitochondria have such a high myokinase activity that AMP may be used instead of ADP as phosphate acceptor in Chance and Williams' procedure (Kemp[69]).

Cooper and Lehninger[70] showed in 1956 that digitonin particles (see p. 372) oxidizing β-hydroxybutyrate do not phosphorylate added IDP, GDP, UDP or CDP. Later, however, it was found that sub-mitochondrial particles prepared by sonic treatment can phosphorylate GDP and UDP (Ref. 71), and IDP (Refs. 71, 72). CDP is not phosphorylated. This apparent discrepancy has been recently resolved. It appears that the respiratory-chain phosphorylation system is relatively non-specific for the phosphate acceptor, but that the mitochondrial membrane is selectively permeable to ADP and ATP. Thus, the failure of digitonin fragments, which probably contain a more or less intact membrane structure, to phosphorylate added IDP, UDP, or GDP is due to the impermeability of the membrane to those nucleotide diphosphates. Heldt and Klingenberg[73–76] have shown that the phosphorylation of added ADP is preceded by phosphorylation of the endogenous ADP of the mitochondria. The ATP thereby formed is transferred to the outside of the mitochondrial membrane by a specific adenine nucleotide translocase, and is replaced by exogenous ADP.

The substrate-linked phosphorylation involved in α-ketoglutarate oxidation, catalysed by succinyl-CoA synthetase (EC 6.2.1.4), requires GDP in the primary reaction[77,78a,74] with subsequent transfer of the phosphate group to ADP in a reaction catalysed by nucleosidediphosphate kinase (EC 2.7.4.6).

Oxidative phosphorylation is almost completely specific for phosphate. Arsenate can readily replace phosphate in the substrate-linked phosphorylation, but the primary arsenate product is rapidly hydrolysed and does not react with ADP. Arsenate can also replace phosphate in the reactions of respiratory-chain phosphorylation[78], but is much less effective than phosphate.

The affinity for phosphate is less than for ADP, but is nevertheless quite high. Lardy[50] found a sharp "cut-off" in the O_2 uptake (measured manometrically) when phosphate was exhausted by rat-liver mitochondria oxidizing α-ketoglutarate (Fig. 4). Chance and Hagihara[79] found a K_m of 130 μM for phosphate with pigeon-heart mitochondria oxidizing a mixture of glutamate and succinate.

4. Location of phosphorylation steps in the respiratory chain

Three methods have been used to locate the phosphorylation steps in the respiratory chain: (*a*) Calculations from the observed P:O ratios; (*b*) observations on isolated portions of the chain; (*c*) observations of the effect of ADP on the state of oxidation of various members of the chain.

(*a*) *Calculations from the observed P:O ratios*

Two types of calculations have been made: (*i*) based on the P:O ratio with different substrates; (*ii*) based on thermodynamic calculations.

(*i*) *P:O ratios*

There is general agreement that the P:O ratio obtained with those substrates which react directly with NAD, *e.g.* β-hydroxybutyrate, is less than that obtained with α-ketoglutarate, and is higher than that obtained with succinate. On the basis of the assumption that oxidative phosphorylation is a quantised phenomenon and that the unit of hydrogen transfer is two H atoms (equivalent to 1 O atom), it follows that one phosphorylation step is localized between α-ketoglutarate and NAD^+ and one between NADH and the point at which succinate enters the respiratory chain (in the region of ubiquinone or cytochrome *b*). This may be formulated

$$\begin{array}{ccccccc} \alpha\text{-kg} & \xrightarrow{\sim} & NAD^+ & \xrightarrow{\sim} & Q & \longrightarrow & O_2 \\ (-0.68) & & (-0.34) & & (+0.11) & & (+0.80) \\ & & \uparrow & & \uparrow & & \\ & & \beta\text{-OH} & & \text{succinate} & & \\ & & (-0.27) & & (+0.02) & & \end{array}$$

where the oxidation–reduction potentials (E'_0 in volts) are given in brackets.

It is clearly important to know how many phosphorylation steps are associated with the oxidation of succinate to fumarate. Two difficulties complicate such measurements. In the first place, it is apparent from all published work, although it is seldom emphasized, that the oxidation of succinate by mitochondrial preparations is not very tightly coupled to phosphorylation. When phosphorylation is prevented by removing ADP or by adding oligomycin, the rate of oxidation is inhibited, but usually by not more than 65–80%. It is difficult to determine to what extent this non-phosphorylating respiration is also operative when ADP and P_i are present in the absence of inhibitor. Secondly, measurements of the O_2 uptake alone do not give a reliable indication of the amounts of succinate oxidized to fumarate, since the malate formed from the fumarate can undergo further oxidation. The extent of this further oxidation, under the conditions used by many authors (*e.g.* 6 m*M* succinate, rat-liver mitochondria[80]) is illustrated by the data of Table II. Since the oxidation of malate is associated with a higher P:O ratio than the oxidation of succinate to fumarate, it is

TABLE II

EFFECT OF SUCCINATE CONCENTRATION ON RELATIONSHIP BETWEEN OXYGEN CONSUMED AND (MALATE + FUMARATE) FORMED

Data taken from Ref. 81

Expt.	*Preparations*	*Succinate (mM)*	*ΔO (μatoms)*	*Δ (fumarate + malate) (μmoles)*	*ΔO:Δ(fumarate + malate)*
1	Liver	6.6	5.8	3.2	1.83
		66	7.7	7.0	1.10
2	Liver	6.6	1.6	1.0	1.66
		66	4.8	4.7	1.03
3	Heart	6.6	1.0	1.0	1.02
		66	2.9	2.9	0.99
4	Heart	6.6	1.0	1.0	1.04
		66	3.1	3.1	1.00

clear that, under these conditions, the measured P:O ratio will be greater than that associated with the oxidation of succinate to fumarate.

As Whittam *et al.*[82] first showed, the further oxidation of the malate II). be suppressed by using very high concentrations of succinate (*cf.* Table can This is presumably the reason for the decline in P:O ratio with increasing succinate concentration shown for liver mitochondria in Table III. The value obtained with 60 m*M* succinate (1.62) probably reflects more closely that associated with the succinate → fumarate step, and on the basis of the assumption mentioned above, warrants the conclusion that there are two phosphorylative steps*.

Similar values (*e.g.* Ref. 85) are obtained with glycerol 1-phosphate, which enters the chain at the same point as succinate, and yields an oxidation product (dihydroxyacetone phosphate) which is not further oxidized.

(ii) Thermodynamic calculations

This method, which was introduced by Ball[86], Lipmann[87], and Ogston and Smithies[88], depends upon a comparison of the free energy available in each reaction of the chain with that required to bring about the synthesis of ATP. The calculations are based on the premise that each step of the

* It might be thought that high concentrations of succinate uncouple oxidative phosphorylation. However, the same P:O ratio was obtained with 60 m*M* succinate as with 6 m*M* in the case of heart mitochondria which oxidize succinate stoichiometrically to fumarate (Table II). Moreover, the amount of glutamate synthesized from α-ketoglutarate + NH_3, coupled to the oxidation of succinate by oxygen, a process which is also susceptible to uncoupling, is scarcely affected by varying the succinate concentration between 24 m*M* and 72 m*M* (Ref. 83). Smith and Hansen[84] agree that up to 50 m*M* succinate does not uncouple oxidative phosphorylation in intact mitochondria, although it acts as an uncoupling agent in concentrations greater than 5 m*M* with mitochondria which have been frozen and thawed.

respiratory chain can proceed only when ΔG is negative. For each step ($AH_2 \rightarrow B$) two calculations of ΔG are made
(*1*) for the reaction $AH_2 + B \rightleftharpoons A + BH_2$
(*2*) for the reaction $AH_2 + B + \text{ADP} + P_i \rightleftharpoons A + BH_2 + \text{ATP} + H_2O$

$$\Delta G_1 = \Delta G_0' + RT \ln \frac{[A][BH_2]}{[AH_2][B]} \text{ cal} \cdot \text{mole}^{-1}$$

$$\Delta G_2 = \Delta G_1 + 7000 + RT \ln \frac{[\text{ATP}]}{[\text{ADP}][P_i]} \text{ cal} \cdot \text{mole}^{-1}$$

where $\Delta G_0'$ is the change of standard free energy for the reaction

$$AH_2 + B \rightleftharpoons A + BH_2$$

and 7000 calories[89,90] is the value of the standard free-energy change for the reaction

$$\text{ADP} + P_i \rightleftharpoons \text{ATP} + H_2O$$

TABLE III

EFFECT OF SUCCINATE CONCENTRATION ON P:O RATIO WITH SUCCINATE

Data taken from Ref. 81

Preparation	*Succinate (mM)*	Q_{O_2} *(µl O₂/mg protein/h)*	*P:O*
Liver	3	15	2.20
	6	23	2.17
	15	34	1.94
	60	109	1.62
Heart	6	43	0.95
	15	56	0.93
	60	165	0.93

In the absence of the necessary experimental data to make more elaborate calculations, the earlier calculations of Ball[86], Lipmann[87], and Ogston and Smithies[88] were based on considerations of the standard free energy, without taking into account the actual concentrations of the reactants. In fact, the concentrations of P_i, ADP and ATP at which oxidative phosphorylation takes place may depart very greatly from the standard conditions ($[P_i] = 1.0\,M$; [ADP]=[ATP]). By coincidence, the large error thereby introduced was balanced by an approximately equally large error in the value assumed for the free-energy change in the hydrolysis of ATP (12000–16000 cal).

The experiments of Chance and Williams[91] provide data which enable more reliable thermodynamic calculations, which have been made by Chance and Williams[92] and by Slater[93]. The latter calculations are corrected and brought up to date in Table IV, from which the conclusion may be drawn that phosphorylation is possible between NADH and ubiquinone, ubiquinone (or ferrocytochrome *b*) and ferricytochrome *c*, and ferrocytochrome *c* (or ferrocytochrome *a*) and oxygen.

However, many assumptions of doubtful validity have had to be made to enable these calculations to be completed. The best that can be said at the moment is that the thermodynamic calculations do not give results in conflict with those obtained by other methods.

(*b*) *Observations on isolated portions of the chain*

Already in their papers in which they postulated the existence of respiratory-chain phosphorylation, Ochoa[23] and Belitzer and Tsibakowa[17] attempted to localize the region of the chain in which the phosphorylation took place. The latter authors found no phosphorylation with *p*-phenylenediamine as donor and concluded that there is no phosphorylation in the cytochrome oxidase reaction. Ochoa[23] found no phosphorylation with NADH as substrate, a result which, when it became clear that the Szent-Gyorgyi's theory of the respiratory chain was incorrect, became difficult to reconcile with the concept of respiratory-chain phosphorylation, as Ogston and Smithies[88] pointed out.

In 1948 Lehninger[30,103,38] succeeded in demonstrating phosphorylation with NADH as substrate, and thereby established the reality of respiratory-chain phosphorylation. His attempts at further localizing the phosphorylation, however, failed, no phosphorylation being demonstrated when ferricytochrome *c* was used as acceptor, or when ferrocytochrome *c* (kept reduced by various reducing agents) was used as donor[103]. In the following year, Slater[104] demonstrated phosphorylation with ferricytochrome *c* as acceptor (α-ketoglutarate as donor), but his early attempts convincingly to demonstrate phosphorylation in the cytochrome oxidase reaction failed (unpublished experiments). This and the fact that the phosphorylation efficiency measured with ferricytochrome *c* as acceptor approached that with oxygen led him to postulate[104] that all the phosphorylation was localized between substrate and ferricytochrome *c*, a conclusion which was abandoned when more accurate determinations showed a distinctly higher phosphorylation efficiency with oxygen[105]. In the meantime, Nielsen and Lehninger[106] in 1954 demonstrated phosphorylation with ferrocytochrome *c* as donor (see also Refs. 107, 108), a finding shortly afterwards confirmed by Slater[109].

It is noteworthy that every success in demonstrating phosphorylation associated with a portion of the respiratory chain was achieved after a previous failure had been published. What were the special difficulties?

(*1*) The concentrations of hydrogen or electron donors and acceptors which could be used in these experiments were necessarily very low, in com-

TABLE IV

CALCULATION OF ΔG VALUES FOR STEPS OF RESPIRATORY CHAIN

$\Delta G'_0$ (cal) is the change of standard free energy for the reaction as written. It is calculated from the difference between the standard oxidation potentials (E'_0 in millivolts) of the oxidant and reductant, according to the equation

$$\Delta G'_0 = -46.1\ \Delta E'_0$$

The following values have been used for E'_0 at pH 7.3:

Reaction		*Value of E'_0 at pH 7.3 (mV)*	*Reference*
β-hydroxybutyrate	⇌ acetoacetate	−248	94
NADH	⇌ NAD^+	−311	95
QH_2	⇌ Q	89	96
cytochrome b^{2+}	⇌ cytochrome b^{3+}	59	97, 98
cytochrome c^{2+}	⇌ cytochrome c^{3+}	260	99
cytochrome a^{2+}	⇌ cytochrome a^{3+}	278	100
O_2		790	

ΔG_1 (cal) is the change of free energy for the reaction as written, under the "State-3" conditions of Chance and Williams[91]. It is assumed that

[β-hydroxybutyrate] = 12.5 mM
[acetoacetate] = 0.48 mM
[NADH]/[NAD^+] = 1.13
[QH_2]/[Q] = 0.25 (*i.e.* the same as the ratio of reduced to oxidized flavoprotein in the experiments of Chance and Williams[91])
[cyt.b^{2+}]/[cyt.b^{3+}] = 0.19
[cyt.c^{2+}]/[cyt.c^{3+}] = 0.064
[cyt.a^{2+}]/[cyt.a^{3+}] = 0.042
p_{O_2} = 0.02 atm (*cf.* Refs. 92, 101)

The following expressions were used to calculate ΔG_1:

Reaction a $$\Delta G_1 - \Delta G'_0 = 1360 \log \frac{[\text{AcAc}]}{[\beta\text{-OH}]} \cdot \frac{[\text{NADH}]}{[\text{NAD}^+]}$$

Reaction b $$\Delta G_1 - \Delta G'_0 = 1360 \log \frac{[\text{NAD}^+]}{[\text{NADH}]} \cdot \frac{[\text{QH}_2]}{[\text{Q}]}$$

Reaction c $$\Delta G_1 - \Delta G'_0 = 1360 \log \frac{[\text{Q}]}{[\text{QH}_2]} \cdot \frac{[\text{cyt.}b^{2+}]^2}{[\text{cyt.}b^{3+}]^2}$$

Reaction d $$\Delta G_1 - \Delta G'_0 = 2 \times 1360 \log \frac{[\text{cyt.}b^{3+}]}{[\text{cyt.}b^{2+}]} \cdot \frac{[\text{cyt.}c^{2+}]}{[\text{cyt.}c^{3+}]}$$

Reaction e $$\Delta G_1 - \Delta G'_0 = 2 \times 1360 \log \frac{[\text{cyt.}c^{3+}]}{[\text{cyt.}c^{2+}]} \cdot \frac{[\text{cyt.}a^{2+}]}{[\text{cyt.}a^{3+}]}$$

Reaction f $$\Delta G_1 - \Delta G'_0 = 0.5 \times 1360 \log \frac{[\text{cyt.}a^{3+}]^4}{[\text{cyt.}a^{2+}]^4} \cdot \frac{1}{p_{O_2}}$$

ΔG_2 (cal) is the change of free energy of the reaction as written, under the "State-3" conditions of Chance and Williams[91], if the reaction is coupled with the synthesis of 1 molecule of ATP from ADP and P_i.

$$\Delta G_2 - \Delta G_1 = 7000 + 1360 \log \frac{[ATP]}{[ADP]} \cdot \frac{1}{[P_i]}$$

It is assumed that [ATP]/[ADP] = 6.5 and that $[P_i]$ = 0.016 *M* (*cf.* Ref. 93), *i.e.* $\Delta G_2 - \Delta G_1$ = 10540 cal.

*Reaction**	$\Delta G_0'$	ΔG_1	ΔG_2
(*a*) β-OH + NAD^+ → AcAc + NADH + H^+	2910	1040[1]	11580[2]
(*b*) NADH + Q + H^+ → NAD^+ + QH_2	−18500	−19390[3]	−8850[4]
(*c*) QH_2 + 2 cyt.b^{3+} → Q + 2 cyt.b^{2+} + 2 H^+	1390	1110	11650
(*d*) 2 cyt.b^{2+} + 2 cyt.c^{3+} → 2 cyt.b^{3+} + 2 cyt.c^{2+}	− 9300	−10580	− 40
(*e*) 2 cyt.c^{2+} + 2 cyt.a^{3+} → 2 cyt.c^{3+} + 2 cyt.a^{2+}	− 830	− 1330	9210
(*f*) 2 cyt.a^{2+} + ½ O_2 + 2 H^+ → 2 cyt.a^{3+} + H_2O	−23500	−15150	−4610

1 −1090 if [NADH]/[NAD^+] = 0.03 (Ref. 102)
2 9450 if [NADH]/[NAD^+] = 0.03
3 −17250 if [NADH]/[NAD^+] = 0.03
4 −6710 if [NADH]/[NAD^+] = 0.03

* Abbreviations: β-OH, β-hydroxybutyrate
AcAc, acetoacetate
cyt., cytochrome

parison with the amount of substrate consumed in the more usual type of experiments with oxidizable substrates. Although "feeder systems" (*e.g.* ethanol + alcohol dehydrogenase (EC 1.1.1.1) to reform NADH from NAD^+, ascorbate or other reducing agents to reform ferrocytochrome *c* from the ferri form) could be used, these often introduced complications, or the possibility of complications, so that both Lehninger and Slater preferred to dispense with them, and found it necessary, therefore, to develop sensitive analytical methods specially for the problem.

(*2*) In the early studies, the NADH[23] and the cytochrome *c* (Ref. 103) used were not completely pure, and contained inhibitors of oxidative phosphorylation.

(*3*) In 1951, Lehninger[110] showed that the respiratory chain in intact mitochondria is not readily accessible to nicotinamide nucleotide added from outside. When NADH is added to a preparation of carefully prepared liver mitochondria, it is only slowly oxidized, and with very little phosphorylation. It is probable in fact that most of the oxidation of the NADH is brought about by fragments of mitochondria in which the phosphorylative activity has been lost. Fortunately, Lehninger did not meet this difficulty in his early studies[30,103,38], but it is possibly the reason why Ochoa found no phosphorylation with NADH as donor. Lehninger[110] overcame this dif-

References p. 388

ficulty by giving the mitochondria an initial hypotonic treatment, which caused them to swell. It seems likely that the mitochondria used in his first work were already swollen.

(*4*) In 1954, Lehninger[111] showed that swelling liver mitochondria also increased the rate of oxidation of ferrocytochrome *c* with increased P:O ratios. Slater's initial failure to demonstrate phosphorylation with ferrocytochrome *c* was due to the poor penetration of the cytochrome into the rat-heart sarcosomes used, and the presence in his preparations of considerable amounts of sarcosomal fragments which rapidly oxidized the cytochrome without any phosphorylation. The sarcosomes require a much more drastic hypotonic treatment than the rat-liver mitochondria in Lehninger's experiments[105,112].

(*5*) Lehninger[110] further showed that mitochondrial preparations contain a still little-understood antimycin-insensitive NADH-cytochrome *c* oxido-reductase, which is not coupled with phosphorylation. This activity is not affected by swelling the mitochondria. The presence of this system accounts for Lehninger's[38] failure to demonstrate phosphorylation in this portion of the respiratory chain, but does not account for the initial failure with β-hydroxybutyrate as substrate, since this substrate reacts with mitochondrial NAD which reacts primarily via the antimycin-sensitive pathway of mitochondria. Slater[104] using α-ketoglutarate as substrate did not meet this difficulty. Swelling the mitochondria increased the rate of reduction of ferricytochrome *c* by α-ketoglutarate, without however affecting the phosphorylation quotient[105].

(*6*) Isolated mitochondrial preparations contain appreciable amounts of endogenous substrate which is oxidized with considerable phosphorylation[113,114]. It is not always easy to separate the contribution from this reaction from that studied.

To summarize, the difficulty lies in "cutting in or out" of the respiratory chain at precisely determined points without introducing complicating side-reactions. Although the hypotonic treatment introduced by Lehninger has proved useful, it is essentially a compromise. The mitochondrial structure must be damaged sufficiently to allow access to the donors and acceptors, without too much damage to the phosphorylative machinery.

The results finally obtained by Lehninger and Slater using this technique were as given below.

$$\beta\text{-OH} \longrightarrow \text{NAD}^+ \xrightarrow{2.6} \text{O}_2 \qquad \text{Lehninger}^{115}$$

$$\beta\text{-OH} \searrow \text{O} \searrow \text{OxAc} \qquad \text{NAD}^+ \downarrow \text{OxAc}$$

$$\alpha\text{-kg} \xrightarrow{1.8} \text{cyt.}c \xrightarrow{0.34} \text{O}_2 \qquad \text{Slater}^{105,109,116}$$

$$\beta\text{-OH} \xrightarrow{1.3} \text{cyt.}c$$
$$\text{Succinate} \xrightarrow{0.2} \text{cyt.}c$$
Slater[105]

$$\beta\text{-OH} \xrightarrow{1.5} \text{cyt.}c \xrightarrow{0.63} O_2$$
Lehninger[45,106,117]

$$\text{NADH} \xrightarrow{0.8} \text{fumarate}$$
Haas[118]

α-kg = α-ketoglutarate; β-OH = β-hydroxybutyrate; cyt. = cytochrome; OxAc = oxaloacetate; the numbers indicate the experimentally determined P:O and P:2e ratios.

These results, together with the demonstration by HUNTER[25] of the substrate-linked phosphorylation with α-ketoglutarate, may be summarized by the scheme

$$\alpha\text{-kg} \xrightarrow{\sim} \text{NAD}^+ \xrightarrow{\sim \quad \sim} \text{cyt.}c \xrightarrow{\sim} O_2$$

↑ β-OH ↑ succinate

Ramirez and Mujica[119] presented evidence based on the "cross-over" phenomenon (see below) for the existence of two phosphorylation sites between cytochrome *c* and oxygen. Howland[120] has obtained P:O ratios of about 1.3 with tetramethyl-*p*-phenylenediamine, which is thought to enter the respiratory chain at cytochrome *c*, as donor. The P:O ratio was halved by the addition of antimycin but 2-heptyl-4-hydroxyquinoline-*N*-oxide, which inhibits the respiratory chain at the same point as antimycin, had no effect. Howland concluded that there are two phosphorylation sites spanned by the oxidation of tetramethyl-*p*-phenylenediamine and that one is eliminated by antimycin. It seems possible, then, that there are two phosphorylation steps between cytochrome *c* and oxygen, but this is not yet proven. There is sufficient energy for this.

(c) *Observations on the effect of ADP on the state of oxidation of various members of the chain*

Chance and Williams[92] in 1955 introduced another method of locating the phosphorylating steps in the respiratory chain. As already discussed, the operation of the respiratory chain is almost compulsorily linked to phosphorylation, *i.e.* the reaction

$$\text{ADP} + P_i \rightarrow \text{ATP}$$

is necessary for respiration. In the absence of ADP (or P_i) the respiration is inhibited, and the inhibition is relieved by adding ADP.

References p. 388

When a typical respiratory inhibitor, antimycin, is added to mitochondria, cytochrome b and the components of the chain on the substrate side of cytochrome b are reduced, while cytochromes c_1, c, a and a_3 are oxidized. Thus, if the inhibition is relieved, for example by adding albumin, cytochrome b and the components on the substrate side of cytochrome b become more oxidized, while cytochrome c_1 and the other cytochromes become more reduced, *i.e.* there is a "cross-over point" between cytochromes b and c_1. From these experiments, we learn that the inhibitor (I) interferes with the reaction between cytochromes b^{2+} and $c_1{}^{3+}$.

$$b^{2+} + c_1{}^{3+} \rightarrow b^{3+} + c_1{}^{2+}$$

There are three possible ways in which it can do this

(*i*) $b^{2+} + \mathrm{I} \rightleftharpoons b^{2+} \cdot \mathrm{I}$

(*ii*) $c_1{}^{3+} + \mathrm{I} \rightleftharpoons c^{3+} \cdot \mathrm{I}$

(*iii*) I combines with a catalyst necessary for reaction between the two cytochromes

Chance and Williams found that when ADP was added to liver mitochondria suspended in a solution containing β-hydroxybutyrate, P_i (and ATP), the cross-over point was between cytochromes c and a. In other experiments, in the presence of 92 μM azide, the cross-over was between cytochromes b and c, and in yet other experiments between NAD^+ and flavoprotein.

Each of these three sites has the three possible explanations (or two if it is assumed that there are no additional components in the respiratory chain). Chance chose the first explanation, and concluded that, in the absence of ADP, inhibited forms of NADH, ferrocytochrome b and ferrocytochrome c are formed. He considered that these inhibited forms are energy-rich compounds which can react with ADP and P_i to form ATP.

$$\mathrm{NADH{\sim}I + ADP + P_i \rightleftharpoons NADH + ATP + I}$$

$$b^{2+}{\sim}\mathrm{I + ADP + P_i} \rightleftharpoons b^{2+} + \mathrm{ATP + I}$$

$$c^{2+}{\sim}\mathrm{I + ADP + P_i} \rightleftharpoons c^{2+} + \mathrm{ATP + I}$$

However, it does not seem to others that this conclusion is the only one which can be drawn from the experimental observations (*cf.* Ref. 93).

Perhaps the most interesting finding of Chance and Williams is the magnitude of the changes on adding ADP. When inhibition by antimycin is relieved, the components of the chain on the substrate side of the inhibition site change from being completely reduced to being largely oxidized (see, for example, Ref. 121). The corresponding changes for the relief by ADP of the inhibition are:

cytochrome *a*	< 1% reduced to	4% reduced
cytochrome *c*	14% reduced to	6% reduced
cytochrome *b*	35% reduced to	16% reduced
flavoprotein	40% reduced to	20% reduced
NAD	100% reduced to	50% reduced

(Klingenberg and Slenczka[102] showed that the observations of Chance and Williams on NAD in rat-liver mitochondria were obscured by the large amount of NADP present. By extraction procedures they showed that, in absence of ADP, NAD is only 43% reduced and becomes 3% reduced on the addition of ADP). These relatively small changes suggest that ADP relieves the inhibition at more than one site of the respiratory chain, which provides independent confirmation of this conclusion drawn from other types of experiments.

5. Mechanism of oxidative phosphorylation

Two types of oxidative phosphorylation may be distinguished: (*a*) substrate-linked phosphorylation, where AH_2 in Eqn. 1.1 is an aldehyde, pyruvate or α-ketoglutarate; (*b*) respiratory-chain phosphorylation, where AH_2 and B are both members of the respiratory chain.

(*a*) *Substrate-linked phosphorylation*

(*i*) *Glyceraldehyde phosphate*

$$\mathrm{R \cdot CHO + NAD^+ + ADP + P_i \rightleftharpoons R \cdot COOH + NADH + H^+ + ATP} \quad (5.1)$$

Negelein and Brömel[5] showed in 1939 that 1,3-diphosphoglyceric acid (R · CO*OP*) is an intermediate in this reaction which may then be written

$$AH_2 + B + \mathrm{P_i} \rightleftharpoons A \sim \mathrm{P} + BH_2$$
$$A \sim \mathrm{P} + \mathrm{ADP} \rightleftharpoons A + \mathrm{ATP}$$
$$\textit{Sum}\ AH_2 + B + \mathrm{ADP} + \mathrm{P_i} \rightleftharpoons A + BH_2 + \mathrm{ATP}$$

The second reaction is catalysed by phosphoglycerate kinase (EC 2.7.2.3).

Warburg and Christian[4] suggested that glyceraldehyde phosphate formed a loose compound with $\mathrm{P_i}$

$$AH_2 + \mathrm{P_i} \rightleftharpoons AH_2\text{-P}$$

which was then oxidized by NAD^+

$$AH_2\text{-P} + \mathrm{NAD^+} \rightleftharpoons A \sim \mathrm{P} + \mathrm{NADH} + \mathrm{H^+}$$

Racker and Krimsky[122] showed, however, that oxidation proceeds in the absence of $\mathrm{P_i}$ with formation of the energy-rich thiol ester of the enzyme which then reacts with $\mathrm{P_i}$

References p. 388

$$AH_2 + B + C \rightleftharpoons A{\sim}C + BH_2$$
$$A{\sim}C + P_i \rightleftharpoons A{\sim}P + C$$

where C is the –SH group on a cysteine residue in the enzyme.

Aspartate semialdehyde dehydrogenase (EC 1.2.1.11) and aspartate kinase (EC 2.7.2.4) catalyse a reaction similar to that given by Eqn. 5.1, except that $NADP^+$ is the acceptor[123]. A thiol ester has not been identified as an intermediate.

The oxidation of acetaldehyde by NAD^+ in certain micro-organisms[124] is coupled with the synthesis of ATP, the reaction proceeding in the following steps

$AH_2 + B + C \rightleftharpoons A{\sim}C + BH_2$	aldehyde dehydrogenase (EC 1.2.1.10)
$A{\sim}C + P_i \rightleftharpoons A{\sim}P + C$	phosphate acetyltransferase (EC 2.3.1.8)
$A{\sim}P + ADP \rightleftharpoons A + ATP$	acetate kinase (EC 2.7.2.1)

where C is coenzyme A, $A{\sim}C$ acetyl-CoA and $A{\sim}P$ acetyl phosphate.

This mechanism resembles that of the glyceraldehydephosphate dehydrogenase reaction in that a thiol ester and an acyl phosphate are intermediates. However, the thiol is not part of the enzyme and a separate enzyme is required for the phosphorolysis reaction.

(ii) Pyruvate

$$CH_3 \cdot CO \cdot COOH + NAD^+ + ADP + P_i \rightleftharpoons CH_3 \cdot COOH + CO_2 + NADH + H^+ + ATP \quad (5.2)$$

The oxidation of pyruvate by NAD^+ is coupled with phosphorylation in some micro-organisms, but not in animal tissues. Acetyl phosphate was early recognized as an intermediate[14], the transfer of phosphate to ADP being catalysed by acetate kinase. Further fractionation of the system at first showed a close analogy with the phosphoglyceraldehyde dehydrogenase system (see Ref. 125 for a review).

Still further fractionation revealed some differences. The first hydrogen acceptor was found to be lipoic acid[126], which also formed a thiol ester with the acetate. Thus the mechanism may be written

$$\left.\begin{aligned} AH_2 + B &\rightleftharpoons A \sim BH_2 \\ A \sim BH_2 + C &\rightleftharpoons A \sim C + BH_2 \end{aligned}\right\} \text{pyruvate dehydrogenase}$$

$$A \sim C + P_i \rightleftharpoons A \sim P + C \qquad \text{phosphate acetyltransferase}$$

$$A \sim P + ADP \rightleftharpoons A + ATP \qquad \text{acetate kinase}$$

Sum: $AH_2 + B + ADP + P_i \rightleftharpoons A + BH_2 + ATP$

(iii) α-Ketoglutarate

$$\mathrm{HOOC \cdot CH_2 \cdot CH_2 \cdot CO \cdot COOH + H_2O + NAD^+ + ADP + P_i \rightleftharpoons HOOC \cdot CH_2 \cdot CH_2 \cdot COOH + CO_2 + NADH + H^+ + ATP + H_2O} \quad (5.3)$$

In both animal cells and micro-organisms, the initial oxidative decarboxylation of α-ketoglutarate is accompanied by phosphorylation[25]. The mechanism resembles closely that of pyruvate in micro-organisms with the differences: (*i*) succinyl phosphate ($A \sim \mathrm{P}$) is not an intermediate[127–129]; (*ii*) GDP replaces ADP[77,78a,74]. The reaction may be written

$$\left.\begin{aligned} AH_2 + B &\rightleftharpoons A \sim BH_2 \\ A \sim BH_2 + C &\rightleftharpoons A \sim C + BH_2 \end{aligned}\right\} \text{α-ketoglutarate dehydrogenase}$$

$$A \sim C + \mathrm{P_i} + \mathrm{GDP} \rightleftharpoons A + C + \mathrm{GTP} \quad \text{succinyl-CoA synthetase (EC 6.2.1.4)}$$

$$\mathrm{GTP + ADP \rightleftharpoons GDP + ATP} \quad \text{nucleosidediphosphate kinase (EC 2.7.4.6)}$$

$$\textit{Sum}: AH_2 + B + \mathrm{ADP} + \mathrm{P_i} \rightleftharpoons A + BH_2 + \mathrm{ATP}$$

Protein-bound phosphohistidine has been shown to be an intermediate in both the succinyl-CoA synthetase[130–133] and the nucleosidediphosphate kinase[134,135] reactions. Enzyme-bound succinyl phosphate[136] and a non-phosphorylated high-energy intermediate of the enzyme[137] have also been suggested as intermediates in the succinyl-CoA synthetase reaction.

(iv) Summary of substrate-linked phosphorylation

The reactions may be summarized as follows:

$$AH_2 + B + C \rightleftharpoons A \sim C + BH_2 \ (5.4) \left\{\begin{array}{l}\text{Pyruvate,}\\ \text{α-ketoglutarate}\end{array}\right. \left\{\begin{array}{ll} AH_2 + B & \rightleftharpoons A \sim BH_2 \\ A \sim BH_2 + C & \rightleftharpoons A \sim C + BH_2 \end{array}\right.$$

$$A \sim C + \mathrm{ADP} + \mathrm{P_i} \rightleftharpoons A + C + \mathrm{ATP} \ (5.5) \left\{\begin{array}{ll} \begin{array}{l}\text{glyceraldehyde}P\\ \text{acetaldehyde,}\\ \text{pyruvate}\end{array} & \left\{\begin{array}{ll} A \sim C + \mathrm{P_i} & \rightleftharpoons A \sim \mathrm{P} + C \\ A \sim \mathrm{P} + \mathrm{ADP} & \rightleftharpoons A + \mathrm{ATP} \end{array}\right. \\ \text{α-ketoglutarate} & \left\{\begin{array}{ll} A \sim C + \mathrm{P_i} & \rightleftharpoons C \sim \mathrm{P} + A \\ C \sim \mathrm{P} + \mathrm{GDP} & \rightleftharpoons C + \mathrm{GTP} \\ \mathrm{GTP} + \mathrm{ADP} & \rightleftharpoons \mathrm{GDP} + \mathrm{ATP} \end{array}\right. \end{array}\right.$$

There are three common features: (*i*) a high-energy intermediate is formed before the intervention of $\mathrm{P_i}$ or ADP; (*ii*) $\mathrm{P_i}$ reacts before ADP; (*iii*) C is –SH.

Racker[138] and Lehninger and Wadkins[139] include the enolase reaction

$$\begin{array}{c} \mathrm{CH_2OH} \\ | \\ \mathrm{CHO}P \\ | \\ \mathrm{COOH} \end{array} \rightleftharpoons \begin{array}{c} \mathrm{CH_2} \\ \| \\ \mathrm{CO}P \\ | \\ \mathrm{COOH} \end{array} + \mathrm{H_2O}$$

References p. 388

as a type of substrate-linked oxidative phosphorylation, the oxido-reduction being an intramolecular reaction. Racker considers this significant since it is the only well-established mechanism of ATP formation in which attachment of the transferable phosphate group takes place before the oxido-reduction step. In the writer's opinion the removal of water to form a C=C double bond is not a typical oxido-reduction reaction, so that this reaction can have little relevance for the mechanism of oxidative phosphorylation.

(*b*) *Respiratory-chain phosphorylation*

Much less is known about the mechanism of respiratory-chain phosphorylation than about that of substrate-linked phosphorylation. There are probably at least three separate phosphorylation reactions in the respiratory chain, but in no case is the identity of the hydrogen donor or acceptor known with certainty. For this reason, it is necessary still to discuss the mechanism of oxidative phosphorylation in terms of general symbols, such as AH_2, B and C. There is, in fact, no paucity of plausible chemical mechanisms involving NAD, flavin, ubiquinone or the cytochromes. There are, however, at present insufficient data to enable a choice to be made between the various possibilities.

Mitchell[140] has proposed a mechanism for oxidative phosphorylation, called a chemi-osmotic theory, which dispenses with any high-energy intermediate. This mechanism will be discussed before the chemical mechanisms.

(*i*) *Chemi-osmotic theory**

The Mitchell theory is based on Lipmann's[141] suggestion that ATP should be considered a phosphorylium compound,

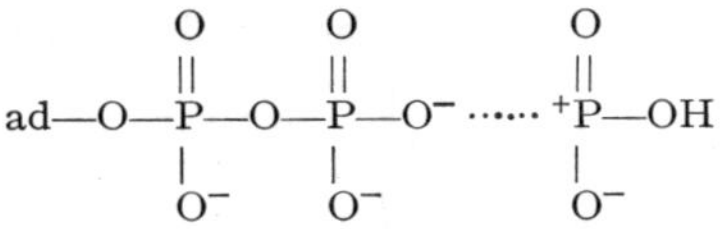

$$\text{ad—O—}\overset{\overset{\displaystyle O}{\|}}{\underset{\underset{\displaystyle O^-}{|}}{P}}\text{—O—}\overset{\overset{\displaystyle O}{\|}}{\underset{\underset{\displaystyle O^-}{|}}{P}}\text{—O}^- \cdots\cdots {}^+\overset{\overset{\displaystyle O}{\|}}{\underset{\underset{\displaystyle O^-}{|}}{P}}\text{—OH}$$

The essence of the theory is that the function of the respiratory chain is to produce a sufficiently low product of the effective concentration of H^+ and OH^- ions (and thus of the concentration of water) in the active-centre region of an ATPase located in a membrane, so that the ATPase can catalyse the synthesis of ATP. The ATPase is accessible from one side (which we shall term the left-hand side) to OH^-, to the other side (the right-hand) to ATP, ADP, P_i and H^+, and to water as such from neither side. The reaction catalysed by the ATPase may be written

* It is a pleasure to acknowledge the help from Dr. Mitchell in writing this section.

$$\mathrm{ADP{-}O^- \cdots\cdots {}^+\overset{OH}{\overset{|}{\underset{\underset{O}{\|}}{P}}}{-}OH + RH \rightleftharpoons R^- \cdots\cdots {}^+\overset{OH}{\overset{|}{\underset{\underset{O}{\|}}{P}}}{-}OH + ADP{-}OH}$$

$$\mathrm{R^+ \cdots\cdots {}^+\overset{OH}{\overset{|}{\underset{\underset{O}{\|}}{P}}}{-}OH + OH^-_L \rightleftharpoons R^- + HO{-}\overset{OH}{\overset{|}{\underset{\underset{O}{\|}}{P}}}{-}OH}$$

$$\mathrm{R^- + H^+_R \rightleftharpoons RH}$$

$$\textit{Sum}\text{: } \mathrm{ATP_R + OH^-_L + H^+_R \rightleftharpoons ADP_R + P_R} \tag{5.6}$$

where the suffixes L and R indicate the left- and right-hand sides and R^- is a nucleophilic grouping in the ATPase*.

The equilibrium constant of Eqn. 5.6 is given by

$$K = \frac{[\mathrm{ADP}][\mathrm{P_i}]}{[\mathrm{ATP}][\mathrm{OH^-_L}][\mathrm{H^+_R}]}$$

* This reaction is written for undissociated ATP, ADP and P_i, which may very well be the reactive species in the non-aqueous membrane. The ionic species present on the right-hand side will be governed by the pH of that side. At pH 7.5, an additional acid radical is formed on hydrolysis. At this pH the ATPase may be written

$$\mathrm{ADP^{2-}{-}O^- \cdots\cdots {}^+\overset{O^-}{\overset{|}{\underset{\underset{O}{\|}}{P}}}{-}OH + R^- \rightleftharpoons R^- \cdots\cdots {}^-\overset{O^-}{\overset{|}{\underset{\underset{O}{\|}}{P}}}{-}OH + ADP^{2-}{-}O^-}$$

$$\mathrm{R^- \cdots\cdots {}^+\overset{O^-}{\overset{|}{\underset{\underset{O}{\|}}{P}}}{-}OH + OH^-_L \rightleftharpoons R^- + HO{-}\overset{O^-}{\overset{|}{\underset{\underset{O}{\|}}{P}}}{-}OH}$$

$$\mathrm{HO{-}\overset{O^-}{\overset{|}{\underset{\underset{O}{\|}}{P}}}{-}OH + ADP^{2-}{-}O^- \rightleftharpoons HO{-}\overset{O^-}{\overset{|}{\underset{\underset{O}{\|}}{P}}}{-}O^- + ADP^{2-}{-}OH}$$

$$\begin{aligned} \mathrm{ATP_R} &\rightleftharpoons \mathrm{ATP^{3-} + 3H^+_R} \\ \mathrm{ADP^{2-} + 2H^+_R} &\rightleftharpoons \mathrm{ADP_R} \\ \mathrm{P^{2-} + 2H^+_R} &\rightleftharpoons \mathrm{P_R} \end{aligned}$$

$$\textit{Sum}\text{: } \mathrm{ATP_R + OH^-_L + H^+_R \rightleftharpoons ADP_R + P_R}$$

Thus the sum reaction is the same as that given by Eqn. 5.6. The H^+_R in the sum reaction is derived by the dissociation of ADP and P_i. This is why ATP, ADP and P_i are put in the right-hand compartment in Eqn. 5.6. The sum of the first 3 equations is $ATP^{3-} + OH^-_L \rightleftharpoons ADP^{2-} + P^{2-}$. The $\Delta G'_0$ of the hydrolysis of ATP is about -7 kcal between pH 1 and 6 and is about -8.2 kcal at pH 7.5 (Ref. 141).

Thus, the enzyme will catalyse the synthesis of ATP if $[OH_L^-]$ can be made sufficiently low, without a corresponding increase in $[H_R^+]$. According to the Mitchell theory, OH^- ions are removed from the left-hand side of the membrane by reacting with H^+ ions produced on this side of the membrane by the operation of the respiratory chain, and H^+ ions are removed from the right-hand side of the membrane by reacting with OH^- ions formed by reduction of O_2 by cytochrome *c* oxidase*.

The two reactions producing H^+ ions are described by Eqns. 5.7 and 5.8

$$SH_2 + NAD^+ \rightleftharpoons S + NADH + H^+ \qquad (5.7)$$

$$QH_2 + 2\,Fe^{3+} \rightleftharpoons Q + 2\,Fe^{2+} + 2\,H^+ \qquad (5.8)$$

The theory applied to succinate oxidation is illustrated in Fig. 5. Succinate, *via* succinate dehydrogenase and ubiquinone, reduces two molecules of ferricytochrome *b* on the left-hand side of the membrane which contains the respiratory chain in a specific orientation. The H^+ ions formed by Reaction 5.7, unable to diffuse through the membrane, react with OH^- on the left-hand side. The electrons travel along the cytochrome chain and react with

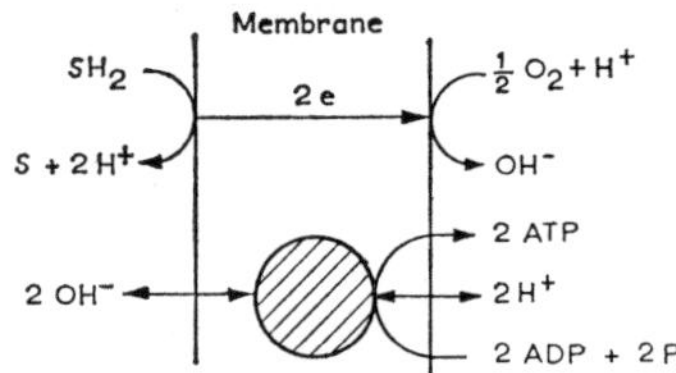

Fig. 5. Mitchell theory of the mechanism of ATP synthesis coupled to the oxidation of succinate (SH_2). The cross-hatched area represents an ATPase, accessible to ATP, ADP, P_i and H^+ from the oxygen side of the membrane and to OH^- from the substrate side.

oxygen, with the production of OH^- ions, at the other side of the membrane. The OH^- ions, also unable to diffuse through the membrane, are neutralized by H^+ ions on the right-hand side. The removal of OH^- ions from the left-hand side and of H^+ ions from the right-hand side of the membrane drives Eqn. 5.6 to the left. The reactions may be described by the following equations:

* At pH 7.5, the equilibrium constant is given by

$$K = \frac{[ADP^{2-}][P_i^{2-}]}{[ATP^{3-}][OH_L^-]}$$

Thus, at this pH the driving force for ATP synthesis is the neutralization of OH_L^- by H^+ produced by Eqns. 5.7 and 5.8, and neutralization of H_R^+ by OH^- produced by the reduction of O_2 is of no great significance.

$$SH_2 + 2\ Fe^{3+} \rightleftharpoons S + 2\ H_L^+ + 2\ Fe^{2+}$$
$$2\ ADP_R + 2\ P_R \rightleftharpoons 2\ ATP_R + 2\ OH_L^- + 2\ H_R^+$$
$$2\ H_L^+ + 2\ OH_L^- \rightleftharpoons 2\ H_2O_L$$
$$2\ Fe^{2+} + \tfrac{1}{2}\ O_2 + 2\ H_R^+ \rightarrow 2\ Fe^{3+} + H_2O_R$$

$$\textit{Sum}: SH_2 + \tfrac{1}{2}\ O_2 + 2\ ADP_R + 2\ P_R \rightarrow S + H_2O_R + 2\ ATP_R + 2\ H_2O_L$$

where the suffixes L and R indicate the left- and right-hand sides of the membrane given in Fig. 5.

Fig. 6 illustrates the theory applied to NAD-linked substrates. One H^+ ion is formed on the "left-hand side" by reduction of NAD^+. The NADH then travels across the membrane where it reacts with flavoprotein, utilizing a H^+ from the medium on the right-hand side of the membrane. The NAD^+

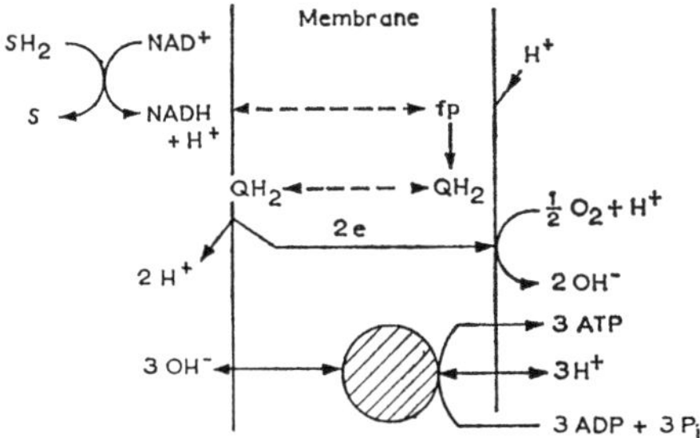

Fig. 6. Mitchell theory of the mechanism of ATP synthesis coupled to the oxidation of NAD-linked substrates.

formed must be free to return to the other side of the membrane. The reduced flavoprotein reduces ubiquinone and the ubiquinol travels across to the other side of the membrane where it reacts with ferricytochrome *b*. The following reactions are the same as in Fig. 5. The complete sequence may be described by the following equations:

$$SH_2 + NAD^+ \rightleftharpoons S + NADH + H_L^+$$
$$NADH + fp + H_R^+ \rightleftharpoons NAD^+ + fpH_2$$
$$fpH_2 + Q \rightleftharpoons fp + QH_2$$
$$QH_2 + 2\ Fe^{3+} \rightleftharpoons Q + 2\ Fe^{2+} + 2\ H_L^+$$
$$3\ ADP_R + 3\ P_R \rightleftharpoons 3\ ATP_R + 3\ OH_L^- + 3\ H_R^+$$
$$3\ H_L^+ + 3\ OH_L^- \rightleftharpoons 3\ H_2O_L$$
$$2\ Fe^{2+} + \tfrac{1}{2}\ O_2 + 2\ H_R^+ \rightarrow 2\ Fe^{3+} + H_2O_R$$

$$\textit{Sum}: SH_2 + \tfrac{1}{2}\ O_2 + 3\ ADP_R + 3\ P_R \rightarrow S + H_2O_R + 3\ ATP_R + 3\ H_2O_L$$

References p. 388

The Mitchell theory has the following interesting features:

(*1*) It gives a chemical explanation of the observed P:O ratios (3 with NAD-linked substrates, 2 with succinate).

(*2*) It explains the coupling between the respiratory chain and phosphorylation without the necessity of any direct connection between the chain and a phosphorylating enzyme system. The two must be in the same membrane, but need not be at the same place in the membrane.

(*3*) It requires that the components of the chain of low molecular weight — NAD and ubiquinone — should be freely diffusible in the membrane, whereas the flavoprotein and the cytochrome system are fixed in position.

(*4*) According to this theory, there are no phosphorylating steps in the sense considered in the previous section. The function of the respiratory chain is merely to deliver H^+ ions on one side of a membrane impermeable to H^+ or OH^- ions.

(*5*) It dispenses with high-energy intermediates of oxidative phosphorylation and all except one ATPase.

(*6*) It gives a special significance to the positively charged N atom of NAD and to the iron atom of cytochrome.

(*7*) It readily explains uncoupling by damage to the mitochondria, since this might well lead to impairment of selective permeability of the membrane and cause the H^+ ions formed by the respiratory chain to react with OH^- ions on the wrong side of the membrane.

(*8*) A steady-state concentration of $[OH^-]$ of about 10^{-14} (pH = 0) would be required to promote the synthesis of ATP by this mechanism. Since this is highly unlikely, Mitchell suggests that exchange diffusion carriers are present in the membrane and that they will allow strictly coupled one-to-one exchange of H^+ against K^+ or of OH^- against Cl^-, for example. The pH differential would thus be reduced to a relatively small figure and would be equivalently replaced by a membrane potential. Indeed, as will be discussed later, mitochondria are capable of taking up large amounts of cations.

(*9*) It provides a ready explanation for the P:O ratios exceeding 1 found by Howland[120] with tetramethyl-*p*-phenylenediamine as substrate, since reduction of ferricytochrome *c* might be expected to have the same effect as reduction of ferricytochrome *b*. Phosphorylation with ferrocytochrome *c* as donor and the lower ratios obtained with ferricytochrome *c* compared with oxygen are more difficult to accommodate in the theory (*cf.* Lehninger and Wadkins[139]) but are not conclusive evidence against it.

The idea that one of the functions of the respiratory chain is to cause a separation of electric charges has formed the basis of many theories of the mechanism of active ion transport proposed in the last 20 or 30 years (see Ref. 142 for a recent review). Robertson[142] suggested that the separation of charges by a lipid membrane might be the dinitrophenol-sensitive process preceding the synthesis of ATP in oxidative phosphorylation. However, Mitchell's theory is the first that links this separation of charges to an anisotropic ATPase also present in the membrane, and is also the first theory to account for the experimentally observed P:O ratios.

Mitchell's theory is beautifully simple, and as we have seen it explains all the experimental findings concerning oxidative phosphorylation which we have discussed to date. We shall see below that it also explains in a simple way many other findings. There are, however, a number of observations which are more easily explained on the basis of discrete phosphorylation steps. In general, oxidative phosphorylation appears to be more complicated than envisaged by the Mitchell theory*.

(ii) Chemical theory

The first mechanism of oxidative phosphorylation, proposed by Lipmann[87] in 1964 and developed by Hunter[145], has been discussed in detail elsewhere[93]. The essential feature of this theory is that, as in Warburg's theory of the glycolytic phosphorylation reaction, AH_2 reacts with P_i to form a low-energy compound (AH_2-P) which is converted to a high-energy compound ($A \sim$P) on oxidation.

In 1953, Slater[146] suggested the mechanism of oxidative phosphorylation given by the equations

$$AH_2 + B + C \rightleftharpoons A \sim C + BH_2 \quad (5.9)$$

$$A \sim C + \text{ADP} + P_i \rightleftharpoons A + C + \text{ATP} \quad (5.10)$$

$$\textit{Sum:}\ AH_2 + B + \text{ADP} + P_i \rightleftharpoons A + BH_2 + \text{ATP}$$

The experimental basis for this suggestion was:

(1) Unlike the oxidative phosphorylation of phosphoglyceraldehyde, the respiratory chain can operate in the absence of P_i. The non-phosphoryla-

* Since the above was written, some important developments in the Mitchell theory have been reported. When a small amount of oxygen was added to an anaerobic mitochondrial suspension containing oxidizable substrate, a temporary decrease in the pH of the suspension was detected[143]. Thus, in terms of Figs. 5 and 6, the left-hand side is outside the mitochondrion. The ratio of H^+ produced to oxygen added (in μatoms) was 6 with β-hydroxybutyrate as substrate and 4 with succinate. When ATP was added, in the absence of substrate or O_2, 2 moles of H^+ were produced by the mitochondria for each mole of ATP hydrolyzed, in addition to the 0.8 mole H^+ expected for the hydrolysis of ATP to ADP and P_i at this pH. Thus, the mechanism of the ATPase reaction has to be modified in order to explain this finding, and the schemes given in Figs. 5 and 6 have to be extended in order to explain the production of 4 H^+ ions for each two reducing equivalents of succinate oxidized and of 6 H^+ ions for each two reducing equivalents of β-hydroxybutyrate (*cf.* Ref. 144). Because of this stoichiometry a differential of only 3.5 pH units on the two sides of the membrane would be sufficient to give an ATP/ADP ratio of 1 at a P_i concentration of 10 mM.

References p. 388

tive Keilin and Hartree preparation oxidizes succinate and NADH at maximal rates when the phosphate concentration is less than 1 μM (Ref. 147; *cf.* Ref. 148).

(*2*) Loomis and Lipmann[24] had shown in 1948 that dinitrophenol can replace the inorganic phosphate which is necessary for optimal oxidation rates with a kidney-cyclophorase preparation oxidizing glutamate.

(*3*) Lardy and Wellman[34,149], Hunter[145] and others[150–152], in 1952–3, developed an earlier suggestion of Lardy and Elvehjem[153] that uncoupling by dinitrophenol is due to catalysis by this compound of the hydrolysis of an intermediate phosphate compound.

(*4*) Although in the presence of ADP and phosphate, dinitrophenol has no effect on the rate of oxidation of α-ketoglutarate by rat-heart mitochondria, it greatly stimulated the respiration of some preparations of mitochondria isolated from the thoracic muscle of the blowfly under the same conditions. Since dinitrophenol stimulated more than ADP or phosphate, it appeared likely that it functions at a point closer to the respiratory chain than ADP or phosphate[154].

(*5*) Recent studies on substrate-linked phosphorylation (see Section 5a) had revealed a general mechanism which could be formulated by Eqns. 5.9 and 5.10.

The new feature of the mechanism was the introduction of *C* into Eqn. 5.1. None of the evidence brought forward in its favour was in fact conclusive and the mechanism was not at first generally accepted. In particular, it did not explain the results of Teply[155] or Judah[107], who had found that if the mitochondria were pretreated so as to remove endogenous inorganic phosphate, maximum rates of oxidation were not obtained unless phosphate was also added. Judah[107] concluded that dinitrophenol split a phosphate-containing intermediate, a point of view which he re-emphasized in 1959 (Ref. 156).

A second objection was raised by Ernster and coworkers[157–159]. They developed the alternative suggestion of Lardy and Elvehjem[153] for the mechanism of action of dinitrophenol, *viz.* that it allows oxidation to proceed without phosphorylation. Until 1961, Ernster maintained that phosphate enters the first oxidative reaction.

Since 1961, however, it has become generally agreed that a component similar to *C* in Eqn. 5.4 is involved before phosphate. The new evidence brought forward which led to the general acceptance of this view included the following:

(*1*) Borst and Slater[160] showed that dinitrophenol can, in fact, abolish the requirement of the respiratory chain for phosphate and that the requirement of phosphate for glutamate oxidation found by Teply[155] and Judah[107] is due to the fact that, in opposition to the view generally held at that time, glutamate is oxidized by isolated mitochondria not to α-ketoglutarate *via* glutamate dehydrogenase but to aspartate by a cyclic mechanism involving transamination and part of the Krebs cycle, and including the phosphate-requiring substrate-linked phosphorylation of α-ketoglutarate oxidation[52].

(*2*) By carrying out similar experiments in the presence of oligomycin (see below), Chappell and Greville[161] closed one possible loophole in these experiments, namely that, on addition of dinitrophenol, ATP formed from ADP by myokinase could form sufficient P_i to operate a phosphate-requiring respiratory chain.

(*3*) Lardy *et al.*[162,163] showed that oligomycin inhibits phosphorylating respiration, that this inhibition is relieved by dinitrophenol, and that the dinitrophenol-induced ATPase, the exchange of $^{32}P_i$ with ATP and the loss of ^{18}O from ^{18}O-labelled P_i are also inhibited by oligomycin. Estabrook[164] and Huijing and Slater[165] showed that, in contrast to dinitrophenol, arsenate does not relieve inhibition by oligomycin.

(*4*) Ernster[166] showed that an energy-requiring reaction which will be discussed later can proceed in the absence of P_i and this was confirmed by Snoswell[167].

While the essential feature of Eqn. 5.9, the formation of a high-energy intermediate not containing phosphate derived from P_i, is generally accepted (*cf.* Ref. 139), there are differences in detail between formulations used by different workers. A trivial difference is that other letters (I, X, Y, Z, E) are used instead of C: I to emphasize that the high-energy intermediate is an inhibited form[92] (*cf.* Ref. 168), X, Y and Z[169] to indicate the three phosphorylating steps and E to indicate an enzyme[170]. More recently C has been replaced by more elaborate formulations, such as RCCF (reduced cytochrome *c* coupling factor)[171] and by M bound to an enzyme (E) in intact mitochondria[172]. More important, Chance and Williams[92] and Ernster[166] propose that the energy-rich compound is with a reduced member of the chain, *e.g.* $BH_2{\sim}C$ rather than $A{\sim}C$ in Eqn. 5.9.

Moreover, in order to overcome thermodynamic difficulties, Chance *et al.*[173] proposed in 1955 that more than one step of the respiratory chain is required to form the high-energy intermediate, and this was adopted by Ernster[157–159,166], and also by Slater and Colpa-Boonstra[174] in more elaborate and speculative mechanisms. Eqn. 5.9 should be regarded only as the formal expression of an oxidation reaction requiring the participation of a third substance, which does not undergo oxido-reduction but forms an energy-rich compound with the oxidized product.

Eqn. 5.10 is probably the sum reaction of perhaps several. The experiments of Estabrook[164] and Huijing and Slater[165] already mentioned suggest that dinitrophenol might act on an earlier high-energy compound than arsenate,

References p. 388

and that oligomycin acts in the region of this second energy-rich compound*. For example, Eqn. 5.10 could be the sum of Eqns. 5.11 and 5.12.

$$A \sim C + D \rightleftharpoons A + C \sim D \qquad (5.11)$$

$$C \sim D + \text{ADP} + \text{P}_i \rightleftharpoons C + D + \text{ATP} \qquad (5.12)$$

Whether or not a high-energy phosphate compound is an intermediate in Eqn. 5.12 will be discussed later (see p. 386).

The three most important characteristics of oxidative phosphorylation — respiratory control, inhibition by oligomycin and uncoupling by dinitrophenol — are illustrated in the experiment shown in Fig. 7. The O_2 disappears very slowly at first even in the presence of glutamate because the reaction medium contains no ADP. As soon as ADP is added, there is an immediate sharp increase in the rate of O_2 consumption until all the ADP is converted to ATP. The reaction then runs slowly owing to lack of ADP.

Mito
Glutamate
[O2] =
250 μM
ADP
Oligomycin
ADP
Dinitrophenol
1 min
[O2] = 0

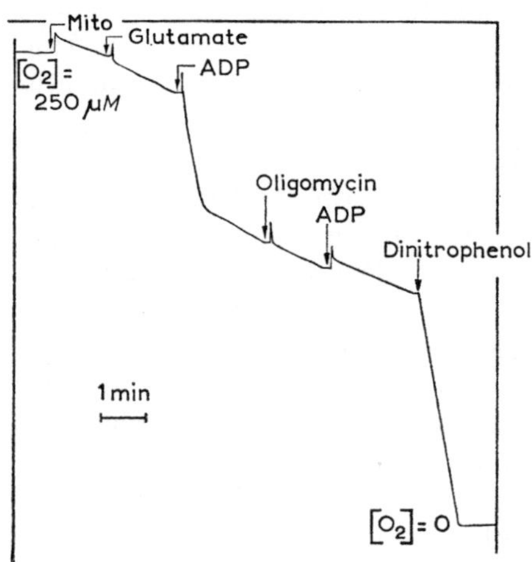

Fig. 7. Inhibition by oligomycin of the ADP-stimulated oxidation of glutamate by rat-liver mitochondria (*cf.* Fig. 1, p. 333) and reversal of inhibition by dinitrophenol. Photograph of a record with an oxygen polarograph, where the concentration of the O_2 is given on the ordinate and time on the abscissa.

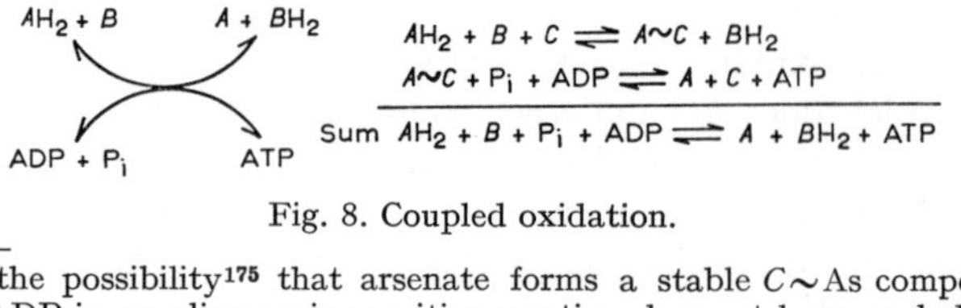

AH2 + B
A + BH2
ADP + Pi
ATP
AH2 + B + C ⇌ A~C + BH2
A~C + Pi + ADP ⇌ A + C + ATP
Sum AH2 + B + Pi + ADP ⇌ A + BH2 + ATP

Fig. 8. Coupled oxidation.

* However, the possibility[175] that arsenate forms a stable $C \sim$As compound, which reacts with ADP in an oligomycin-sensitive reaction, has not been excluded.

A second addition of ADP would have restored the respiration (*cf.* Fig. 1, p. 333) had not oligomycin been added previously. The respiration is restored by the addition of dinitrophenol.

The mechanism summarized in Eqns. 5.9 and 5.10 is shown schematically in Fig. 8, which is drawn in such a way as to emphasize the compulsory coupling between oxidation and phosphorylation. One cannot proceed without the other, since *C* is present in small concentrations compared with the amount of O_2 uptake.

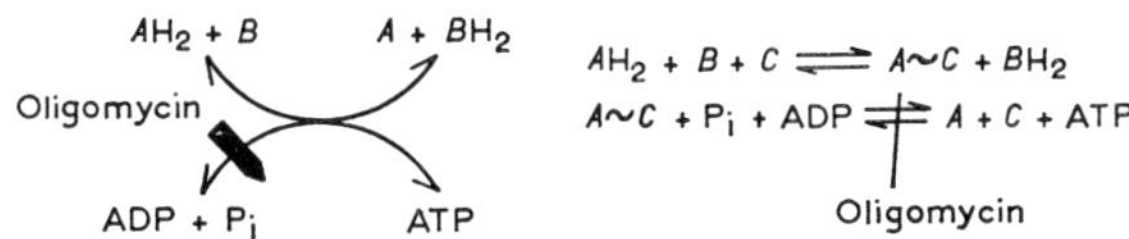

Fig. 9. Effect of oligomycin on coupled oxidation.

Fig. 9 illustrates inhibition by oligomycin, which is primarily on the phosphorylation reaction. Respiration is inhibited secondarily as a result of the compulsory link between oxidation and phosphorylation.

Dinitrophenol, on the contrary, does not inhibit phosphorylation, but uncouples it from respiration. In its presence, respiration proceeds at maximum speed even in the absence of P_i and ADP, and there is no phosphorylation even in the presence of P_i and ADP. This is illustrated in Fig. 10. We explain the uncoupling in chemical terms by adopting Lardy's[149,153] suggestion that dinitrophenol causes the splitting of the high-energy intermediate ($A \sim C$* in our scheme in place of a $\sim$P compound in Lardy's), so that $A \sim C$ is split without intervention of P_i or ADP, which are, therefore,

* In 1953 (Ref. 146) it was suggested that dinitrophenol acts on $A \sim C$. In 1957 (Ref. 176), when it appeared that reduction of A to AH_2 had no effect on the dinitrophenol-induced ATPase, it was concluded that dinitrophenol acts on a subsequent high-energy intermediate ($C \sim D$ in Eqn. 5.11), in agreement with Chance and Williams[92], who termed the dinitrophenol-sensitive intermediate $X \sim I$. In 1959, however, Wadkins and Lehninger[177] and a little later Chefurka[178] showed that addition of a high concentration of cyanide or careful removal of oxygen markedly inhibits the ATPase. Thus, the minimum hypothesis is to revert to $A \sim C$ as the site of action of dinitrophenol.

Recently, Chance and Ito[179,180] have shown that the addition of succinate to pigeon-heart mitochondria causes, after an initial stimulation, an inhibition of the endogenous ATPase activity and have correlated this inhibition with the reduction of endogenous NAD^+. They propose that the NADH reacts with $X \sim I$ to form NADH $\sim I$ (Ref. 92), thereby removing the dinitrophenol-sensitive $X \sim I$ from the system. However, this finding, which is essentially similar to that of Wadkins and Lehninger[177] and Chefurka[178], can also be easily interpreted on the basis that NAD^+ (*i.e.* A) is necessary for forming the dinitrophenol-sensitive intermediate ($A \sim C$) and that reduction of A to AH_2 removes A from the system. The initial hydrolysis of ATP, the amount of which is proportional to the mitochondria concentration[179], is roughly stoichiometric with the NAD^+ that is reduced.

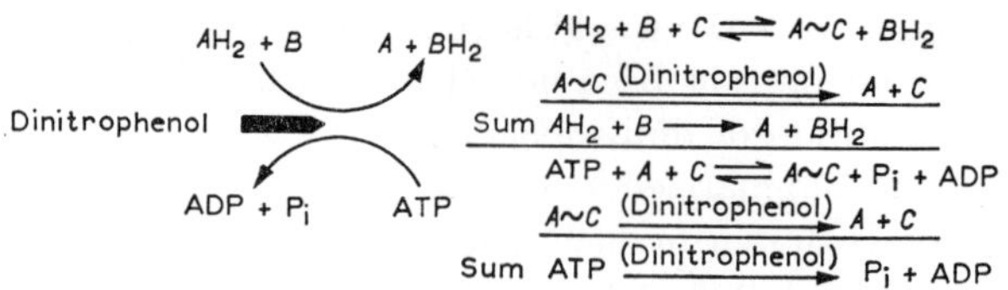

Fig. 10. Uncoupled oxidation and dinitrophenol-induced ATPase.

not necessary for respiration. Since the reaction of $A \sim C$ with P_i and ADP is reversible, dinitrophenol can induce an ATPase as shown[33,145,149,181]. Thus, dinitrophenol converts a reversible coupled oxidative phosphorylation into an irreversible oxidation running separately from the phosphorylation reaction which proceeds in the direction of hydrolysis.

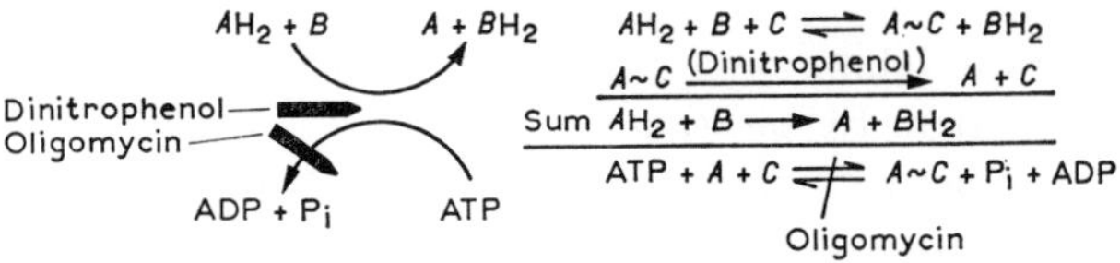

Fig. 11. Lack of effect of oligomycin on uncoupled oxidation and inhibition of dinitrophenol-induced ATPase.

The effects of dinitrophenol and oligomycin together[162,163] are illustrated in Fig. 11. In the presence of dinitrophenol, oligomycin has no effect on the oxidation reaction since this is uncoupled from the phosphorylation reaction, the site of action of the oligomycin. However, it inhibits the dinitrophenol-induced ATPase, because it prevents the reaction between A, C and ATP. This, and the similar effect on the $^{32}P_i$–ATP exchange and on the exchange of oxygen between P_i and water[163], is the proof that oligomycin acts on the phosphorylation reaction.

Respiratory control, inhibition by oligomycin and uncoupling by dinitrophenol can also be explained by Mitchell's chemi-osmotic theory[140]. In the absence of ADP or P_i, or in the presence of oligomycin which can be thought of as an inhibitor of the anisotropic ATPase, no OH^- ions are formed on the substrate side of the membrane to neutralize the H^+ ions, so that, by exchange of cations for H^+ ions, a very high membrane potential would be built up, until the passage of electrons along the respiratory chain would be inhibited.

The effects of dinitrophenol can be explained by the Mitchell theory if it is assumed that the ATPase is accessible to the undissociated phenol on the right-hand side and to the phenolate ion on the left-hand side, and further that the membrane is readily permeable to undissociated phenol from both sides. Hemker[182] has shown that the uncoupling activity of nitrophenols is correlated with the solubility of the undissociated phenol in the mitochondrial lipid (*cf*. Ref. 183). If the phenol (Φ–OH) can replace H^+ ions in the action of the anisotropic ATPase, we have

$$ATP_R + \Phi\text{–}OH_R + OH^-_L \rightleftharpoons ADP_R + P_R + \Phi\text{–}O^-_L$$

since the phenolate ion can only be discharged to the left-hand side. There it can react with H^+_L

$$\Phi\text{–}O^- + H^+_L \rightleftharpoons \Phi\text{–}OH_L$$

and the undissociated phenol may readily pass through the membrane

$$\Phi\text{–}OH_L \rightleftharpoons \Phi\text{–}OH_R$$

The sum reaction is

$$ATP_R + OH^-_L + H^+_L \rightleftharpoons ADP_R + P_R$$

the equilibrium of which lies far to the right. Thus, in the presence of an uncoupling phenol, the ATPase can function only to cause the hydrolysis of ATP and not its synthesis. The negligible ATPase activity of freshly prepared mitochondria in the absence of uncouplers can be explained if it is assumed that the OH^- ion concentration on the substrate side of the membrane is normally very low*.

Both the chemi-osmotic and the chemical theories explain other properties of the oxidative phosphorylation system, which will now be enumerated.

(*1*) In the presence of ATP, or of substrate in the absence of phosphate acceptor, mitochondria catalyse a rapid exchange of the oxygen atoms of inorganic phosphate and water[47,184–186], and this reaction is dinitrophenol-[186,187] and oligomycin-sensitive[163].

The fact that water is formed by the esterification of ADP with P_i (Eqn. 1.1) is not incorporated in the formal representation of the mechanism of oxidative phosphorylation given in Eqns. 5.9 and 5.10. In order to account for the oxygen exchange reactions, it is necessary to bring oxygen into these reactions. One possible explanation is to assume that Eqn. 5.12 involves reaction with P_i before ADP, that C contains an exchangeable –OH group (*cf*. Refs. 93, 187, 188) and that $C \sim D$ is formed by removal of a hydrogen atom from D and the –OH group from C. In the presence of $C \sim D$, formed from ATP or by coupled oxidation, the following exchange reaction would then be expected

$$C \sim D + P\text{–}{}^{18}OH \rightleftharpoons D \sim P + C\text{–}{}^{18}OH \rightleftharpoons C^+ + {}^{18}OH^- \qquad (5.13)$$

The anisotropic ATPase proposed by Mitchell would catalyse an exchange of oxygen atoms between P_i and OH^-_L, which by one-to-one exchange with

* It may be significant that there is an appreciable ATPase activity at higher pH's (Ref. 176).

Cl^- ions could be transferred to the oxygen side of the mitochondrion.

(*2*) In net oxidative phosphorylation, the bridge oxygen atom is supplied by the ADP while the P_i loses oxygen to water[188]. Similarly, in the dinitrophenol-induced ATPase, the ATP is cleaved between the terminal P atom and the bridge O atom[187].

This is to be expected according to Eqn. 5.13 which would be followed by

$$D{\sim}P + \text{ADP–OH} \rightleftharpoons DH + \text{ADP–O–}P \tag{5.14}$$

It would also be expected on the basis of the Mitchell theory, which proposes that the ADP provides the bridge O atom in the ATP formed.

(*3*) Both in the presence and absence of substrate, the terminal oxygen atom of ATP exchanges with water even more rapidly than the exchange of P_i with water[189,186]. A possible explanation of this has been discussed[93] (but see Ref. 139).

(*4*) When oxidative phosphorylation is uncoupled by 2,4-dinitrophenol, no oxygen is lost from the phenolic hydroxyl[188].

This would eliminate a carbonium ion form of the phenol as the active species of the uncoupler and would further imply that any compound between the uncoupler and A or C, which might be an intermediate in the dinitrophenol-induced splitting of $A \sim C$, must contain the phenolic oxygen of the uncoupler.

This observation is clearly not inconsistent with Mitchell's mechanism of uncoupling.

(*5*) In the absence of net hydrogen transfer, mitochondria also catalyse an exchange between the phosphorus atoms of P_i and of ATP (Refs. 47, 190, 185) and between ADP and ATP (Refs. 191, 169).

Wadkins and Lehninger[172] have provided evidence that these exchange activities in intact mitochondria are related to oxidative phosphorylation. They are inhibited by oligomycin as well as by dinitrophenol, and by reduction of the respiratory chain. This exchange will be discussed further (p. 374).

Clearly, these exchange reactions are readily explained by Eqn. 5.10 (or 5.12) or by Mitchell's anisotropic ATPase.

(*iii*) *Uncoupling of oxidative phosphorylation*

(*1*) *Phenols*. The stimulatory effects of nitrophenols on the overall metabolism of the animal were known to the pharmacologist as long ago as 1885, when Cazeneuve and Lepine[192] found that ingestion of dinitro-α-naphthol by the dog caused a high fever. Heymans and Bouchaert[193] and Magne *et al.*[194,195] in 1928–1932 demonstrated that the dinitrophenol acts directly on the tissues and not by stimulating the heat-regulating centre. The effects on isolated tissues were first studied in 1932–1936 by Von Euler[196,197], Ehrenfest and Ronzoni[198,199] and Dodds and Greville[200]. Ronzoni and

Ehrenfest[199] showed that 2,4-dinitrophenol increases the rate of hydrolysis of creatine phosphate. Further studies led to the generalization that nitrophenols stimulate intracellular respiration, whereas energy-requiring functions such as cell-division in sea-urchin eggs, growth of yeast, assimilation in micro-organisms, sperm mobility and phosphate uptake in yeast are inhibited.

De Meio and Barron[201] suggested in 1934 that dinitrophenol acts by combining with some of the substances acting as agents for the control of the speed of cellular oxidations, thus increasing the activity of oxidizing enzymes. In 1945, Lardy and Elvehjem[153] suggested that dinitrophenol and other uncoupling compounds act either by allowing oxidation to occur without phosphorylation or by catalysing the hydrolysis of an intermediate phosphate compound. In either case, oxidation would proceed without phosphorylation. This idea was first given experimental support in 1948 by Loomis and Lipmann[24] and Green and co-workers[26] when they found that 2,4-dinitrophenol and a number of other compounds inhibit the synthesis of ATP by mitochondrial preparations without affecting respiration. This was followed in 1951–1952 by the demonstration that these uncouplers induce an ATPase in freshly prepared liver mitochondria which in their absence do not hydrolyse added ATP (Refs. 33, 145, 181, 149).

In 1957, Myers and Slater[176] concluded that three separate dinitrophenol-induced ATPases are present in mitochondria, corresponding to the three phosphorylating steps, distinguishable from one another by different pH optima (6.5, 7.4 and 8.3). Moreover, Hülsmann and Slater[202] showed that, with different substrates, the number of peaks in the pH–activity curve of the P:O ratio equalled the number of phosphorylation steps with the particular substrate, and that the pH values of these peaks were the same in the ATPase reaction. It was thought that the three different Reactions 5.10, corresponding to the three phosphorylating steps, had been identified by this procedure.

Subsequent studies from the same laboratory by Hemker[182] showed that the interpretation by Myers and Slater[176] of the pH–activity curves of the dinitrophenol-induced ATPase was incorrect. Myers and Slater found that the pH optimum of the ATPase varied with the concentration of the 2,4-dinitrophenol; it was at 6.3 with 10 μM, 7.4 with 100 μM and 8.5 with 1 mM. Two possible interpretations were considered: (*1*) dinitrophenol inhibits at higher concentrations, and the effects of pH merely reflect the higher concentration of undissociated phenol at lower pH, the pK for 2,4-dinitrophenol being 4.1; (*2*) the effects of pH reflect the different sensitivities of three different enzyme systems, with different pH optima, to dinitrophenol. The first explanation appeared to be excluded by the observation that *p*-nitrophenol (pK 7.2) and 2,4-dinitrophenol (pK 4.1) are about equally

References p. 388

effective at pH 7 in inducing ATPase activity. This appeared to prove that the phenolate ion is the active species of the nitrophenols, since the concentration of the undissociated *p*-nitrophenol molecule under these circumstances is about 480 times as large as the concentration of the undissociated 2,4-dinitrophenol. Hemker[182] showed, however, that the effectiveness of an uncoupler depends not only on the pK but also on the lipid solubility of the phenol (*cf.* also Refs. 203, 204), and that dinitrophenol is 320 times more soluble than *p*-nitrophenol. Thus the difference of the concentration of the undissociated phenol molecule in the aqueous phase is largely counteracted by the difference in lipid solubility, resulting in approximately equal concentrations in the lipid phase.

Hemker[182] studied the effects of the pK and lipid solubility of a number of uncoupling agents, including a homologous series of 2,6-dinitro-4-alkylphenols (the largest substituent at the 4-position was iso-octyl), and of the pH of the medium on the ATPase activity of rat-liver mitochondria. Within a homologous series, the maximum ATPase activity induced was independent of the size of the alkyl substituent. He developed Eqn. 5.15.

$$\mathrm{p}c_1 = \mathrm{p}c_{\mathrm{aq}} + \mathrm{pH} + \mathrm{p}Q + \log(K + [\mathrm{H}^+] + fQ[\mathrm{H}^+]) \tag{5.15}$$

to describe the relationship between the concentration (c_1) of an uncoupling phenol in a lipid phase within the mitochondrion and the concentration (c_{aq}) in the surrounding aqueous phase, where Q is the partition coefficient of the undissociated phenol between lipid and water, K is its acid dissociation constant, and f is the ratio of volumes of lipid and aqueous phases. $(c_1)_{\mathrm{opt}}$ is defined as c_1 when c_{aq} is the concentration in the aqueous phase giving maximum ATPase activity ($(c_{\mathrm{aq}})_{\mathrm{opt}}$). By using this equation, Hemker was able to show that $\mathrm{p}(c_1)_{\mathrm{opt}}$ was independent of the size of the alkyl substituent in the homologous series of alkyl-2,6-dinitrophenols. Depending upon the conditions, Eqn. 5.15 can be reduced to the limiting cases

I. When $K \gg [\mathrm{H}^+]$ and $K \gg fQ[\mathrm{H}^+]$

$$\mathrm{p}c_1 = \mathrm{p}c_{\mathrm{aq}} + \mathrm{p}Q + \mathrm{pH} - \mathrm{p}K \tag{5.16}$$

II. When $[\mathrm{H}^+] \gg K$ and $fQ \ll 1$

$$\mathrm{p}c_1 = \mathrm{p}c_{\mathrm{aq}} + \mathrm{p}Q \tag{5.17}$$

III. When $fQ[\mathrm{H}^+] \gg K$ and $fQ[\mathrm{H}^+] \gg [\mathrm{H}^+]$

$$\mathrm{p}c_1 = \mathrm{p}c_{\mathrm{aq}} + \log f \tag{5.18}$$

Case I, in which there is a linear relationship between pc_1 and pH, is normally applicable at pH's above the pK. Case II, in which pc_1 becomes independent of the pH, is normally applicable at pH's below the pK. In practice, this is the case with *p*-nitrophenol (pK 7.1), 2,6-dibromophenol (pK 8.0) and 2,6-dichlorophenol (pK 7.8). In Case III, the value of pc_1 is independent of both the pH and the pQ but becomes a linear function of the log f. This was found to be the case with liver mitochondria oxidizing pyruvate + malate in the absence of P_i or ADP and presence of alkyl-substituted dinitrophenols.

Having shown that the measurement of the dinitrophenol-induced ATPase at different pH's and dinitrophenol concentrations could not be used to determine whether the ATPase measured in the presence of dinitrophenol represents one or more enzyme systems, Hemker[205] re-examined the question using other methods. He obtained evidence for the existence of two systems, which differ in the concentration of 2,4-dinitrophenol required for maximum activity and in sensitivity to Amytal and antimycin. The dinitrophenol-induced activity at pH 7.0 is made up of two systems: 62% by an Amytal-sensitive system (optimal dinitrophenol concentration, 0.2 mM) and 33% by an antimycin-sensitive system (optimal dinitrophenol concentration, 0.1 mM)*. The ATPase activity was almost completely suppressed by the addition of Amytal and antimycin together. Hemker proposed that the Amytal-sensitive system corresponds to the first phosphorylating step and the antimycin-sensitive to the second step.

This conclusion is clearly consistent with the chemical theory, since it is known that Amytal and antimycin are respiratory inhibitors acting in the region of the first and second phosphorylating steps, respectively. Hemker's findings are more difficult to reconcile with the Mitchell theory which requires only one ATPase acting independently of the respiratory chain. The inhibitory effect on the dinitrophenol-induced ATPase of reduction of the chain, referred to above, also indicates a more intimate relationship between the respiratory chain and the ATPase than is involved in Mitchell's theory.

Hemker's data provide good experimental support for an earlier suggestion by Hülsmann[203] that respiratory inhibitors of the type of Amytal and antimycin act in essentially the same way as uncouplers of the type of dinitrophenol. According to this theory, both react with $A \sim C$ forming a compound with C, thus

$$A \sim C + \Phi \rightarrow A + \Phi\text{–}C \qquad (5.19)$$

where Φ represents Amytal, antimycin or an uncoupling phenol. The compounds with Amytal and antimycin are stable, resulting in removal of C from the system, with consequent inhibition of respiration. Amytal combines specifically with the C corresponding to the first phosphorylating step, antimycin with that corresponding to the second phosphorylating step. The compounds with uncoupling phenol are, on the other hand, unstable and readily split, yielding C.

$$\Phi\text{–}C \rightleftharpoons \Phi + C \qquad (5.20)$$

* The pH optimum of the first is at 6.8 (contrast 8.5 proposed by Hülsmann and Slater[202]) and of the second at 7.5 (*cf.* 7.4 proposed by Hülsmann and Slater).

References p. 388

Thus, uncoupling phenols cause the splitting of $A \sim C$, leading to uncoupling, but C remains available for the oxidation reaction. Hülsmann suggested, however, that the reaction given by Eqn. 5.20 is reversible and that the formation of Φ–C from C and Φ in high concentrations is the reason for the inhibitory action of uncouplers at higher concentrations. Thus, the difference between an uncoupler and an inhibitor is merely quantitative, depending upon the relative ease of decomposition of Φ–C by Reaction 5.20.

According to this theory, one might expect that a competition between dinitrophenol and Amytal or antimycin could be demonstrated. In fact, Chance *et al.*[206,207] showed that inhibition by Amytal could be reversed by uncouplers, and Howland[208] obtained the analogous result with 2-heptyl-4-hydroxyquinoline-*N*-oxide and 2-hydroxy-3(3-methylbutyl)-1,4-naphthoquinone (hydrolapachol) which act in the same way as antimycin. Reversal of antimycin inhibition by uncouplers has not been demonstrated, probably because of the very high affinity of the corresponding $A \sim C$ for antimycin.

Hemker[209] made a detailed study of the inhibitory action of dinitrophenols on the dinitrophenol-induced ATPase and on respiration, in order to examine the other mechanism for the uncoupling action of dinitrophenols, first proposed (as an alternative explanation) by Lardy and Elvehjem[153] (see p. 363), *viz.* that an uncoupling phenol allows oxidation to proceed without phosphorylation.

According to this theory, the reaction mechanism of uncoupled oxidation is given by

$$AH_2 + B \xrightarrow{(\Phi)} A + BH_2 \tag{5.21}$$

and the mechanism of dinitrophenol-induced ATPase by

$$\begin{array}{ll} & \mathrm{ATP} + A + C \rightleftharpoons \mathrm{ADP} + A \sim C + \mathrm{P_i} \\ & A \sim C + BH_2 \rightleftharpoons AH_2 + B + C \\ & AH_2 + B \xrightarrow{(\Phi)} A + BH_2 \\ \hline \textit{Sum:} & \mathrm{ATP} \xrightarrow{(\Phi)} \mathrm{ADP} + \mathrm{P_i} \end{array}$$

This mechanism of uncoupling has been supported more recently by Ernster[166] in the specific form

$$\begin{aligned} &\mathrm{ATP} + X \rightleftharpoons X{\sim}\mathrm{P} + \mathrm{ADP} \\ &X{\sim}\mathrm{P} + \mathrm{fpH_2} \rightleftharpoons \mathrm{P_i} + \mathrm{fpH}{\sim}X \\ &\mathrm{fpH}{\sim}X + \mathrm{NAD^+} + \mathrm{OH^-} \rightleftharpoons \mathrm{fp} + X + \mathrm{NADH} \\ &\mathrm{NADH} + \mathrm{fp} + \mathrm{H^+} \xrightarrow{(\Phi)} \mathrm{NAD^+} + \mathrm{fpH_2} \end{aligned}$$

According to this theory, Reaction 5.21 is involved in both the dinitrophenol-induced ATPase and the uncoupled respiration, and since this is the only reaction affected by the presence of an uncoupler, it is presumably also the site of the inhibitory action by higher concentrations of dinitrophenols. Hemker's finding that $(c_{aq})_{opt}$ for 2,6-dinitrophenol is more than 10 times greater for the ATPase than for the oxidation of β-hydroxybutyrate or pyruvate + malate is difficult to reconcile with this theory. On the other hand, according to the theory of uncoupling represented by Eqns. 5.19 and 5.20, there is no reason why the binding of I by Φ should have the same effect on the uncoupled oxidation and the ATPase, since the dinitrophenol-induced ATPase does not include an oxidation reaction.

It is important to note that, although the third phosphorylating step is as easily uncoupled as the others, there is now no evidence that it contributes to the dinitrophenol-induced ATPase[205], nor is the oxidation reaction in this step inhibited by higher concentrations of dinitrophenols.

Finally, a study by Hemker[210] of the relationship between $(c_{aq})_{opt}$ and pH gave further information on the nature of Reaction 5.20. In the case of respiration with NAD-linked substrates, in the absence of P_i or ADP, $(pc_1)_{opt}$ was found to be a linear function of pH, the slope of the line relating these quantities being equal to -0.5. Respiration with pyruvate (+ malate) as substrate, uncoupled by alkyldinitrophenols, formed an exception in that $(c_1)_{opt}$ was independent of pH. This was also the case with succinate as substrate, both with non-alkylated and alkylated dinitrophenols. From a consideration of the kinetic equations derived for the mechanism suggested above, Hemker concluded that, in those cases when $(c_1)_{opt}$ was independent of pH, Φ–C dissociates into Φ and C (Eqn. 5.20) without the intervention of water, whereas in those cases where $d(c_1)_{opt}/dpH$ equalled -0.5, a hydrogen ion is involved, thus

$$\Phi\text{–}C + H^+ \rightleftharpoons \Phi + C$$

In both cases the undissociated phenol molecule is involved. From the different behaviour of pyruvate as substrate, compared with glutamate and β-hydroxybutyrate, Hemker concluded that mitochondrial NAD associated with the different substrates is present in different compartments, differing in their lipophilic character, and that the whole phosphorylation system connected with a particular substrate must be localized in the same mitochondrial compartment. The phosphorylation step at site II and also that at site I when pyruvate (+ malate) is substrate would appear to take place in a much more lipophilic region of the mitochondrion than the phosphorylation at site I with other substrates.

There is no doubt that Hemker's studies have considerably deepened our knowledge of the mechanism by which dinitrophenols uncouple respiration. It should be remembered, however, that some of the conclusions, although they follow logically from the mechanism of oxidative phosphorylation adopted, are entirely dependent upon the correctness of that mecha-

References p. 388

nism. Although it can be stated that the mechanism provides a satisfactory framework on which to hang Hemker's results, it would be going too far to claim that Hemker's results provide important confirmatory evidence of the mechanism. The inhibitory effects of dinitrophenols, which are satisfactorily explained by Hülsmann's modification of Slater's mechanism, cannot easily be explained by Mitchell's theory.

(*2*) *Other uncoupling agents.* A number of compounds are active uncouplers in low concentrations, including: dicoumarol (3,3′-methylene bis(4-hydroxycoumarin))[211], gramicidin[212,26], aureomycin[213], valinomycin[214], long-chain unsaturated fatty acids[53–55,215–220], carbonyl cyanide *m*-chlorophenylhydrazone[221,222] and the fluorine analogue[223]. Gramicidin and valinomycin uncouple only in the presence of alkali metal ions. The uncoupling activity is associated with the uptake of these ions by the mitochondria. Gramicidin acts with Na^+, Li^+,K^+, Rb^+ and Cs^+, whereas valinomycin is active only with K^+, Rb^+ and Cs^+ (Refs. 224–226).

Arsenate, the classical uncoupler of substrate-linked phosphorylation[227,228] also uncouples respiratory-chain phosphorylation, as first shown by Crane and Lipmann[78]. It can replace P_i in stimulating respiration[160,164,165] but, in contrast to dinitrophenol-stimulated respiration, ADP is also necessary for maximum respiration[229,230]. Despite reports to the contrary [231,232], arsenate does not induce an appreciable ATPase activity (Ref. 233). It inhibits the P_i–ATP exchange[186,232], the ADP–ATP exchange reaction[231], and the exchange of oxygen atoms between P_i and water[186]. Chappell and Crofts[234] have proposed that ADP participates in the uncoupling activity of arsenate.

(*iv*) *Inhibition of oxidative phosphorylation*

Phosphorylating respiration may be inhibited by compounds of the type of antimycin or Amytal which also inhibit uncoupled respiration, although, except in the case of antimycin, less effectively.

In 1955, Hollunger[235] introduced a new type of respiratory inhibitor, guanidine, which inhibits respiration coupled with phosphorylation, without having any effect on the non-phosphorylating respiration of mitochondrial fragments or of mitochondria in the presence of dinitrophenol. Guanidine was not widely used, probably because the mitochondria must be preincubated with rather high concentrations for complete inhibition. In 1958, Lardy[162] introduced the fungicide oligomycin which, in very low concentrations, has effects somewhat similar to those brought about by guanidine.

(*1*) *Guanidine and derivatives.* The effects of guanidines have recently formed the subject of a series of papers from Chance's laboratory[236–239]. Pressman[236] showed that the effectiveness of guanidines increases with increasing size of an alkyl substituent up to $C_{12}H_{23}$. The substitution of a

Elsevier's Scientific Publications

You received this card in one of our publications. It would greatly assist us in serving you further if, when returning it for more information, you would indicate below how you heard of the book or books now in your possession. We thank you for your co-operation.

- ☐ **Bookseller's recommendation**
- ☐ **Books sent on approval by bookseller**
- ☐ **Displays in bookshops**
- ☐ **Reviews**
- ☐ **Advertisements**
- ☐ **Personal recommendation**
- ☐ **References in books and journals**
- ☐ **Publisher's catalogue**
- ☐ **Circular received from publisher**
- ☐ **Circular received from bookseller**
- ☐ **Listing in a subject catalogue of bookseller**

POSTCARD

ELSEVIER PUBLISHING COMPANY

P.O. BOX 211

AMSTERDAM-W.

THE NETHERLANDS

second amino hydrogen, either on the same or on different nitrogen atoms, resulted in a considerable loss of activity despite the increase of lipophilicity. Similarly, straight-chain substituents were more effective than branched-chain of the same size.

Guanidine and its alkyl derivatives were found to differ in their effect from oligomycin in the following respects: (*i*) they are much more effective in inhibiting the phosphorylation at site I than at the other sites[236,240,241], (*ii*) inhibition by guanidines sets in relatively slowly, in comparison with almost instantaneous inhibition by oligomycin, (*iii*) reversal by 2,4-dinitrophenol of inhibition is not instantaneous, while neither 4-isooctyl-2,6-dinitrophenol nor dicoumarol is able to reverse the effect of octylguanidine although these uncouplers are quite effective against inhibition by oligomycin or unsubstituted guanidine. Moreover, octylguanidine inhibits the dicoumarol-stimulated respiration in the presence of oligomycin, (*iv*) the guanidines do not inhibit the dinitrophenol-induced ATPase.

Chappell[237] (*cf.* Ref. 238) showed that inhibition by galegine (4-methyl-3-butenylguanidine) or hexylguanidine is greater when the inhibitor is added to mitochondria the respiration of which is limited by P_i or ADP, indicating that the guanidines combine with an energy-rich intermediate (such as $A \sim C$). In contrast, oligomycin inhibits oxidation equally well whether it is added in the active or the "resting" (due to lack of P_i or ADP) phases of respiration. Spectrophotometric measurements[237,239] localized the site of action of the alkylguanidines between NAD^+ and cytochrome *b*.

It appears, then, that the guanidines act at a point closer to the respiratory chain than oligomycin. In fact, the effects of alkylguanidines resemble in many respects those of Amytal, and can be explained by the type of mechanism indicated in Eqns. 5.19 and 5.20*. Unlike Amytal, however, the guanidines do not inhibit the dinitrophenol-induced ATPase or the NADH oxidase activity of the non-phosphorylating Keilin and Hartree heart-muscle preparation. This difference may, however, only be a reflection of the different values of the rate constants in Eqns. 5.19 and 5.20.

Pressman[238] (*cf.* Ref. 237) showed that phenylethylbiguanide (DBI) inhibits in a manner analogous to the guanidines, but that it selectively acts on Site II. Thus, addition of this compound causes reduction of cytochrome *b*, in contrast to the alkylguanidines. Haas[240] confirmed that it has no action on Site-I phosphorylation.

Synthalin (decamethylene diguanidine) differs from the alkylguanidines and DBI in that it inhibits Site-III phosphorylation[241]. It is also the only guanidine compound that inhibits the ADP–ATP exchange reaction. In this respect, it resembles oligomycin.

* The explanations given by Pressman[236], Chappell[237] and Chance and Hollunger[239] differ in detail from one another, and from that given in Eqns. 5.19 and 5.20.

References p. 388

(2) *Oligomycin*. Preparations used are a mixture of three structurally related compounds (A, B and C) of molecular weights 425, 397 and 479, respectively[242–244]. The relative proportions of the three components can be determined by paper chromatography[243]. Rutamycin (Lilly compound A 272)[245] is a related compound of molecular weight 439. Some differences in activity between the different compounds have been reported[244]. The chemical structures of these compounds have not been determined. They have been described as neutral, unsaturated, optically active alcohols which may also contain a ketone group. No elements besides carbon, hydrogen and oxygen are present.

The inhibitory effects of oligomycin have been fully described above. In lower concentrations, oligomycin stimulates oxidative phosphorylation and ATP-driven reactions in sub-mitochondrial particles[246,247]. Lee and Ernster suggest that oligomycin, in addition to its inhibitory action illustrated in Figs. 9 and 11, inhibits the hydrolysis of the high-energy intermediate ($A \sim C$ in Figs. 9 and 11). At low concentrations, the latter action of oligomycin predominates.

(3) *Aurovertin*. The structure of this compound is not known. Lardy and co-workers[162,248,175,250] showed that it acts rather like oligomycin. However, it is much less effective than oligomycin in inhibiting ATPases induced by uncoupling agents.

(4) *Atractyloside*. Atractyloside is a glycoside, the carbohydrate portion consisting of a single glucose unit containing two residues of potassium sulphate, one residue of isovaleric acid, and an aglycone of perhydrophenanthrenic structure[251]. It inhibits the phosphorylation of added ADP[251,252], without having any effect on that of the endogenous ADP of the mitochondria[253,254,234]. The inhibition is competitive with respect to ADP[252,256]. Heldt and Klingenberg[73–76] have suggested that it inhibits the adenine nucleotide translocase (see p. 337).

(5) *Dio-9*. The structure of a toxic antibiotic Dio-9 is not known. Guillory[257] found that, in the absence of P_i, this compound acts like an uncoupling agent. Like 2,4-dinitrophenol, Dio-9 reverses inhibition by 4-hydroxyquinoline-*N*-oxide. In the presence of P_i, there is a short period in which it acts as an uncoupler, but this is soon followed by an inhibition. As in the case of the alkylguanidines, inhibition requires addition to the mitochondria under such conditions that high-energy intermediates are present. Thus, Dio-9 has little inhibitory effect even in the presence of P_i when added in the presence of ADP or of 2,4-dinitrophenol. On the other hand, dinitrophenol is unable to reverse the inhibition when added after the inhibitor. Dio-9 differs from the alkylguanidines in that, like oligomycin and atractyloside, it inhibits all three phosphorylating steps.

Guillory suggests a mechanism of action of Dio-9 indicated in the following equations (d stands for Dio-9)

$$A \sim C + d \rightleftharpoons A + d \sim C \tag{5.22}$$

$$d \sim C \rightarrow d + C \tag{5.23}$$

$$d \sim C + P_i \rightarrow d\text{-}C\text{-}P \tag{5.24}$$

It is suggested that Reaction 5.23 is sufficiently rapid to account for the initial uncoupling action, even in the presence of P_i, but that C becomes slowly bound in the compound d-C-P by the slow reaction 5.24, until all the C, necessary for respiration, is removed from the system.

The suggested points of action of the various inhibitors are summarized in Fig. 12.

(*v*) *Fractionation studies*

In recent years, much effort has gone into attempts to gain further information on the mechanism of oxidative phosphorylation by subjecting mitochondria to the fractionation procedures which have been so successful in the study of other biochemical systems. It was found in 1950 that extraction of mitochondria with saline yielded a particle with decreased oxidative and phosphorylative ability, both (but particularly the phosphorylative) being restored by adding the soluble extract[104,258]. The active component of

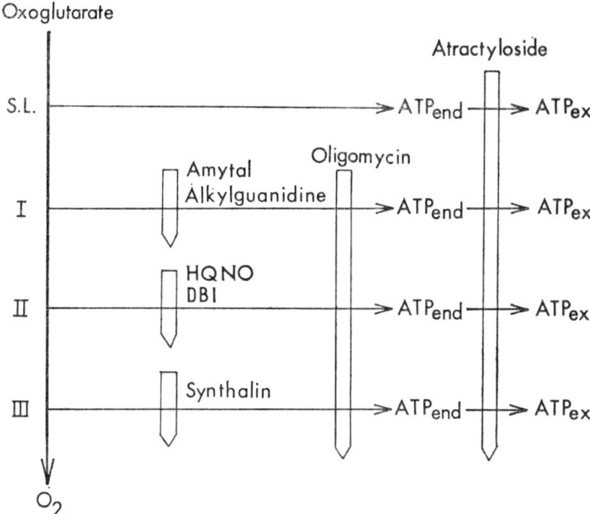

Fig. 12. Site of action of inhibitors of oxidative phosphorylation. The vertical line represents the respiratory chain with the sites of the substrate-linked phosphorylation (SL) and the three respiratory-chain phosphorylation steps (I, II and III) indicated. The horizontal lines represent the sequence of energy-transferring steps leading to the synthesis of ATP. The broad arrows indicate the site of action of inhibitors. HQNO, 4-hydroxyquinoline-N-oxide; DBI, phenylethylbiguanide.

the soluble extract was found to be cytochrome *c* (Ref. 258, *cf.* Ref. 259). Bacterial extracts are readily separated into particulate and soluble fractions which are needed together for both oxidation and phosphorylation (*e.g.* Brodie[260,261]). A more useful fractionation is into a particle which catalyses maximal oxidation without phosphorylation and a supernatant fraction specifically required for phosphorylation.

(*1*) *Bacterial systems.* The first successful fractionation of this type was made by Pinchot[42] in 1953. He separated the system required for oxidative phosphorylation in extracts of *Alcaligenes faecalis* with NADH as substrate into three fractions: (*i*) a particulate fraction containing the cytochrome system which catalysed the oxidation of NADH without accompanying phosphorylation, (*ii*) a soluble heat-labile fraction which when added to the particulate fraction caused a substantial stimulation of respiration with no phosphorylation and (*iii*) a soluble heat-stable component, which when added to the other two fractions promoted phosphorylation without any effect on respiration. The heat-stable factor was found to be an oligonucleotide containing adenine, guanine and uracil in the molar ratio 2:1:1. The oligonucleotide and magnesium act together to bind the heat-labile fraction to the particles.

Hovenkamp[262] fractionated the system in particles isolated from *Azotobacter vinelandii* by reducing the salt concentration to less than 0.01 *M* KCl or 0.8 m*M* $MgCl_2$ and centrifuging at high speed. The particles retained their oxidative activity but had lost their phosphorylative. This was regained by incubating the high-speed supernatant with the particles in the presence of $MgCl_2$. The supernatant factor was heat-labile. Ishikawa and Lehninger[263] used a similar method to fractionate particles isolated from *Micrococcus lysodeikticus* into a particulate fraction containing the oxidizing enzymes and a soluble fraction necessary for phosphorylation.

(*2*) *Linnane's and Racker's factors.* Mitochondria isolated from animal tissues proved much more difficult to fractionate. At first attention was concentrated on the preparation of sub-mitochondrial particles capable of carrying out oxidative phosphorylation with certain substrates. The first success in this direction was achieved in 1956 by Cooper and Lehninger[70] by treating rat-liver mitochondria with digitonin. The most recent preparation from Lehninger's laboratory is described by Lehninger and Gregg[264].

Haas and Elliott[265] have used digitonin to prepare submitochondrial particles from heart mitochondria. Lardy *et al.*[266] and Kielley and Bronk[267] disintegrated the mitochondria by sonic treatment. This method was also used by Linnane and Ziegler[268] in Green's laboratory to isolate a sub-mitochondrial particle (called "heavy electron-transport particle" or ETP_H). An improved preparation has been described by Hansen and Smith[269].

Although these sub-mitochondrial preparations are free from some of the complications inherent in using intact mitochondria, with their complex internal structure, they are still very complicated systems and suffer from the disadvantage that the phosphorylation is less firmly coupled with respiration than in intact mitochondria. An early claim[70] that oxidative phosphorylation in digitonin particles did not require magnesium was later refuted[270] (*cf.* Ref. 271). Also, the low concentration of NAD reported by Lehninger[272] was not supported by later measurements by Fugmann and Estabrook[273].

In 1958–1960, Linnane[274,275] and Racker and co-workers[276] fractionated ETP_H and intact beef-heart mitochondria, respectively, into a particulate and a soluble protein fraction, both of which were required for oxidative phosphorylation. Linnane[274] found that no fractionation took place in the presence of magnesium and that the latter was necessary for restoration of the phosphorylation (*cf.* Refs. 42, 262). Hansen and Smith[269] have shown that Mn^{2+} as well as Mg^{2+} is required to bind the soluble factor to the particles. The possible role of Mn^{2+} in oxidative phosphorylation was first suggested by Lindberg and Ernster[277] in 1954.

Extension of Linnane's work in Green's laboratory led to the claim that site-specific coupling factors had been isolated[278]. The claim with respect to the Site-III factor was later withdrawn by Green (*cf.* Ref. 279). Beyer, working in the same laboratory, isolated from beef-heart mitochondria a protein that was claimed to be involved in oxidative phosphorylation specifically at Site II[280]. This protein was originally given the name "Coupling Factor II (CF_{II})" and more recently "Site-II-linked synthetase".

Further fractionation of Racker's particulate fraction yielded a second factor[276]. The two are now termed F_1 and F_2 (see Ref. 281). F_2 is probably identical with Linnane's factor[282]. More recently, two other factors (F_3 and F_4) which are required to restore oxidative phosphorylation in particles treated in other ways have been separated by Racker and Connover[281]. F_1 has ATPase activity, stimulated by about 50% by dinitrophenol, and is more labile at 2° than at 25°. Yet another factor (F_0) has been isolated which confers oligomycin sensitivity on the ATPase activity of F_1. An ATPase inhibitor has also been described[282a].

F_1 is required for all reactions associated with oxidative phosphorylation that involve a transphosphorylation with ATP. These reactions include the ATP-dependent reduction of NAD^+ (Ref. 283), the ATP-dependent reduction of $NADP^+$ (Ref. 284), the $^{32}P_i$–ATP exchange[276], and the $H_2{}^{18}O-P_i$ exchange[284a]. On the other hand F_1 is not required for the energy-linked reduction of NAD^+ or $NADP^+$ when the energy is provided by the operation of the respiratory chain[284]. Racker and co-workers[284a] suggest that the function of F_1 is to catalyse the transphosphorylation step from a $\sim$P intermediate to ADP (Eqn. 5.14), with the intermediate formation of an ADP–F_1

References p. 388

complex, the existence of which has been demonstrated with the pure enzyme

$$\text{ADP} + F_1 \rightleftharpoons \text{ADP}-F_1$$
$$\text{ADP}-F_1 + D{\sim}\text{P} \rightleftharpoons \text{ATP} + F_1 + D$$

F_1 does not itself catalyse an ADP–ATP exchange.

F_4 (Refs. 281, 284b), which appears to be identical with the water-insoluble structural protein[284c], binds phospholipids, cytochrome *b* and the uncoupler desaspidin. Since it increases the binding of F_1 to deficient particles, its main function may be in promoting the orientation of the components of the phosphorylation system, without itself having any specific catalytic function.

None of these factors is site-specific[284]. Factor-deficient particles are still able to form high-energy intermediates of oxidative phosphorylation that are able to drive the energy-dependent transhydrogenase reaction. It appears, then, that the factors are concerned in the primary energy-conserving reactions of oxidative phosphorylation[247].

(3) *Lehninger's factors*. Using the digitonin particles as starting material, Wadkins and Lehninger[285–287] isolated an enzyme catalysing an exchange between ADP and ATP, and obtained evidence that this enzyme forms part of the oxidative phosphorylation mechanism. This exchange activity of digitonin particles had been discovered in 1957 by Cooper and Lehninger[152], and studied in detail by Wadkins and Lehninger[288,285,288a,289]. The ATP–ADP exchange activity measured in mitochondrial preparations is often due not only to this enzyme, but also to nucleosidediphosphate kinase (EC 2.7.4.6) and adenylate kinase (EC 2.7.4.3), both of which catalyse an ADP–ATP exchange, especially in the presence of Mg^{2+}. In intact mitochondria, the exchange enzyme associated with oxidative phosphorylation is almost completely sensitive to oligomycin, but damage to the mitochondrial structure causes a loss of oligomycin sensitivity[163,287,289,241], so that sensitivity to oligomycin cannot be used to distinguish between the exchange associated with oxidative phosphorylation and that due to other kinases. According to Wadkins and Lehninger[287,289] the exchange reaction in digitonin particles is almost completely insensitive to oligomycin, but Kulka and Cooper[290] found 56–84% inhibition with their particles. Wadkins and Lehninger ascribe this to differences in the particle preparations. The exchange activity is, however, sensitive to dinitrophenol even in digitonin particles, but the sensitivity disappears on ageing or on the addition of azide or oligomycin[289]. The exchange activity in intact mitochondria is inhibited by reduction of the respiratory chain.

Wadkins and Lehninger[285,286] extracted from digitonin particles and purified an enzyme catalysing a dinitrophenol-insensitive ADP–ATP exchange and showed that the enzyme could be re-incorporated into digitonin particles, upon which it became dinitrophenol-sensitive. More recently[287] this enzyme has been resolved into two protein fractions by chromatography on DEAE-cellulose.

It seems probable, then, that the ADP–ATP exchange enzyme of Wadkins and Lehninger is related to oxidative phosphorylation, but that it is very readily dissociated from the other oxidative phosphorylation enzymes. Its exact function is still obscure. The complete insensitivity to oligomycin of the exchange activity in digitonin particles which catalyse an oligomycin-sensitive oxidative phosphorylation is not readily explained by Eqns. 5.9 and 5.10, even when extended to Eqns. 5.11 and 5.12. Wadkins and Lehninger[289] have suggested an ingenious modification in which the two coupling factors C and D (called M and E by Wadkins and Lehninger) are bound together in intact mitochondria, but become dissociated during the preparation of sub-mitochondrial particles. In terms of the symbolism of this review the mechanism in intact mitochondria may be written

$$AH_2 + C\cdot D \rightleftharpoons AH_2\text{–}C\cdot D \tag{5.25}$$

$$AH_2\text{–}C\cdot D + B \rightleftharpoons A\sim C\cdot D + BH_2 \tag{5.26}$$

$$A\sim C\cdot D + P_i \rightleftharpoons A + D\cdot C\sim P \tag{5.27}$$

$$D\cdot C\sim P \rightleftharpoons C\cdot D\sim P \tag{5.28}$$

$$C\cdot D\sim P + ADP \rightleftharpoons C\cdot D + ATP \tag{5.29}$$

The ADP–ATP exchange reaction, given by Eqn. 5.29, will be inhibited by reduction of the chain (which will cause binding of $C\cdot D$ to AH_2), by dinitrophenol (which will drain the system of high-energy intermediates, including $C\cdot D\sim P$, by causing the splitting of $A\sim C\cdot D$), and by oligomycin which is thought to bind $C\cdot D$ (as $D\cdot C$–oligomycin) by substituting for phosphate in Reaction 5.27.

In sub-mitochondrial particles C is dissociated from D and the intramolecular phosphate transfer shown in Eqn. 5.28 is replaced by an intermolecular reaction between $C\sim P$ and D, thus

$$AH_2 + C \rightleftharpoons AH_2\text{–}C \tag{5.30}$$

$$AH_2\text{–}C + B \rightleftharpoons A\sim C + BH_2 \tag{5.31}$$

$$A\sim C + P_i \rightleftharpoons A + C\sim P \tag{5.32}$$

$$C\sim P + D \rightleftharpoons C + D\sim P \tag{5.33}$$

$$D\sim P + ADP \rightleftharpoons D + ATP \tag{5.34}$$

The ADP–ATP exchange reaction now involves only D and is insulated from the effects of reduction of the respiratory chain or of combination of C with oligomycin. Dinitrophenol will still inhibit by draining the system of high-energy intermediates, including $D\sim P$, but oligomycin (by removing

References p. 388

C) will protect the exchange reaction from these effects of dinitrophenol. In both systems, azide is thought to act similarly to oligomycin.

According to this explanation, the isolated and purified ADP–ATP exchange enzyme would represent *D*, which is the reason why Wadkins and Lehninger use *E* (for enzyme) in place of *D* in the above equations. Wadkins and Lehninger[286,287] have also isolated and purified a protein factor (called *M* factor) which when added to digitonin particles increases the dinitrophenol sensitivity of the exchange. A factor acting like *C* in the above mechanism would be expected to have this effect, which is presumably the reason why Wadkins and Lehninger write *M* where we write *C*.

Although this mechanism explains satisfactorily the important work of Lehninger and Wadkins on the ATP–ADP exchange enzyme, it cannot yet be completely excluded that the synthesis of ATP in Reaction 5.10 proceeds by a concerted mechanism, without the intermediate formation of high-energy phosphate compounds. Kulka and Cooper[290] found, in opposition to Wadkins and Lehninger[288], that the rate of the ADP–ATP exchange is equal to that of the $^{32}P_i$–ATP exchange under all conditions tried. This would not be expected if ADP enters the mechanism two reactions after P_i as depicted above. The isolation by Chiga and Plaut[291] from mitochondria of an enzyme catalysing both an ADP-dependent $^{32}P_i$–ATP exchange and a P_i-dependent ADP–ATP exchange would also favour this view. It is also unexpected that the isolated ATP–ADP exchange enzyme does not catalyse the exchange of oxygen between water and ATP (Ref. 186).

Yet another factor (contraction (*C*) factor), required for the ATP-induced contraction of mitochondria previously swollen by treatment with glutathione[286], has been shown to be a mixture of glutathione peroxidase (EC 1.11.1.9), catalase (EC 1.11.1.6) and a heat-stable component, each of which appears to be active on its own[292,293]. The heat-stable component was identified as phosphatidyl inositol[294–296]. It seems unlikely that the *C* factors are directly related to oxidative phosphorylation as originally believed, although they increase the P:O ratio when added to pretreated digitonin particles.

(*vi*) *High-energy intermediates of oxidative phosphorylation*

(*1*) *Utilization of energy accumulated in absence of* P_i *or ADP*

The essential feature of the chemical theory of oxidative phosphorylation discussed above (p. 355) is that high-energy compounds, containing components of the respiratory chain, formulated as $A \sim C$, are intermediates in the chain of reactions leading from oxidation to synthesis of ATP from ADP and P_i. The chemi-osmotic theory, on the other hand, envisages the building up of a membrane potential which may be utilized to synthesize ATP. Both theories agree in postulating the accumulation of energy (as $A \sim C$ or a membrane potential) in the absence of P_i and ADP.

The first proof of this concept came from studies of what became known as "reversal of the respiratory chain". Chance[297] reported in 1956 that succinate added to mitochondria in the absence of ADP brings about the rapid and extensive reduction of mitochondrial nicotinamide nucleotides. In fact, this reduction is greater with succinate than with NAD- or NADP-requiring substrates. The reaction is sensitive to dinitrophenol and to Amytal. Chance and Hollunger[298,299] suggested that this reduction of NAD by succinate is due to a reversal of electron flow in the respiratory chain, the necessary energy being provided by the oxidation of the succinate. This theory was supported by Klingenberg and Slenczka[300,301], who used glycerol-1-*P* instead of succinate and thereby avoided certain difficulties inherent in using the latter substrate, by Ernster[302,166] and by Snoswell[303,167] and Tager and Slater[83,304,305].

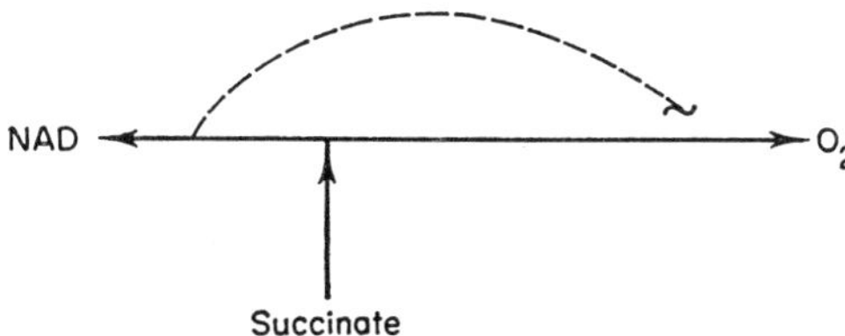

Fig. 13. The Chance reaction. Reduction of NAD^+ by succinate coupled with oxidation of succinate by O_2.

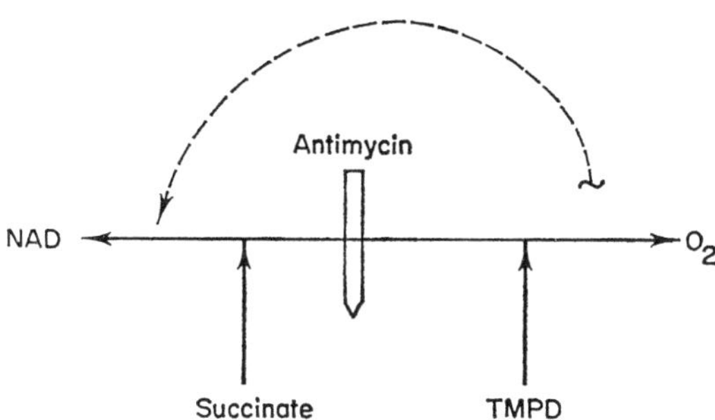

Fig. 14. Reduction of NAD^+ by succinate coupled with oxidation of tetramethyl-*p*-phenylenediamine (TMPD) by O_2.

The essential features of the mechanism of the reaction bringing about the reduction of NAD^+ are shown in Fig. 13. The oxidation of succinate by oxygen is coupled with the oxidation of succinate by NAD^+, or, in other words, the energy generated in the oxidation of succinate by O_2 can be utilized, not only for the synthesis of ATP from P_i and ADP, but also for the energy-requiring reduction of NAD^+ by succinate.

Here succinate provides reducing equivalents to both NAD^+ and oxygen. However, this is not necessary, since succinate can be replaced as donor for the energy-requiring reaction as shown in Fig. 14. Antimycin blocks the energy-generating reaction with succinate as donor, without affecting its ability to reduce NAD^+ when energy is supplied to the system. The aerobic oxidation of tetramethyl-*p*-phenylenediamine provides the energy[306,307].

Tetramethyl-*p*-phenylenediamine can also provide the reducing equivalents to ubiquinone[308] and to NAD^+ (Refs. 307, 309, 310; *cf.* Ref. 311), as is illustrated in Fig. 15.

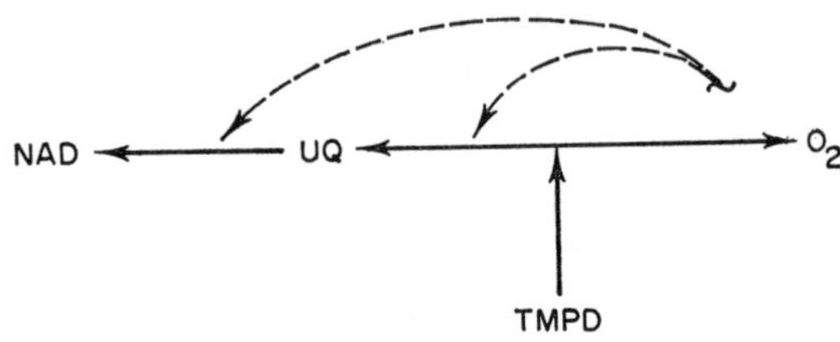

Fig. 15. Reduction of NAD^+ by TMPD coupled with oxidation of TMPD by O_2.

Ernster[302,166] and Snoswell[303,167] showed independently that oligomycin has no effect on the utilization of the energy of respiration for reversal of the respiratory chain. Indeed, the addition of oligomycin often causes a substantial increase in the degree of reduction of the NAD^+ (*cf.* p. 370). Thus, the energy need not be provided by ATP formed by oxidative phosphorylation; ~ formed prior to ATP suffices. This was the first experimental demonstration of a proposal made in 1953 (Ref. 146) that the energy of intermediates of oxidative phosphorylation might be utilized directly for energy-requiring reactions without conversion to ATP being necessary.

This important conclusion was supported by the following experiments:

(*1*) When the oxidation of succinate is inhibited by antimycin, the reduction of NAD^+ by succinate is also inhibited since no ~ is formed. The reduction can be partly restored by adding ATP from outside, but now the reaction is oligomycin-sensitive, showing that ATP cannot be utilized directly for reversal of the respiratory chain, but that its energy can be used to make ~ by an oligomycin-sensitive reaction. This is illustrated in Fig. 16. Löw and Vallin[312] showed that added NAD^+ could be reduced by succinate in the presence of sub-mitochondrial particles and cyanide on the addition of ATP.

(*2*) Ernster[166] showed that the reduction of acetoacetate by succinate (presumably *via* NAD^+) coupled with the oxidation of succinate by oxygen can proceed in the absence of phosphate. This was confirmed by Snoswell[167], who followed directly the reduction of mitochondrial NAD^+, and by Slater *et al.*[313] who used the same experimental procedure as Ernster, after a preincubation with glucose and hexokinase to remove endogenous phosphate (*cf.* Ref. 160).

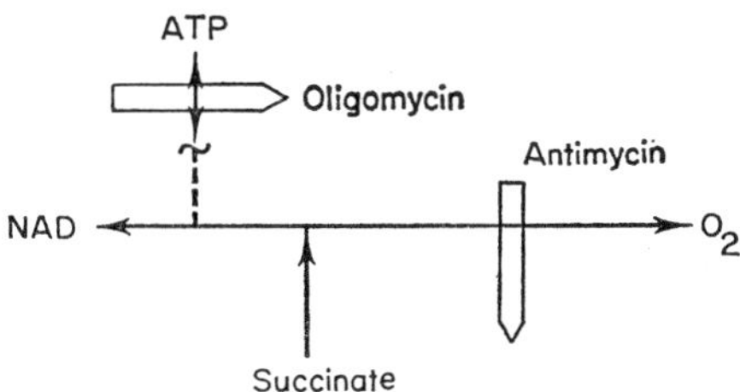

Fig. 16. Reduction of NAD^+ by succinate coupled with hydrolysis of ATP.

(*3*) According to both the chemi-osmotic and chemical theories of oxidative phosphorylation, respiration is inhibited by oligomycin owing to the accumulation of ~. Respiration is restored by adding dinitrophenol which releases the accumulated ~. One might also expect it to be restored if ~ is utilized for other reactions. Fig. 17 shows that the addition of α-ketoglutarate (+NH_3), which by oxidizing NADH to NAD^+ promotes the further

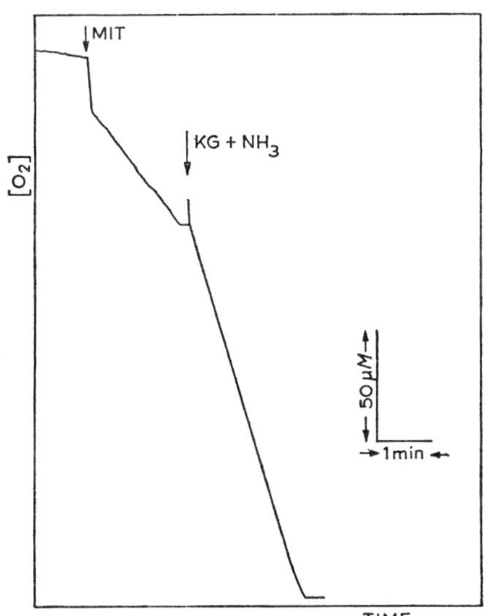

Fig. 17. Stimulation by α-ketoglutarate + NH_3 of the oxidation of succinate by rat-liver mitochondria, in the presence of oligomycin.

References p. 388

reduction of NAD^+, stimulates the respiration[305]. Ernster[166] reported similar results using acetoacetate instead of α-ketoglutarate ($+NH_3$). In other words, the utilization of the energy of the accumulated $\sim$ to bring about the reduction of NAD^+ by succinate is an uncoupling of oxidative phosphorylation.

(*4*) The uncoupling can be shown in a second way. In the presence of ADP and P_i and absence of oligomycin, there will be a competition between NAD^+ and P_i + ADP for $\sim$. In other words, the amount of oxidative phosphorylation (measured by ATP formation) will be inhibited by the addition of α-ketoglutarate ($+ NH_3$). Slater and Tager[83] showed that this was the case and by comparing the decline in ATP synthesis with the amount of α-ketoglutarate reduced (measured as glutamate) found that the stoichiometry of the energy-requiring reduction of NAD^+ by succinate is that given by Eqn. 5.35.

$$\text{Succinate} + NAD^+ + \sim \rightarrow \text{fumarate} + NADH + H^+ \qquad (5.35)$$

These first demonstrations that $\sim$ could be utilized for energy-requiring reactions in the mitochondria were soon followed by other examples. Van Rossum[314] showed that oligomycin inhibits only partially the uptake of K^+ and extrusion of Na^+ in respiring rat-liver slices and, more significantly, that ion movements supported by glycolysis in rat-liver slices isolated from late-foetal rats were inhibited by about 50% by oligomycin. These findings are strongly suggestive that part of the energy for ion movements in rat-liver slices is supplied by $\sim$ formed directly by the respiratory chain or, in the case of slices from late-foetal rats, *via* ATP formed in glycolysis.

Van Rossum[314] found that the respiration of rat-liver slices is inhibited by only about 20% by oligomycin. This relatively slight effect of oligomycin on repiration has been confirmed for other tissues[315–318]. It indicates that, when the conversion of the high-energy intermediates of oxidative phosphorylation to ATP in the cells of these preparations is inhibited by oligomycin, the energy is either largely dissipated or directly utilized, *i.e.* the mitochondria are "loosely coupled".

Harary and Slater[319] showed that the beating of cultured heart cells is supported by ATP synthesised either by glycolysis or by oxidative phosphorylation. High-energy intermediates synthesised before the site of oligomycin inhibition are not able to maintain beating.

In 1952, Bartley and Davies[320] showed that isolated kidney mitochondria can maintain metabolism-dependent concentration gradients of Na^+, K^+, and P_i, as well as of organic anions, between themselves and the external fluid. MacFarlane and Spencer[321], Spector[322] and Stanbury and Mudge[323] obtained similar results. Bartley and Davies[320] found also that Mg^{2+} was accumulated in the mitochondria but could find no clear effect of metabolism on this accumulation. Earlier, Slater and Cleland[324] had shown that isolated heart mitochondria have a high affinity for added Ca^{2+}, and suggested that this binding is not dependent on metabolism. However, Chance[325] showed that the addition of Ca^{2+} to mitochondria in the absence of ADP caused a temporary stimulation of respiration and oxidation of nicotinamide nucleotide. More recently, DeLuca and Engstrom[326], Chappell *et al.*[327,328,226], Brierley *et al.*[329–331], Lehninger *et al.*[332–335] and Vasington[336] have shown that the uptake of Ca^{2+}, Mg^{2+}, Mn^{2+} and Sr^{2+} (Ref. 337) requires energy and is inhibited by dinitrophenol, but is not inhibited by oligomycin. The uptake of alkali-metal ions in the presence of valinomycin and gramicidin is also an energy-requiring process[224–226].

Another mitochondria-catalysed energy-requiring reaction which can be supported by $\sim$ is the reaction shown in Eqn. 5.36

$$\text{NADH} + \text{NADP}^+ + \sim \;\rightarrow\; \text{NAD}^+ + \text{NADPH} \qquad (5.36)$$

This reaction was discovered by Danielson and Ernster[338], and has been further studied by Lee and Ernster[339,247] and by Van Dam and Ter Welle[340]. There is a stoichiometric rather than a catalytic requirement for energy[339,341,247]. On the other hand, there is a catalytic requirement for energy, which can also be supplied by $\sim$, for Reaction 5.37 (Refs. 342, 343)

$$\text{malate} + \text{NH}_3 \overset{\sim}{\rightleftharpoons} \text{aspartate} \qquad (5.37)$$

There is, thus, now overwhelming evidence that energy can accumulate in mitochondria under conditions in which it cannot be converted to ATP. There is no evidence, however, that allows a firm choice to be made between $A \sim C$ or a membrane potential as the form of accumulated energy. If $\sim$ were a membrane potential, it is to be expected that ion transport would proceed without the intervention of ATP, as Robertson[142] has pointed out. On the other hand, it is certainly easier for the biochemist to write mechanisms involving $A \sim C$ to explain the reversal of the respiratory chain. For example, Slater and Tager[83] have proposed the following mechanism of the Chance[297] reaction.

$$\begin{array}{c} \text{NAD}^+ \longleftrightarrow A \rightarrow B \rightarrow \text{O}_2 \\ \uparrow \\ \text{Succinate} \end{array}$$

$$\begin{array}{ll}
3\ \text{succinate} + 3\,A & \rightleftharpoons 3\ \text{fumarate} + 3\,A\text{H}_2 \\
A\text{H}_2 + B + C^{\text{II}} & \rightleftharpoons A \sim C^{\text{II}} + B\text{H}_2 \\
B\text{H}_2 + \tfrac{1}{2}\,\text{O}_2 + C^{\text{III}} & \rightleftharpoons B \sim C^{\text{III}} + \text{H}_2\text{O} \\
A \sim C^{\text{II}} + \text{NAD}^+ + C^{\text{I}} & \rightleftharpoons A + C^{\text{II}} + \text{NAD} \sim C^{\text{I}} \\
B \sim C^{\text{III}} + \text{NAD}^+ + C^{\text{I}} & \rightleftharpoons B + C^{\text{III}} + \text{NAD} \sim C^{\text{I}} \\
2\,A\text{H}_2 + 2\,\text{NAD} \sim C^{\text{I}} & \rightleftharpoons 2\,A + 2\,\text{NADH} + 2\,C^{\text{I}} + 2\,\text{H}^+ \\
\hline
\textit{Sum}\text{: } 3\ \text{succinate} + \tfrac{1}{2}\,\text{O}_2 + 2\,\text{NAD}^+ & \rightleftharpoons 3\ \text{fumarate} + 2\,\text{NADH} + 2\,\text{H}^+
\end{array}$$

References p. 388

A and *B* represent two regions of the respiratory chain and C^{I}, C^{II} and C^{III} are *C*'s corresponding to the three phosphorylating sites. According to this mechanism it is the energy-rich NAD$\sim C^{I}$ which is reduced rather than NAD^+ itself.

Schachinger *et al.*[344] and Vignais[345] presented evidence of the accumulation of $\sim$ compounds in mitochondria by a different type of experiment. When ADP is added to mitochondria after pre-incubation in the presence of substrate and $^{32}P_i$ (Ref. 344) or when ADP + $^{32}P_i$ are added after pre-incubation in the presence of substrate only[345], there is an initial "jump" in synthesis of [^{32}P]ATP, followed by a slower steady synthesis. Schachinger *et al.*[344] found a jump corresponding to 1.6 μmoles/g protein in intact mitochondria. Vignais[345] reported much less in digitonin particles (about 0.3 μmole/g protein). The "jump" in ATP synthesis was ascribed to the reaction with ADP of high-energy intermediates accumulated during the pre-incubation. However, Van Dam[346] showed that the "jump" can be accounted for by the rapid oxidation of intramitochondrial NADH that occurs on adding ADP to an acceptor-deficient system. Thus, the "jump" phenomenon cannot be brought forward in favour of the accumulation of high-energy intermediates. Indeed, Van Dam[346] concluded that the concentration of high-energy intermediates accumulated in mitochondria under acceptor-deficient conditions must be at least one order of magnitude smaller than that of the endogenous NAD. This underlines the difficulty of isolating these hypothetical intermediates.

(2) *Attempted isolation of A$\sim$C intermediates*

The most important experimental evidence required in support of the chemical theory of oxidative phosphorylation is the isolation of the postulated $A \sim C$ compounds. Any such compound should preferably satisfy the following criteria: (*1*) it should contain *A*, *i.e.* a component of the respiratory chain; (*2*) its formation should be inhibited by dinitrophenol; (*3*) in the presence of mitochondria or of a mitochondrial extract, it should react with ADP and P_i to form equimolar amounts of *A* and ATP; (*4*) the latter reaction should be inhibited by oligomycin.

Three compounds satisfying some but not all of these criteria have been described in the literature — in chronological order, Purvis' "Extra NAD" (NAD$\sim I$), Pinchot's "NAD$\sim E$", and Webster's "RCCF$\sim$cyt.*c*". A closely related intermediate is Griffiths' NADH$\sim$P, which differs from the proposed $A \sim C$ compounds by the fact that it contains AH_2 rather than *A* and P_i rather than *C*.

(α) *Purvis' "Extra NAD" (NAD$\sim I$).* In 1958, Purvis[347,348] showed that the sum of the NAD^+ (determined in acid extracts) and of NADH (determined in alkali extracts) contents of freshly prepared liver mitochondria was considerably less than the total NAD+, determined by incubating the mitochondria in hypotonic phosphate or in the presence of dinitrophenol. He suggested that the "Extra NAD" compound, not measured as NAD+ or NADH by his analytical procedure, was the postulated high-energy intermediate of NAD+ (NAD$\sim$*I*). The amount of "Extra NAD" was increased by a short incubation (90 sec at 0°) with succinate. A large part of the "Extra NAD" was found in the alkali extract from which NAD+ in an amount greatly in excess of the NADH in the alkali extract could be liberated by incubation with aged (and therefore NAD-free) mitochondria.

Although Slater *et al.*[349] found that most preparations of rat-liver mitochondria did not contain Purvis' "Extra NAD" it was found regularly in preparations of muscle mitochondria. Snoswell[167] found that the (NAD++ NADH) content of rabbit-heart sarcosomes declined on the addition of succinate, indicating the formation of "Extra NAD". It should be noted that no evidence has yet been presented for the formation of ATP by reaction of "Extra NAD" with ADP and P_i. Indeed, the amount of "Extra NAD" found by Purvis greatly exceeds the upper limit of the amount of high-energy intermediates revealed by the experiments of Van Dam[346]. Moreover, Van Dam[350] has shown that, although under certain conditions "Extra NAD" can accumulate and can be converted to NAD in the way described by Purvis[348], it is not present under conditions in which a high-energy intermediate of oxidative phosphorylation would be expected to accumulate (see also Refs. 351–353).

(β) *Pinchot's NAD$\sim$E*. Pinchot[170,354,355] found that when particles from *Alcaligenes faecalis* were incubated with NADH in air and the particles removed by centrifugation, the supernatant fraction (termed S^{NADH}) was able to bring about the synthesis of ATP from ADP and P_i. He concluded that the supernatant contained a high-energy form of NAD (NAD$\sim$*E*) which could react first with P_i and then with ADP to form ATP. In the presence of ATP, [^{14}C]NAD+ became bound to the particle and remained bound after treatment with trichloroacetic acid. Pandit-Hovenkamp[356] has, however, brought forward the following evidence against this view (*i*) incubation at pH 9.0 in the absence of O_2 (during treatment with NADH the suspension goes anaerobic) yielded as much phosphorylating activity in the supernatant as incubation with NADH; (*ii*) when $^{32}P_i$ and ADP were added to S^{NADH}, under the conditions used by Pinchot, a more rapid labelling was found in the ADP than in the ATP, especially in the presence of fluoride. It appears, then, that reduced S^{NADH} contains, in addition to factors necessary for oxidative phosphorylation (see p. 372), NAD+, polynucleotide phosphorylase (EC 2.7.7.8) and adenylate kinase. Polynucleotide phosphorylase

References p. 388

catalyses an exchange between ADP and P_i (Ref. 357) according to the equation

$$n \text{ ADP} \rightleftharpoons (\text{AMP})_n + n \text{ P}_i$$

while adenylate kinase would cause labelling of ATP from labelled ADP.

Thus, the evidence for the formation of NAD$\sim E$ in Pinchot's system is inadequate at present.

(γ) *Webster's RCCF$\sim$cyt.c.* Webster[171,358,359] reported the isolation of a high-energy form of cytochrome *c*, that was formed during the oxidation of ferrocytochrome *c* and that reacted with ADP and P_i to yield ferricytochrome *c* and ATP in stoichiometric amounts. It corresponded therefore exactly to an $A\sim C$ where A is ferricytochrome *c*. (The RCCF stood for "reduced cytochrome *c* coupling factor"). These claims by Webster have been repudiated by the director of the laboratory in which this work was carried out (*cf.* Ref. 279).

(δ) *Griffiths' NADH$\sim$P.* Although this compound does not satisfy the definition of $A\sim C$ since it contains phosphate (and AH_2 rather than A), it is most conveniently discussed in this section. Griffiths[360] incubated mitochondria with $^{32}P_i$, NAD^+ and succinate for 2–3 min at 0° and then precipitated the mitochondria by bringing the suspension into a boiling-water bath for 20 sec. When an aliquot of the deproteinized supernatant was transferred to a second medium containing ADP, Mg^{2+}, antimycin and mitochondria or submitochondrial particles, ATP and smaller amounts of NADH were formed. Griffiths concluded that NADH$\sim$P was formed in the first incubation and the $\sim$P transferred to ADP in the second. The formation of the intermediate required succinate and P_i and was inhibited by antimycin or dinitrophenol, but not by oligomycin; the synthesis of ATP was inhibited by oligomycin or dinitrophenol. The intermediate was isolated by paper electrophoresis and found to have 1 labile and 2 stable phosphorus atoms per molecule of NAD^+. It was labile and yielded $P_i + NAD^+$ on standing. In the presence of mitochondria and antimycin, however, it yielded NADH together with P_i in the absence of ADP, and ATP in its presence. Oligomycin and dinitrophenol inhibited ATP formation without affecting the formation of NADH.

This compound satisfies most of the criteria for an $A\sim C$ intermediate, except that it contains phosphate. The experimental data do not allow a final choice to be made between a formulation of NAD$\sim$P or NADH$\sim$P. Heldt and Klingenberg[353] could not find any evidence for the existence of phosphorylated NAD compounds in mitochondria. Indeed, they conclude that the "existence of any acid stable and acid soluble phosphate containing intermediate of oxidative phosphorylation can be excluded".

(ε) *Brodie's chromanyl phosphate.* Brodie[260,261] showed that vitamin K_1 or the naphthoquinone present in *Mycobacterium phlei* (dihydromenaquinone-9, Ref. 361) could restore both oxidation and phosphorylation to irradiated extracts of *M.phlei* and that reduced intermediates of phylloquinone (vitamin K_1, I) were found to accumulate when untreated extracts were incubated with substrate amounts of phylloquinone and either NADH or malate as hydrogen donor. The products were trapped by acetylation. One was spectrally identical with synthetic phylloquinol diacetate (II), the other was spectrally and chromatographically similar to acetyl phyllochromanol (III, $R = CH_3CO-$). Phyllochromanol-like compounds could also be isolated by extraction with ether in the absence of a trapping agent. Similar results were obtained with dihydromenaquinone-9.

The phyllochromanol-like compound was readily auto-oxidizable, yielding P_i in amounts equivalent to the amount of phylloquinone formed. It was also oxidized by *M. phlei* extracts yielding ATP by a dinitrophenol-sensitive reaction. These results suggested that the compound was phyllochromanol 6-phosphate (III, R = *P*). A synthetic preparation behaved similarly[362]. However, a direct transfer of phosphate from phyllochromanol 6-phosphate to ADP has not been demonstrated.

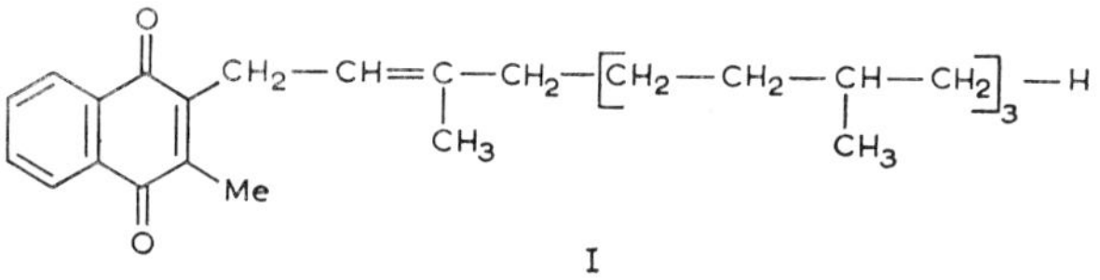

I

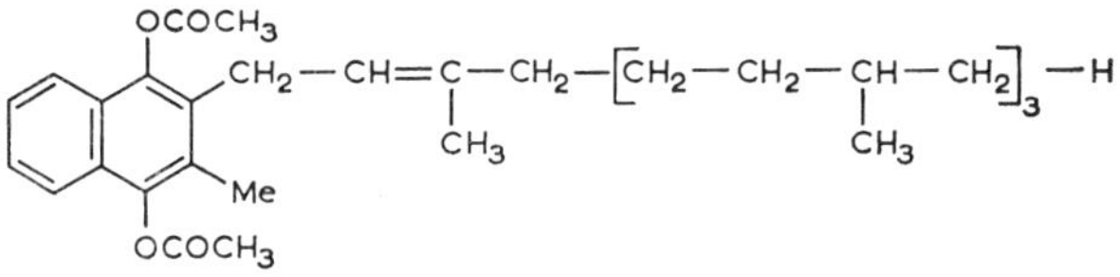

II

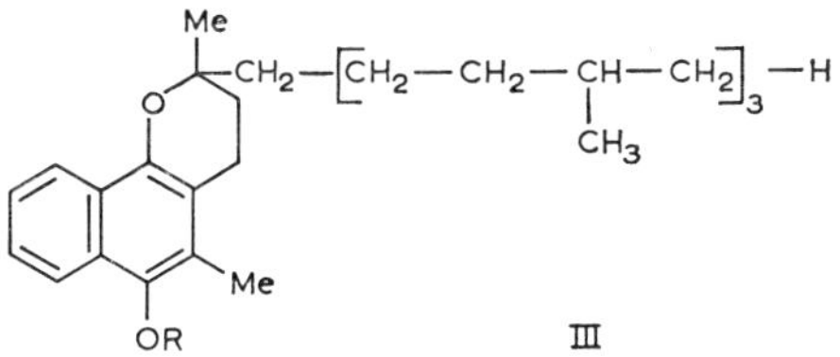

III

References p. 388

Like Griffiths' NAD compound, Brodie's compound can be formally written $BH_2{\sim}P$. Compounds of this type could be formed by the sequence

$$AH_2 + B + C \rightleftharpoons A + BH_2{\sim}C$$
$$BH_2{\sim}C + P_i \rightleftharpoons C + BH_2{\sim}P$$
$$BH_2{\sim}P + ADP \rightleftharpoons BH_2 + ATP$$

(3) C ~ P

Boyer and colleagues[363–366] showed that when mitochondria are incubated with $^{32}P_i$ in the absence of added ADP there is a rapid labelling of protein-bound phosphorus, identified as phosphohistidine. Rapid labelling also occurs with [^{32}P]ATP. Boyer[367] concluded that these experiments gave convincing evidence that protein-bound phosphohistidine participates as an intermediate in oxidative phosphorylation. In terms of the chemical mechanism discussed above protein-bound phosphohistidine would be an intermediate in the reaction

$$A{\sim}C + ADP + P_i \rightleftharpoons A + C + ATP$$

This conclusion was contested by Slater *et al.*[313], on kinetic grounds and because of the ineffectiveness of oligomycin in inhibiting the incorporation of $^{32}P_i$ into phosphohistidine under conditions in which the labelling of ATP was inhibited 95–99%. They concluded that phosphohistidine might be an intermediate in a slow oligomycin-insensitive pathway for the synthesis of ATP. Pressman[368] reported evidence of a different nature which also cast doubts on the rôle of phosphohistidine as an intermediate of respiratory-chain phosphorylation. Shortly afterwards, Boyer[369,370] showed that succinyl-coenzyme A synthetase is responsible for the incorporation of $^{32}P_i$ into protein-bound phosphohistidine by mitochondrial extracts. On the basis of the sensitivity of the labelling of mitochondrial phosphohistidine to arsenite, Slater and Kemp[132] concluded that the same is true for the labelling of protein-bound phosphohistidine in intact mitochondria (see also Refs. 74, 76, 133). Although there has been some discussion of the validity of the kinetic agreement used by Slater and coworkers (*cf.* Refs. 371–373), it is now generally accepted that there is no evidence that phosphohistidine is an intermediate of respiratory-chain phosphorylation.

Beyer[280] claimed that the mitochondrial protein known as Coupling Factor II (see p. 373) was labelled with $^{32}P_i$ in a system containing a sonicate of beef-heart mitochondria and oxidizable substrate. The protein could also be labelled with [γ-^{32}P]ATP. Kemp[133], although confirming the experiments of Beyer, has raised doubts on the participation of a labelled form of Coupling Factor II in oxidative phosphorylation.

It must be concluded that no compound corresponding to a hypothetical $A{\sim}C$ or a $\sim$P intermediate has been isolated.

BIBLIOGRAPHY

Reviews in Chronological Order

F. Lipmann, *Advan. Enzymol.*, 1 (1941) 99.
H. A. Lardy and C. A. Elvehjem, *Ann. Rev. Biochem.*, 14 (1945) 1.
F. Lipmann, in D. E. Green (Ed.), *Currents in Biochemical Research*, Interscience, New York, 1946, p. 137.
F. E. Hunter Jr., in W. D. McElroy and B. Glass (Eds.), *Phosphorus Metabolism*, Vol. 1, Johns Hopkins, Baltimore, Md., 1951, p. 297.
A. L. Lehninger, *Harvey Lectures, Ser.* 49 (1953–4) 176.
E. C. Slater, *Proc. 3rd Intern. Congr. Biochem., Brussels, 1955*, Academic Press, New York, 1956, p. 264.
B. Chance and G. R. Williams, *Advan. Enzymol.*, 17 (1956) 65.
A. L. Lehninger, C. L. Wadkins, C. Cooper, T. M. Devlin and J. L. Gamble Jr., *Science*, 128 (1958) 450.
E. C. Slater. *Rev. Pure Appl. Chem.*, 8 (1958) 221.
A. L. Lehninger, *Federation Proc.*, 19 (1960) 952.
E. Racker, *Advan. Enzymol.*, 23 (1961) 323.
A. L. Lehninger and C. L. Wadkins, *Ann. Rev. Biochem.*, 31 (1962) 47.
E. C. Slater (Ed.), *Symposium on Intracellular Respiration: Phosphorylating and Non-Phosphorylating Oxidation Reactions, Proc. 5th Intern. Congr. Biochem., Moscow, 1961*, Vol. 5, Pergamon, Oxford, 1963.
L. Ernster and C.-P. Lee, *Ann. Rev. Biochem.*, 33 (1964) 729.
A. L. Lehninger, *Bioenergetics*, Benjamin, New York, 1965.
E. Racker, *Mechanisms in Bioenergetics*, Academic Press, New York, 1965.
J. M. Tager, S. Papa, E. Quagliariello and E. C. Slater (Eds.), *Regulation of Metabolic Processes in Mitochondria, (BBA Library, Vol. 7)*, Elsevier, Amsterdam, 1966.

References p. 388

REFERENCES

1 A. Harden and W. J. Young, *Proc. Roy. Soc. (London), Ser. B*, 77 (1906) 405.
2 W. J. Young, *Proc. Roy. Soc. (London), Ser. B*, 81 (1909) 528.
3 A. Harden and W. J. Young, *Proc. Roy. Soc. (London), Ser. B*, 80 (1908) 299.
4 O. Warburg and W. Christian, *Biochem. Z.*, 303 (1939) 40.
5 E. Negelein and H. Brömel, *Biochem. Z.*, 303 (1939) 132.
6 K. Lohmann, *Biochem. Z.*, 233 (1931) 460.
7 F. Lipmann, *Advan. Enzymol.*, 1 (1941) 99.
8 O. Meyerhof, *Arch. Ges. Physiol.*, 185 (1920) 11.
9 P. Eggleton and G. P. Eggleton, *Biochem. J.*, 21 (1927) 190.
10 C. H. Fiske and Y. SubbaRow, *J. Biol. Chem.*, 81 (1929) 629.
11 W. A. Engelhardt, *Biochem. Z.*, 227 (1930) 16.
12 H. Kalckar, *Enzymologia*, 2 (1937) 47.
13 H. Kalckar, *Biochem. J.*, 33 (1939) 631.
14 F. Lipmann, *Nature*, 143 (1939) 281.
15 S. Ochoa, *Nature*, 146 (1940) 267.
16 S. Ochoa, *J. Biol. Chem.*, 138 (1941) 751.
17 V. A. Belitzer and E. T. Tsibakowa, *Biokhimiya*, 4 (1939) 516.
18 E. Annau, I. Banga, B. Gözsy, St. Huszák, K. Laki, B. Straub and A. Szent-Györgyi, *Z. Physiol. Chem.*, 236 (1935) 1; E. Annau, I. Banga, A. Blazsó, V. Bruckner, K. Laki, F. B. Straub and A. Szent-Györgyi, *Z. Physiol. Chem.*, 244 (1936) 105.
19 V. R. Potter, *Medicine*, 19 (1940) 441.
20 F. B. Straub, *Enzymologia*, 9 (1940) 148.
21 V. R. Potter and H. G. Albaum, *J. Gen. Physiol.*, 26 (1943) 443.
22 E. C. Slater, *Biochem. J.*, 46 (1950) 484.
23 S. Ochoa, *J. Biol. Chem.*, 151 (1943) 493.
24 W. F. Loomis and F. Lipmann, *J. Biol. Chem.*, 173 (1948) 807.
25 F. E. Hunter Jr., *J. Biol. Chem.*, 177 (1949) 361.
26 R. J. Cross, J. V. Taggart, G. A. Covo and D. E. Green, *J. Biol. Chem.*, 177 (1949) 655.
27 L. Berger, M. W. Slein, S. P. Colowick and C. F. Cori, *J. Gen. Physiol.*, 29 (1946) 379.
28 E. P. Kennedy and A. L. Lehninger, *J. Biol. Chem.*, 172 (1948) 847.
29 A. L. Lehninger and E. P. Kennedy, *J. Biol. Chem.*, 173 (1948) 753.
30 M. Friedkin and A. L. Lehninger, *J. Biol. Chem.*, 174 (1948) 757.
31 E. P. Kennedy and A. L. Lehninger, *J. Biol. Chem.*, 179 (1949) 957.
32 W. C. Schneider and G. H. Hogeboom, *J. Biol. Chem.*, 183 (1950) 123.
33 W. W. Kielley and R. K. Kielley, *J. Biol. Chem.*, 191 (1951) 485.
34 H. A. Lardy and H. Wellman, *J. Biol. Chem.*, 195 (1952) 215.
35 G. H. Hogeboom, in S. P. Colowick and N. O. Kaplan (Eds.), *Methods in Enzymology*, Vol. 1, Academic Press, New York, 1955, p. 16.
36 S. Ochoa, *J. Biol. Chem.*, 155 (1944) 87.
37 F. E. Hunter and W. S. Hixon, *J. Biol. Chem.*, 181 (1949) 73.
38 A. L. Lehninger, *J. Biol. Chem.*, 178 (1949) 625.
39 E. C. Slater, *Biochem. J.*, 53 (1953) 157.
40 E. C. Slater, *Biochem. J.*, 53 (1953) 521.
41 E. Racker, *J. Biol. Chem.*, 167 (1947) 843.
42 G. B. Pinchot, *J. Biol. Chem.*, 205 (1953) 65.
43 M. E. Pullman and E. Racker, *Science*, 123 (1956) 1105.
44 L. Ernster, R. Zetterström and O. Lindberg, *Acta Chem. Scand.*, 4 (1950) 942.
45 S. O. Nielsen and A. L. Lehninger, *J. Biol. Chem.*, 215 (1955) 555.
46 H. A. Krebs, A. Ruffo, M. Johnson, L. V. Eggleston and R. Hems, *Biochem. J.*, 54 (1953) 107.
47 P. D. Boyer, A. B. Falcone and W. H. Harrison, *Nature*, 174 (1954) 401.
48 B. Chance and G. R. Williams, *Nature*, 175 (1955) 1120.
49 W. A. Engelhardt, *Biochem. Z.*, 251 (1932) 343.

[50] H. A. LARDY, in L. F. WOLTERINK (Ed.), *The Biology of Phosphorus, East Lensing, 1951*, Michigan State College Press, East Lensing, 1952, p. 131.
[51] B. HAGIHARA, *Biochim. Biophys. Acta*, 46 (1961) 134.
[52] P. BORST, *Biochim. Biophys. Acta*, 57 (1962) 256.
[53] B. C. PRESSMAN AND H. A. LARDY, *Biochim. Biophys. Acta*, 21 (1956) 458.
[54] W. C. HÜLSMANN, W. B. ELLIOTT AND E. C. SLATER, *Biochim. Biophys. Acta*, 39 (1960) 267.
[55] L. WOJTCZAK AND A. L. LEHNINGER, *Biochim. Biophys. Acta*, 51 (1961) 442.
[56] A. L. SMITH AND M. HANSEN, *Biochem. Biophys. Res. Communs.*, 15 (1964) 431.
[57] J. M. HASLAM, *Biochim. Biophys. Acta*, 105 (1965) 184.
[58] G. LENAZ AND R. E. BEYER, *J. Biol. Chem.*, 240 (1965) 3653.
[59] G. P. BRIERLEY, *Biochem. Biophys. Res. Communs.*, 19 (1965) 500.
[60] C. GURBAN AND E. CRISTEA, *Rev. Roum. Biochim.*, 1 (1964) 51.
[61] C. GURBAN AND E. CRISTEA, *Biochim. Biophys. Acta*, 96 (1965) 195.
[62] M. KOIVUSALO AND E. C. SLATER, *Biochem. Z.*, 342 (1965) 246.
[63] M. KOIVUSALO, R. D. CURRIE AND E. C. SLATER, *Biochem. Z.*, 344 (1966) 221.
[64] W. S. LYNN AND R. H. BROWN, *Biochim. Biophys. Acta*, 105 (1965) 15.
[65] E. C. SLATER AND F. A. HOLTON, *Biochem. J.*, 55 (1953) 530.
[66] A. L. LEHNINGER AND S. W. SMITH, *J. Biol. Chem.*, 181 (1949) 415.
[67] S. P. COLOWICK AND H. M. KALCKAR, *J. Biol. Chem.*, 148 (1943) 117.
[68] S. S. BARKULIS AND A. L. LEHNINGER, *J. Biol. Chem.*, 190 (1951) 339.
[69] A. KEMP JR., unpublished results.
[70] C. COOPER AND A. L. LEHNINGER, *J. Biol. Chem.*, 219 (1956) 489.
[71] H. LÖW, I. VALLIN AND B. ALM, in B. CHANCE (Ed.), *Energy-Linked Functions of Mitochondria*, Academic Press, New York, 1963, p. 5.
[72] C. T. GREGG, *Biochim. Biophys. Acta*, 74 (1963) 573.
[73] H. W. HELDT, H. JACOBS AND M. KLINGENBERG, *Biochem. Biophys. Res. Communs.*, 18 (1965) 174.
[74] H. W. HELDT, in J. M. TAGER, S. PAPA, E. QUAGLIARIELLO AND E. C. SLATER (Eds.), *Regulation of Metabolic Processes in Mitochondria, (BBA Library, Vol. 7)*, Elsevier, Amsterdam, 1966, p. 51.
[75] E. PFAFF, M. KLINGENBERG AND H. W. HELDT, *Biochim. Biophys, Acta*, 104 (1965) 312.
[76] M. KLINGENBERG AND E. PFAFF, in J. M. TAGER, S. PAPA, E. QUAGLIARIELLO AND E. C. SLATER (Eds.), *Regulation of Metabolic Processes in Mitochondria, (BBA Library, Vol. 7)*, Elsevier, Amsterdam, 1966, p. 180.
[77] D. R. SANADI, D. M. GIBSON AND P. AYENGAR, *Biochim. Biophys. Acta*, 14 (1954) 434.
[78] R. K. CRANE AND F. LIPMANN, *J. Biol. Chem.*, 201 (1953) 235.
[78a] R. MAZUMDER, D. R. SANADI AND V. W. RODWELL, *J. Biol. Chem.*, 235 (1960) 2546.
[79] B. CHANCE AND B. HAGIHARA, in E. C. SLATER (Ed.), *Symposium on Intracellular Respiration: Phosphorylating and Non-Phosphorylating Oxidation Reactions, Proc. 5th Intern. Congr. Biochem., Moscow, 1961*, Vol. 5, Pergamon, Oxford, 1963, p. 3.
[80] J. H. COPENHAVER AND H. A. LARDY, *J. Biol. Chem.*, 195 (1952) 225.
[81] P. GREENGARD, K. MINNAERT, E. C. SLATER AND I. BETEL, *Biochem. J.*, 73 (1959) 637.
[82] R. WHITTAM, W. BARTLEY AND G. WEBER, *Biochem. J.*, 59 (1955) 590.
[83] E. C. SLATER AND J. M. TAGER, *Biochim. Biophys. Acta*, 77 (1963) 276.
[84] A. L. SMITH AND M. HANSEN, *Biochem. Biophys. Res. Communs.*, 8 (1962) 33.
[85] P. BORST, *11th Yearbook for Cancer Research and Fight against Cancer in The Netherlands*, 1961, p. 227.
[86] E. BALL, *Ann. N.Y. Acad. Sci.*, 45 (1944) 363.
[87] F. LIPMANN, in D. E. GREEN (Ed.), *Currents in Biochemical Research*, Interscience, New York, 1946, p. 137.
[88] A. G. OGSTON AND O. SMITHIES, *Physiol. Rev.*, 28 (1948) 283.
[89] T. BENZINGER, C. KITZINGER, R. HEMS AND K. BURTON, *Biochem. J.*, 71 (1959) 400.
[90] M. R. ATKINSON, E. JOHNSON AND R. K. MORTON, *Nature*, 184 (1959) 1925.
[91] B. CHANCE AND G. R. WILLIAMS, *J. Biol. Chem.*, 217 (1955) 409.

92 B. Chance and G. R. Williams, *Advan. Enzymol.*, 17 (1956) 65.
93 E. C. Slater, *Rev. Pure Appl. Chem.*, 8 (1958) 221.
94 H. A. Krebs, J. Mellanby and D. H. Williamson, *Biochem. J.*, 82 (1962) 96.
95 K. Burton and T. H. Wilson, *Biochem. J.*, 54 (1953) 86.
96 E. C. Slater, J. P. Colpa-Boonstra and J. Links, *Ciba Foundation Symp. on Quinones in Electron Transport*, Churchill, London, 1961, p. 161.
97 F. A. Holton and J. P. Colpa-Boonstra, *Biochem. J.*, 76 (1960) 179.
98 J. P. Straub and J. P. Colpa-Boonstra, *Biochim. Biophys. Acta*, 60 (1962) 650.
99 E. Stotz, A. E. Sidwell Jr. and T. R. Hogness, *J. Biol. Chem.*, 124 (1938) 11.
100 K. Minnaert, *Federation Proc.*, 20 (1961) 42; *Biochim. Biophys. Acta*, 110 (1965) 42.
101 E. C. Slater, in W. Ruhland (Ed.), *Encyclopedia of Plant Physiology*, Vol. 12, Springer, Berlin, 1960, p. 114.
102 M. Klingenberg and W. Slenczka, *Biochem. Z.*, 331 (1959) 486.
103 M. Friedkin and A. L. Lehninger, *J. Biol. Chem.*, 178 (1949) 611.
104 E. C. Slater, *Nature*, 166 (1950) 982.
105 E. C. Slater, *Biochem. J.*, 59 (1955) 392.
106 S. O. Nielsen and A. L. Lehninger, *J. Am. Chem. Soc.*, 76 (1954) 3860.
107 J. D. Judah, *Biochem. J.*, 49 (1951) 271.
108 G. F. Maley and H. A. Lardy, *J. Biol. Chem.*, 210 (1954) 903.
109 E. C. Slater, *Nature*, 174 (1954) 1143.
110 A. L. Lehninger, *J. Biol. Chem.*, 190 (1951) 345.
111 A. L. Lehninger, M. Ul Hassan and H. C. Sudduth, *J. Biol. Chem.*, 210 (1954) 911.
112 E. C. Slater, *Proc. 3rd Intern. Congr. Biochem., Brussels, 1955*, Academic Press, New York, 1956, p. 264.
113 K. Minnaert and A. R. van Kammen-Wertheim, *Biochim. Biophys. Acta*, 44 (1960) 593.
114 E. C. Weinbach, *J. Biol. Chem.*, 236 (1961) 1526.
115 A. L. Lehninger, *Harvey Lectures, Ser.* 49 (1953–4) 176.
116 E. C. Slater, *Biochim. Biophys. Acta*, 48 (1961) 117.
117 B. Borgström, H. C. Sudduth and A. L. Lehninger, *J. Biol. Chem.*, 215 (1955) 571.
118 D. W. Haas, *Biochim. Biophys. Acta*, 92 (1964) 433.
119 J. Ramirez and A. Mujica, *Federation Proc.*, 20 (1961) 49.
120 J. L. Howland, *Biochim. Biophys. Acta*, 77 (1963) 419.
121 B. Chance, *Nature*, 169 (1952) 215.
122 I. Krimsky and E. Racker, *Science*, 122 (1955) 319.
123 S. Black and N. G. Wright, *J. Biol. Chem.*, 213 (1955) 27, 39.
124 R. M. Burton and E. R. Stadtman, *J. Biol. Chem.*, 202 (1953) 873.
125 E. C. Slater, *Ann. Rev. Biochem.*, 22 (1953) 17.
126 I. C. Gunsalus, in W. D. McElroy and B. Glass (Eds.), *The Mechanism of Enzyme Action*, Johns Hopkins, Baltimore, Md., 1954, p. 545.
127 S. Kaufman, C. Gilvarg, O. Cori and S. Ochoa, *J. Biol. Chem.*, 203 (1953) 869.
128 H. Hift, L. Ouellet, J. W. Littlefield and D. R. Sanadi, *J. Biol. Chem.*, 204 (1953) 565.
129 S. Kaufman, *J. Biol. Chem.*, 216 (1955) 153.
130 R. A. Mitchell, L. G. Butler and P. D. Boyer, *Biochem. Biophys. Res. Communs.*, 16 (1964) 545.
131 G. Kreil and P. D. Boyer, *Biochem. Biophys. Res. Communs.*, 16 (1964) 551.
132 E. C. Slater and A. Kemp Jr., *Nature*, 204 (1964) 1268.
133 A. Kemp Jr., in J. M. Tager, S. Papa, E. Quagliariello and E. C. Slater (Eds.), *Regulation of Metabolic Processes in Mitochondria, (BBA Library, Vol. 7)*, Elsevier, Amsterdam, 1966, p. 264.
134 N. Mourad and R. E. Parks Jr., *Biochem. Biophys. Res. Communs.*, 19 (1965) 312.
135 A. W. Norman, R. T. Wedding and M. K. Black, *Biochem. Biophys. Res. Communs.*, 20 (1965) 703.
136 J. S. Nishimura and A. Meister, *Biochemistry*, 4 (1965) 1457.
137 S. Cha, C.-J. M. Cha and R. E. Parks Jr., *J. Biol. Chem.*, 240 (1965) PC 3700.

138 E. Racker, *Advan. Enzymol.*, 23 (1961) 323.
139 A. L. Lehninger and C. L. Wadkins, *Ann. Rev. Biochem.*, 31 (1962) 47.
140 P. Mitchell, *Nature*, 191 (1961) 144.
141 F. Lipmann, in *Molecular Biology*, Academic Press, New York, 1960, p. 37.
142 R. N. Robertson, *Biol. Rev. Cambridge Phil. Soc.*, 35 (1960) 231.
143 P. Mitchell and J. Moyle, *Nature*, 208 (1965) 147.
144 P. Mitchell, in J. M. Tager, S. Papa, E. Quagliariello and E. C. Slater (Eds.), *Regulation of Metabolic Processes in Mitochondria, (BBA Library, Vol. 7)*, Elsevier, Amsterdam, 1966, p. 65.
145 F. E. Hunter Jr., in W. D. McElroy and B. Glass (Eds.), *Phosphorus Metabolism*, Vol. 1, Johns Hopkins, Baltimore, Md., 1951, p. 297.
146 E. C. Slater, *Nature*, 172 (1953) 975.
147 W. D. Bonner Jr., *Biochem. J.*, 49 (1951) viii; 56 (1954) 274.
148 D. Keilin and E. F. Hartree, *Biochem. J.*, 44 (1949) 205.
149 H. A. Lardy and H. Wellman, *J. Biol. Chem.*, 201 (1953) 357.
150 D. E. Green, *Biol. Rev. Cambridge Phil. Soc.*, 26 (1951) 410.
151 K. H. Lee and J. J. Eiler, *J. Biol. Chem.*, 203 (1953) 719.
152 C. Cooper and A. L. Lehninger, *J. Biol. Chem.*, 224 (1957) 547, 561.
153 H. A. Lardy and C. A. Elvehjem, *Ann. Rev. Biochem.*, 14 (1945) 1.
154 E. C. Slater and S. E. Lewis, *Biochem. J.*, 58 (1954) 337.
155 L. J. Teply, *Arch. Biochem.*, 24 (1949) 383.
156 M. J. R. Dawkins, J. D. Judah and K. R. Rees, *Biochem. J.*, 73 (1959) 16.
157 H. Löw, P. Siekevitz, L. Ernster and O. Lindberg, *Biochim. Biophys. Acta*, 29 (1958) 392.
158 B. Grabe, *Biochim. Biophys. Acta*, 30 (1958) 560.
159 H. Löw, *Biochim. Biophys. Acta*, 32 (1959) 1.
160 P. Borst and E. C. Slater, *Biochim. Biophys. Acta*, 48 (1961) 362.
161 J. B. Chappell and G. D. Greville, *Nature*, 190 (1961) 502.
162 H. A. Lardy, D. Johnson and W. C. McMurray, *Arch. Biochem. Biophys.*, 78 (1958) 587.
163 H. A. Lardy and W. C. McMurray, *Federation Proc.*, 18 (1959) 269.
164 R. W. Estabrook, *Biochem. Biophys. Res. Communs.*, 4 (1961) 89.
165 F. Huijing and E. C. Slater, *J. Biochem. (Tokyo)*, 49 (1961) 493.
166 L. Ernster, in E. C. Slater (Ed.), *Symposium on Intracellular Respiration: Phosphorylating and Non-Phosphorylating Oxidation Reactions, Proc. 5th Intern. Congr. Biochem., Moscow, 1961*, Vol. 5, Pergamon, Oxford, 1963, p. 115.
167 A. M. Snoswell, *Biochim. Biophys. Acta*, 60 (1962) 143.
168 C. N. Peiss and J. Field, *J. Biol. Chem.*, 175 (1948) 49.
169 A. L. Lehninger, C. L. Wadkins, C. Cooper, T. M. Devlin and J. L. Gamble, *Science*, 128 (1958) 450.
170 G. B. Pinchot, *Proc. Natl. Acad. Sci. (U.S.)*, 46 (1960) 929.
171 G. Webster, *Biochem. Biophys. Res. Communs.*, 13 (1963) 399.
172 C. L. Wadkins and A. L. Lehninger, *J. Biol. Chem.*, 238 (1963) 2555.
173 B. Chance, G. R. Williams, W. F. Holmes and J. Higgins, *J. Biol. Chem.*, 217 (1955) 439.
174 E. C. Slater and J. P. Colpa-Boonstra, in *Symp. Intern. Union of Biochem. on Haematin Enzymes, Canberra, 1959*, Part 2, Pergamon Oxford, 1961, p. 575.
175 H. A. Lardy, J. L. Connelly and D. Johnson, *Biochemistry*, 3 (1964) 1961.
176 D. K. Myers and E. C. Slater, *Biochem. J.*, 67 (1957) 572.
177 C. L. Wadkins and A. L. Lehninger, *J. Biol. Chem.*, 234 (1959) 681.
178 W. Chefurka, *Can. J. Biochem. Physiol.*, 38 (1960) 1195.
179 B. Chance and T. Ito, *J. Biol. Chem.*, 238 (1963) 1509.
180 B. Chance, T. Ito, P. K. Maitra and R. Oshino, *J. Biol. Chem.*, 238 (1963) 1516.
181 V. R. Potter and R. O. Recknagel, in W. D. McElroy and B. Glass (Eds.), *Phosphorus Metabolism*, Vol. 1, Johns Hopkins, Baltimore, 1951, p. 377.
182 H. C. Hemker, *Biochim. Biophys. Acta*, 63 (1962) 46.
183 C. Hansch, K. Kiehs and G. L. Lawrence, *J. Am. Chem. Soc.*, 87 (1965) 5770.
184 M. Cohn, *J. Biol. Chem.*, 201 (1953) 735.

185 P. D. Boyer, W. W. Luchsinger and A. B. Falcone, *J. Biol. Chem.*, 223 (1956) 405.
186 P. C. Chan, A. L. Lehninger and T. Enns, *J. Biol. Chem.*, 235 (1960) 1790.
187 G. R. Drysdale and M. Cohn, *J. Biol. Chem.*, 233 (1958) 1574.
188 P. D. Boyer, *Proc. Intern. Symp. on Enzyme Chem., Tokyo and Kyoto*, Maruzen, Tokyo, 1957, p. 301.
189 M. Cohn and G. R. Drysdale, *J. Biol. Chem.*, 216 (1955) 831.
190 M. A. Swanson, *Biochim. Biophys. Acta*, 20 (1956) 85.
191 J. R. Bronk and W. W. Kielley, *Biochim. Biophys. Acta*, 29 (1958) 369.
192 P. Cazeneuve and R. Lepine, *Compt. Rend.*, 101 (1885) 1167.
193 C. Heymans and J. J. Bouchaert, *Arch. Intern. Pharmacodyn.*, 35 (1928) 63.
194 H. Magne, A. Mayer and L. Plantefol, *Ann. Physiol. Physicochim. Biol.*, 7 (1931) 269.
195 H. Magne, A. Mayer and L. Plantefol, *Ann. Physiol. Physicochim. Biol.*, 8 (1932) 1, 51, 70, 157.
196 U. S. von Euler, *Arch. Intern. Pharmacodyn.*, 43 (1932) 67.
197 U. S. von Euler, *Arch. Intern. Pharmacodyn.*, 44 (1933) 464.
198 E. Ehrenfest and E. Ronzoni, *Proc. Soc. Exptl. Biol. Med.*, 31 (1933) 318.
199 E. Ronzoni and E. Ehrenfest, *J. Biol. Chem.*, 115 (1936) 749.
200 E. C. Dodds and G. D. Greville, *Nature*, 132 (1933) 966.
201 R. H. De Meio and E. S. G. Barron, *Proc. Soc. Exptl. Biol. Med.*, 32 (1934–1935) 36.
202 W. C. Hülsmann and E. C. Slater, *Nature*, 180 (1957) 372.
203 W. C. Hülsmann, *Over het Mechanisme van de Ademhalingsketenphosphorylering*, M.D. Thesis, Poortpers, Amsterdam, 1958.
204 E. Gladtke and E. Liss, *Biochem. Z.*, 331 (1959) 65.
205 H. C. Hemker, *Biochim. Biophys. Acta*, 73 (1963) 311.
206 B. Chance, G. Hollunger and B. Hagihara, *Biochem. Biophys. Res. Communs.*, 8 (1962) 180.
207 B. Chance and G. Hollunger, *J. Biol. Chem.*, 238 (1963) 418.
208 J. L. Howland, *Biochim. Biophys. Acta*, 73 (1963) 665.
209 H. C. Hemker, *Biochim. Biophys. Acta*, 81 (1964) 1.
210 H. C. Hemker, *Biochim. Biophys. Acta*, 81 (1964) 9.
211 C. Martius and N. Nitz-Litzow, *Biochim. Biophys. Acta*, 12 (1953) 134.
212 R. D. Hotchkiss, in D. E. Green (Ed.), *Currents in Biochemical Research*, Wiley (Interscience), New York, 1946, p. 379.
213 W. F. Loomis, *Science*, 111 (1950) 474.
214 W. C. McMurray and R. W. Begg, *Arch. Biochem. Biophys.*, 84 (1959) 546.
215 B. C. Pressman and H. A. Lardy, *J. Biol. Chem.*, 197 (1952) 547.
216 B. C. Pressman and H. A. Lardy, *Biochim. Biophys. Acta*, 18 (1955) 482.
217 W. C. Hülsmann, W. B. Elliott and H. Rudney, *Biochim. Biophys .Acta*, 27 (1958) 663.
218 W. B. Elliott, W. C. Hülsmann and E. C. Slater, *Biochim. Biophys. Acta*, 33 (1959) 509.
219 W. C. Hülsmann, W. B. Elliott and E. C. Slater, *Biochim. Biophys. Acta*, 39 (1960) 267.
220 P. Borst, J. A. Loos, E. J. Christ and E. C. Slater, *Biochim. Biophys. Acta*, 62 (1962) 509.
221 P. G. Heytler, *Biochemistry*, 2 (1963) 357.
222 R. A. Goldsby and P. G. Heytler, *Biochemistry*, 2 (1963) 1142.
223 P. G. Heytler and W. W. Prichard, *Biochem. Biophys. Res. Communs.*, 7 (1962) 272.
224 C. Moore and B. C. Pressman, *Biochem. Biophys. Res. Communs.*, 15 (1964) 562.
225 B. C. Pressman, *Proc. Natl. Acad. Sci. (U.S.)*, 53 (1965) 1076.
226 J. B. Chappell and A. R. Crofts, in J. M. Tager, S. Papa, E. Quagliariello and E. C. Slater (Eds.), *Regulation of Metabolic Processes in Mitochondria, (BBA Library, Vol. 7)*, Elsevier, Amsterdam, 1966, p. 293.
227 D. M. Needham and R. K. Pillai, *Biochem. J.*, 31 (1937) 1837.

228 D. R. Sanadi, D. M. Gibson, P. Ayengar and L. Ouellet, *Biochim. Biophys. Acta*, 13 (1954) 146.
229 R. W. Estabrook and N. Itada, *Federation Proc.*, 21 (1962) 55.
230 S. G. van den Bergh, *Respiration and Energy Production in the Flight Muscle of the Housefly Musca domestica L.*, Ph.D. Thesis, Rototype, Amsterdam, 1962.
231 C. L. Wadkins, *J. Biol. Chem.*, 235 (1960) 3300.
232 G. F. Azzone and L. Ernster, *J. Biol. Chem.*, 236 (1961) 1510.
233 H. F. ter Welle and E. C. Slater, *Biochim. Biophys. Acta*, 89 (1964) 385.
234 J. B. Chappell and A. R. Crofts, *Biochem. J.*, 95 (1965) 707.
235 G. Hollunger, *Acta Pharmacol. Toxicol., Suppl. 1*, 11 (1955).
236 B. C. Pressman, *J. Biol. Chem.*, 238 (1963) 401.
237 J. B. Chappell, *J. Biol. Chem.*, 238 (1963) 410.
238 B. C. Pressman, in B. Chance (Ed.), *Energy-Linked Functions of Mitochondria*, Academic Press, New York, 1963, p. 181.
239 B. Chance and G. Hollunger, *J. Biol. Chem.*, 238 (1963) 432.
240 D. W. Haas, *Biochim. Biophys. Acta*, 92 (1964) 433.
241 R. J. Guillory and E. C. Slater, *Biochim. Biophys. Acta*, 105 (1965) 221.
242 S. Masamune, J. M. Sehgal, E. E. van Tamelen, F. M. Strong and W. H. Peterson, *J. Am. Chem. Soc.*, 80 (1958) 6092.
243 J. Visser, D. E. Weinauer, R. C. Davis, W. H. Peterson, W. Nazarewicz and H. Oroway, *J. Biochem. Microbiol. Technol. Eng.*, 2 (1960) 31.
244 H. A. Lardy, P. Witoncky and D. Johnson, *Biochemistry*, 4 (1965) 552.
245 R. Q. Thompson, M. M. Hoehn and C. E. Higgins, *Antimicrobial Agents and Chemotherapy*, Am. Soc. of Microbiologists, Detroit, 1961, p. 474.
246 C.-P. Lee and L. Ernster, *Biochem. Biophys. Res. Communs.*, 18 (1965) 523.
247 C.-P. Lee and L. Ernster, in J. M. Tager, S. Papa, E. Quagliariello and E. C. Slater (Eds.), *Regulation of Metabolic Processes in Mitochondria, (BBA Library, Vol. 7)*, Elsevier, Amsterdam, 1966, p. 218.
248 H. A. Lardy, *IUB/IUBS Symp. on Biological Structure and Function, Stockholm, 1960*, Vol. 2, Academic Press, New York, 1961, p. 265.
250 J. L. Connelly and H. A. Lardy, *Biochemistry*, 3 (1964) 1969.
251 A. Bruni, A. R. Contessa and S. Luciani, *Biochim. Biophys. Acta*, 60 (1962) 301.
252 A. Bruni, S. Luciana and A. R. Contessa, *Nature*, 201 (1964) 781.
253 A. Kemp Jr. and E. C. Slater, *Biochim. Biophys. Acta*, 92 (1964) 178.
254 H. W. Heldt, H. Jacobs and M. Klingenberg, *Biochem. Biophys. Res. Communs.*, 18 (1965) 174.
256 A. Bruni, in J. M. Tager, S. Papa, E. Quagliariello and E. C. Slater (Eds.), *Regulation of Metabolic Processes in Mitochondria, (BBA Library, Vol. 7)*, Elsevier, Amsterdam, 1966, p. 275.
257 R. J. Guillory, *Biochim. Biophys. Acta*, 89 (1964) 197.
258 E. C. Slater and K. W. Cleland, *Biochem. J.*, 53 (1953) 557.
259 E. E. Jacobs and D. R. Sanadi, *J. Biol. Chem.*, 235 (1960) 531.
260 A. F. Brodie and P. J. Russell, in E. C. Slater (Ed.), *Symposium on Intracellular Respiration: Phosphorylating and Non-Phosphorylating Oxidation Reactions, Proc. 5th Intern. Congr. Biochem., Moscow, 1961*, Vol. 5, Pergamon, Oxford, 1963, p. 89.
261 A. F. Brodie, *Federation Proc.*, 20 (1961) 955.
262 H. G. Hovenkamp, *Nature*, 184 (1959) 471.
263 S. Ishikawa and A. L. Lehninger, *J. Biol. Chem.*, 237 (1962) 2401.
264 A. L. Lehninger and C. T. Gregg, *Biochim. Biophys. Acta*, 78 (1963) 12.
265 D. W. Haas and W. H. Elliott, *J. Biol. Chem.*, 238 (1963) 1132.
266 W. C. McMurray, G. F. Maley and H. A. Lardy, *J. Biol. Chem.*, 230 (1958) 219.
267 W. W. Kielley and J. R. Bronk, *J. Biol. Chem.*, 230 (1958) 521.
268 A. W. Linnane and D. M. Ziegler, *Biochim. Biophys. Acta*, 29 (1958) 630.
269 M. Hansen and A. L. Smith, *Biochim. Biophys. Acta*, 81 (1964) 214.
270 J. L. Purvis and E. C. Slater, *Exptl. Cell Res.*, 16 (1959) 109.
271 W. W. Kielley and J. R. Bronk, *Biochim. Biophys. Acta*, 23 (1957) 448.
272 A. L. Lehninger, in *Ciba Foundation Symp. on the Regulation of Cell Metabolism*, Churchill, London, 1959, p. 88.

273 U. Fugmann and R. W. Estabrook, Transactions of the Plenary Sessions and Abstracts of Papers, *Proc. 5th Intern. Congr. Biochem., Moscow, 1961*, Vol. 9, Pergamon Press, London, 1963, p. 530.
274 A. W. Linnane, *Biochim. Biophys. Acta*, 30 (1958) 221.
275 A. W. Linnane and E. B. Titchener, *Biochim. Biophys. Acta*, 39 (1960) 469.
276 M. E. Pullman, H. S. Penefsky, A. Datta and E. Racker, *J. Biol. Chem.*, 235 (1960) 3322, 3330.
277 O. Lindberg and L. Ernster, *Nature*, 173 (1954) 1038.
278 G. Webster and D. E. Green, *Proc. Natl. Acad. Sci. (U.S.)*, 52 (1964) 1170.
279 D. R. Sanadi, *Ann. Rev. Biochem.*, 34 (1965) 21.
280 R. E. Beyer, *Biochem. Biophys. Res. Communs.*, 16 (1964) 460; 17 (1964) 184, 764.
281 E. Racker and T. E. Conover, *Federation Proc.*, 22 (1963) 1088.
282 E. Racker, M. E. Pullman, H. S. Penefsky and M. Silverman, in E. C. Slater (Ed.), *Symposium on Intracellular Respiration: Phosphorylating and Non-Phosphorylating Oxidation Reactions, Proc. 5th Intern. Congr. Biochem., Moscow, 1961*, Vol. 5, Pergamon, Oxford, 1963, p. 303.
282a M. E. Pullman and G. C. Monroy, *J. Biol. Chem.*, 238 (1963) 3762.
283 R. L. Prairie, T. E. Conover and E. Racker, *Biochem. Biophys. Res. Communs.*, 10 (1963) 422.
284 E. Racker and G. Monroy, *Abstr. 6th Intern. Congr. Biochem., New York, 1964*, Vol. 10, p. 760.
284a H. Zalkin, M. E. Pullman and E. Racker, *J. Biol. Chem.*, 240 (1965) 4011.
284b H. Zalkin and E. Racker, *J. Biol. Chem.*, 240 (1965) 4017.
284c R. S. Criddle, R. M. Bock, D. E. Green and H. Tisdale, *Biochemistry*, 1 (1962) 827.
285 C. L. Wadkins and A. L. Lehninger, *Proc. Natl. Acad. Sci. (U.S.)*, 46 (1960) 1576.
286 A. L. Lehninger, in E. C. Slater (Ed.), *Symposium on Intracellular Respiration: Phosphorylating and Non-Phosphorylating Oxidation Reactions, Proc. 5th Intern. Congr. Biochem., Moscow, 1961*, Vol. 5, Pergamon, Oxford, 1963, p. 239.
287 C. L. Wadkins and A. L. Lehninger, *Federation Proc.*, 22 (1963) 1092.
288 C. L. Wadkins and A. L. Lehninger, *J. Biol. Chem.*, 233 (1958) 1589.
288a C. L. Wadkins, *J. Biol. Chem.*, 236 (1961) 221.
289 C. L. Wadkins and A. L. Lehninger, *J. Biol. Chem.*, 238 (1963) 2355.
290 R. C. Kulka and C. Cooper, *J. Biol. Chem.*, 237 (1962) 936.
291 M. Chiga and G. W. E. Plaut, *J. Biol. Chem.*, 234 (1959) 3059.
292 D. Neubert, A. B. Wojtczak and A. L. Lehninger, *Proc. Natl. Acad. Sci. (U.S.)*, 48 (1962) 1651.
293 D. Neubert, in J. M. Tager, S. Papa, E. Quagliariello and E. C. Slater (Eds.), *Regulation of Metabolic Processes in Mitochondria, (BBA Library, Vol. 7)*, Elsevier, Amsterdam, 1966, p. 351.
294 P. V. Vignais, P. M. Vignais and A. L. Lehninger, *J. Biol. Chem.*, 239 (1964) 2002.
295 P. M. Vignais, P. V. Vignais and A. L. Lehninger, *J. Biol. Chem.*, 239 (1964) 2011.
296 P. V. Vignais and P. M. Vignais, in J. M. Tager, S. Papa, E. Quagliariello and E. C. Slater (Eds.), *Regulation of Metabolic Processes in Mitochondria, (BBA Library, Vol. 7)*, Elsevier, Amsterdam, 1966, p. 368.
297 B. Chance, in O. H. Gaebler (Ed.), *Enzymes: Units in Biological Structure and Function*, Academic Press, New York, 1956, p. 447.
298 B. Chance and G. Hollunger, *Federation Proc.*, 16 (1957) 163.
299 B. Chance and G. Hollunger, *Nature*, 185 (1960) 666.
300 M. Klingenberg and W. Slenczka, *Biochem. Z.*, 331 (1959) 486.
301 M. Klingenberg, W. Slenczka and E. Ritt, *Biochem. Z.*, 332 (1959) 47.
302 L. Ernster, *IUB/IUBS Symp. on Biological Structure and Function, Stockholm, 1960*, Vol. 2, Academic Press, New York, 1961, p. 139.
303 A. M. Snoswell, *Biochim. Biophys. Acta*, 52 (1961) 216.
304 J. M. Tager and E. C. Slater, *Biochim. Biophys. Acta*, 77 (1963) 227.
305 J. M. Tager and E. C. Slater, *Biochim. Biophys. Acta*, 77 (1963) 246.
306 L. Packer and M. D. Denton, *Federation Proc.*, 21 (1962) 53.

[307] J. M. TAGER, J. L. HOWLAND, E. C. SLATER AND A. M. SNOSWELL, *Biochim. Biophys. Acta*, 77 (1963) 266.
[308] H. S. PENEFSKY, *Biochim. Biophys. Acta*, 58 (1962) 619.
[309] L. PACKER, *J. Biol. Chem.*, 237 (1962) 1327.
[310] H. LÖW AND I. VALLIN, *Biochem. Biophys. Res. Communs.*, 9 (1962) 307.
[311] B. CHANCE AND U. FUGMANN, *Biochem. Biophys. Res. Communs.*, 4 (1961) 317.
[312] H. LÖW AND I. VALLIN, *Biochim. Biophys. Acta*, 69 (1963) 361.
[313] E. C. SLATER, A. KEMP JR. AND J. M. TAGER, *Nature*, 201 (1964) 781.
[314] G. D. V. VAN ROSSUM, *Biochem. J.*, 84 (1962) 35P; *Biochim. Biophys. Acta*, 82 (1964) 556.
[315] S. MINAKAMI, K. KAKINUMA AND H. YOSHIKAWA, *Biochim. Biophys. Acta*, 78 (1963) 808.
[316] R. WU, *Biochim. Biophys. Acta*, 82 (1964) 212.
[317] R. WHITTAM, K. P. WHEELER AND A. BLAKE, *Nature*, 203 (1964) 720.
[318] R. B. TOBIN AND E. C. SLATER, *Biochim. Biophys. Acta*, 105 (1965) 214.
[319] I. HARARY AND E. C. SLATER, *Biochim. Biophys. Acta*, 99 (1965) 227.
[320] W. BARTLEY AND R. E. DAVIES, *Biochem. J.*, 52 (1952) xx; 57 (1954) 37.
[321] M. G. MACFARLANE AND A. G. SPENCER, *Biochem. J.*, 54 (1953) 569.
[322] W. G. SPECTOR, *Proc. Roy. Soc. (London), Ser. B*, 141 (1953) 268.
[323] S. W. STANBURY AND G. H. MUDGE, *Proc. Soc. Exptl. Biol. Med.*, 82 (1953) 675.
[324] E. C. SLATER AND K. W. CLELAND, *Biochem. J.*, 55 (1953) 566.
[325] B. CHANCE, *Proc. 3rd Intern. Congr. Biochem., Brussels, 1955*, Academic Press, New York, 1956, p. 300.
[326] H. F. DELUCA AND G. W. ENGSTROM, *Proc. Natl. Acad. Sci. (U.S.)*, 47 (1961) 1744.
[327] J. B. CHAPPELL, G. D. GREVILLE AND K. E. BICKNELL, *Biochem. J.*, 84 (1962) 61P.
[328] J. B. CHAPPELL, M. COHN AND G. D. GREVILLE, in B. CHANCE (Ed.), *Energy-linked Functions of Mitochondria*, Academic Press, New York, 1963, p. 219.
[329] G. P. BRIERLEY, E. BACHMANN AND D. E. GREEN, *Proc. Natl. Acad. Sci.(U.S.)*, 48 (1963) 1928.
[330] G. P. BRIERLEY, E. MURER AND D. E. GREEN, *Science*, 140 (1963) 60.
[331] G. P. BRIERLEY, E. MURER, E. BACHMANN AND D. E. GREEN, *J. Biol. Chem.*, 238 (1963) 3482.
[332] A. L. LEHNINGER, C. S. ROSSI AND J. W. GREENAWALT, *Biochem. Biophys. Res. Communs.*, 10 (1963) 444.
[333] C. S. ROSSI AND A. L. LEHNINGER, *Biochem. Z.*, 338 (1963) 698.
[334] E. CARAFOLI, C. S. ROSSI AND A. L. LEHNINGER, *J. Biol. Chem.*, 239 (1964) 3055.
[335] C. S. ROSSI, E. CARAFOLI, Z. DRAHOTA AND A. L. LEHNINGER, in J. M. TAGER, S. PAPA, E. QUAGLIARIELLO AND E. C. SLATER (Eds.), *Regulation of Metabolic Processes in Mitochondria, (BBA Library, Vol. 7)*, Elsevier, Amsterdam, 1966, p. 317.
[336] F. D. VASINGTON, *J. Biol. Chem.*, 238 (1963) 1841.
[337] E. CARAFOLI, *Biochim. Biophys. Acta*, 97 (1965) 99, 107.
[338] L. DANIELSON AND L. ERNSTER, *Biochem. Z.*, 338 (1963) 188.
[339] C.-P. LEE AND L. ERNSTER. *Biochim. Biophys. Acta*, 81 (1964) 190.
[340] K. VAN DAM AND H. F. TER WELLE, in J. M. TAGER, S. PAPA, E. QUAGLIARIELLO AND E. C. SLATER (Eds.), *Regulation of Metabolic Processes in Mitochondria, (BBA Library, Vol. 7)*, Elsevier, Amsterdam, 1966, p. 235.
[341] D. W. HAAS, *Biochim. Biophys. Acta*, 82 (1964) 200.
[342] J. M. TAGER, *Biochim. Biophys. Acta*, 77 (1963) 258.
[343] M. KLINGENBERG, *Symp. über Redoxfunktionen cytoplasmatischer Strukturen*, Gemeinsame Tagung der deutschen Gesellschaft für physiologische Chemie und der österreichischen biochemischen Gesellschaft, Wien, 1962, p. 163.
[344] L. SCHACHINGER, R. EISENHARDT AND B. CHANCE, *Biochem. Z.*, 333 (1960) 182.
[345] P. V. VIGNAIS, *Biochim. Biophys. Acta*, 78 (1963) 404.
[346] K. VAN DAM, *Biochim. Biophys. Acta*, 92 (1964) 181.
[347] J. L. PURVIS, *Nature*, 182 (1958) 711.
[348] J. L. PURVIS, *Biochim. Biophys. Acta*, 38 (1960) 435.
[349] E. C. SLATER, M. J. BAILIE AND J. BOUMAN, *IUB/IUBS Symp. Biol. Structure and Function, Stockholm, 1960*, Vol. 2, Academic Press, 1961, p. 207.

350 K. VAN DAM, *Proc. 6th Intern. Congr. Biochem., New York, 1964, Abstr. Vol. X*, p. 791.
351 E. C. SLATER, in J. M. TAGER, S. PAPA, E. QUAGLIARIELLO AND E. C. SLATER (Eds.), *Regulation of Metabolic Processes in Mitochondria, (BBA Library, Vol. 7)*, Elsevier, Amsterdam, 1966, p. 541.
352 M. KLINGENBERG, in J. M. TAGER, S. PAPA, E. QUAGLIARIELLO AND E. C. SLATER (Eds.), *Regulation of Metabolic Processes in Mitochondria, (BBA Library, Vol. 7)*, Elsevier, Amsterdam, 1966, p. 542.
353 H. W. HELDT AND M. KLINGENBERG, *Biochem. Z.*, 343 (1965) 443.
354 G. B. PINCHOT AND M. HORMANSKI, *Proc. Natl. Acad. Sci. (U.S.)*, 48 (1962) 1970.
355 G. B. PINCHOT, *Federation Proc.*, 22 (1963) 1076.
356 H. G. PANDIT-HOVENKAMP, *Biochim. Biophys. Acta*, 99 (1965) 552.
357 M. GRUNBERG-MANAGO AND S. OCHOA, *J. Am. Chem. Soc.*, 77 (1955) 3165.
358 G. WEBSTER, *Biochem. Biophys. Res. Communs.*, 7 (1962) 245.
359 G. WEBSTER, A. L. SMITH AND M. HANSEN, *Proc. Natl. Acad. Sci. (U.S.)*, 49 (1963) 259.
360 D. E. GRIFFITHS, *Federation Proc.*, 22 (1963) 1064.
361 P. H. GALE, B. H. ARISON, N. R. TRENNER, A. C. PAGE JR., K. FOLKERS AND A. F. BRODIE, *Biochemistry*, 2 (1963) 200.
362 A. ASANO, A. F. BRODIE, A. F. WAGNER, P. E. WITTREICH AND K. FOLKERS, *J. Biol. Chem.*, 237 (1962) PC 2411.
363 C. H. SUELTER, M. DELUCA, J. B. PETER AND P. D. BOYER, *Nature*, 192 (1961) 43.
364 P. D. BOYER, M. DELUCA, K. E. EBNER, D. E. HULTQUIST AND J. B. PETER, *J. Biol. Chem.*, 237 (1962) PC 3306.
365 J. B. PETER AND P. D. BOYER, *J. Biol. Chem.*, 238 (1963) PC 1180.
366 P. D. BOYER, D. E. HULTQUIST, J. B. PETER, G. KREIL, R. A. MITCHELL, M. DELUCA, J. W. HINKSON, L. G. BUTLER AND R. W. MOYER, *Federation Proc.*, 22 (1963) 1080.
367 P. D. BOYER, *Science*, 141 (1963) 1147.
368 B. C. PRESSMAN, *Biochem. Biophys. Res. Communs.*, 15 (1964) 556.
369 R. A. MITCHELL, L. G. BUTLER AND P. D. BOYER, *Biochem. Biophys. Res. Communs.*, 16 (1964) 545.
370 G. KREIL AND P. D. BOYER, *Biochem. Biophys. Res. Communs.*, 16 (1964) 551.
371 L. L. BIEBER, O. LINDBERG, J. J. DUFFY AND P. D. BOYER, *Nature*, 202 (1964) 1316.
372 P. D. BOYER, *Nature*, 207 (1965) 409.
373 E. C. SLATER, *Nature*, 207 (1965) 411.

Chapter VIII

Photosynthetic Phosphorylation *

ALBERT W. FRENKEL AND KONSTANTINE COST**

Department of Botany, University of Minnesota, Minneapolis, Minn. (U.S.A.)

1. Introduction

One of the important processes of the photochemical activity of chlorophyll containing organelles of photosynthetic organisms is the production of high-energy phosphate; usually observed in the form of ATP. This photosynthetic phosphorylation process is generally considered to be an important component reaction of the over-all process of photosynthesis.

In general terms, the process of photosynthesis[1-4] is thought to involve a primary photochemical act resulting from the absorption of light quanta by the photosynthetic pigment system; this gives rise to the formation of relatively short-lived oxidizing and reducing equivalents which, depending upon the nature of the system, produce a number of different end products.

In "normal" photosynthesis, carried out by green plants, the process results in the production of molecular oxygen and the reduction of CO_2 to the level of carbohydrate.

$$CO_2 + H_2O \xrightarrow{\text{light}} (CHOH) + O_2 \qquad (1a)$$

In addition, isolated chloroplasts, chloroplast fragments, or intact algal cells can reduce suitable oxidants, other than CO_2, with the concomitant production of molecular oxygen.

$$4\,Fe^{3+} + 2\,H_2O \xrightarrow{\text{light}} 4\,Fe^{2+} + 4\,H^+ + O_2 \qquad (1b)$$

* Study supported by grants from the National Institute of Allergy and Infectious Diseases (E-2218) and the National Science Foundation (G9888).

** Holder of fellowship from the Charles F. Kettering Foundation for Photosynthetic Research.

References p. 420

$$2\ PN^+ + 2\ H_2O \xrightarrow{\text{light}} 2\ PNH + 2\ H^+ + O_2 \qquad (1c)$$

$$2\ B + 2\ H_2O \xrightarrow{\text{light}} 2\ BH_2 + O_2 \qquad (1d)$$

Fe^{3+} in reaction (1b) is ferricyanide (Hill-chloroplast reaction) or oxidized cytochrome *c*; reaction (1c) involves the production of reduced pyridine nucleotides and will be discussed in more detail below; (1d) is a generalized Hill reaction involving the reduction of a Hill oxidant and the production of molecular oxygen.

In contrast, bacterial systems do not produce molecular oxygen and the presence of a reductant is required to react directly or indirectly with the photochemically produced oxidant. The over-all reaction of bacterial photosynthesis[5,6] is:

$$CO_2 + 2\ H_2A \xrightarrow{\text{light}} (CHOH) + 2\ A + H_2O \qquad (2a)$$

(where H_2A may be either an organic or an inorganic reductant). When CO_2 is not the oxidant:

$$NAD^+ + H_2A \xrightarrow{\text{light}} NADH + H^+ + A \qquad (2b)$$

In more general terms, the reaction may be expressed:

$$B + H_2A \xrightarrow{\text{light}} BH_2 + A \qquad (2c)$$

Reactions (2b) and (2c) may represent energetically uphill reactions and can be considered as the bacterial variants of the Hill-chloroplast reaction.

In reactions (1) and (2), a net accumulation of oxidized and reduced products can be readily observed. Other situations, however, may arise where such accumulation does not occur even though the system can be shown to be otherwise active. Franck[7], some time ago, postulated that under certain conditions the photochemical oxidant and reductant can back-react with one another, releasing energy, and thus returning the system to its pre-illumination state. A modified back-reaction resulting in some storage of light energy in the form of thermochemical energy was recognized later[8,9] as the production of ATP by illuminated chloroplasts or bacterial chromatophores, without the concomitant accumulation of oxidized or reduced products (reaction 3a):

$$ADP^{3-} + HPO_4^{2-} + H_2O \xrightarrow{\text{light}} ATP^{4-} + OH^- \qquad (3a)$$

This reaction has been referred to as cyclic photophosphorylation[10] or phosphorylation linked to light-induced cyclic electron transport[11]. This terminology is based upon the assumption that an electron-transport system exists in chloroplasts and bacterial chromatophores which can accept electrons or hydrogens from the photochemical reductant, transferring them to the photochemical oxidant, and in the process, giving rise to high-energy phosphate. Evidence for the existence and operation of such an electron-transport system will be discussed below. An additional phosphorylation reaction in chloroplasts was described by Arnon *et al.*[12], which was shown to accompany the reduction of ferricyanide or of NADP with the simultaneous production of molecular oxygen according to the following over-all reaction:

$$ADP^{3-} + HPO_4^{2-} + NADP^+ + H_2O \xrightarrow{\text{light}} ATP^{4-} + NADPH + \tfrac{1}{2}\,O_2 \qquad (4)$$

This reaction has been referred to by Arnon and coworkers as non-cyclic photophosphorylation or also can be considered as phosphorylation linked to light- induced non-cyclic electron transport[12] (Fig. 1).

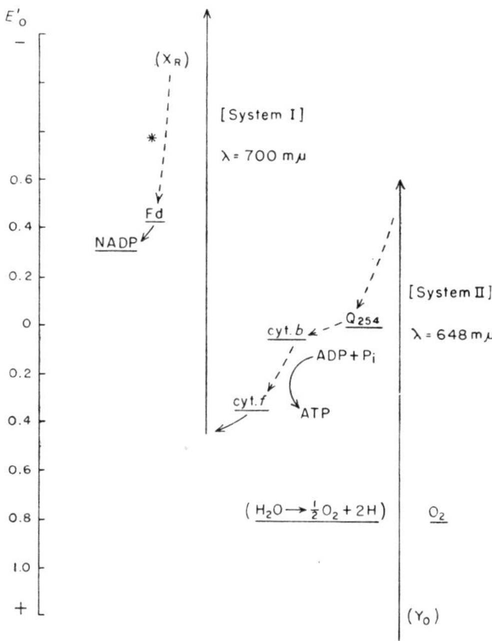

Fig. 1. Energy diagram of green-plant photosynthesis[149,154]. Upon illumination of system II, O_2 and reduced plastoquinone (Q_{254}) are formed, while absorption of quanta by system I leads to the oxidation of cytochrome *f* and the production of reduced ferredoxin (Fd); the latter is capable of reducing NADP in the presence of a specific flavoprotein[149]. Cytochrome *f* is reduced in a dark reaction by electrons moving from reduced Q_{254} *via* an electron-transport system. It is believed that phosphorylation is coupled to this portion of the electron-transport system (* indicates another proposed site for phosphorylation). Q_{254}, 2,3-Dimethyl-6-solanesylbenzoquinone (plastoquinone). (X_R), Intermediate reductant. (Y_O), Intermediate oxidant.

References p. 420

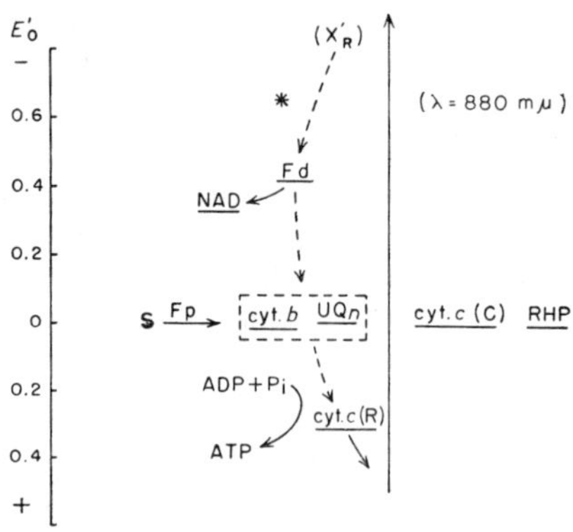

Fig. 2. Energy diagram of bacterial photosynthesis. Excitation of bacteriochlorophyll by far-red light leads to the oxidation of cytochrome *c*, and the reduction of an unknown intermediate (X_R'). (At present there is no conclusive evidence regarding the requirement of quanta at two different wavelengths[155,156].) In *cyclic electron transport* electrons move through an endogenous electron-transport system, presumably via ferredoxin (Fd), ubiquinone and cytochrome *b* to oxidized cytochrome *c*. In *non-cyclic electron transport* a suitable oxidant such as NAD^+ may act as electron acceptor from Fd; a reductant like succinate (S) may supply electrons for the re-reduction of cytochrome *c via* ubiquinone and cytochrome *b*. X_R', Intermediate reductant. UQ_n, 2,3-Dimethoxy-5-methyl benzoquinone with *n* unsaturated isoprenoid units at position 6 (ubiquinone$_n$) (Fig. 7). ($n = 9$, ref. 93; $n = 10$, Rudney, ref. 150, p. 217). Cyt. *c* (C), *Chromatium* cytochrome. Cyt. *c* (R), *Rhodospirillum* cytochrome. RHP, *Rhodospirillum* haemoprotein.

Illuminated bacterial chromatophores can catalyze reaction (3a) and in addition can carry out a modification[13] of reaction (4):

$$ADP^{3-} + HPO_4^{2-} + NAD^+ + AH_2 \xrightarrow{\text{light}} ATP^{4-} + NADH + A + H_2O \quad (5)$$

where AH_2 can be ascorbate or some other suitable reductant.

Reaction (5) differs from reaction (4) in that molecular oxygen is not produced but instead, a reductant is required to satisfy the photochemically produced oxidant.

If one wishes to make a comparison of the over-all reactions of PS-P* with those of respiratory phosphorylation, one may take as an example, the substrate phosphorylation linked to the oxidation of phosphoglyceraldehyde in glycolysis:

$$ADP^{3-} + HPO_4^{2-} + \text{3-phosphoglyceraldehyde}^{2-} + NAD^+ \rightleftharpoons ATP^{4-} + 3\ PGA^{3-} + NADH + H^+ \quad (6)$$

and oxidative phosphorylation:

$$3\ ADP^{3-} + 3\ HPO_4^{2-} + AH_2 + \tfrac{1}{2}\ O_2 \longrightarrow 3\ ATP^{4-} + 3\ OH^- + A + H_2O \quad (7)$$

* PS-P will be commonly used hereafter for "photosynthetic phosphorylation", "photophosphorylation", or "light-induced phosphorylation".

(AH_2 represents a substrate such as NADH whose oxidation by mitochondria results in P/O values of $\leqq 3.0$).

In comparing the photosynthetic and respiratory phosphorylation reactions, it is apparent that reactions (5) and (6) are formally quite similar. They differ, however, in one important respect. In reaction (6), the energy for the reduction of pyridine nucleotide and the formation of ATP from ADP and P_i is derived from the oxidation of phosphoglyceraldehyde to phosphoglyceric acid. In reaction (5), the oxidation of ascorbate to dehydroascorbate, or of succinate to fumarate, yields little if any free energy at pH 7.0; the energy thus required for the pyridine nucleotide reduction and ATP formation must be derived from light energy.

2. Conversion of light energy into thermochemical energy

(a) *General considerations*

There appears to be general agreement that in the conversion of photochemical energy into thermochemical energy by photosynthetic systems, an initial separation of charges occurs with the production of oxidants (Y_O) and reductants (X_R) (Figs. 1, 2), which then participate in the further reactions of the photosynthetic systems. The mechanism of this quantum-conversion process is under active experimental and theoretical investigation and the reader is referred to a number of interesting papers and reviews on the subject[1,3,14–19].

The manner in which reducing equivalents are transported to intermediates in the process of carbon dioxide reduction, is still an open question. Some investigators believe that hydrogen transfer occurs from chlorophyll to intermediate reductants (Ref. 3, p. 693), while others prefer to think in terms of electron-transfer reactions[14–19]. Furthermore, there is much discussion and experimentation concerning the possible occurrence of either a direct transfer of electrons from donor to acceptor[17], or an electron migration *via* conduction bands, analogous to their behavior in semi-conductors[18].

There has been much speculation concerning the fate of the photochemical oxidant, but relatively little experimental evidence is available. From the experiments of Duysens[20], it has become clear that certain cytochromes are oxidized in the light. The process of cytochrome oxidation in bacterial chromatophores[22] has been shown to occur at −196°C, and thus, one is forced to the conclusion that this cytochrome must be closely associated with the primary oxidant of photosynthesis. The data for bacterial systems indicate a high efficiency of light-dependent cytochrome oxidation[23], which appears to show that all, or most of, the light-induced oxidizing power passes through specific cytochromes.

References p. 420

A light-dependent oxidation of cytochrome *f* has been observed in green plants[24–28]. The quantum efficiency of this process has not yet been established, and therefore, it is difficult to estimate the importance of this reaction for oxygen production. Several suggestions have been made to account for a possible role of cytochromes in oxygen production[27–34]. A very interesting suggestion made by Kamen[30,31] is the oxidation of a cytochrome to a +4 oxidation state by the primary oxidant. This highly oxidized cytochrome would then have the capacity to generate molecular oxygen from water. The various hypotheses proposed thus far have not been tested extensively, and the nature of the oxygen-producing process in photosynthesis still represents one of the challenging riddles of biochemistry.

The role of cytochromes in photosynthetic phosphorylation is based primarily on investigations carried out with bacterial chromatophores[21,22,35]. The suggested relationships from these investigations have been incorporated into various schemes including the ones presented here (Figs. 1, 2). Smith and Baltscheffsky[21] demonstrated with chromatophore preparations from *Rhodospirillum rubrum* an enhancement of the light-dependent oxidation of cytochrome *c* upon the addition of ADP to an otherwise complete phosphorylating system. This observation has been interpreted as evidence for the existence of a phosphorylation site between cytochrome *c* and the photochemical oxidant and such a hypothetical phosphorylation site has been incorporated into schemes of photosynthesis[68,69]. Studies by Kamen[31], Witt[19] and others in due time should yield further clues to the role of cytochromes in photosynthetic reactions.

(*b*) *Action spectra of photosynthetic phosphorylation*

That the pigments which are involved in photosynthesis also play a role in PS-P, can be shown by measuring the action spectra of PS-P. Black *et al.*[36] demonstrated that the action spectrum of PS-P in general follows the absorption of chlorophyll and provides some evidence for the participation of carotenoids in the process. In similar measurements with the photosynthetic bacteria, Fuller *et al.*[37] showed that the light absorbed by the bacteriochlorophyll was active in PS-P, and that, under certain conditions, the light absorbed by the carotenoids could be utilized for PS-P, though not as effectively as in *in vivo* CO_2 fixation. Chromatophores which were isolated in Tris buffer (pH 7.8) had little activity when they were illuminated with light absorbed primarily by the carotenoids, while addition of 0.5 *M* sucrose in the Tris buffer-isolating medium caused over a two-fold increase in PS-P over the Tris buffer alone. That the PS-P activity of Tris-isolated chromatophores could be increased by the subsequent addition of sucrose was interpreted to be due to a swelling of the chromatophores in the dilute medium leading to an "uncoupling" (quotation theirs) of energy transfer from carotenoids to bacteriochlorophyll.

(c) *Relationship of action spectra of photosynthetic phosphorylation to other photochemical processes carried out by photosynthetic organelles*

Black *et al.*[36] measured absolute action spectra and found that the action spectra for PS-P and for NADP reduction were rather similar. They observed peaks for NADP reduction at 450, 500 and 675 mμ, and peaks for concomitant phosphorylation at 430 and 680 mμ with a shoulder at 500 mμ. In the presence of phenazine methylsulfate, the peaks remained in the same place but the shoulder at 500 mμ developed into a definite peak. Arnon *et al.*[38] have presented relative action spectra, in the red region, for the formation of ATP, oxygen production, and NADP reduction. Oxygen production in a Hill-reaction mixture with ferricyanide had a maximum at 644 mμ, while NADP reduction (in the presence of 3-(4-chlorophenyl)-1,1-dimethylurea, to block oxygen production, ascorbate, and 2,3',6-trichlorophenol indophenol) had a minimum at 661 mμ and no maxima between 630 and 699 mμ; ATP formation by cyclic PS-P in the presence of vitamin K_3 (menadione; Fig. 5) had a peak at 677 mμ. Kok and Hoch[39] have presented an action spectrum of PS-P in the presence of phenazine methylsulfate and

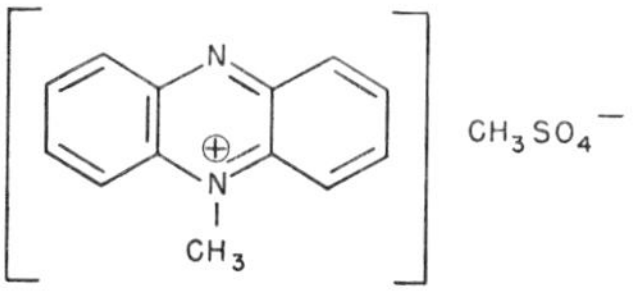

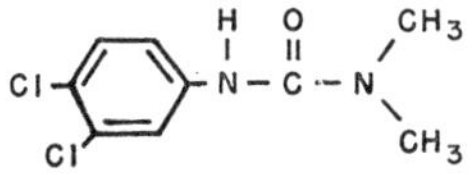

$CH_3SO_4^-$

Fig. 3. 5-Methylphenazinium methylssulfate (phenazine methylsulfate: PMS).

Fig. 4. 3-(3,4-Dichlorophenyl)-1,1-dimethylurea: DCMU. [3-(4-Chlorophenyl)-1,1-dimethylurea: CMU.]

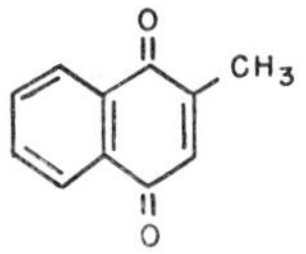

Fig. 5. 2-Methyl-1,4-naphthoquinone (menadione; vitamin K_3).

References p. 420

TABLE I

QUANTUM REQUIREMENTS REPORTED FOR PHOTOSYNTHETIC PHOSPHORYLATION AND FOR CERTAIN LIGHT-INDUCED OXIDATION–REDUCTION REACTIONS

(Quanta required per molecule formed as indicated)

Reference:	23	44	43	36	45	46
A. Cyclic PS-P		6/ATP	4–6/ATP			
Cyclic PS-P in presence of phenazine methylsulfate		8–10/ATP				
B. Non-cyclic PS-P			4–6/ATP	15/ATP		
NADP reduction and O_2 production			8–12/O_2	18/O_2		
C. NADP reduction and O_2 production without PS-P			8–12/O_2		16/NADPH	
D. Ferricyanide reduction and O_2 production						$7.9 \pm 0.3/O_2$
E. Cytochrome *c* oxidation	1/cyt. *c* (0.6–1.5) (2 est.)[42]					

23 cytochrome *c* oxidized in *Chromatium* cells at 6 wavelengths from 860–890 mμ.
42 same, estimated.
44 ATP formed by *Rhodospirillum rubrum* chromatophores at 862 mμ.
43 ATP and O_2 produced by spinach chloroplasts. Band from 620–660 mμ.
36 ATP and O_2 produced by spinach chloroplasts at 675 mμ.
45 NADPH produced by spinach chloroplasts at 672 mμ.
46 O_2 produced (ferricyanide reduction) by *Beta vulgaris* chloroplast fragments at 675 mμ.

3-(3,4-dichlorophenyl-1,1-dimethylurea (Fig. 4) which had a maximum at about 710 mμ and a minimum at about 664 mμ. This shift towards the longer wavelengths is attributed to the action of phenazine methylsulfate on the pigment system.

A study of the action spectra of the individual components of photosynthetic reactions is interesting for several reasons. Should the spectra for these reactions turn out to be the same, then the assumption could be made that the primary photochemical process underlying all these reactions is most likely identical. However, if they are even slightly different, then it is quite possible that there may be subtle differences in the operation of these photosynthetic reactions. The study of these differences might aid in separating the processes involved in the over-all photosynthetic process. This type of study is particularly important since the discovery of the so-called second Emerson effect[40] and the observation of chromatic transients in photosynthesis by Blinks[41].

At the present time there does not appear to exist any convincing evidence that the action spectrum for photosynthetic phosphorylation differs significantly from that of other photochemical processes which are catalyzed by illuminated photosynthetic particulates. Where striking differences have been claimed to be demonstrable, it appears that experimental conditions used for measuring different processes were not always comparable. This does not preclude the possibility that critical experiments eventually will demonstrate that reproducible and significant differences do exist.

(d) *Quantum efficiency of PS-P and of light-induced oxidation–reduction reactions in partial systems*

Some recent estimates and measurements of the quantum requirement for PS-P, NADP reduction, oxygen evolution, with and without concomitant phosphorylation, and for bacterial cytochrome *c* oxidation are listed in Table I. The most efficient process listed is that for cytochrome oxidation (column 2) which has a mean quantum-requirement value[23] approaching 1.0. Thus far, the lowest requirements reported for PS-P are 4–6 quanta[43]. It is interesting that the data for cyclic and non-cyclic PS-P, as reported by Yin *et al.*[43], are the same. These investigators conclude that in non-cyclic PS-P, the reduction of NADP and the formation of ATP must be coupled, as originally proposed by Arnon[10], otherwise there should be observed an increase in the quantum requirement in going from cyclic to non-cyclic PS-P.

Calculations from the data presented by Yin *et al.*[43] show that the mean energy efficiency of PS-P at 640 mμ represents a conversion of light energy into chemical energy of about 3.5%. The comparable energy conversion for

References p. 420

NADP reduction and oxygen production is about 23.5%, and the overall efficiency of simultaneous NADP reduction, oxygen production, and ATP production is about 27.0%. In comparison, the energy efficiency of photosynthesis is 27% for a quantum requirement of ten, or 34% for a quantum requirement of eight (quanta per molecule of CO_2 fixed or per molecule of oxygen produced for a photosynthetic quotient of 1.0).

The energy efficiency of *Chromatium* cytochrome oxidation is about 1%, and on the assumption that a reductant is formed simultaneously with a potential close to the hydrogen electrode, an energy conversion of about 30% has been calculated by Olson[23] for such a process.

(*e*) *Rates of photosynthetic phosphorylation*

The rates of PS-P compare very favorably with those of respiratory phosphorylation when based on the protein-nitrogen content of the respective particulates. It was pointed out by Allen *et al.*[47], that rates of 600–800 μmoles P_i esterified per mg of protein-N per hour or 400–500 μmoles P_i esterified per mg chlorophyll per hour were achieved in chloroplasts as compared to about 100 μmoles P_i esterified per mg protein-N per hour for fragments of heart mitochondria, or 200 μmoles P_i esterified per mg protein-N per hour for sweet potato mitochondria. Rates as high as 2500 μmoles P_i esterified per mg chlorophyll per hour have been reported by Avron[48] in swiss chard chloroplasts, and comparable rates have been reported for bacterial chromatophores[49].

3. Basic requirements for photosynthetic phosphorylation

(*a*) *Requirements for photosynthetic phosphorylation linked to cyclic electron transport*

It is relatively simple to demonstrate PS-P with chloroplasts or chromatophores, or with fragments derived from these organelles; few cofactors are required to elicit this process upon illumination. The chromatophores of *Rhodospirillum rubrum* require only the presence of divalent cations such as magnesium or manganese, inorganic phosphate, ADP, and traces of a mild reducing agent such as succinate, and preferably anaerobic conditions[9,50–54]. With chloroplasts, the condition is somewhat more complex. In addition to magnesium ions, P_i, and ADP, catalytic amounts of ascorbate, FMN, vitamin K_3, or certain other quinone derivatives, are required to give good rates of PS-P[8,55–57]. Oxygen is capable of replacing the requirement of FMN or vitamin K (Refs. 58–60). In both the chloroplast and the chromatophore systems, phenazine methylsulfate can bring about an increase in

PS-P rates at high light intensities[61,62]. The different reaction mixtures which have been employed in the chloroplast system have been summarized by Kandler[63].

Experiments demonstrating the importance of disulfide linkages for bacterial photophosphorylation have been reported by Newton[64].

(*b*) *Requirements for phosphorylation linked to light-induced non-cyclic electron transport*

The basic requirements for this reaction are chloroplasts which are capable of carrying out the Hill-chloroplast reaction (reactions 1b and 1c). Hill-reaction activity is, in general, more stable than phosphorylation activity; thus, chloroplasts capable of carrying out PS-P, in general also can carry out the Hill reaction in the presence of suitable oxidants and chloride ion[34]. The only additional requirements for non-cyclic PS-P are magnesium ions, inorganic phosphate and ADP. The stoichiometric relations expressed in Eqn. (4) have been achieved with such reaction mixtures[10]. Arnon and coworkers, in general, have postulated that the Hill reaction and the accompanying phosphorylation reaction are coupled. On the basis of the excellent one to one stoichiometry of the ratio of moles of NADP reduced and moles of ATP produced, this has appeared to be quite convincing. Such perfect stoichiometry, however, has not always been obtained[65], thus the assumed coupling of the two reactions could be questioned. Evidence from quantum-yield determinations discussed earlier, has forced other investigators[43] to agree with the original hypothesis[10] that the two reactions are coupled. Nevertheless, the problem does not yet appear to be satisfactorily settled. More information is needed about the mechanism of light-induced electron transport and phosphorylation to give us a better insight into the interrelationships of these processes.

(*c*) *Cyclic versus non-cyclic photosynthetic phosphorylation*

Detailed studies of the process of cyclic PS-P by chloroplasts[59,66] have raised the problem as to whether the Hill reaction was operative under conditions where cyclic PS-P could be observed. This problem was investigated by Krall *et al.*[67] by using isotopically enriched oxygen in the gas phase. It was observed, that under conditions where chloroplasts did produce ATP without accumulating oxygen or without a net reduction of the Hill oxidant, these chloroplasts did carry out a vigorous exchange of oxygen; that is, they produced $^{16}O–^{16}O$ (mass 32) from un-enriched water while consuming $^{16}O–^{18}O$ (mass 34) from the ^{18}O-enriched gas phase. With the addition of either FMN or menadione as catalysts in a reaction mixture which

References p. 420

contained chloride, the oxygen exchange observed was equal to, or greater than the amount of ATP synthesized on the basis of atoms of oxygen exchanged per molecule of ATP formed. Under these experimental conditions, it became apparent that the oxygen-producing system of the chloroplast was in full operation, and that oxygen consumption must have been due to the photoreduction of substances which were readily re-oxidized by molecular oxygen, *e.g.*, reduced flavin or menadione. The observed oxygen exchange was greatly inhibited in the presence of phenazine methylsulfate or pyocyanine, and a more truly cyclic PS-P was elicited. The effect of chloride on the oxygen exchange was not elucidated during the course of this investigation; one might predict from the observations of Arnon[34] that such an exchange would be dependent upon the presence of chloride. It is evident, therefore, that in many investigations of cyclic PS-P the investigators were really dealing with a non-cyclic or pseudo-cyclic system.

The situation is somewhat different with bacterial chromatophores, as molecular oxygen is not produced during bacterial photosynthesis. It has been claimed that cyclic PS-P was the only type of photophosphorylation carried out by these particles[68]. It was possible to demonstrate, however, that chromatophores can produce high-energy phosphate along with the simultaneous reduction of pyridine nucleotides[11,69,70], even though evidence did not always point to a coupled process. More recently, Nozaki *et al.*[13] have presented evidence of bacterial PS-P coupled to a reduction of NAD and oxidation of ascorbate under conditions where cyclic electron transport was blocked by antimycin A.

Biochemically, it appears that the most important difference between the products of bacterial photosynthesis and of green-plant photosynthesis is the ability of the latter to produce molecular oxygen. This, more than anything else, is the most striking difference in the overall phosphorylation reactions as indicated in Eqns. 3–5, pp. 398–400, 410.

At the present time there is insufficient evidence about the true nature of the actual photophosphorylation reactions; consequently, we have no basis for assuming that they are different under conditions of cyclic or non-cyclic electron transport. It is apparent that all the differences which have been uncovered thus far are related to the nature of the electron-transport system.

(*d*) *Specificity of the phosphate acceptor*

Unwashed preparations of chloroplasts or of bacterial chromatophores can utilize both AMP and ADP as acceptors of the high-energy phosphate generated upon illumination[48,50,71]. When such chloroplasts or chromatophores are washed with buffer solutions, their activity toward AMP is lost and only ADP will act as an acceptor[12,48,50,71]. It has been demonstrated that adenylate kinase (myokinase) is present in the crude preparations, and that this enzyme can be removed from the particles by repeated washing[48,50]. Adenylate kinase, from higher plants, has been investigated in more detail by Mazelis[72].

Among the nucleotides which have been tested, in addition to AMP and ADP, are IDP, GDP, and CDP, which are active as phosphate acceptors with unwashed spinach chloroplasts. The corresponding nucleoside monophosphates, IMP, GMP and UMP, are inactive under these conditions. When chloroplasts are washed, their activity toward UDP and CDP is lost[71]. Krall and Purvis[71] have concluded from these observations that washed chloroplasts show specificity toward the purine nucleoside diphosphates, yet with the available evidence, one cannot decide whether there is an *in vivo* specific acceptor among the nucleotides. Similar observations have been made by Avron[48] with swiss chard chloroplasts.

Washed chromatophores from *Rhodospirillum rubrum* can utilize both ADP and IDP as high-energy phosphate acceptors[50], and Newton and Kamen[52] have observed a light-dependent incorporation of ^{32}P into added GDP in chromatophores from *Chromatium*.

Crude preparations of spinach and swiss chard chloroplasts contain nucleotide diphosphokinase[48,71]. Krall and Purvis demonstrated that this enzyme would transfer terminally labelled ^{32}P-phosphate from ATP to CDP and UDP at a more rapid rate than to GDP and IDP.

It may be of interest to note that the primary phosphorylation reaction appears to be specific for the purine nucleoside diphosphates, while the nucleoside diphosphokinase favors the transfer of the terminal phosphate from ATP to the pyrimidine nucleoside diphosphates; thus, we may observe here part of a mechanism which can control the rate of production of purine and pyrimidine nucleoside triphosphates.

(*e*) *The origin of the bridge oxygen of the terminal phosphate group of ATP*

Jagendorf and Avron[73] established that the orthophosphate taken up in PS-P of chloroplasts appeared almost exclusively in the γ-position of ATP; this observation was confirmed by Schulz and Boyer[74]. These observations simplify the analysis of experiments in which ^{18}O-labelled inorganic phosphate has been used to trace the fate of oxygen during PS-P. Schulz and Boyer thus demonstrated that in reaction (3b) only the terminal phosphoryl group of ATP contained ^{18}O label. When this terminal phosphoryl group was removed by means of hexokinase, which cleaves the O—P bond of the phosphoryl residue and transfers it to glucose, the residual ADP did not contain any detectable amount of ^{18}O, demonstrating that the bridge oxygen between the β- and the γ-phosphate of ATP must be derived from ADP and

References p. 420

$$\mathrm{Ad{-}O{-}\underset{\underset{\alpha}{O^-}}{\overset{O}{\overset{\|}{P}}}{-}O{-}\underset{\underset{\beta}{O^-}}{\overset{O}{\overset{\|}{P}}}{-}O^-} + \mathrm{HO^*{-}\underset{O^{*-}}{\overset{O^*}{\overset{\|}{P}}}{-}O^{*-}} \xrightarrow{\text{light}} \mathrm{Ad{-}O{-}\underset{\underset{\alpha}{O^-}}{\overset{O}{\overset{\|}{P}}}{-}O{-}\underset{\underset{\beta}{O^-}}{\overset{O}{\overset{\|}{P}}}{-}O{-}\underset{\underset{\gamma}{O^{*-}}}{\overset{O^*}{\overset{\|}{P}}}{-}O^{*-}} + \mathrm{OH^{*-}} \quad (3b)$$

not from orthophosphate. Schulz and Boyer therefore suggested that the results are consistent with the participation of a phosphoryl intermediate, but they did not rule out a mechanism in which the first covalent compound formed from P_i and ADP is ATP, with the loss of an oxygen from P_i in the process. Schulz and Boyer observed little if any exchange of ^{18}O in labelled orthophosphate under conditions of PS-P; these observations are in contrast to the extensive exchange observable during oxidative phosphorylation by mitochondria[75]. On the other hand, Avron and Sharon[76] observed a small exchange between the ^{18}O of labelled water and non-enriched orthophosphate in chloroplasts. This exchange, however, was not light-dependent and according to these investigators may not be related to the process of PS-P proper. They also observed a light-dependent incorporation of oxygen into ATP from labelled water, which was equivalent to one atom of oxygen per molecule of ATP formed. These authors indicate that they did not observe any ATPase activity in their preparations. Since then, however, Avron[77] has reported in some detail on a light-induced ATPase activity of swiss chard chloroplasts. Whether this observed exchange is due to such ATPase activity or has a deeper significance for the mechanism of PS-P remains to be decided. The good stoichiometry reported for these experiments might speak in favor of some importance in the mechanism of the synthetic reaction. These observations in no way invalidate the conclusions reached about the source of the bridge oxygen, and the observations of Avron and Sharon, while not as direct, are in general agreement with the observations of Schulz and Boyer on this point.

(*f*) *ADP–ATP exchange reaction*

Kahn and Jagendorf[78] and Jagendorf and Kahn[79] have described a partially purified enzyme system from spinach chloroplasts which catalyzes the exchange of the terminal phosphate of ATP with ADP. An enzyme system from mitochondria, which also carries out such an exchange, has been described by Lehninger[80]. The reaction is measured by incubating unlabelled ATP with ^{14}C-labelled ADP and then following the appearance of ^{14}C in the ATP formed. The enzyme has a pH optimum between 7–8. There is a requirement for Mg ions which can be replaced by Mn, Fe or Co ions. The enzyme does not catalyze an ATP–^{32}P exchange and does not show adenylatekinase activity. The enzyme may play a role in the light-induced phosphorylation reaction.

(g) *ATPase*

ATPase activity has been demonstrated in both chromatophores and chloroplasts. There are reports of at least two ATPases in chloroplasts which are active in the dark[81,82], whose role in PS-P has not yet been clarified. Petrak first demonstrated a light-dependent ATPase activity[83,84], and since then Petrak and Lipmann[84], and Avron[77] have studied this activity in greater detail. Since light-induced ATPase activity can be elicited at appreciable rates only in the presence of inhibitors of PS-P, or in the presence of phenazine methylsulfate, its physiological importance, at this time, appears to be uncertain; nevertheless, further studies of ATPase reactions may give us more information about the PS-P process.

4. Components of the electron-transport apparatus of photophosphorylating systems

(a) *Photosynthetic pigments*

(i) Chlorophyll

Chlorophyll in its native state appears to exist as a lipoprotein complex; it is normally associated with carotenoids and in certain plant groups with other accessory pigments. In addition a great variety of lipids, such as plastoquinones, may be present. These pigment–lipoprotein complexes may act as an oxidation–reduction system in the process of transforming light energy into thermochemical energy (*cf.* p. 401). Oxidized and reduced forms of chlorophyll have been recognized *in vivo* and *in vitro*; their role in photosynthetic reactions is under active investigation and may become clarified within a few years (*cf.* Refs. 1–3).

(ii) Accessory pigments

Carotenoids and other accessory pigments, like the phycobilins, may be of importance in the transfer of light energy absorbed by these pigments to chlorophyll *via* inductive resonance[1,85]. Carotenoids, furthermore, have been shown to be of importance in inhibiting photo-oxidations under aerobic conditions[86,87]. Carotenoid-free chromatophores, prepared from diphenylamine treated *Chromatium* cells, showed good PS-P activity under anaerobic conditions, indicating that carotenoids in this system are not directly involved in the phosphorylation process. Observations of Petrack[83] and Petrack and Lipmann[84] indicate that in the blue-green alga, *Anabaena variabilis*, the accessory pigment phycocyanin is not required for PS-P and that this pigment also may protect the photochemical system against photo-oxidation.

References p. 420

(b) *Low molecular weight organic co-factors*

(i) *Quinones and naphthoquinones*

A good deal of work is being carried out on the possible role of quinones and naphthoquinones in photosynthesis, in the Hill reaction, and in PS-P. Arnon *et al.*[89], early reported that cyclic PS-P was catalyzed by either vitamin K derivatives and FMN; however, since certain vitamin K derivatives and FMN were about equally effective and could be replaced by oxygen[59], the action of these derivatives did not appear to be highly specific. A number of quinones and naphthoquinones are now recognized as being associated with photosynthetic systems[90–97].

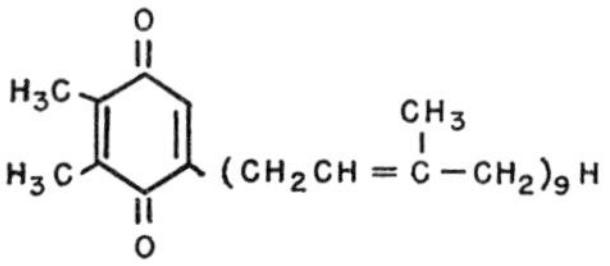

Fig. 6. 2,3-Dimethyl-6-solanesylbenzoquinone (plastoquinone, PQ_9, also Q_{254}, Q_{255}).

Plastoquinone was shown to be present in chloroplasts by Crane[90], and was demonstrated by Bishop[91] to have the capacity to reactivate the Hill reaction. It has been also shown by Krogman[92] to reactivate the PS-P activity of lyophilized and extracted chloroplasts. When *Rhodospirillum* is grown in the presence of diphenylamine, the concentration of the native quinone, $ubiquinone_9$, was severely depressed and the chromatophores

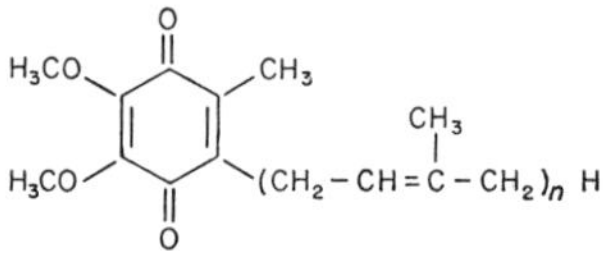

Fig. 7. 2,3-Dimethoxy-5-methylbenzoquinone with side-chain in 6-position containing *n* unsaturated isoprenoid units ($ubiquinone_n$).

isolated from such cells showed a marked depression of PS-P activity; this activity could be markedly restored by addition of either UQ_2 or UQ_3; vitamin K_1 or K_3 were much less effective[93]. Phenazine methylsulfate had the same stimulating effect as UQ_2 or UQ_3 and the authors proposed that phenazine methylsulfate bypassed the electron step(s) *via* the endogenous quinones. This hypothesis is based on the action of antimycin *A*, which inhibits the quinone effect but does not affect the stimulating action of phenazine methylsulfate.

Crane *et al.*[94], and Redfearn and Friend[95], have reported that illuminated chloroplasts will reduce endogenous plastoquinone which is subsequently re-oxidized in the dark. Witt *et al.*[19] have also reported on spectral changes which they believe are due to endogenous plastoquinone.

It appears that quinones are part of the electron-transport system of photosynthetic organelles and thus play at least an indirect role in PS-P. Evidence that they are associated directly with a phosphorylation site, thus far, is lacking.

(ii) Flavins

Baltscheffsky[98] has shown that FAD, rather than FMN, will stimulate PS-P in extracts of *Rhodospirillum rubrum*. Furthermore, PS-P is inhibited by atebrin, whose effect can be overcome with FAD and only partially with FMN; the inhibition produced by atebrin cannot be overcome by phenazine methylsulfate. Baltscheffsky suggests that FAD participates in electron transport associated with PS-P in *Rhodospirillum* extracts.

Other aspects of the possible role of flavins in PS-P will be discussed under "enzyme components of electron-transport systems".

(iii) Flavones

Krogman and Stiller[99] have shown that non-aqueous extracts of chloroplasts will not show Hill reaction or PS-P, but that they contain a co-factor which will support PS-P in conventionally isolated chloroplasts, without added FMN. Flavones, such as chlorogenic acid and catechin, were found to be active in such systems.

(c) *Proteins*

Chloroplasts and bacterial chromatophores contain enzymes and enzyme systems which are not only concerned with the elaboration of the primary photosynthetic reactants, but also with the synthesis of the components, such as the pigments and proteins of these organelles. It should be kept in mind that some of the enzymes and enzyme systems cited here represent only a portion of reaction systems of these complex organelles. Until more is known about these organelles, they should be considered as complex multi-enzyme systems.

(i) Photosynthetic pyridine nucleotide reductase (ferredoxin[148])

A very interesting system which catalyzes the reduction of NADP in the presence of illuminated chloroplasts has been described by San Pietro and Lang[100]. This protein, which has been purified a great deal, has been called photosynthetic pyridine nucleotide reductase (PPNR) and appears to be identical with the methemoglobin reducing factor which has been described by Davenport *et al.*[101]. The properties of this enzyme have been described in

References p. 420

some detail[102,103], and the methemoglobin reducing factor has been crystallized[104]. Keister *et al.*[105] have reported that the reduction of NADP is greatly stimulated in the presence of a complete phosphorylating system, and in the presence of high concentrations of PPNR. This is somewhat at variance with the earlier observations[61] in which NADP reduction was measured with chloroplasts which had not been supplied with excess PPNR. Uncouplers of PS-P, such as arsenate or NH_4^+, also produce a stimulating effect on NADP reduction. These observations would support the assumption that the phosphorylation and electron-transport processes leading to the formation of ATP and the reduction of NADP (and production of oxygen) are coupled. Nevertheless, from present evidence, one cannot decide whether the phosphorylation site is on the oxidizing or reducing side of the electron-transport system. As a consequence, we have no evidence thus far that PPNR is directly involved in the phosphorylation reaction.

(ii) Pyridine nucleotide transhydrogenase

The photochemical reduction of NAD in the presence of grana has been shown by Keister *et al.*[106] to require the presence of NADP, PPNR and a transhydrogenase which they obtained from spinach. This probably accounts for the reports in the literature that both NAD and NADP were capable of stimulating PS-P at high chloroplast concentrations[12], and that chloroplasts were capable of reducing both NAD and NADP in the light[100].

Chromatophores of *Rhodospirillum rubrum* will react with NAD as oxidant, in the light, in the presence of suitable reductants such as succinate[69,107]. Tagawa *et al.*[108] have reported transhydrogenase activity in *Rhodospirillum rubrum* chromatophores, which catalyzes the reduction of NADP in the light, in the presence of trace amounts of NAD.

Such transhydrogenases may well be important in controlling the flow of reducing power into either synthetic or energy-release channels[109–111].

(iii) NADPH-, NADH-cytochrome c reductases and reduced pyridine nucleotide oxidase activities

Marré and Servettez[112] have purified an enzyme from an acetone powder of spinach or pea chloroplasts which catalyzes the reduction of mammalian cytochrome *c* by NADPH; the enzyme requires FMN or FAD for full activity. The crude chloroplast preparation also showed NADH-cytochrome *c* reductase activity. Whole chloroplasts could reduce cytochrome *c* in the dark with either NADH or NADPH; FMN enhanced this activity, especially with NADPH as reductant. Cytochrome *c* was found to increase the PS-P activity of chloroplasts particularly in the presence of NADP. The latter observation is of interest, and it may implicate this chloroplast NADPH-cytochrome reductase in a cyclic electron-transport system associated with photophosphorylation.

Marré and Servettez[112] also observed a NADPH oxidase activity associated with their purified NADPH-cytochrome *c* reductase preparation. Chromatophores from *Rhodospirillum rubrum* will oxidize reduced NAD, but not reduced NADP, with molecular oxygen[69].

(*iv*) *NADPH diaphorase*

Avron and Jagendorf[113] have isolated an enzyme from spinach leaf chloroplasts which catalyzes the reduction of a number of oxidants such as 2,3,6-trichlorophenol indophenol, ferricyanide, etc., but not mammalian cytochrome *c*. Flavin adenine dinucleotide was identified as being associated with the enzyme preparation. This preparation was specific for NADPH as reductant while NADH, even at concentrations twenty times that of NADPH, did not reduce the oxidants tested.

(*v*) *Succinic dehydrogenase*

Purified chromatophores from *Rhodospirillum rubrum* have been shown to contain considerable succinic dehydrogenase activity[49]; the enzyme has been partially purified by Woody and Lindstrom[114]. It is not known whether this bacterial succinic dehydrogenase is an FMN or FAD enzyme.

The enzyme appears to participate in the light-induced reduction of NAD with succinate as hydrogen donor. This photo-reduction can be inhibited by malonate, and the inhibition, in turn, can be reversed by excess succinate[69]. There is no evidence, however, that this enzyme participates in PS-P linked to light-induced electron transport.

(*vi*) *Haem proteins*

The isolation, characterization and properties of the haem proteins, obtained from photosynthetic organisms, have been reviewed in considerable detail by Kamen[115], and by Smith and Chance[116].

Evidence for the possible role of haem proteins stems from two different types of experimental observations: (*a*) changes in the absorption spectra of these pigments as a result of illumination; and, (*b*) effects of added haem proteins on the photochemical activities of cell-free photosynthetic systems.

The earliest report on spectroscopic changes of endogenous cytochromes upon illumination were those of Duysens[20], who observed an oxidation of cytochrome *c* when *Rhodospirillum rubrum* cells were illuminated. This observation has been amply confirmed. Chance and Olson[117] have made measurements of the relative rates of cytochrome oxidation and pyridine nucleotide reduction in *Rhodospirillum rubrum* and *Chromatium*, and have found that the cytochrome oxidation is far more rapid than the pyridine

References p. 420

nucleotide reduction at 26°C. Another extremely interesting observation is that of Smith and Baltscheffsky[21], Smith and Ramirez[118], and Smith[35], that illuminated chromatophores, when transformed from a non-phosphorylating to a phosphorylating state by the addition of ADP, will show an oxidation of endogenous cytochrome *c*. It is also of interest that the bacterial cytochrome *c* usually is in the reduced form within the cell, and that it is not oxidized under aerobic conditions, even though *Rhodospirillum rubrum* has an oxidative metabolism. Smith and Baltscheffsky[21] further showed that in the presence of 3-hydroxy-1-heptylquinoline *N*-oxide, in the light, the cytochrome *c* becomes more oxidized and a pigment, which appears to be a *b*-type cytochrome[119], becomes reduced. This is in agreement with the observations on mitochondria, that this type of inhibitor can act to break the electron-transport chain between cytochromes *b* and *c*. Observations along these lines also have been carried out with chloroplasts[28].

Another bit of evidence for the possible role of cytochromes in phosphorylation comes from the work of Horio and Kamen[120], who found that washed chromatophores continue to lose cytochrome *c*, and that this is accompanied by loss in PS-P activity. Upon addition of purified cytochrome *c* to the extensively washed chromatophores, the PS-P rate could be increased linearly but could not be saturated even with high concentrations of the added cytochrome c_2. The stimulating action of cytochrome *c* on PS-P by chloroplasts has been mentioned earlier[112].

On the basis of the experiments of Smith and Baltscheffsky[21], it was proposed that a phosphorylation site may exist between the photochemical oxidant and cytochrome *c*. The evidence for this is not too firm; the original observations should be extended and the kinetics of the reaction should be further studied. Nevertheless, many schemes now include this supposed phosphorylation site for both bacterial and chloroplast PS-P as if it were firmly established.

Bartsch and Kamen[121,122] have described a haem protein from *Rhodospirillum rubrum* and from *Chromatium* which they call RHP. This haem protein is auto-oxidizable and, at least in *Rhodospirillum rubrum*, it could play a part in electron transport to molecular oxygen.

(*vii*) *Hydrogenase*

A particulate hydrogenase has been isolated from *Rhodospirillum rubrum* by Gest[123] and has been shown to be associated with the chromatophores. Since intact cells can carry out the photoreduction of CO_2 with molecular hydrogen, one would expect that this enzyme should be able to reduce pyridine nucleotides with molecular hydrogen. This reaction has been demonstrated, thus far, only under conditions where certain surface active agents were added, which in turn inhibited the photochemical activities of these particulates[124]. Thus, the nature of the biochemical link between the hydrogenase and the photochemical system of the chromatophores still represents a problem. *Rhodospirillum rubrum* hydrogenase can reduce mammalian cytochrome *c* with molecular hydrogen[125]; whether this reaction is of physiological significance has not been established. Another striking phenomenon of intact cells of *R. rubrum* is their ability to produce molecular hydrogen in the light[126]. Ormerod *et al.*[127], who have studied this phenomenon in detail, believe that ATP is required for H_2 production, but direct evidence to support this hypothesis is still lacking. Paneque and Arnon[128] have reported a simultaneous production of molecular hydrogen and ATP in a rather complex system involving chloroplasts, a hydrogenase from *Clostridium pasteurianum*, and ascorbate.

Hydrogenase activity can also be observed in certain algae which can carry out photoreduction of CO_2 with molecular hydrogen and also may be able to produce H_2 in the light[129–131]. The relation of these reactions to PS-P has not yet been investigated.

(viii) Plastocyanin and allagochrome

Plastocyanin, a copper protein isolated from chloroplasts by Katoh *et al.*[132], which appears to play a role in the Hill reaction, and which is not present in *Rhodopseudomonas palustris*, has not yet been demonstrated to play a role in PS-P.

The pigment allagochrome, described by Habermann[133], isolated from sunflower leaves, is capable of undergoing reversible oxidation–reduction reactions. According to Habermann and Krall[134], allagochrome may play a role in PS-P.

5. The role of phosphorylation in photosynthesis

In comparing rates of photosynthesis and respiration in algae and higher plants, it is quite apparent that in most cases rates of photosynthesis at saturating light intensities are far higher than the rates of respiration observed in the same organisms. For instance, the green alga, *Chlorella*, is capable of fixing CO_2 at rates 20–40 times that of respiratory CO_2 production. If we assume that the P/O value for respiration is about three, and if we further assume that three molecules of ATP are required for each molecule of CO_2 fixed according to the Calvin–Benson scheme[135], and if the required ATP were to come from respiration, then photosynthesis could not proceed at rates much higher than twice those of respiration. It would appear from these considerations that the requirement for high-energy phosphate at high rates of photosynthetic carbon dioxide fixation can only be met through the process of PS-P and not by ATP formed in respiration.

References p. 420

A direct demonstration for the requirement of ATP in photosynthetic CO_2 fixation has been shown, in preliminary experiments, by Levine[136]. A mutant of *Chlamydomonas reinhardi* with impaired ability to fix carbon dioxide photosynthetically was selected. Sonic extracts prepared from this organism were capable of carrying out the Hill reaction almost as effectively as preparations derived from the wild type, but their photophosphorylation activity was severely impaired. When extracts from cells of this mutant strain were supplied with exogenous ATP, they then became capable of fixing carbon dioxide in the light. These experiments appear to indicate that the extracts from the mutant cells contain all the enzymes necessary for the photosynthetic process except for the ability to synthesize ATP, and that this ATP is vital for the complete photosynthetic process.

The high-energy phosphate formed in photosynthetic structures may play a role in a variety of synthetic reactions, but only a few will be mentioned here. It should be kept in mind that the evidence for direct utilization in these reactions of high-energy phosphate produced in the light is either indirect or only suggestive.

Leaves which are supplied with an exogenous source of carbohydrates are capable of converting them to starch in the presence of light under anaerobic conditions, where the source[137] of the ATP must be from PS-P. The role of ATP in the synthesis of β-hydroxybutyrate polymer from acetate by *Rhodospirillum rubrum* has been described by Stanier and coworkers[138,139]. ATP is thought to play an important role in the synthesis of acetyl-CoA and in the condensation reactions leading to polymer formation. Stumpf[140] recently has reviewed the role of PS-P in the lipid metabolism of leaves.

Chloroplasts appear to be capable of protein synthesis[141], and it is possible that the energy-rich phosphate formed in PS-P can be utilized for condensation reactions of this process. Nucleoside triphosphates formed directly as a result of PS-P and through the activity of nucleotide diphosphokinase, mentioned earlier, may possibly participate in the synthesis of RNA[142], and possibly also in the synthesis of phospholipids[143] which are abundantly present in photosynthetic organelles. Photosynthetic bacteria are capable of motility under anaerobic conditions in the light[144]; the energy required for this activity may well come from photosynthetic phosphorylation.

6. Conclusions

Photosynthetic phosphorylation, although it has some properties in common with oxidative phosphorylation, like the requirement for electron-transport systems, also has characteristics which are quite different from respiratory phosphorylation processes. The most striking characteristic of PS-P is the ability to convert light energy into thermochemical energy in the form of high-energy phosphate. In attempting to study the individual reaction steps of PS-P it will be useful to separate more effectively the photochemical reactions from the thermochemical reactions of PS-P[145]. Much of the work reviewed here deals with indirect efforts to achieve these aims. In the study of thermochemical reactions, pioneering work in oxidative and substrate phosphorylation should continue to be a useful guide, but judging from the information available already, we should not expect to find exact copies of thermochemical reaction systems between such structures as chloroplasts and mitochondria. In the photochemical reactions and in the problem of quantum conversion more information will have to come through biophysical studies. In the meanwhile another technique is beginning to bridge these different approaches. Biochemical genetics of photosynthetic organisms, first used effectively with pigment mutants[146] is extending to photosynthetic mutants with impaired electron transport and phosphorylation systems[136,147]; it is anticipated that a detailed study of such mutants will make important contributions to our knowledge of photosynthesis and of photophosphorylation.

ADDENDUM

This review, except for Figs. 1 and 2, was completed in August 1962. Since then many contributions related directly or indirectly to photosynthetic phosphorylation have appeared. A few key references[149–154] to the more recent literature and relating[149,154–156] to Figs. 1 and 2, have been added.

References p. 420

REFERENCES

1 E. I. RABINOWITCH, *Photosynthesis and Related Processes*, Vol. I, Vol. II, Parts 1 and 2, Interscience, New York, 1945, 1951, 1956.
2 H. GAFFRON, in F. C. STEWARD (Ed.), *Plant Physiology*, Vol. IB, Academic Press, New York, 1960, p. 3–277.
3 W. RUHLAND, *Encyclopedia of Plant Physiology*, Vol. V, Parts 1 and 2, Springer, Berlin, 1960.
4 R. HILL and C. P. WHITTINGHAM, *Photosynthesis*, 2nd ed., Methuen, London, 1957.
5 C. B. VAN NIEL, *Advan. Enzymol.*, 1 (1941) 263.
6 C. B. VAN NIEL, *Ann. Rev. Plant Physiol.*, 13 (1962) 1.
7 J. A. FRANCK AND K. F. HERZFELD, *J. Phys. Chem.*, 45 (1941) 978.
8 D. I. ARNON, F. R. WHATLEY AND M. B. ALLEN, *J. Am. Chem. Soc.*, 76 (1954) 6324.
9 A. FRENKEL, *J. Am. Chem. Soc.*, 76 (1954) 5568.
10 D. I. ARNON, *Brookhaven Symp. Biol.*, 11 (1959) 181.
11 A. W. FRENKEL, in W. D. MCELROY AND B. GLASS (Eds.), *Light and Life*, Johns Hopkins, Baltimore, 1961, p. 587.
12 D. I. ARNON, F. R. WHATLEY AND M. B. ALLEN, *Nature*, 180 (1957) 182.
13 M. NOZAKI, K. TAGAWA AND D. I. ARNON, *Proc. Natl. Acad. Sci. U.S.*, 47 (1961) 1334.
14 W. D. MCELROY AND B. GLASS, (Eds.), *Light and Life*, Johns Hopkins, Baltimore, 1961.
15 R. LIVINGSTON, *Quart. Rev. (London)*, 14 (1960) 174.
16 A. A. KRASNOVSKY, *Ann. Rev. Plant Physiol*,. 11 (1960) 363.
17 G. TOLLIN, *J. Theoret. Biol.*, 2 (1962) 105.
18 R. K. CLAYTON, *Bacteriol. Rev.*, 26 (1962) 151.
19 H. T. WITT, A. MÜLLER AND B. RUMBERG, *Nature*, 191 (1961) 194.
20 L. N. M. DUYSENS, *Nature*, 173 (1954) 692.
21 L. SMITH AND M. BALTSCHEFFSKY, *J. Biol. Chem.*, 234 (1959) 1575.
22 B. CHANCE AND M. NISHIMURA, *Proc. Natl. Acad. Sci. U. S.*, 46 (1960) 19.
23 J. M. OLSON, *Science*, 135 (1962) 101.
24 H. LUNDEGÅRDH, *Physiol. Plantarum*, 7 (1954) 375.
25 H. LUNDEGÅRDH, *Nature*, 192 (1962) 243.
26 L. N. M. DUYSENS, *Science*, 121 (1955) 210.
27 B. CHANCE AND R. SAGER, *Plant Physiol.*, 32 (1957) 548.
28 R. HILL AND W. D. BONNER, in W. D. MCELROY AND B. GLASS (Eds.), *Light and Life*, Johns Hopkins, Baltimore, 1961, p. 424–435.
29 R. HILL AND F. BENDALL, *Nature*, 186 (1960) 136.
30 M. D. KAMEN, in W. D. MCELROY AND B. GLASS (Eds.), *Light and Life*, Johns Hopkins, Baltimore, 1961, p. 483.
31 M. D. KAMEN, in T. W. GOODWIN AND O. LINDBERG (Eds.), *Biological Structure and Function*, Academic Press, New York, 1961, p. 277.
32 M. CALVIN, in W. D. MCELROY AND B. GLASS (Eds.), *Light and Life*, Johns Hopkins, Baltimore, 1961, p. 317.
33 D. D. HENDLEY AND B. L. STREHLER, in W. D. MCELROY AND B. GLASS (Eds.), *Light and Life*, Johns Hopkins, Baltimore, 1961, p. 593.
34 D. I. ARNON, *Bull. Torrey Botan. Club*, 88 (1961) 215.
35 L. SMITH, in W. D. MCELROY AND B. GLASS (Eds.), *Light and Life*, Johns Hopkins, Baltimore, 1961, p. 436.
36 C. C. BLACK, J. F. TURNER, M. GIBBS, D. W. KROGMANN AND S. A. GORDON, *J. Biol. Chem.*, 237 (1962) 580.
37 R. C. FULLER, J. A. BERGERON AND I. C. ANDERSON, *Arch. Biochem. Biophys.*, 92 (1961) 273.
38 D. I. ARNON, M. LOSADA. F. R. WHATLEY, H. Y. TSUJIMOTO, D. O. HALL AND A. A. HORTON, *Proc. Natl. Acad. Sci. U. S* , 47 (1961) 1314.
39 B. KOK AND G. HOCH, in W. D. MCELROY AND B. GLASS (Eds.), *Light and Life*, John Hopkins, Baltimore, 1961, p. 397.
40 R. EMERSON, R. V. CHALMERS AND C. CEDERSTRAND, *Proc. Natl. Acad. Sci. U. S.*, 43 (1957) 133.

41 L. R. Blinks, in H. Gaffron *et al.* (Eds.), *Research in Photosynthesis*, Interscience, New York, 1957, p. 444.
42 J. M. Olson and B. Chance, *Biochim. Biophys. Acta*, 28 (1958) 227.
43 H. C. Yin, Y. K. Chen, G. M. Shen, S. Y. Yang and K. S. Chiu, *Sci. Sinica (Peking)*, 10 (1961) 976.
44 H. M. Baltscheffsky, M. Baltscheffsky and J. M. Olson, *Biochim. Biophys. Acta*, 50 (1961) 380.
45 A. San Pietro, S. B. Hendricks, J. Giovanelli and F. E. Stolzenbach, *Science*, 128 (1958) 845.
46 R. Lumry, R. E. Wayrynen and J. D. Spikes, *Arch. Biochem. Biophys.*, 67 (1957) 453.
47 M. B. Allen, F. R. Whatley and D. I. Arnon, *Biochim. Biophys. Acta*, 27 (1958) 16.
48 M. Avron, *Biochim. Biophys. Acta*, 40 (1960) 257.
49 G. Cohen-Bazire and R. Kunisawa, *Proc. Natl. Acad. Sci. U. S.*, 46 (1960) 1543.
50 A. W. Frenkel, *J. Biol. Chem.*, 222 (1956) 823.
51 A. W. Frenkel, in H. Gaffron *et al.* (Eds.), *Research in Photosynthesis*, Interscience, New York, 1957, p. 303.
52 J. W. Newton and M. D. Kamen, *Biochim. Biophys. Acta*, 25 (1957) 462.
53 D. M. Geller and J. D. Gregory, *Federation Proc.*, 15 (1956) 260.
54 D. M. Geller and F. Lipmann, *J. Biol. Chem.*, 235 (1960) 2478.
55 F. R. Whatley, M. B. Allen and D. I. Arnon, in H. Gaffron *et al.* (Eds.), *Research in Photosynthesis*, Interscience, New York, 1957, p. 340.
56 F. R. Whatley, M. B. Allen and D. I. Arnon, *Biochim. Biophys. Acta*, 32 (1959) 32.
57 J. S. C. Wessels, *Biochim. Biophys. Acta*, 25 (1957) 97.
58 J. S. C. Wessels, *Biochim. Biophys. Acta*, 29 (1958) 113.
59 T. Nakamoto, D. W. Krogmann and B. Vennesland, *J. Biol. Chem.*, 234 (1959) 2783.
60 A. Trebst and H. Eck, *Z. Naturforsch.*, 16b (1961) 455.
61 A. T. Jagendorf, *Federation Proc.*, 18 (1959) 974.
62 J. F. Turner, C. C. Black and M. Gibbs, *J. Biol. Chem.*, 237 (1962) 577.
63 O. Kandler, *Ann. Rev. Plant Physiol.*, 11 (1960) 37.
64 J. W. Newton, *Nature*, 195 (1962) 349.
65 F. R. Whatley, M. B. Allen, A. V. Trebst and D. I. Arnon, *Plant Physiol.*, 35 (1960) 188.
66 T. Nakamoto, D. W. Krogmann and B. Mayne, *J. Biol. Chem.*, 235 (1960) 1843.
67 A. R. Krall, N. E. Good and B. C. Mayne, *Plant Physiol.*, 36 (1961) 44.
68 D. I. Arnon, in W. D. McElroy and B. Glass (Eds.), *Light and Life*, Johns Hopkins, Baltimore, 1961, p. 489.
69 A. W. Frenkel, *Brookhaven Symp. Biol.*, 11 (1959) 276.
70 L. P. Vernon and O. K. Ash, *J. Biol. Chem.*, 235 (1960) 2721.
71 A. R. Krall and M. R. Purvis, *Arch. Biochem. Biophys.*, 94 (1961) 14.
72 M. Mazelis, *Plant Physiol.*, 31 (1956) 37.
73 A. T. Jagendorf and M. Avron, *J. Biol. Chem.*, 231 (1958) 277.
74 A. R. Schulz and P. D. Boyer, *Arch. Biochem. Biophys.*, 93 (1961) 335.
75 P. D. Boyer, W. W. Luchsinger and A. B. Falcone, *J. Biol. Chem.*, 223 (1956) 405.
76 M. Avron and N. Sharon, *Biochem. Biophys. Res. Comm.*, 2 (1960) 336.
77 M. Avron, *J. Biol. Chem.*, 237 (1962) 2011.
78 J. S. Kahn and A. T. Jagendorf, *Biochem. Biophys. Res. Comm.*, 2 (1960) 259.
79 A. T. Jagendorf and J. S. Kahn, in T. W. Goodwin and O. Lindberg (Eds.), *Biological Structure and Function*, Academic Press, New York, 1961, p. 455.
80 A. L. Lehninger, in T. W. Goodwin and O. Lindberg (Eds.), *Biological Structure and Function*, Academic Press, New York, 1961, p. 31.
81 H. Baltscheffsky, *Acta Chem. Scand.*, 13 (1959) 393.
82 J. S. C. Wessels and H. Baltscheffsky, *Acta Chem. Scand.*, 14 (1960) 233.
83 B. Petrack, *Federation Proc.*, 18 (1959) 302.

84 B. PETRACK AND F. LIPMANN, in W. D. MCELROY AND B. GLASS (Eds.), *Light and Life*, Johns Hopkins, Baltimore, 1961, p. 621.
85 L. N. M. DUYSENS, *Ph.D. Thesis*, University of Utrecht, 1952.
86 G. COHEN-BAZIRE AND R. Y. STANIER, *Nature*, 181 (1958) 250.
87 R. C. FULLER AND J. C. ANDERSON, *Nature*, 181 (1958) 252.
88 G. D. DOROUGH AND M. CALVIN, *J. Am. Chem. Soc.*, 73 (1951) 2362.
89 D. I. ARNON, F. R. WHATLEY AND M. B. ALLEN, *J. Am. Chem. Soc.*, 76 (1954) 6324.
90 F. L. CRANE, *Plant Physiol.*, 34 (1959) 128.
91 N. I. BISHOP, *Proc. Natl. Acad. Sci. U. S.*, 45 (1959) 1696.
92 D. W. KROGMAN, *Biochem. Biophys. Res. Comm.*, 4 (1961) 275.
93 H. RUDNEY, *J. Biol. Chem.*, 236 (1961) PC 39.
94 F. L. CRANE, B. EHRLICH AND L. P. KEGEL, *Plant Physiol. Suppl.*, 35 (1960) xxi.
95 E. R. REDFEARN AND J. FRIEND, *Nature*, 191 (1961) 806.
96 R. C. FULLER, R. M. SMILLIE, N. RIGOPOULOS AND V. YOUNT, *Arch. Biochem. Biophys.*, 95 (2) (1961) 197.
97 D. I. ARNON, *Federation Proc.*, 20 (1961) 1012.
98 H. BALTSCHEFFSKY, *Biochim. Biophys. Acta*, 40 (1960) 1.
99 D. W. KROGMANN AND M. L. STILLER, *Biochem. Biophys. Res. Comm.*, 7 (1962) 46.
100 A. SAN PIETRO AND H. M. LANG, *J. Biol. Chem.*, 231 (1958) 211.
101 H. E. DAVENPORT, R. HILL AND F. R. WHATLEY, *Proc. Roy. Soc. (London) Ser. B.*, 139 (1952) 346.
102 H. E. DAVENPORT, *Biochem. J.*, 77 (1960) 471.
103 H. E. DAVENPORT, in T. W. GOODWIN AND O. LINDBERG (Eds.), *Biological Structure and Function*, Academic Press, New York, 1961, p. 449.
104 R. HILL AND F. BENDALL, *Nature*, 187 (1960) 417.
105 D. L. KEISTER, A. SAN PIETRO AND F. E. STOLZENBACH, *Arch. Biochem. Biophys.*, 94 (1961) 187.
106 D. L. KEISTER, A. SAN PIETRO AND F. E. STOLZENBACH, *J. Biol. Chem.*, 235 (1960) 2989.
107 L. P. VERNON AND K. ASH, *J. Biol. Chem.*, 234 (1959) 1878.
108 K. TAGAWA, M. NOZAKI AND D. I. ARNON, *Plant Physiol. Suppl.*, 37 (1962) vi.
109 M. KLINGENBERG AND T. BÜCHER, *Ann. Rev. Biochem.*, 29 (1960) 669.
110 T. OH-HAMA AND S. MIYACHI, *Plant Cell Physiol.*, 1 (1960) 155.
111 D. C. PRATT, A. W. FRENKEL AND D. D. HICKMAN, in T. W. GOODWIN AND O. LINDBERG (Eds.), *Biological Structure and Function*, Academic Press, New York, 1961, p. 295.
112 E. MARRÉ AND O. SERVETTEZ, *Arch. Biochem. Biophys.*, 75 (1958) 309.
113 M. AVRON AND A. T. JAGENDORF, *Arch. Biochem. Biophys.*, 65 (1956) 475.
114 B. R. WOODY AND E. S. LINDSTROM, *J. Bacteriol.*, 69 (1955) 353.
115 M. D. KAMEN, in M. B. ALLEN (Ed.), *Comparative Biochemistry of Photoreactive Systems*, Academic Press, New York, 1960, p. 323.
116 L. SMITH AND B. CHANCE, *Ann. Rev. Plant Physiol.*, 9 (1958) 449.
117 B. CHANCE AND J. M. OLSON, *Arch. Biochem. Biophys.*, 88 (1960) 54.
118 L. SMITH AND J. RAMIREZ, *Brookhaven Symp. Biol.*, 11 (1959) 310.
119 L. P. VERNON AND M. D. KAMEN, *J. Biol. Chem.*, 211 (1954) 643.
120 T. HORIO AND M. D. KAMEN, *Biochemistry*, 1 (1962) 144.
121 R. G. BARTSCH AND M. D. KAMEN, *J. Biol. Chem.*, 230 (1958) 41.
122 R. G. BARTSCH AND M. D. KAMEN, *J. Biol. Chem.*, 235 (1960) 825.
123 H. GEST, *J. Bacteriol.*, 63 (1952) 111.
124 S. K. BOSE AND H. GEST, *Nature*, 195 (1962) 1168.
125 A. W. FRENKEL AND K. COST, *Nature*, 195 (1962) 1171.
126 H. GEST AND M. D. KAMEN, *Science*, 109 (1949) 558.
127 J. G. ORMEROD, K. S. ORMEROD AND H. GEST, *Arch. Biochem. Biophys.*, 94 (1961) 449.
128 A. PANEQUE AND D. I. ARNON, *Plant Physiol. Suppl.*, 37 (1962) iv.
129 H. GAFFRON, *Biol. Revs. Cambridge Phil. Soc.*, 19 (1944) 1.
130 E. KESSLER, in W. RUHLAND (Ed.), *Encyclopedia of Plant Physiology*, Springer, Berlin, 1960, p. 951.

131 A. W. Frenkel, *Arch. Biochem. Biophys.*, 38 (1952) 219.
132 S. Katoh, I. Suga, I. Shiratori and A. Takamiya, *Arch. Biochem. Biophys.*, 94 (1961) 136.
133 H. M. Habermann, in M. B. Allen (Ed.), *Comparative Biochemistry of Photoreactive Systems*, Academic Press, New York, 1960, p. 73.
134 H. M. Habermann and A. R. Krall, *Biochem. Biophys. Res. Comm.*, 4 (1961) 109.
135 J. A. Bassham and M. Calvin, *The Path of Carbon in Photosynthesis*, Prentice Hall, New Jersey, 1957.
136 R. P. Levine, *Proc. Natl. Acad. Sci. U. S.*, 46 (1960) 972.
137 C. S. MacLachlan and H. K. Porter, *Proc. Roy. Soc. (London), Ser. B*, 150 (1959) 460.
138 R. Y. Stanier, M. Doudoroff, R. Kunisawa and R. Contopoulou, *Proc. Natl. Acad. Sci. U. S.*, 45 (1959) 1246.
139 R. Y. Stanier, *Bacteriol. Rev.*, 25 (1961) 1.
140 P. K. Stumpf, *Nature*, 194 (1962) 1158.
141 U. Heber, *Nature*, 195 (1962) 91.
142 A. O. Pogo, G. Brawerman and E. Chargaff, *Biochemistry*, 1 (1962) 128.
143 A. A. Benson, in W. D. McElroy and B. Glass (Eds.), *Light and Life*, Johns Hopkins, Baltimore, 1961, p. 392.
144 T. W. Engelmann, *Arch. Ges. Physiol.*, 30 (1883) 95.
145 M. Nishimura, *Biochim. Biophys. Acta*, 59 (1962) 183.
146 W. R. Sistrom, M. Griffith and R. Y. Stanier, *J. Cellular Comp. Physiol.*, 48 (1956) 473.
147 N. Bishop, *Nature*, 195 (1962) 55.
148 K. Tagawa and D. I. Arnon, *Nature*, 193 (1962) 537.
149 B. Kok and A. Jagendorf (Eds.), Photosynthetic Mechanisms of Green Plants, *Natl. Acad. Sci., Natl. Res. Council, Publ. 1145* (1963).
150 H. Gest, A. San Pietro and L. P. Vernon (Eds.), *Bacterial Photosynthesis*, The Antioch Press, Yellow Springs, Ohio, 1963.
151 M. D. Kamen, *Primary Process in Photosynthesis*, Academic Press, New York, 1963.
152 M. Losada and D. I. Arnon, in H. F. Linskens, B. B. Sanwal and M. V. Tracy (Eds.), *Modern Methods of Plant Analysis*, Springer, Berlin, 1964, p. 569.
153 L. P. Vernon, *Ann. Rev. Plant Physiol.*, 15 (1964) 73.
154 B. Rumberg and H. T. Witt, *Z. Naturforsch.*, 19b (1964) 693.
155 L. R. Blinks and C. B. van Niel, in *Microalgae and Photosynthetic Bacteria*, Japan. Soc. Plant Physiol., University of Tokyo Press, Tokyo, 1963, p. 297.
156 R. K. Clayton, *Proc. Natl. Acad. Sci. (U.S.)*, 50 (1963) 583.

Chapter IX

Enzymatic Activation of Oxygen

LLOYD L. INGRAHAM

Department of Biochemistry and Biophysics, University of California, Davis, Calif. (U.S.A.)

1. Introduction

Living in a bath of 20% oxygen, we tend to forget that oxygen is a powerful oxidizing agent. Paper, wood and many other organic materials will exist for thousands of years in air if kept sterile. Organisms however, possess oxygenases that will cause oxygen to burn organic materials at a tremendous rate. One mole of copper, properly chelated in an enzyme, can burn all the air in a 20 × 20 foot room with an eight foot ceiling in one second. Two questions arise: why is oxygen so kinetically stable without a catalyst, and how do the biological catalysts cause it to suddenly become so reactive? We shall attempt to answer these questions in this Chapter.

2. Non-enzymatic oxidations

(*a*) *Oxygen stability*

The primary reason for the extremely slow reactions of oxygen in the absence of a catalyst at room temperature is that the strong bonding between the oxygen atoms must be broken when an oxygen molecule oxidizes a compound. The oxygen molecule is held together not only by one normal 2-electron bond but also by two 3-electron bonds.

An oxygen atom has six electrons in the second shell (outer) distributed among the 2s, $2p_x$, $2p_y$ and $2p_z$ atomic orbitals[1]. When two oxygen atoms combine to form an oxygen molecule there are now 12 electrons and we might at first guess that the distribution would be 2 electrons in each of the 2s orbitals of the oxygens, O_1 and O_2. Similarly, there would be 2 electrons in each of the $2p_z$ orbitals. The $2p_x$ and $2p_y$ orbitals could combine to form $2p\sigma$ and $2p\pi$ bonds, respectively, containing 2 electrons each.

O_1		O_2			
2s	○○	2s	○○		
$2p_x$		$2p_x$		$2p\sigma$	○○
$2p_y$		$2p_y$		$2p\pi$	○○
$2p_z$	○○	$2p_z$	○○		

This structure would give oxygen a double bond made of $2p\sigma$ and $2p\pi$ bonds. However, a more stable structure for oxygen is one in which a $2p\sigma$ bond is formed and the $2p_y$ and $2p_z$ electrons are distributed between the extremes designated by structures *A* and *B*.

A

O_1		O_2			
2s	○○	2s	○○		
$2p_x$		$2p_x$		$2p\sigma$	○○
$2p_y$	○○	$2p_y$	○		
$2p_z$	○	$2p_z$	○○		

B

O_1		O_2			
2s	○○	2s	○○		
$2p_x$		$2p_x$		$2p\sigma$	○○
$2p_y$	○	$2p_y$	○○		
$2p_z$	○○	$2p_z$	○		

Both the $2p_y$ and $2p_z$ orbitals combine on each oxygen to form two 3-electron bonds.

:O ⁝⁝⁝ O:

In molecular-orbital description the p_y orbitals overlap to give a $\pi_u{}^y$ and a higher $\pi_g{}^y$ orbital; the p_z orbitals similarly overlap to give a $\pi_u{}^z$ and a $\pi_g{}^z$ orbital. The subscripts g and u stand for "gerade" and "ungerade", meaning the total π orbital either does or does not have a center of symmetry.

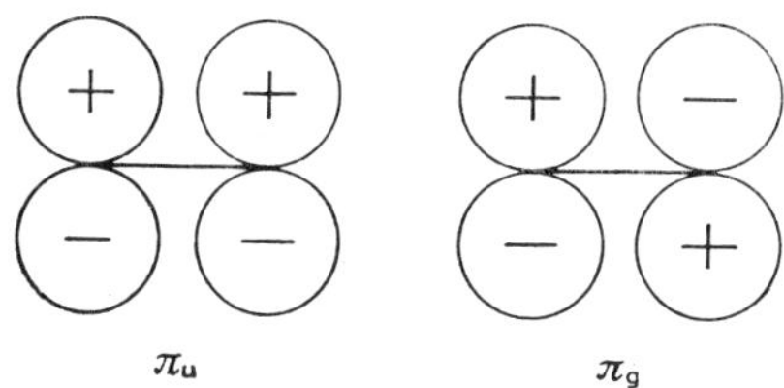

π_u π_g

References p. 444

In the π_u orbital the atom-wave functions are of the same sign so that they add together in the area between the oxygen atoms to form a stable molecular orbital corresponding to a chemical bond, whereas in π_g the opposite signs cancel to make a molecular orbital of higher energy. The six electrons in the p orbitals are therefore distributed with 2 electrons in each of the lower π_u orbitals and only 1 electron in each higher π_g orbital.

$$(2s_1)^2(2s_2)^2(2p\sigma)^2(\pi_u{}^y)^2(\pi_u{}^z)^2(\pi_g{}^y)^1(\pi_g{}^z)^1$$

The higher two electrons would rather be unpaired than suffer electrostatic repulsion in the same orbital (Hund's rule). Because they are unpaired it is clear why the ground state of oxygen is paramagnetic.

If one or two more electrons are added to the system, resonance is prevented and the bond between the oxygen may be more easily broken. For example, if two electrons are added, only a single bond remains and the structure is isoelectronic with the fluorine molecule.

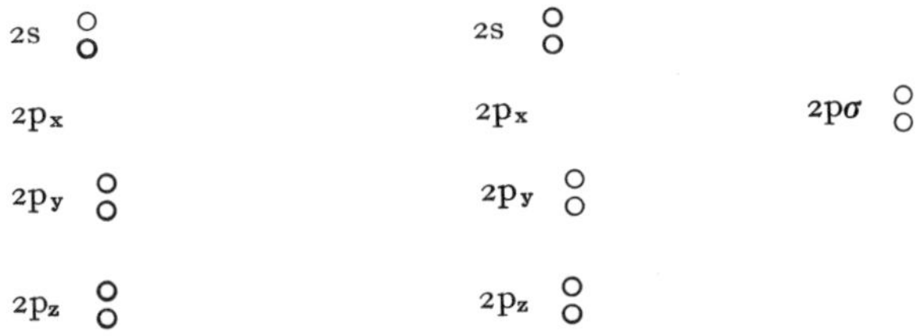

2s ○○	2s ○○	
$2p_x$	$2p_x$	$2p\sigma$ ○○
$2p_y$ ○○	$2p_y$ ○○	
$2p_z$ ○○	$2p_z$ ○○	

Any catalyst that even partially donates an electron to oxygen should catalyze the oxidation. This gives us a clue to how an enzyme can "activate" oxygen. The idea that the first electron is hard to add to oxygen but that the rest are added easily is borne out by the oxygen potentials in acid solution[2].

First electron	—0.13 V
Second electron	+1.5 V
Third electron	+0.72 V
Fourth electron	+2.82 V

Thus considering the first electron only, oxygen is a poorer oxidizing agent than H^+ and about as poor an oxidizing agent as Sn^{2+} going to Sn.

(b) *Oxygen activation*

The oxidation by molecular oxygen may be catalyzed by two general mechanisms: (*1*) a catalyst (usually a metal) may donate an electron to the oxygen and thus allow the strong bonding in the oxygen molecule to be broken more easily or (*2*) the oxygen may react with a compound with an easily available electron (usually a free radical) so that the oxygen molecule need not be activated. Although, it is the first mechanism, oxygen activation, that this chapter is primarily concerned with, a brief discussion of substrate activation and examples will occur in later sections.

The oxygen molecule may be activated by combining with a metal so that the first part of the discussion will concern oxygen binding by metals. Oxygen is bound primarily by ferrous or cuprous ions in biological systems so that our discussion of oxygen binding will be limited to these metals. The oxygen complexes of these ions are called perferryl ion and percupryl ion.

Essentially two things occur in oxygen–metal binding. The oxygen donates a pair of electrons to the metal as a normal ligand and the d orbitals donate electrons back to the oxygen to form a π bond. The σ bond may be formed from the lone s (or sp^2) electron pair on the oxygen or one of the π_u pairs in the double bond of the oxygen. These give the two structures A and B respectively.

M←O=O (A) M←‖O=O (B)

Griffith[3] prefers structure B over A because the ionization potential of a sp^2 electron is 4.3 eV higher than of a π_u electron. Donation of a π_u electron to the metal should therefore be easier than donation of an sp^2 electron. The electron pair on the oxygen is accepted by an empty d^2sp^3 orbital on iron or probably an empty sp^3 orbital on copper.

Ferrous iron has three d orbitals filled with 6 electrons, thus two d orbitals, one s orbital, and three p orbitals are available to accept electron pairs from the ligand. These orbitals hybridize to form octahedral d^2sp^3 bonds. Because in cuprous ion all the d orbitals are filled, the ligands form tetrahedral sp^3 bonds.

As mentioned before, the d orbitals of the metal contribute to the binding of the metal through π bonds. d Orbitals may form either σ bonds or π bonds according to the symmetry of the ligand orbitals.

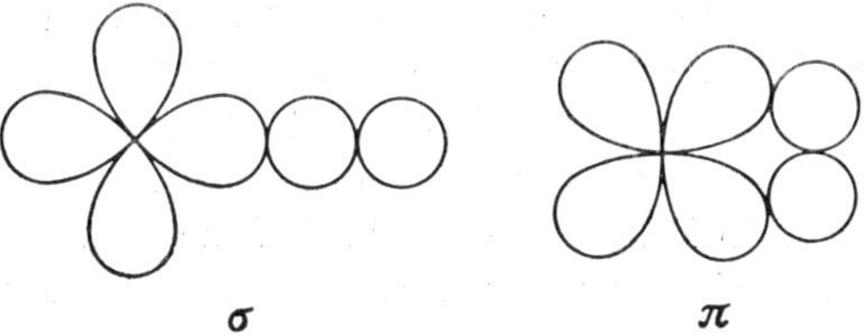

In an octahedral or square planar complex only the d_{xy}, d_{xz}, and d_{yz} orbitals can form π bonds. However, in a tetrahedral complex where the ligands are not on the coordinates all d orbitals are able to form π bonds*[4].

The total picture of the metal–oxygen binding is one in which oxygen donates an electron pair to the metal and then the metal donates an electron pair from a filled d orbital back to the oxygen to form a double bond.

$$\mathrm{M}::\overset{\oplus}{\mathrm{O}}:\overset{\cdot\cdot\ominus}{\underset{\cdot\cdot}{\mathrm{O}}}: \qquad \mathrm{M}::\begin{matrix}\mathrm{O}:\\ \mathrm{O}:\end{matrix}$$

A B

The complexed oxygen molecule in these ions is now "activated" because the single bond between the oxygen atoms is much easier to break than the strong bonding which occurs in the uncomplexed oxygen molecule. Since the overall charge on a metal–oxygen complex is positive, the ion can more readily accept electrons in oxidations than a neutral oxygen molecule. A metallic ion may thus catalyze a reaction by virtue of its ability to change the electronic structure of the substrate and by virtue of its ability to form positively charged complexes.

One of the considerations of metal–oxygen binding is that the oxygen may oxidize the metal instead of forming a complex. This problem is not as great as it might seem at first because both one-electron and two-electron reactions are difficult in metal–oxygen complexes. The one-electron reaction is prevented because it is difficult to add one electron to oxygen.

The one-electron oxidations of both ferrous and cuprous ion have positive free energies for the uncomplexed ion in aqueous solution[2].

$$\Delta F$$

$$Cu^{+} + O_2 \rightarrow Cu^{2+} + O_2^{-} + 16.5 \text{ kcal}$$

$$Fe^{2+} + O_2 \rightarrow Fe^{3+} + O_2^{-} + 30.8 \text{ kcal}$$

The two-electron reaction is prevented because it is difficult to obtain two electrons from cuprous or ferrous ions. The problem in a ferrous–oxygen or cuprous–oxygen complex in neutral aqueous solution is not to prevent autoxidation of the metal but to aid donation of electrons to oxygen for double bond formation. The field of the protein may help in the donation of electrons from metal to oxygen. Cuprous ion tends to form tetrahedral chelates because of the four vacant sp^3 orbitals. When cuprous ion is placed in a tetrahedral field some of the d-orbital levels are displaced to a higher energy than in uncomplexed cuprous ion. This would aid in donation of d orbitals to oxygen to form the second half of the double bond and may be one of the functions of the protein. The same arguments may be made for

* The π orbitals of the ligands are of symmetry e, t_1 and t_2 in a tetrahedral field, the d_{xy}, d_{xz} and d_{yz} orbitals are of symmetry t_2, and the d_{x^2} and $d_{x^2-y^2}$ orbitals are of symmetry e, thus all are available for overlap with π orbitals of the ligand[5].

ferrous ion. Ferrous ion has vacant d^2sp^3 orbitals and tends to form octahedral complexes. In an octahedral field, d orbitals are available for π bonding at the same energy as d orbitals in the free ion[6]. However, another field could raise the level of these orbitals and make them again more easily donated to oxygen.

Perferryl and percupryl ions are only known as transient intermediates in inorganic chemistry. Perferryl ion has been postulated as an intermediate in the aerobic oxidation of ferrous ion[7] and percupryl ion has been proposed to occur in the autoxidation of cuprous salts[8,9].

(c) *Substrate activation*

The rapid aerobic oxidation of hydroquinones in basic solution falls into the second general mechanism type[10] in which the oxygen reacts with an easily oxidizable free radical.

$$R + O_2 \rightarrow S + O_2^- \quad (1)$$

$$S + O_2 \rightarrow T + O_2^- \quad (2)$$

$$R + T \rightarrow 2S \quad (3)$$

$$2S \rightarrow R + T \quad (4)$$

The symbol R stands for reduced hydroquinone, S for semiquinone (radical) and T for totally oxidized quinone. Reaction (1) is the initiation reaction, (2) and (3) are chain-propagating reactions and (4) or other similar reactions are chain-terminating reactions. Most of the consumption of oxygen occurs in (2) in which oxygen pulls an easily available electron off a semiquinone radical. This type of reaction may be catalyzed by increasing the amount of radical. One method to increase the amount of radical is to stabilize the radical.

3. Enzymatic reactions

(a) *Oxygen-carrying proteins*

(i) *Hemoglobin*

Although hemoglobin is not an enzyme it will be discussed briefly because it points out some of the problems arising in metallo–oxygen complexes. The reversible reaction of ferrous hemoglobin with oxygen brings up two questions: Why is the ferrous iron not oxidized to ferric iron by the oxygen and why is the ferrous iron able to bind oxygen?

The first question becomes even more important when we realize that ferroheme, or dipyridine hemochromes, are easily oxidized to the ferriheme with oxygen[11]. There may be two reasons for this effect. First, the autoxida-

References p. 444

$$Fe^{2+} + O_2 \rightarrow Fe^{3+} + O_2^-$$

tion of iron has a positive free energy of reaction in water. However, the potential of the ferrohemoglobin–ferrihemoglobin couple is only 0.16 V compared to 0.77 for the ferric–ferrous couple which indicates that the ferrihemoglobin is 10^{10} more stable to dissociation than the ferrohemoglobin[12]. Even with this great stabilization George reports that the autoxidation of hemoglobin to give ferrihemoglobin and O_2 is endothermic[13].

The stabilization of the ferriheme must in part take place through electron exchange between iron and the porphyrin. Because ferriheme has a magnetic moment of 5.8 Bohr magnetons corresponding to the 5 unpaired electrons of ferric ion, the iron is usually described as "essentially ionic". However, the Lande splitting factor, g, is 6.0 for ferriheme and 5.9 for ferrihemoglobin[14] instead of the value 2.00, expected for ionic ferric iron. This higher value for g must mean that there are strong interactions between the iron orbital and those of the porphyrin.

Possibly the autoxidation of ferroheme is second order in ferroheme. This is an attractive mechanism because although oxygen adds one electron with

$$Fe^{2+} + O_2 \rightarrow FeO_2^{2+}$$
$$FeO_2^{2+} + Fe^{2+} \rightarrow 2Fe^{3+} + O_2^{2-}$$

difficulty it adds two electrons quite readily. The ferroheme is able to undergo such a bimolecular reaction whereas steric hindrance prevents the second reaction with hemoglobin because the oxygen and iron are buried in the protein. Possibly another effect may be the difference in dielectric constant. The low dielectric constant of the protein will decrease the rate of the reac-

$$Fe^{2+} + O_2 \rightarrow Fe^{3+} + O_2^-$$

tion because the species on the right side of the equation are more strongly charged. However, the dielectric constant will not change the free energy of the reaction[15] because the dielectric constant of the solution has not been changed. Very likely the effect of the low dielectric constant on the rate is less important than equilibrium effects because ionic reactions are commonly fast.

In order to test the effect of dielectric constant Wang made films of a matrix of 1-(2-phenylethyl)-imidazole carbonmonoxyheme diethylester in 25% polystyrene and 75% of excess 1-(2-phenylethyl)-imidazole. Films of this material were found to reversibly absorb oxygen without being autoxidized. The polystyrene not only lowered the dielectric constant but also prevented bimolecular reactions[16,17].

The general principles of how iron is able to bind oxygen has been discussed in the previous section. A drastic change in electron configuration must take place when hemoglobin binds oxygen or carbon monoxide because the ferrohemoglobin has a magnetic moment of 5.46 Bohr magnetons[18] whereas the oxygen and carbon monoxide adducts are diamagnetic[18]. The primary bond must be a σ bond, formed by donation of oxygen electrons to the vacant d^2sp^3 orbitals of iron. In addition, an important part of the binding energy must be $d\pi$ electron donation from iron to oxygen. The fact that the potential of heme is lower than aqueous iron means the iron electrons are more easily donated to oxygen from heme iron. Small amounts of pyridine greatly enhance the CO-binding power of ferroheme[19] and imidazole will enable ferroheme to absorb oxygen[20,21]. Similarly, ferrous dimethylglyoxime in 50% aqueous dioxane will absorb oxygen if a base is added. Histidine causes a greater absorption of oxygen than pyridine[22]. The fifth ligand thus greatly affects the binding capacity of the iron for the sixth ligand. Presumably donation of electrons from base to iron must aid donation of electrons from iron to the sixth ligand, the oxygen or carbon monoxide. This donation of electrons from iron to oxygen or carbon monoxide must draw heavily on electrons in the rest of the protein because the protein becomes more rigid on oxygenation. Entropy considerations[23] show that the protein becomes more ordered as the first molecule of oxygen or carbon monoxide is added to the hemoglobin.

(ii) Hemocyanin

Hemocyanin is an oxygen-carrying copper protein found in the blood of many invertebrates. It will be briefly discussed because of its relation to the copper enzymes.

The copper is very tightly bound to the protein. The binding constant[24] has been found to be $10^{18.7}$ for the first 50% of the copper and $10^{20.5}$ for the second 50%. No exchange occurs between copper of the protein and solution even during oxygenation and deoxygenation[25]. The groups binding the copper to the protein are unknown except for the observation that one new mercapto group appears in hemocyanin when the four coppers are removed by dialysis against cyanide ion[26]. The copper in the unoxygenated hemocyanin is in the cuprous state, but it can be oxidized to the cupric state by hydrogen peroxide[27]. Hemocyanin in the cupric state is called methemocyanin.

The stoichiometry of the reaction of hemocyanin with oxygen is one oxygen molecule for each two copper atoms in the protein[28]. Very likely the oxygen forms a bridge between two of the copper atoms. Hemocyanin is colorless in the deoxygenated state, but it is blue with an absorption band at 600 mμ when oxygen is added. This blue color is often ascribed to cupric ion complexes but the color is 5–10 times as intense as known chemical cupric complexes. When oxygenated hemocyanin is added to glacial acetic acid, both cuprous and cupric ions are formed[29]. The irreversible oxidation to cupric ion must occur.

$$(CuO_2Cu)^{2+} + H^+ \rightarrow Cu^{2+} + HO_2\cdot + Cu^+$$

References p. 444

Speculation on the structure of $(CuO_2Cu)^{2+}$ is interesting. As discussed previously the ionization potentials lead us to prefer structure B. The binding of oxygen by cuprous ion in structure B must be very similar to the binding of olefins by cuprous ion[30–32]. In structure B the double bond between copper and oxygen is formed by donation of a pair of π_u electrons of oxygen to the sp^3 orbitals of copper and by the donation of 2-electrons from the d orbitals of copper back to the π_g orbitals of oxygen to form a bridged

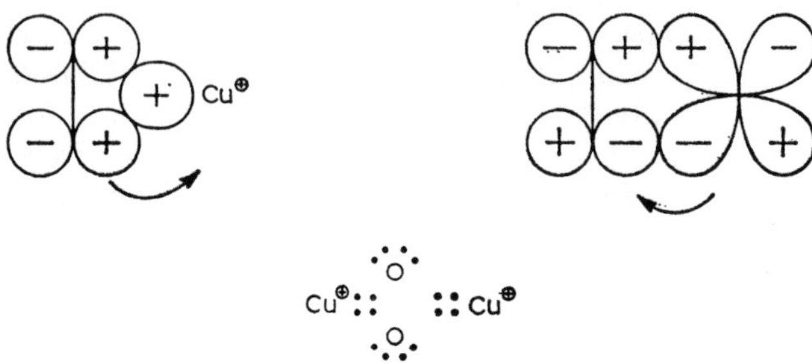

structure. This structure would be expected to be paramagnetic if the copper ions are equivalent and experiment has shown that oxyhemocyanin is diamagnetic[33]. Very likely the copper ions are not equivalent. Because the two π_u orbitals of oxygen are at right angles this requires the copper–oxygen bonds to be at right angles. The observation that hemocyanin will not

Cu^+---O_2
Cu^+

bind carbon monoxide strongly[34], is in support of this structure. Since the ionization potential of an sp^2 electron of carbon monoxide is less than of a π_u electron, A would be expected[3] to be the best structure for carbon

monoxide and B for oxygen. Because the mode of binding is different it is possible, for steric reasons, to explain why structure A may be less readily formed and, therefore, why carbon monoxide is not bound whereas most cuprous compounds do bind carbon monoxide.

The optical rotation of hemocyanin[35] is found to change on oxygenation. This means the secondary structure of the protein must change on oxygenation, again presumably because of a drain on electrons of the protein.

(b) *Double-bond cleavage*

These are reactions of molecular oxygen with double bonds to cleave the bond. Both atoms of oxygen are found in the cleaved products. Enzymes catalyzing reactions of this type are called oxygen transferases[36]. Because these enzymes are all activated by ferrous ion and transfer molecular oxygen, the intermediate must be some type of perferryl ion, such as FeO_2^{2+}, comparable to oxyhemoglobin. In enzymes perferryl ion is called complex III. The reaction must transfer the oxygen molecule directly from complex III to the substrate.

$$FeO_2^{2+} + >C{=}C< \longrightarrow >C{=}O + O{=}C< + Fe^{2+}$$

Many of these enzymes have an essential thiol group. Its exact function is unknown.

(i) *Pyrocatechase*

Pyrocatechase is the enzyme that catalyzes the aerobic oxidation of catechol to *cis,cis*-muconic acid and is found in *Pseudomonas*[37]. The enzyme has an essential thiol group, contains two atoms of iron per mole and requires ferrous iron for activity. Both oxygen atoms of molecular oxygen are transferred directly to the *cis,cis*-muconic acid[38,39].

An intermediate peroxide has been proposed but has not been detected. Peroxide intermediates probably occur in non-enzymatic cleavage of certain enols by molecular oxygen. For example, β-phenylethylethyl ketone will cleave with oxygen in the presence of tertiary butoxide ion to give β-phenylacetaldehyde and benzoate ion[40]. Such a mechanism would account

$$C_6H_5{-}CH_2{-}CH_2{-}CO{-}C_6H_5 + \textit{tert.}\text{-}BuO^{\ominus} \longrightarrow C_6H_5{-}CH_2{-}\bar{C}H{-}CO{-}C_6H_5 + \textit{tert.}\text{-}BuOH$$

$$\xrightarrow{O_2} C_6H_5{-}CH_2{-}CH{-}C(O^{\ominus}){-}C_6H_5 \text{ (with } {-}O{-}O{-} \text{ bridge)} \longrightarrow C_6H_5{-}CH_2{-}CH{=}O + C_6H_5{-}C(=O)O^{\ominus}$$

for the fact that atoms of oxygen are found in *cis,cis*-muconic acid when the catechol is enzymatically cleaved. Non-enzymatic aromatic ring cleavage in low yields is also found when *o*-quinones are oxidized by hydrogen peroxide to *cis,cis*-muconic acid[40,41].

Metapyrocatechase catalyzes the cleavage of pyrocatechol by oxygen in

References p. 444

the 2,3-positions to give the corresponding hydroxy-aldehyde[42–44]. This enzyme is inhibited by reagents specific for sulfhydryl groups.

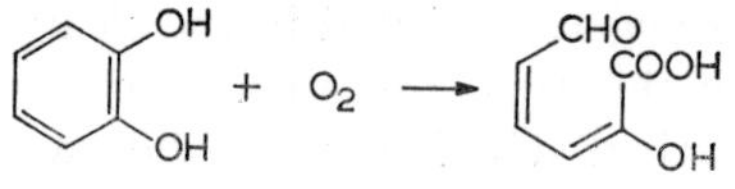

$$\text{catechol (OH, OH)} + O_2 \longrightarrow \text{(CHO, COOH, OH)}$$

(ii) Protocatechuic oxidase

This enzyme, first discovered by Ingraham[45,46] and co-workers in *Pseudomonas fluorescens*, cleaves the aromatic ring of protocatechuic acid.

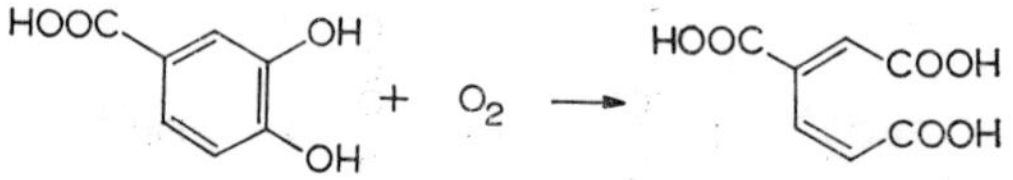

$$\text{HOOC–C}_6\text{H}_3\text{(OH)}_2 + O_2 \longrightarrow \text{HOOC–(COOH)(COOH)}$$

This enzyme also requires Fe^{2+} ion and is inhibited by sulfhydryl reagents[47].

(iii) Homogentisic acid oxidase

This enzyme cleaves the aromatic ring of homogentisic acid with molecular oxygen to form maleylacetoacetate[48]. It is inhibited by substances that complex iron and by sulfhydryl reagents and is activated by ferrous ion[49–51]. Only one of the atoms of molecular oxygen is found in the product but the newly formed keto group exchanges so rapidly with water that it is likely that both atoms of oxygen are incorporated and one is lost before it can be detected[52].

(iv) Tryptophan oxidase

Tryptophan oxidase cleaves the indole ring of tryptophan with molecular

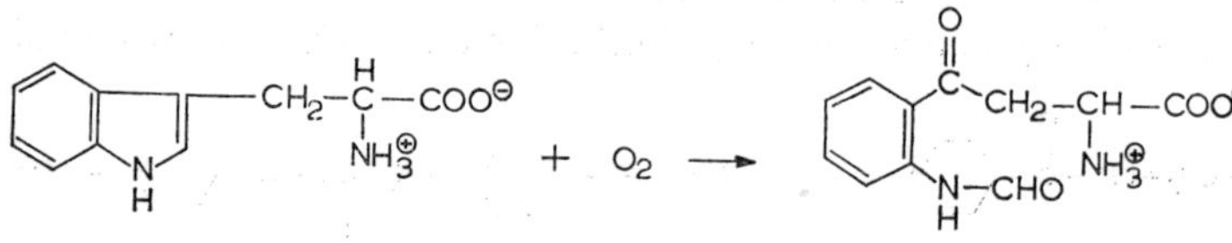

$$\text{Indole–}CH_2\text{–}\underset{NH_3^{\oplus}}{\overset{H}{C}}\text{–}COO^{\ominus} + O_2 \longrightarrow \text{C}_6\text{H}_4(\text{NH–CHO})\text{–}\overset{O}{\overset{\|}{C}}\text{–}CH_2\text{–}\underset{NH_3^{\oplus}}{CH}\text{–}COO^{\ominus}$$

oxygen. Both atoms of the oxygen molecule are incorporated in the product[53]. This enzyme is unique among oxygen transferases in that it is inhibited by catalase.

(c) *Hydroxylation at an unsaturated atom*

In these reactions enzymes use molecular oxygen to hydroxylate at an unsaturated atom. The substrate is usually an aromatic compound. In all reactions a reducing agent other than the substrate to be hydroxylated is required.

Because only one atom of the oxygen molecule appears in the product and the other is reduced to water these enzymes are called mixed-function oxidases[36].

With our present knowledge of these enzymes, the most likely mechanism is one in which the metal combines with oxygen to form complex III, MO_2^{n+}, this is reduced to complex II, MO^{n+}, by a reducing agent and this in turn adds to the unsaturated carbon.

$$M^{n+} + O_2 \rightleftharpoons MO_2^{n+}$$

$$MO_2^{n+} + 2H^+ + 2e \longrightarrow MO^{n+} + H_2O$$

$$MO^{n+} + \text{H}\!-\!\text{C}\!=\!\text{C} \longrightarrow MO^{(n-1)+}\!-\!\text{C(H)}\!-\!\text{C}^{\oplus}$$

$$MO^{(n-1)+}\!-\!\text{C(H)}\!-\!\text{C}^{\oplus} \longrightarrow MO^{(n-1)+}\!-\!\text{C}\!=\!\text{C} + H^+$$

$$MO^{(n-1)+}\!-\!\text{C}\!=\!\text{C} + H^+ + H_2O \longrightarrow \text{HO}\!-\!\text{C}\!=\!\text{C} + M^{n+} + H_2O$$

(*i*) *Tyrosinase*

Tyrosinase, commonly called the phenolase complex[54], will catalyze the aerobic hydroxylation of a phenol in the *ortho* position or the oxidation of a catechol to an *o*-quinone. It is a copper-containing protein with copper in the cuprous form in the reduced enzyme. Very likely two of these cuprous coppers are required to bind one oxygen molecule, as in hemocyanin, because it has been shown that one carbon monoxide is bound by two copper atoms[55,56]. The copper of the resting enzyme will not exchange with radioactive cupric ion in solution[57] but may be removed by dialysis against cyanide ion to produce an apoenzyme which is an inhibitor for tyrosinase[58]. When cupric ion is added to the apoenzyme the activity is gradually regained in spite of the fact that the enzyme appears to be a cuprous enzyme.

Tyrosinase, originally considered one enzyme, has now been found to consist of two protein fractions which may be separated by column chromatography on either hydroxyapatite or DEAE-cellulose*. One fraction has a high catecholase activity (catechol to *o*-quinone) but the other fraction has

* This fact was discovered independently using DEAE-cellulose by Mr. and Mrs. James Brooks in the enzyme laboratory course at Davis, Calif.

References p. 444

cresolase activity (phenol or cresol to catechol) and catecholase activity. These enzymes are quite similar: (*a*) they always occur together and are associated with the same electrophoretic and ultracentrifugal peak[54], (*b*) they are inhibited to the same degree with metal-binding agents and inhibition of one activity competitively inhibits the other, (*c*) each activity is proportional to the copper content and (*d*) both activities are lost when copper is removed and regained when copper is added back again[60]. The fraction of catecholase activity has been found to increase upon rough treatment of the enzyme. This suggests that the catecholase enzyme may be a degraded artifact. However, Smit and Krueger[59] feel that both enzymes occur together naturally but that the cresolase is more sensitive. The first indication that there were two enzymes present was found by Dressler and Dawson who showed that cupric ion exchanges with the functioning catecholase, but not the cresolase enzyme[61]. The cresolase activity will oxidize either free or peptide-bound tyrosine[62] to 3,4-dihydroxyphenylalanine.

Tyrosinase has the interesting property of slowly losing activity while functioning as a catalyst, but it does not lose activity under similar conditions when not functioning. Tyrosinase, thus, resembles many of the normal solid inorganic catalysts. This phenomenon called "reaction inactivation" has been extensively studied kinetically[63–66]. As might be expected, the inactivation is first order in enzyme.

Two pieces of evidence support the theory that the enzyme is an oxygen transferase[67] and carries molecular oxygen. Mason and coworkers[68] have shown that the oxygen in 4,5-dimethylcatechol formed from 3,4-dimethylphenol in the presence of this enzyme is derived from oxygen of molecular oxygen and not from oxygen of the water. Kinetic evidence is also in support of an oxygen transferase.

$$E + O_2 \underset{R_2}{\overset{R_1}{\rightleftarrows}} EO_2$$

$$EO_2 + S \overset{R_3}{\rightarrow} \text{product}$$

At low substrate concentration reaction R_3 becomes very small compared to R_1 and R_2 and under these conditions it is possible to detect a reversible combination between oxygen and enzyme[69].

The structure of the oxygenated enzyme is of interest. Mason *et al.*[68] proposed that the oxygen molecule is held between two cuprous ions on the enzyme as $Cu^+O_2Cu^+$ which is called[70] complex III, corresponding to complex III, FeO_2^{2+} of the iron enzymes. The reactivity of complex III in the copper enzymes is quite different than complex III of the iron enzymes. The species $Cu^+O_2Cu^+$ oxidizes catechols to *o*-quinones whereas the comparable species, complex III, FeO_2^{2+}, in the iron enzymes oxidizes catechol to *cis, cis*-muconic acid.

The reason for this difference in products may lie in the protein structure. There are two marked differences between the oxygenated tyrosinase and oxygenated hemocyanin. Oxygenated tyrosinase has a yellow color instead of the blue color of hemocyanin and binds carbon monoxide much more strongly than hemocyanin. These differences may be only qualitative differences and do not necessarily indicate a different structure. The color may be a result of the amount of electron donation from copper to oxygen and the carbon monoxide binding may mean a larger hole at the active center. The larger cavity seems reasonable when we consider that tyrosinase must act on a large substrate; whereas hemocyanin need only carry oxygen.

Hydroxylation by tyrosinase requires a reducing agent such as catechol or ascorbic acid. This implies that CuO_2^+, or its reduction product, CuO^+, but not both, is the active hydroxylation agent. Because it is difficult to imagine a mechanism for CuO_2^+ we are inclined to believe the hydroxylating agent is CuO^+. Substitutions in aromatic systems with their high electron density, commonly occur via electrophilic attack by positive ions, *e.g.*, bromination by Br^+ and nitration by NO_2^+.

CuO⁺ + [benzene, H] → [(+) ring, H, OCu] → [benzene, O, Cu] + H⁺

Cupryl ion, CuO^+, is called[80] complex II because of its similarity to ferryl ion, FeO^{2+}, complex II, of the iron enzymes. Cupryl ion may be thought of as a stable source of (^+OH). Cupryl ion is probably stabilized by d-orbital overlap in the same manner as discussed for the percupryl ion.

Tyrosinase is inactivated by acid much more rapidly when catalyzing an oxidation than when resting[71]. This occurs probably by the reaction of hydrogen ion with the cupryl form of the enzyme.

$$CuO^+ + H^+ \rightarrow Cu^{2+} + OH\cdot$$

The kinetics support this mechanism because the substrate, catechol, protects the enzyme in a competitive manner against hydrogen ion whereas oxygen does not affect the inactivation with acid. The hydrogen ion–catechol competition is explained by the two reactions

$$CuO^+ + H^+ \rightarrow Cu^{2+} + OH\cdot$$

$$CuO^+ + SH_2 \rightarrow Cu^+ + H_2O + S$$

The resting enzyme is either $Cu^+ — Cu^+$ or $Cu^+O_2Cu^+$, and these species are evidently not as acid sensitive. The much greater acid sensitivity of the

References p. 444

CuO^+ form of the enzyme over the CuO_2^+ form is in agreement with the more negative free energy of the cuprous–oxygen atom reaction, compared to the cuprous–oxygen molecule reaction.

	ΔF
$Cu^+ + O + H^+ \rightarrow Cu^{2+} + OH\cdot$	—43 kcal
$Cu^+ + O_2 + H^+ \rightarrow Cu^{2+} + HO_2\cdot$	+ 6.5 kcal

The tritium rate effect during aromatic hydroxylation of 3,4-dimethylphenol by tyrosinase has been found to be very small[72], $k_H/k_T = 1.2$.

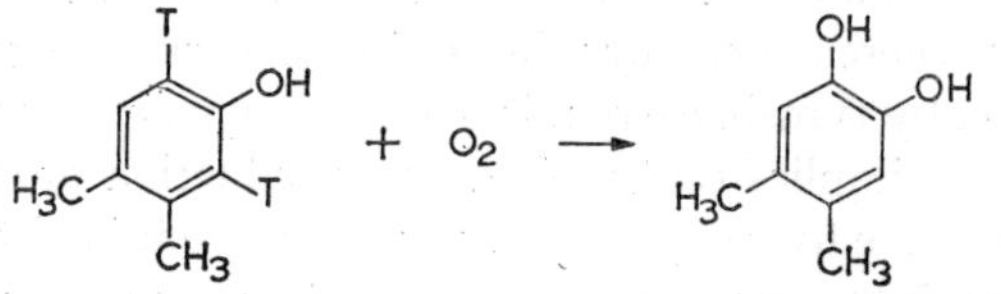

A rate effect is to be expected for an electrophilic displacement reaction on a phenol because the first step to form a comparatively stable oxonium ion should be easy and hence the second step involving C—T bond cleavage is rate determining.

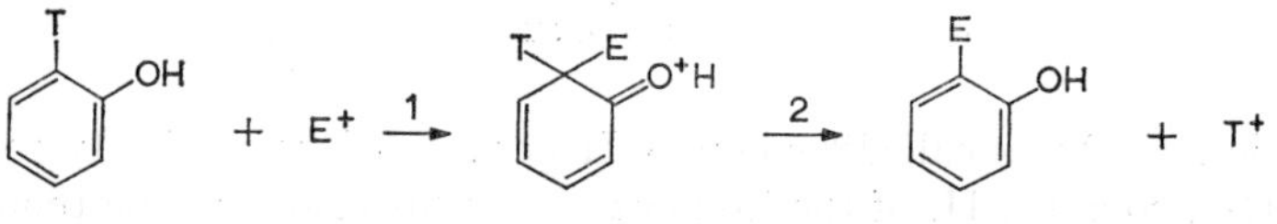

The fact that the rate effect is small indicates that the tritium must be removed very efficiently by the enzyme in the second step.

The catecholase reaction, the oxidation of catechol to *o*-quinone, also appears to be a two-electron reaction because EPR studies have shown that the first product is *o*-quinone and not the intermediate semi-quinone[73].

(*ii*) *Rat-liver hydroxylating system*

There is an hydroxylating system in rat-liver microsomes that is fairly non-specific, consisting of either one or several enzymes[74]. The system requires the reducing agent NADPH[75] and is also a mixed-function oxidase. These two facts are certainly similar to those for tyrosinase and one might speculate on a similar mechanism. First complex III is formed which is reduced to complex II by NADPH, and complex II in turn hydroxylates by an electrophilic attack on the substrate. However, no metal has been found in either this or the following aliphatic hydroxylases. The rat-liver hydroxylating system[76–78] will hydroxylate benzene, diphenylindole, acetanilide, naphthalene and aniline. The hydroxylation of acetanilide and aniline is in the 2 and 4 positions as would be expected for an electrophilic attack on aniline.

A similar hydroxylating enzyme will open the ring in imidazole acetic acid by oxygen to give *N*-formimino aspartic acid[79]. This enzyme requires NADH and transfers one oxygen atom to the substrate.

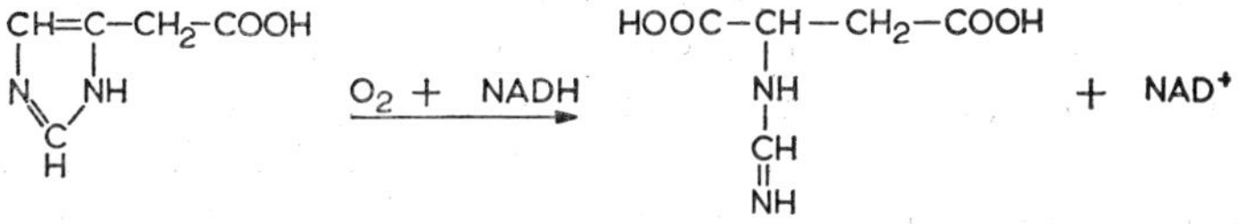

CH=C–CH₂–COOH (imidazole ring: N, NH, C–H) $\xrightarrow{O_2 + NADH}$ HOOC–CH(NH–CH=NH)–CH₂–COOH + NAD^+

The reaction probably proceeds through a hydroxylation, followed by a ketonization and ring opening.

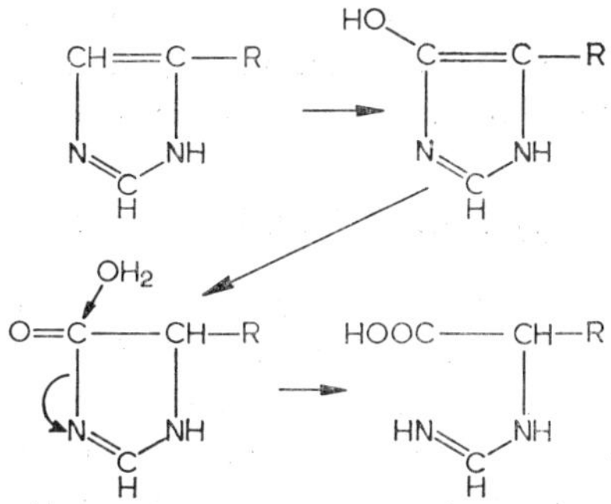

CH=C–R (ring N, NH, C–H) → HO–C=C–R (ring N, NH, C–H) → O=C–CH–R (OH_2; ring N, NH, C–H) → HOOC–CH–R (HN, NH, C–H)

A hydroxylating system causes the cyclization of squalene to lanosterol. This system uses molecular oxygen and one of the atoms of the oxygen molecule appears in the lanosterol[80].

(*d*) *Hydroxylation at a saturated atom*

The enzymes that hydroxylate aliphatic compounds are less well-known than the aromatic hydroxylases. These enzymes commonly require NADPH as a reducing agent and transfer one atom of the oxygen molecule to the substrate. Although there is no good evidence for metals in these enzymes, it is possible that these enzymes also hydroxylate by a mechanism similar to an attack on a double bond with the exception that the hydroxylation is now a direct electrophilic displacement of hydrogen ion by complex II, instead of a prior addition to the double bond.

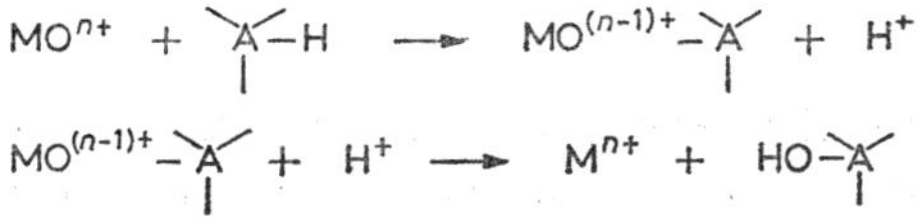

$$MO^{n+} + \;\geq A{-}H \longrightarrow MO^{(n-1)+}{-}A\leq \; + H^+$$

$$MO^{(n-1)+}{-}A\leq \; + H^+ \longrightarrow M^{n+} + HO{-}A\leq$$

References p. 444

Most of the known aliphatic hydroxylases act on steroids. For example, cultures of *Bacillus megatherium* will hydroxylate progesterone in the 15β position and *Bacillus cereus* will hydroxylate the steroid in the 11α position[81]. In general these enzymes seem to transfer only one of the atoms of oxygen to the substrate. Adrenal microsomes will hydroxylate steroids in the 21 position[82,83] and require NADPH for reduction of the other atom of oxygen[84]. These enzymes hydroxylate with retention of configuration. Both the 11α and the 11β hydroxylation[85,86] of pregnanedione proceeds with retention of configuration as does the 7α hydroxylation of cholesterol[87]. This fact is mechanistically important because electrophilic displacement reactions are known to proceed with retention of configuration[88,89].

The 11β-hydroxylating enzyme has been separated into two heat-labile extracts[90]; thus, the ultimate mechanism may involve two steps.

A rat-liver hydroxylating system will hydroxylate trimethylamine to trimethylamine-*N*-oxide. This reaction again requires NADPH and incorporates an oxygen atom from O_2 into the *N*-oxide[91].

(*e*) *Electron-transfer reactions*

These are reactions which use molecular oxygen but both atoms are reduced to water and only electrons are transferred from the substrate. These enzymes are commonly called electron transferases[36]. The examples discussed here are all copper enzymes. Perhaps the cytochromes could be included in this group. The reaction presumably involves the oxidation by molecular oxygen of the cuprous enzyme to a cupric enzyme and the oxidation of the substrate by the cupric enzyme. The reduction product of the oxygen is water.

$$4H^+ + 4Cu^+ + O_2 \rightarrow 4Cu^{2+} + 2H_2O$$

$$4Cu^{2+} + 2SH_2 \rightarrow 2S + 4H^+ + 4Cu^+$$

(*i*) *Ascorbic acid oxidase*[92]

Ascorbic acid oxidase is a copper enzyme that catalyzes the aerobic oxidation of ascorbic acid to dehydroascorbic acid. The enzyme is colorless in the reduced form but blue in the oxidized form. Although listed in this section as an electron transferase, there is no evidence regarding the formation of an oxygen complex.

As with tyrosinase, this enzyme also undergoes reaction inactivation. This reaction inactivation is accelerated by cupric ion[93].

(*ii*) *Laccase*

Laccase catalyzes the aerobic oxidation of hydroquinones to *p*-quinone. It contains four copper atoms per mole which react with one mole of oxygen[94].

This appears to be a simple one-electron oxidation of each copper atom. The reduced enzyme is diamagnetic (cuprous) but becomes paramagnetic (cupric) upon oxidation by oxygen[95]. The cupric enzyme then reacts with hydroquinone to give a one-electron oxidized free-radical product[96], presumably a semiquinone, which subsequently non-enzymatically disproportionates to diamagnetic products.

4. Enzyme-catalyzed substrate activation

(a) *Flavin enzymes*

The flavin enzymes fall into a class in which most of the catalytic effect of the enzyme is to produce an easily oxidizable substrate for the oxygen. In this sense we will consider the flavin as a substrate for the oxygen.

Amino acid oxidases

Kinetics of the L-amino acid oxidase have led to the following mechanism[97]:

$$E\begin{matrix}\diagup FAD \\ \diagdown FAD\end{matrix} + \text{amino acid} \longrightarrow E\begin{matrix}\diagup FADH^{\oplus} \\ \diagdown FADH^{\oplus}\end{matrix} + \text{imino acid}$$

$$E\begin{matrix}\diagup FADH^{\oplus} \\ \diagdown FADH^{\oplus}\end{matrix} + O_2 \longrightarrow E\begin{matrix}\diagup FAD \\ \diagdown FAD\end{matrix} + H_2O_2$$

Other reactions occur but they are slower. The interesting point about this mechanism is that the oxygen molecule reacts with a free radical instead of fully reduced flavin. The flavin semiquinone intermediate has been detected[98] in L-amino acid oxidase by means of its broad absorption at 500–650 mμ.

The oxidation of α-amino acids to the corresponding α-keto acids probably proceeds through an intermediate imino acid instead of a vinyl amine

$$R-\underset{\underset{NH}{\|}}{C}-COOH$$

$$R-\overset{\overset{H}{|}}{C}=\underset{\underset{NH_2}{|}}{C}-COOH$$

because there is no exchange of deuterium with solvent at the β-position during the oxidation[99]. Further evidence for an imino acid is found by the use of a keto–enol tautomerase. If the tautomerase is added during the L-amino acid oxidase catalyzed oxidation of phenylalanine, a new intermediate absorption peak appears at 300 mμ. This peak corresponds to the

References p. 444

vinyl amine so that the tautomerase must catalyze the reaction between imine and vinyl amine[100].

Very likely there is an essential sulfhydryl group in D-amino acid oxidase because sulfhydryl reagents inhibit D-amino acid oxidase. Flavins tend to prevent this inhibition[101].

(*b*) *Miscellaneous enzymes*

Lipoxidases

Lipoxidase catalyzes the aerobic oxidation of linoleic acid to an optically active conjugated hydroperoxide[102–104]. It is unique among oxygenases in that no cofactor has been found. The mechanisms proposed for this enzyme are similar to ordinary fat oxidation.

$$R\cdot + O_2 \rightarrow RO_2\cdot$$

$$RO_2\cdot + RH \rightarrow R\cdot + RO_2H$$

or variations of this[105]. The kinetics[106] of lipoxidase action show that a ternary complex[107] is formed between enzyme, linoleate and oxygen. An induction period has been observed[108] for this reaction. The induction is presumably the time for the relatively slow reaction between hydrocarbon and oxygen to produce the initial enzyme-bound radical.

$$RH + O_2 \rightarrow R\cdot + HO_2\cdot$$

The induction period may be eliminated by adding oxidized linoleic acid. The essential problem in lipoxidase action concerns how the enzyme can stabilize a free radical in order to react with the oxygen. Two factors may be operative. First, the enzyme may hold the radical in a planar position so that resonance stabilization is possible.

$$—CH{=}CH—\dot{C}H—CH{=}CH—$$

$$—\dot{C}H—CH{=}CH—CH{=}CH—$$

$$—CH{=}CH—CH{=}CH—\dot{C}H—$$

Second, aromatic compounds are known to stabilize radicals[109–112] and an aromatic amino acid in the protein may be operative.

5. Summary

The kinetic stability of molecular oxygen is the result of the strong bonding between the atoms. This bonding can be partially destroyed by adding one electron. Thus, if one electron can be added, the rest will be added easily.

The electron may be added in biological systems in two ways. A metal may donate electrons to oxygen in a metal–oxygen complex or a free radical may donate its odd electron to the oxygen. The first complex of metal and oxygen is called complex III, and the two-electron reduction product is called complex II. Enzymes are classified as (*1*) those with only complex III (oxygen transferases), (*2*) those with both complex II and III (mixed-function oxidases), and (*3*) those in which the metal is oxidized by the oxygen (electron transferases). Finally, a few examples of reactions of oxygen with free radicals are discussed.

References p. 444

BIBLIOGRAPHY

1 J. M. Nelson and C. R. Dawson, *Advan. Enzymol.*, 4 (1944) 99.
2 A. B. Lerner, *Advan. Enzymol.*, 14 (1953) 73.
3 I. W. Sizer, *Advan. Enzymol.*, 14 (1953) 129.
4 H. S. Mason, *Advan. Enzymol.*, 16 (1955) 105.
5 H. S. Mason, *Science*, 125 (1957) 1185.
6 H. S. Mason, *Advan. Enzymol.*, 19 (1957) 457.
7 L. Massart and R. Vercauteren, *Ann. Rev. Biochem.*, 28 (1957) 527.

REFERENCES

1 L. L. Ingraham, *Biochemical Mechanisms*, John Wiley and Sons, New York, 1962.
2 W. M. Latimer, *Oxidation Potentials*, Prentice-Hall, New Jersey, 1952.
3 J. S. Griffith, *Proc. Roy. Soc. (London) Ser. A*, 235 (1956) 23.
4 M. Wolfsberg and L. Helmholz, *J. Chem. Phys.*, 20 (1952) 837.
5 F. A. Cotton, *J. Chem. Soc.*, (1960) 5269.
6 K. Nakamota, J. Fujita, M. Kobayashi and R. Tsuchida, *J. Chem. Phys.*, 27 (1957) 439.
7 P. George, *J. Chem. Soc.*, (1954) 4349.
8 R. E. Huffman and N. Davidson, *J. Am. Chem. Soc.*, 78 (1956) 4836.
9 H. Nord, *Acta Chem. Scand.*, 9 (1955) 430.
10 J. E. Lu Valle and A. Weissberger, *J. Am. Chem. Soc.*, 69 (1957) 1567.
11 J. H. Wang, A. Nakahara and E. B. Fleisher, *J. Am. Chem. Soc.*, 80 (1958) 1109.
12 P. George, D. H. Irvine and S. C. Glauser, *Ann. N. Y. Acad. Sci.*, 88 (1960) 393.
13 P. George, *Haematin Enzymes, I.U.B. Symp. Ser.*, 19 (1959) 103.
14 D. J. E. Ingram and J. E. Bennett, *Discussions Faraday Soc.*, 18 (1955) 140.
15 L. F. Larkworthy and R. S. Nyholm, *Nature*, 183 (1957) 1377.
16 J. H. Wang, *J. Am. Chem. Soc.*, 80 (1958) 3198.
17 J. H. Wang, *Haematin Enzymes, I.U.B. Symp. Ser.*, 19 (1959) 98.
18 L. Pauling and C. D. Coryell, *Proc. Natl. Acad. Sci. U.S.*, 22 (1936) 210.
19 A. Hakahara and J. H. Wang, *J. Am. Chem. Soc.*, 80 (1958) 6526.
20 A. H. Corwin and Z. Reya, *J. Am. Chem. Soc.*, 78 (1956) 2437.
21 A. H. Corwin and S. D. Bruck, *J. Am. Chem. Soc.*, 80 (1958) 4736.
22 J. F. Drake and R. J. P. Williams, *Nature*, 182 (1958) 1084.
23 J. Wyman Jr. and D. W. Allen, *J. Polymer Sci.*, 5 (1951) 499.
24 G. Felsenfeld, *J. Cellular Comp. Physiol.*, 43 (1954) 23.
25 M. Joselow and C. R. Dawson, *Science*, 121 (1955) 300.
26 L. C. G. Thomsen, M. Hines and H. S. Mason, *Arch. Biochem. Biophys.*, 83 (1959) 88.
27 G. Felsenfeld and M. P. Printx, *J. Am. Chem. Soc.*, 81 (1959) 6259.
28 W. A. Rawlinson, *Australian J. Exptl. Biol. Med. Sci.*, 18 (1940) 131.
29 I. M. Klotz and T. A. Klotz, *Science*, 121 (1955) 477.
30 L. J. Andrews and R. M. Keefer, *J. Am. Chem. Soc.*, 71 (1949) 2379.
31 R. M. Keefer, L. J. Andrews and R. E. Kepner, *J. Am. Chem. Soc.*, 71 (1949) 2381.
32 R. M. Keefer, L. J. Andrews and R. E. Kepner, *J. Am. Chem. Soc.*, 71 (1949) 3906.
33 T. Nakamura and H. S. Mason, *Biochem. Biophys. Res. Comm.*, 3 (1960) 297.
34 W. A. Rawlinson, *Australian J. Exptl. Biol. Med. Sci.*, 18 (1940) 131.
35 I. M. Klotz and R. E. Heiney, *Proc. Natl. Acad. Sci. U.S.*, 43 (1957) 717.
36 H. S. Mason, *Science*, 125 (1957) 1185.
37 O. Hayaishi and K. Hashimoto, *J. Biochem. (Tokyo)*, 37 (1950) 371.
38 O. Hayaishi, M. Katigiri and S. Rothberg, *J. Am. Chem. Soc.*, 77 (1955) 5450.
39 O. Hayaishi, M. Katigiri and S. Rothberg, *J. Biol. Chem.*, 229 (1957) 905.
40 W. von Doering and R. M. Haines, *J. Am. Chem. Soc.*, 76 (1954) 482.
41 O. Hayaishi, A. A. Patchett and B. Witkop, *Ann. Chem.*, 608 (1957) 158.
42 A. A. Patchett and B. Witkop, *J. Org. Chem.*, 22 (1957) 1477.

43 Y. Kojima, N. Itada and O. Hayaishi, *J. Biol. Chem.*, 236 (1961) 2223.
44 S. Dagley and D. A. Stopher, *Biochem. J.*, 73 (1959) 16.
45 R. Y. Stanier and J. L. Ingraham, *J. Biol. Chem.*, 210 (1954) 799.
46 D. L. MacDonald, R. Y. Stanier and J. L. Ingraham, *J. Biol. Chem.*, 210 (1954) 809.
47 L. Ottley and E. L. Tatum, *J. Biol. Chem.*, 223 (1956) 307.
48 W. E. Knox and S. W. Edwards, *J. Biol. Chem.*, 216 (1955) 489.
49 D. I. Crandall, *J. Biol. Chem.*, 212 (1955) 566.
50 W. E. Knox and S. W. Edwards, *J. Biol. Chem.*, 216 (1955) 479.
51 K. Tokuyama, *J. Biochem. (Tokyo)*, 46 (1959) 1379.
52 D. I. Crandall, R. C. Krulger, F. Anan, K. Yasunobu and H. S. Mason, *J. Biol. Chem.*, 235 (1960) 3011.
53 O. Hayaishi, S. Rothberg, A. H. Mehler and Y. Saito, *J. Biol. Chem.*, 229 (1957) 889.
54 H. S. Mason, *Nature*, 177 (1956) 79.
55 F. Kubowitz, *Biochem. Z.*, 296 (1938) 443.
56 F. Kubowitz, *Biochem. Z.*, 299 (1938) 32.
57 H. Dressler and C. R. Dawson, *Biochim. Biophys. Acta*, 45 (1961) 508.
58 Y. Karkhanis and E. Friedin, *Biochem. Biophys. Res. Comm.*, 4 (1961) 303.
59 J. L. Smith and R. C. Krueger, *J. Biol. Chem.*, 237 (1962) 1121.
60 D. Kertsz, *Nature*, 180 (1957) 506.
61 H. Dressler and C. R. Dawson, *Biochim. Biophys. Acta*, 45 (1961) 515.
62 K. T. Yasunobu, E. W. Peterson and H. S. Mason, *J. Biol. Chem.*, 234 (1959) 3291.
63 W. H. Miller and C. R. Dawson, *J. Am. Chem. Soc.*, 63 (1941) 1168.
64 W. H. Miller, M. F. Mallette, L. J. Roth and C. R. Dawson, *J. Am. Chem. Soc.*, 66 (1944) 515.
65 I. Asimov and C. R. Dawson, *J. Am. Chem. Soc.*, 72 (1950) 820.
66 L. L. Ingraham, *J. Am. Chem. Soc.*, 77 (1955) 2875.
67 H. S. Mason, *Advan. Enzymol.*, 19 (1957) 79.
68 H. S. Mason, W. L. Fowlks and E. Peterson, *J. Am. Chem. Soc.*, 77 (1955) 2914.
69 L. L. Ingraham, *J. Am. Chem. Soc.*, 79 (1957) 666.
70 H. J. Bright, B. J. B. Wood and L. L. Ingraham, *Ann. N.Y. Acad. Sci.*, 100 (1963) 965.
71 L. L. Ingraham in Myron Gordon (Ed.), *4th Conference on Pigment Cell Biology*, Academic Press, New York, 1959.
72 B. J. B. Wood and L. L. Iingraham, *Arch. Biochem. Biophys.*, 98 (1962) 479.
73 H. S. Mason, E. Spencer and I. Yamazaki, *Biochem. Biophys. Res. Comm.*, 49 (1961) 236.
74 H. S. Posner, C. Mitoma and S. Udenfriend, *Arch. Biochem. Biophys.*, 94 (1961) 269.
75 H. S. Posner, C. Mitoma, S. Rothberg and S. Udenfriend, *Arch. Biochem. Biophys.*, 94 (1961) 280.
76 J. Booth and E. Boyland, *Biochem. J.*, 66 (1957) 73.
77 C. Mitoma, H. S. Posner, H. C. Fritz and S. Udenfriend, *Arch. Biochem. Biophys.*, 61 (1956) 431.
78 H. S. Posner, C. Mitoma and S. Udenfriend, *Arch. Biochem. Biophys.*, 94 (1961) 269.
79 S. Rothberg and O. Hayaishi, *J. Biol. Chem.*, 229 (1957) 897.
80 T. T. Tchen and K. Bloch, *J. Am. Chem. Soc.*, 78 (1956) 1516.
81 W. J. Acaleer, T. A. Jacob, L. B. Turnbull, E. F. Schoenwaldt and T. A. Stoudt, *Arch. Biochem. Biophys.*, 73 (1958) 127.
82 K. J. Ryan and L. L. Engel, *J. Am. Chem. Soc.*, 78 (1956) 2654.
83 M. Hayano, M. C. Lindberg, R. I. Dorfman, H. E. H. Hancock and W. Van-Doering, *Arch. Biochem. Biophys.*, 59 (1955) 529.
84 A. C. Brownie and J. K. Grant, *Biochem. J.*, 62 (1956) 29.
85 E. J. Corey, G. A. Gregoriou and D. H. Peterson, *J. Am. Chem. Soc.*, 80 (1958) 2338.

[86] M. HAYANO, M. GUR, R. I. DORFMAN, O. K. DEBEK AND D. H. PETERSON, *J. Am. Chem. Soc.*, 80 (1958) 2336.
[87] S. BERGSTROM, S. LINDSTREDT, B. SAMUELSON, E. J. COREY AND G. A. GREGORIOUS, *J. Am. Chem. Soc.*, 80 (1958) 2337.
[88] S. WINSTEIN AND T. G. TRAYLOR, *J. Am. Chem. Soc.*, 78 (1956) 2597.
[89] F. R. JENSEN AND L. H. GALE, *J. Am. Chem. Soc.*, 81 (1959) 1261.
[90] G. M. TOMKINS, J. F. CURRAN AND P. J. MICHAEL, *Biochim. Biophys. Acta*, 28 (1959) 449.
[91] J. R. BAKER AND S. CHAYKIN, *J. Biol. Chem.*, 237 (1962) 1309.
[92] C. R. DAWSON, *Ann. N.Y. Acad. Sci.*, 88 (1960) 353.
[93] N. BENHAMOU, R. J. MAGEE AND C. R. DAWSON, *Arch. Biochem. Biophys.*, 81 (1959) 135.
[94] T. NAKAMURA, *Biochim. Biophys. Acta*, 30 (1960) 538.
[95] T. NAKAMURA, *Biochim. Biophys. Acta*, 42 (1960) 499.
[96] T. NAKAMURA, *Biochem. Biophys. Res. Comm.*, 2 (1960) 111.
[97] D. WELLNER AND A. MEISTER, *J. Biol. Chem.*, 236 (1961) 2357.
[98] H. BEINERT, *J. Biol. Chem.*, 225 (1957) 465.
[99] C. FRIEDEN AND S. F. VELICK, *Biochim. Biophys. Acta*, 23 (1957) 439.
[100] B. M. PITT, *J. Am. Chem. Soc.*, 80 (1958) 3799.
[101] W. R. FRISELL AND L. HELLERMAN, *J. Biol. Chem.*, 225 (1957) 53.
[102] A. S. PRIVETT, C. NICHELL, W. O. LUNDBERG AND P. O. BOYER, *J. Am. Oil Chemists' Soc.*, 32 (1955) 505.
[103] R. T. HOLMAN, *Arch. Biochem.*, 15 (1947) 403.
[104] S. BERGSTROM AND R. T. HOLMAN, *Nature*, 161 (1948) 55.
[105] A. M. SIDDIQUI AND A. L. TAPPEL, *J. Am. Oil Chemists' Soc.*, 34 (1957) 529.
[106] A. L. TAPPEL, P. D. BOYER AND W. O. LUNDBER, *J. Biol. Chem.*, 199 (1952) 267.
[107] L. L. INGRAHAM AND B. MAKOWER, *J. Phys. Chem.*, 58 (1954) 266.
[108] J. L. HAINING AND B. AXELROD, *J. Biol. Chem.*, 232 (1958) 193.
[109] L. L. INGRAHAM, *J. Chem. Phys.* 18 (1950) 988.
[110] F. R. MAYO, *J. Am. Chem. Soc.*, 75 (1953) 6133.
[111] G. S. HAMMOND, C. E. BOOZER, C. E. HAMILTON AND J. N. SEN, *J. Am. Chem. Soc.*, 77 (1955) 3236.
[112] G. A. RUSSELL, *J. Am. Chem. Soc.*, 79 (1957) 2977.

Chapter X

Peroxidases and Catalase

A. S. BRILL

Department of Molecular Biophysics,
Yale University, New Haven, Conn. (U.S.A.)

1. Introduction

Peroxidases and catalase, as haemoproteins, are classed with haemoglobin, myoglobin, and with the cytochromes. They are enzymes, which haemoglobin and myoglobin are not; and they are naturally soluble, which the cytochromes are not. While the physiological roles of the oxygen transport, storage, and utilization pigments are well defined, the importance of peroxidases and catalase is not clear. Peroxidases are widespread in plant materials and have been implicated in the control of plant growth[1]; they are also occasionally found in animal tissues. Catalase is very generally present in aerobic cells, frequently in sizeable amounts. Very nearly one per cent of the dry weight of *M. lysodeikticus* is catalase. The useful purposes which are apparent—participation in coupled oxidations[2], and safeguard against peroxide poisoning — could be served by a more modest quantity. The interest in these enzymes is largely centered about mechanisms of reaction, but many reasons for the presence of these vigorous catalysts surely remain to be uncovered.

Catalases from different sources are alike; peroxidases are generally different from each other and from catalase. In Table I are listed some molecular properties. Catalase from all sources has a molecular weight of 250 000 $\pm$ 10%. The molecular weights of the peroxidases average about one-fourth that of catalase, but are much more variable. The catalase molecule has four haem groups, the peroxidases one. (One of the myeloperoxidases is said to have two haem groups.) In all catalases the haem is derived from protoporphyrin IX. Lactoperoxidase and the myeloperoxidases have unusual and undetermined porphyrins. Horseradish (HRP) is the most investigated peroxidase, and a large part of this treatment deals with HRP.

References p. 478

TABLE I

MOLECULAR PROPERTIES OF SOME CRYSTALLINE PEROXIDASES AND CATALASES

Enzyme	*Molecular weight*	*Number of haem groups*	*Porphyrin*	*Activity*	*Crystallization*
Horseradish peroxidase	40000	1	Proto-IX	P.Z. 1020–1220	Theorell, 1941
Lactoperoxidase	93000	1	*Not* Proto-IX but unknown	70	Theorell *et al.*, 1941
Japanese radish peroxidase	55000	—	—	—	Morita and Kameda, 1957
Beef-liver catalase	251000	(3)	Proto-IX	Kat.f. 60000	Sumner and Dounce, 1937
Horse-erythrocyte catalase	250000	4	Proto-IX	137000	Bonnichsen, 1947
Human-erythrocyte catalase	220000	4	Proto-IX	80000	Herbert and Pinsent, 1948
M. lysodeikticus catalase	232000	4	Proto-IX	120000	Herbert and Pinsent, 1948

Catalase and peroxidases catalyze reactions between hydroperoxides (H_2O_2, hydrogen peroxide; MeOOH, methyl hydroperoxide; EtOOH, ethyl hydroperoxide; and other hydroperoxides) and many oxidizable compounds. While there are differences in the efficiencies of the two classes of enzymes with respect to the catalytic reduction of certain of the hydrogen donors, the defining difference between peroxidases and catalase is in action toward H_2O_2. In the presence of catalase, H_2O_2 is vigorously decomposed into oxygen and water in the so-called "catalatic" reaction. By comparison, the action of peroxidases is very feeble indeed, about 10^{-4} as effective. However, peroxidases are about 10^2 more effective than methaemoglobin and metmyoglobin[2]; for all three of these pigments, the evolution of oxygen is not normally observable.

Spectrophotometric and rapid titration determinations of catalase activity have supplanted earlier methods[3]. Under the conditions of these tests the time course of the reaction is accurately described by

$$\frac{dx}{dt} = -kex \qquad (1)$$

where x and e are the concentrations of peroxide and enzyme respectively. k, a second-order rate constant, is obtained from the slope of the plot of ln(residual H_2O_2) *versus* time. Consider any mechanism in which an H_2O_2 molecule is presumed bound to a haem group, and a second H_2O_2 molecule reacts with this activated compound to produce an H_2O molecule and an O_2 molecule, freeing the haem group. The number of times per second that the haem group is freed (turnover number = T.N.) is given by

$$\text{T.N. (per haem group)} = \frac{1}{4e}\left|\frac{d}{dt}\left(\frac{x}{2}\right)\right| = \frac{kx}{8} \qquad (2)$$

Under the conditions of the activity tests, at room temperatures, catalase turnover numbers are in the range 20000–40000 sec^{-1}. It must be emphasized that the T.N., an important concept and molecular parameter, has not only been defined in several ways but depends upon the experimental conditions. One must be careful in comparing the turnover numbers from different laboratories.

The parameter which has conventionally been used to compare, on a weight basis, the catalatic efficiencies of catalase preparations is Kat.f. (Katalasefähigkeit).

$$\text{Kat.f.} = \frac{1}{2.30\,W}\left|\frac{1}{x}\frac{dx}{dt}\right| \qquad (3)$$

where W is the weight (in grams) of protein in the reaction mixture, and the

References p. 478

time t is in minutes. In Table I are listed Kat.f. values for several crystalline and highly purified catalases at 20–25°C.

A unique reaction for measuring the activity of peroxidase preparations is not naturally defined as it is for catalase. Furthermore *no* one test of activity is of special merit in rating the catalytic efficiency of all the peroxidases. The reader is referred elsewhere for methods developed for particular peroxidases[3].

The purification of peroxidase and catalase preparations can be followed by activity tests and by a spectrophotometric criterion, the P.V. (purity value), described in Section 2. Highly purified preparations have been crystallized (Table I), and there are now considerable chemical and physical data which have been obtained from such preparations.

2. Physical and chemical properties of the free enzymes*

It is convenient to consider successively the components iron, porphyrin, and apoenzyme.

In both peroxidases and catalases, the high paramagnetic susceptibility values of the free enzymes at neutral pH provide conclusive evidence that the iron is in the ferric form. In alkaline solution, peroxidase, like metmyoglobin, methaemoglobin and ferricytochrome *c*, ionizes. This reaction is accompanied by marked changes in magnetic moment and absorption spectrum. For horseradish peroxidase the pK of this ionization is 9.6, and the magnetic moment drops from a high spin value of 5.5 B.M. (Bohr magnetons) for the acid form to 2.7 B.M. for the alkaline form[4]. Catalase, differing from the above four haemoproteins, does not undergo a transition between the low and the high pH regions of protein denaturation. Another difference is that the iron in catalase cannot be reduced to the ferrous form with dithionite unless the enzyme is denatured. There is substantial evidence (Section 6) for quadrivalent iron, perhaps in the form of the ferryl group (FeO^{2+}), in certain compounds of peroxidase and catalase (and metmyoglobin and methaemoglobin) resulting from reactions with peroxides and other oxidizing agents.

The structure of the metmyoglobin molecule at a resolution of 1.4 Å presented by Kendrew shows the iron atoms to lie 0.3–0.5 Å on one side of the plane of the porphyrin ring, and equally distant from the four pyrrole nitrogen atoms. There is no evidence to suggest that, in the haem groups of peroxidases and catalase, the iron atoms should not also be very nearly in the tetrapyrrole plane, and centrally located. The positions of the six

* The reader is assumed to be familiar with relevant basic information covered in other parts of Comprehensive Biochemistry, such as the Chapter by J. N. Phillips, Physico-Chemical Properties of Porphyrins, Vol. 9, p. 34.

ligands of the octahedral iron complexes found in haemoproteins are conventionally numbered one through four for the pyrrole nitrogens, five for the donor group which is bound as well to the protein, and six for a distinct molecule or ion (such as H_2O or OH^-), or, as has been suggested in several cases, another protein group. In all compounds of a particular haemoprotein, the ligands at positions 1–5 remain the same. However, the iron–protein link is not the only factor involved in the binding of haem to protein, the propionyl carboxyl groups of porphyrins being strongly implicated in some cases. For example, the maximum of the Soret band obtained when protoporphyrin IX reacts with apo-horseradish peroxidase at pH 6.8 has the same position and very nearly the same extinction coefficient as that of horseradish peroxidase itself. When the carboxyl groups are blocked, either in protohaemin or protoporphyrin IX, by forming the dimethyl esters, there is no spectrophotometric indication of binding upon addition of the modified prosthetic group to the apoenzyme[5]. Furthermore, it can be shown that protoporphyrin competes with protohaemin for the same sites on the apo-horseradish peroxidase molecule.

But for the possibility of free radicals, the apoenzyme and the porphyrin ring are not paramagnetic, nor are the molecules and ions that form compounds with peroxidases and catalases. The magnetic moment arises solely from the iron. Whether the iron is of high, low, or intermediate spin depends upon the ligands in all six positions. However, for a particular haemoprotein, provided that the porphyrin structure remains intact, the changes in paramagnetic susceptibility which accompany the formation of a compound are due *only* to the change in binding at ligand position 6. Similarly, the differences in the magnetic moments of the same compounds of catalase, peroxidases, metmyoglobin and methaemoglobin should reflect mainly differences in the protein groups at position 5, with possible secondary influences of the protein groups near position 6 and of the protein groups bound to the propionyl side-chains of the porphyrin.

The absorption spectra of free base (two H atoms in the center) porphyrins are characterized by a strong single peak (Soret band) in the near ultraviolet, at about 400 mμ, and four fairly sharp bands of moderate intensity in the visible, from 500–650 mμ. The coalescence of the four visible bands of the free base to two when a metal ion is bound can be explained from considerations of symmetry alone[6]. The effect of the side-chains is secondary in this connection, and the metalloporphyrins are taken to have a four-fold rotational symmetry (D_{4h}). The visible bands (and the Soret as well) arise from π–π transitions, whence there is no allowed z (perpendicular to the molecular plane) dipole transition. The in-plane dipole transitions are equivalent (x and y belong to the doubly degenerate irreducible representation E_u). One might, therefore, expect but one band. The

References p. 478

TABLE II

SPECTRAL AND MAGNETIC PROPERTIES OF COMPLEXES OF PEROXIDASE, CATALASE. METMYOGLOBIN, AND METHAEMOGLOBIN

Abbreviations: HRP, horseradish peroxidase; BMC, bacterial micrococcus catalase; HBC, horse-blood catalase; C.T., charge-transfer band; λ_{max}, wavelength of absorption peak, in millimicrons, or of shoulder if number appears in parentheses; ε_{mM}, millimolar extinction coefficient; N.M., not measured.

Complex		*Absorption bands*					*Magnetic moment (Bohr magnetons)*	*Refs.*
		C.T.1	*α*	*β*	*C.T.2*	*Soret*		
Peroxidase (HRP)								
Fluoride	λ_{max}	612	560	(530)	488	404	5.9	47,48
	ε_{mM}	6.9	4.8		7.6	130		
Water, pH 5.6	λ_{max}	641	(~580)	(~530)	497	403	5.5	47,48
	ε_{mM}	2.8			10.0	91		
Hydroxide	λ_{max}	~635	572	545	—	416	2.7	47,48
	ε_{mM}	~ 1.5	6.9	8.6		89		
Azide	λ_{max}	635	565	534	(~495)	416	N.M.	47
	ε_{mM}	1.7	5.5	8.2		114		
Cyanide	λ_{max}	—	(570)	538	—	423	2.7	47,48
	ε_{mM}			10.2		94		
Catalase								
Fluoride (BMC)	λ_{max}	(~620)	598	(~535)	~485	406.5	5.7	49,50
	ε_{mM}		12.7		~ 16	109	(HBC)	
Water, pH 6.8 (HBC)	λ_{max}	623	—	541	505	405	5.7	50,51
	ε_{mM}	7.3		9.2	10.5	95	(HBC)	
Azide (BMC)	λ_{max}	621	587	537.5	500	413	5.4	49,50
	ε_{mM}	8.7	6.9	7.8	10.2	116	(HBC)	
Cyanide (BMC)	λ_{max}	—	(~588)	554.5	—	425	2.4	49,50
	ε_{mM}			11.7		92	(HBC)	

TABLE II (*Continued*)

Complex		*Absorption bands*					*Magnetic moment (Bohr magnetons)*	*Refs.*
		C.T.1	*α*	*β*	*C.T.2*	*Soret*		
Metmyoglobin (horse)								
Fluoride	λ_{max}	604	(585)	(550)	487	406	5.9	50,52,61
	ε_{mM}	9.2			9.9	146		
Water, pH 6.4	λ_{max}	630	(580)	(550)	502	408	5.7	50,52,61
	ε_{mM}	3.9			10.2	188		
Hydroxide	λ_{max}	(600)	585	539	(490)	411	5.1	50,52,61
	ε_{mM}		7.8	8.8		119		
Azide	λ_{max}	(635)	570	540	—	420	3.3	52
	ε_{mM}		8.7	11.2		123		
Cyanide	λ_{max}	—	(570)	540	—	422	2.0	11,52
	ε_{mM}			11.3		116		
Methaemoglobin (horse)								
Fluoride	λ_{max}	605	—	(550)	483	403	5.8	47,52
	ε_{mM}	10.9			10.3	144		
Water, pH 6.4	λ_{max}	631	(575)	(540)	500	405	5.6	47,50,52
	ε_{mM}	4.4			10.0	179		
Hydroxide	λ_{max}	(605)	575	540	(485)	409.5	4.7	11,52
	ε_{mM}		9.2	10.9		120		
Azide	λ_{max}	(630)	575	540	—	417	2.4	52
	ε_{mM}		9.9	12.8		134		
Cyanide	λ_{max}	—	(~575)	540	—	419	2.5	47,52
	ε_{mM}			12.5		124		

References p. 478

existence of two bands is ascribed (from the constancy of their energy separation in the spectra of different porphyrins) to different vibrational levels of the excited electronic state (0–0 and 0–1 vibrational transitions). In contrast with the metalloporphyrins, the free bases have only a two-fold rotational symmetry about the z axis, the x and y axes are no longer equivalent, and the allowed transitions are to excited electronic states of different energy. Once again the vibrational energies enter to double the number of bands*.

The *visible* spectra of many ferric porphyrin compounds differ from the two-banded spectra characteristic of most other metalloporphyrins. This is most apparent in haemoprotein compounds of intermediate to high spin. For example, bacterial catalase azide has four distinct peaks, at 621, 587, 537.5, and 500 mμ (Table II). Free catalase has three distinct peaks, and free peroxidase, metmyoglobin and methaemoglobin at neutral pH have two peaks and two pronounced shoulders. Low-spin ferric porphyrin compounds have the usual metalloporphyrin spectra, an α band between 555 and 595 mμ, and a β band between 525 and 555 mμ. An explanation for the extra bands of the intermediate and high-spin ferric porphyrins may be found in the spectra of simpler ferric compounds[7]. Ferric complexes with saturated ligands (other than those coordinating through sulfur), such as acetate and fluoride, have feeble absorption in the visible. However, when a ferric complex is formed with an unsaturated ligand, there may appear intense bands in the regions 450–500 mμ and 600–650 mμ. The condition for the appearance of these bands is that the complex be of high spin. In low-spin compounds, the bands are weak or absent. The origin of these bands, which are not present at all in either the free ferric ion or the free ligands, lies in the formation of excited states characterized by the transfer of an electron from the unsaturated ligand to the ferric ion. Since in ferrihaemoprotein compounds the absorption bands (*1*) just on the red side of the usual α-band region, and (*2*) on the blue side of the β-band region, behave like the charge-transfer bands in simpler ferric compounds, they have been characterized as charge-transfer bands (C.T. 1 and C.T. 2) and are so labeled[7,8] in Tables II and IV. However, the assignments of the visible bands to particular transitions are not certain[62,63].

A potentially important difference exists between the environment of the iron atom in haemoproteins and in simpler coordination complexes. In the latter, the stable configuration of sterically free small ligands results from interaction between each ligand and the central metal ion, with no con-

* Description of the porphyrin molecule as a cyclic polyene, leading to a four-orbital model, has recently been shown to account not only for the appropriate numbers of visible bands, but also for the much greater intensity of the Soret band. The quantitative value of this model is limited[6,64].

straints from outside the coordination sphere. When quadridentate ligands, *e.g.*, porphyrins, occupy positions 1–4, only the ligands in positions 5 and 6 are not hindered. In haemoproteins the group in position 5 is constrained as well, (and possibly the group in position 6 also), for it and the porphyrin ring are both bound to the protein which has a somewhat rigid configuration. The changes in magnetic and spectral properties of coordination complexes which accompany distortions arising from steric hindrance of ligands are currently being investigated.

The ligands available on the protein for binding iron are limited: carboxylate anions, imidazoles of histidine residues, amino groups, the phenolate anion of tyrosine, and, perhaps, the sulfhydryl group of cysteine. The high resolution picture of metmyoglobin available from X-ray diffraction has unequivocally established the imidazole group of histidine in position 5 of the haem group, with a water molecule in position 6, sandwiched between the iron atom and another histidine. This situation appears to be the same in methaemoglobin, but the present degree of refinement does not permit a definite statement. The absorption spectra of methaemoglobin and metmyoglobin are so alike that it is possible to recognize the similar spectrum of peroxidase as being different. The spectral properties of catalase are quite distinct from the other three haemoproteins. These considerations require either that the iron atoms in catalase and peroxidase do not exist in the histidine–Fe–H_2O–histidine arrangement found in methaemoglobin and metmyoglobin, or that the environments of the haem groups in the former proteins differ significantly from those in the latter two. The binding of imidazole groups in both positions 5 and 6 is ruled out for peroxidase because the ferrous form does not have a haemochrome spectrum. Since ferrocatalase cannot be prepared, the criterion of the preceding sentence cannot be applied. However, on the basis of spectral and magnetic properties, it is unlikely that catalase iron is bound directly to two histidine groups, or that a sulfhydryl group is involved in coordination with iron in either catalase or peroxidase. Further discussion of the iron–protein bonds appears in Section 3 on the pH dependence of complex formation.

The spectrophotometric purity criterion, P.V., is defined as the ratio of the maximum absorbance of the Soret band to the maximum absorbance in the region 278–280 mμ. The value of this number is based upon the fact that the Soret absorption is characteristic of haemoproteins, while the absorbance at 278–280 mμ arises from *all* the proteins present (including impurities). The interference of a second haemoprotein with the validity of this criterion is obvious. A less troublesome interference can arise in the early stages of purification when nucleic acids may be present and absorbing greatly at 260 mμ. A shift of the 278-mμ peak downwards indicates that protein is not the only impurity.

References p. 478

No leading information is obtained from the amino acid analyses of peroxidases and catalase, and sequence studies are just being started. It has not been possible to remove haem groups from catalase or peroxidases with some amino acids attached. No method of splitting off the haem groups from myeloperoxidase or lactoperoxidase is very effective. Protohaem comes off cleanly from catalase and horseradish peroxidase in acetone–HCl, but only HRP can be successfully reconstituted. HRP recombined from protohaem IX and the apoenzyme has the same activity and spectral properties as the native enzyme[9]. (It is interesting that apo-HRP bound to mesohaem and haemotohaem is more effective than the protohaem enzyme in catalyzing the peroxidation of pyrogallol[10]. The ferric ion cannot be substituted by other metal ions without loss of activity.)

Ferriperoxidases, within the pH limitations of denaturation, show a single ionization of pK 9.5–11 (depending upon the peroxidase and the ionic strength). The spectrophotometric and magnetic changes accompanying the formation of the hydroxide have been analyzed in detail and with clarity[11]. There is no ionization of catalase; the spectral and magnetic properties are independent of pH within the limits of denaturation. Oxidation–reduction potential measurements of the ferro–ferric complex in HRP have demonstrated an ionization at pH 7 for the lower valence form[12].

3. Complexes of peroxidases and catalase

Peroxidases and catalase react with numerous "simple" compounds such as fluoride, formate, acetate, azide, and cyanide, to form spectroscopically and magnetically distinct complexes (Table II). Considerable data are available on the relative strengths of molecular species in producing ligand-field splitting in transition-metal ion complexes. The ligands of Table II are arranged in this order and the magnetic moments demonstrate that ferriperoxidase and catalase complexes behave in the usual manner. Certain changes in the spectral bands are characteristic of the transition from high to low spin: the Soret band moves to longer wavelengths, the charge-transfer bands decrease in intensity, and the β band increases in intensity.

These complexes have been studied for some time, with the hope that the knowledge acquired would aid in the interpretation of the properties of enzyme–substrate compounds. While progress has been made in understanding chemical and physical characteristics of the simple complexes, such a fundamental question as "Are these ligands bound as anions or undissociated acids?" remains to be answered unequivocally.

The direct interpretation of the effect of pH upon the equilibrium concentration of complex is that the free (undissociated) acid is bound[13]. This follows from the independence of pH of the dissociation constant

$$K_c = \frac{[\text{free enzyme}]\,[\text{HA}]}{[\text{complex}]} \tag{4}$$

where the concentration of complex formed and the remaining free enzyme are determined experimentally, and the free acid concentration is calculated from the pK of the acid and the pH of the solution. Plots of pK_c *versus* pH for hydrofluoric, formic, acetic, hydrazoic, and hydrocyanic acids are very nearly constant over the pH ranges for which experimental data are available. Kinetic measurements of the reaction of formate with catalase also indicate that the free acid is complexed. (An interesting side light of this experiment shows the rate of combination of catalase with formate is almost as rapid as with H_2O_2.)

Objections have been raised to the direct interpretation of these data. In the cases of metmyoglobin and methaemoglobin, where considerably more data are available from thermodynamic studies of complex formation, the evidence heavily favors the binding of the anions[14]. For these pigments, the effect of pH upon equilibrium constants is complicated by the ionization of haem-linked protein groups. It has been suggested that, in the cases of peroxidase and catalase, one or more haem-linked protein groups ionize in such a way as to obscure what would otherwise be the pH dependence of anion binding. The reasons for trying to preserve anion binding for all four haemoproteins in their ferric states are of two kinds. First, there are similarities in the magnetic and spectral properties of each kind of complex. Second, provided that iron is bound to a neutral group on the protein, the binding of a single-charged anion results in a neutral complex. (Two of the four pyrrole nitrogen atoms each contribute a single negative charge. The formation of neutral complexes is favored on energetic and entropic grounds.) The first point is of questionable weight, because nothing is known about the relative effectiveness of acids as compared with their anions in producing ligand-field splitting (upon which the magnetic, and, to a large extent, the spectral properties depend). With regard to the second point, there are reasons not to prefer a neutral protein group bound to the iron[15]. In discussions which have favored the neutral group, peroxidase and catalase have been symbolized

$$\text{Pr—Fe}^{+}\text{—}$$

the single plus sign indicating the resultant charge after neutralization by the two negative charges on the pyrrole nitrogens. Total neutralization by combination with the anion A^- is then shown by

$$\text{Pr—Fe A}$$

Peroxidases and catalase will be symbolized

$$\text{Pr—Fe—}$$

in this treatment, with no pictorial emphasis on the net charge.

References p. 478

It is worthwhile to summarize the explanations which have been given for the pH dependence of complex formation in peroxidases and catalase, for they demonstrate various conceptions of the environment of the haem groups. An early view was that a hydroxyl group is bound to iron in position 6. This preserves anionic binding. For example, in the region of neutrality, the following reactions would apply:

$$\mathrm{Pr-FeOH + F^- + H^+ = Pr-FeF + H_2O} \tag{5}$$

$$\mathrm{Pr-FeOH + HCN = Pr-FeCN + H_2O} \tag{6}$$

However, this theory would not permit the well-known ionization of HRP at p$K \sim 11$ which corresponds to the formation of a hydroxide. It also implies a very unlikely p$K \sim 2$ for the ionization of catalase (which has no ionization from pH 2–12). Another unlikely scheme is the one mentioned in the preceding paragraph where the acid strength of a group or groups on the protein is markedly affected by the binding of the ligand. Thus, when a water molecule is bound in position 6, some group (Z) on the protein is in the form of the conjugate base (Z^-); but when a fluoride ion replaces the H_2O, the pK of Z is sufficiently raised so that the conjugate acid (HZ) is formed. In the region where this mechanism is effective

$$\mathrm{Z^- - Pr - Fe(H_2O) + F^- + H^+ = HZ - Pr - FeF + H_2O} \tag{7}$$

$$\mathrm{Z^- - Pr - Fe(H_2O) + HCN = HZ - Pr - FeCN + H_2O} \tag{8}$$

This scheme is analogous to the well-known Bohr effect in the binding of O_2 to haemoglobin, but requires, instead of the Bohr increment in pK of 1.2, the improbably high increment of 3 pH units. Also, the mechanism can apply only to a limited region of pH, say 5–8.

A third scheme proposes a two-bonded crevice structure[16] where the haem-linked group Z of the preceding theory is directly bound to the iron. When this special group is denoted by Y, the structure can be symbolized

$$\overline{\mathrm{Pr-Fe-Y}}$$

It is conceivable that the properties of this haem-linked group Y might allow a pK increment of 3, but it is very unlikely for Y to exhibit the large range of pK values, from < 4 to > 10, demanded by the ionizations in which it is involved[15]. What is ruled out here is not the two-bonded crevice *per se*, but rather the forced acid–base properties assigned to it to explain the pH independence of complex formation. Indeed the best picture available of haem environment is in metmyoglobin where there is a kind of crevice. The non-polar vinyl groups are buried among interior (non-polar) amino acid side-chains; the iron atom is attached to the imidazole of a histidine on one side, and the water molecule bound in position 6 is in close proximity to another histidine. Only the propionic groups of the haem can be said to be on the "outside", and they are bound to some basic groups of the protein. This brings us back to the direct and most likely interpretation of the effect of pH upon complex formation in peroxidases and catalase: a water molecule in the sixth position is replaced by the undissociated acid.

4. Reactions catalyzed by peroxidases and catalase

The reactions of peroxidases and catalase have been studied mainly in terms of reactants and not products. A large number of hydrogen donors have been tried; but all of the oxidation products from a single donor have been analyzed only in about twenty cases[17], and the oxidation products from a two-donor system, rarely. Table III lists characteristic donors and their products, where known.

Non-enzymatic oxidation reactions involving donors like those in Table III have occasionally been investigated. For example, when either aniline or *p*-toluidine is oxidized by H_2O_2 in the presence of ferrous sulfate, the identifiable products are different than when the reactions are catalyzed by peroxidase[18]. The structures of the products of enzymatic oxidation of two-electron donors by peroxidase are in accord with electron paramagnetic resonance experiments which show: (*1*) the reactive intermediates are donor free radicals (*not* hydroxyl or peroxide radicals); (*2*) the donor free radicals (which exist freely in solution) usually react with each other and not with the enzyme again[19]. The small number of products is related to the limited reactivity and favored reaction sites of donor free radicals, and not to enzymatic function. However, the case of mesidine (just one product) may be analogous to the two-electron transfer reactions of alcohol and formic acid with catalase compound I (Section 7, p. 472). The final product of the mesidine reaction is known to result from the condensation of mesidine with a fully oxidized intermediate compound.

The "peroxidatic" action of catalase and an explanation for it were discovered in studies of "coupled-oxidation" systems in which an oxidase (such as glucose oxidase) continually produces H_2O_2 at a slow rate, and catalase utilizes the H_2O_2 to oxidize alcohols[2,20]. Efficiency in such a system for oxidizing hydrogen donors other than H_2O_2 requires that the steady-state concentration of the peroxide be relatively low. Donor oxidation can also be effected in the absence of an oxidase system (*i.e.*, catalase alone is present) by the addition of small amounts of H_2O_2. As can be seen in Table III, very little is known about the products of peroxidatic reactions catalyzed by catalase. It is not possible to compare, for example, the products of phenol and amine oxidation by peroxidase and catalase. Nor are electron

TABLE III

SOME H_2O_2 REACTIONS

H-donor	*Products*
	A. Catalyzed by peroxidases[17]
Phenols	
Pyrogallol	Purpurogallin, others
p-Cresol	2,2′-dihydroxy-5,5′-dimethyldiphenyl The corresponding triphenyl A furan derivative
Mesitol	2,6-dimethylbenzoquinone 4-hydroxy-3,5-dimethylbenzaldehyde
Primary amines	
Aniline	2,5-dianilinobenzoquinone imine anil Pseudo-mauvine Indulines-3B and -6B Aniline black
p-Toluidine	4-amino-2,5-toluquinone di-*p*-tolylimine 4-*p*-toluidino-2,5-toluquinone di-*p*-tolylimine 4,4′-di-methyldiphenylamine Traces of others
Mesidine	3,5-dimethylbenzoquinone 1-(2,4,6-trimethyl)anil
Enediols	
Ascorbic acid	Dehydro ascorbic acid, presumably (N.A.*)
Triose reductone	2,3-diketopropanal, presumably (N.A.)
Miscellaneous	
Aniline + *p*-toluidine	Mostly *intra*molecular mixtures of intermediate structures from both donors
NADH	NAD
Ferrocytochrome *c*	Ferricytochrome *c*
Indoleacetic acid	Hydroxy-*O*-aminoacetophenone (?), others
Ferrocyanide	Ferricyanide
	B. Catalyzed by catalase[2,20,53]
Phenols	
Pyrogallol	Colored, N.A.
p-Cresol	Colored, N.A.
Primary Amines	
p-Phenylenediamine	Colored, N.A.
Alcohols	
Methanol	Formaldehyde
Ethanol	Acetaldehyde
n-Propanol	Propionaldehyde
Miscellaneous	
H_2O_2	O_2
Formic acid	CO_2
Nitrous acid	Nitric acid
p-Phenylenediamine + α-naphthol	Indophenol purple (?), N.A.
	C. Not catalyzed by peroxidases
Formic acid, methanol, ethanol, *n*-propanol	
	D. Not catalyzed by catalase
Ascorbic acid, *n*-pentanol, ferrocyanide	

* N.A. = not analyzed

paramagnetic resonance data available on (possible) free-radical intermediates in catalase reactions. However, Table III does display differences between the two enzymes. HRP is unable to oxidize either the normal primary alcohols or formic acid, making the catalysis of these reactions specific properties of catalase. Catalase, as distinct from peroxidase, is unable to utilize ascorbic acid or ferrocyanide in coupled oxidation, but these compounds will react with the primary oxidized compound of catalase (see Table V). The formation of aldehydes from alcohols arises from a reaction between the primary peroxide compound of catalase and the donor in which two electrons are transferred in rapid succession (Section 7).

Hydroperoxides other than H_2O_2 can be employed as oxidizing substrates, but do not serve as hydrogen donors for either peroxidases or catalase. A steady-state reaction mixture of methyl, ethyl, *n*-propyl, or isopropyl hydroperoxide with a very pure peroxidase or catalase preparation contains the primary oxidized compound of the enzyme at a high concentration which is constant over periods ranging from several seconds to several minutes, under conditions of concentration where H_2O_2–catalase mixtures react vigorously. The compounds of peroxidases and catalase formed with these hydroperoxides are discussed in Section 6. *tert.*-Butyl hydroperoxide is neither an effective oxidizing substrate nor produces spectroscopic changes in the enzyme.

Peroxidases catalyze the aerobic oxidation of several compounds (*e.g.* indole acetic acid, reduced nicotinamide–adenine dinucleotide, triose reductone), of which dihydroxyfumarate was the first to be found[65]. The experimental evidence which bears upon the role of H_2O_2 in these reactions and upon the inhibitory effects of carbon monoxide and cyanide has appeared to be inconsistent. Some progress has been made in unifying these controversial results[66].

The efficiency of the enzymes in catalyzing reactions of the type shown in Table III can be decreased in several ways. Reversible inhibition is produced by the complexing agents discussed earlier (Section 3)*. These agents are in competition with the hydroperoxides for a site on the iron atom. One exception among this group is azide, which reduces the primary peroxide compound of catalase to a ferrous form in a reaction which is not readily reversible. Catalytically inactive *oxidized* compounds (III and IV), in which apparently only the haem group is affected, are also known. In all cases of reversible or temporary irreversible inhibition, the haem alone is involved. When treatments (such as lyophilization) affect the *protein*

* In addition to reversible inhibition, complex-forming agents can also cause a progressive irreversible component of inhibition of the catalatic and other two-electron transfer reactions of catalase. This component arises from an acceleration of the reduction of compound I to compound II through endogenous donor[21].

References p. 478

moiety in such a way as to reduce enzymatic activity, this inhibition is found to be irreversible. It is interesting that the compound 3-amino-1,2,4-triazole, which irreversibly inhibits catalase action when it reacts with the primary oxidized compound, has been shown to attack the protein[22]. When the haem group is split off from catalase irreversibly inhibited by aminotriazole, the protein moiety is found to have the inhibitor attached. However, the protein sites affected by aminotriazole bear some close relationship to the haem group. Not only is one mole of inhibitor bound per mole of haem, but the inhibited enzyme reacts extremely slowly with complex-forming ligands such as cyanide[23].

The depressed peroxidation of dianisidine by HRP on the basic side of the pH optimum is restored by ammonia, pyridine and imidazole[68]. This effect is upon k_4 (rate constant for the reaction with hydrogen donor, the alkaline depression of which shows an apparent pK of 6.5) and hence appears when k_1 (combination with H_2O_2) is not rate-limiting. A single saturable enzyme site is involved to which one of the nitrogenous molecules is bound reversibly. Cyanide and hydroxide compete with these ligands for the site. The peroxidation of *p*-phenylenediamine is affected analogously to that of dianisidine, but the peroxidation of hydroquinone, guaiacol and uric acid are not affected.

5. Model reactions

The decomposition of H_2O_2 by inorganic iron is vigorous at low pH. As mentioned previously, the oxidation of hydrogen donors (such as alcohols and aromatic amines) can be coupled to this reaction. Many mechanisms of inorganic catalysis have been proposed. One set of theories postulates free-radical intermediates, and the coupling of the H_2O_2 oxidation–reduction system with the ferrous–ferric system[24]. Other mechanisms do not involve free radicals: higher oxidation states than ferric have been considered, and, recently, a mechanism involving the transition from a primary iron–peroxide complex to a secondary compound has been proposed[25,67]. *Active* primary mono-peroxy $[Fe^{3+}(H_2O)_5H_2O_2]$ and *inactive* di-peroxy $[Fe^{3+}(H_2O)_4(H_2O_2)_2]$ complexes have been suggested to explain the dependence of the reaction velocity[26] upon the mole ratio H_2O_2:H_2O. It is not known what relation the catalysis by inorganic iron has to the catalatic reaction. The same can be said of the reactions generated by haematin and model organic–ferric complexes such as

$$H_2NCH_2CH_2NHCH_2CH_2NHCH_2CH_2NH_2Fe(OH_2)^+$$

For this interesting compound[27] the second-order rate constant (at pH 10) of Eqn. (1) is about $4 \cdot 10^3$ times smaller than for catalase, but over $1 \cdot 10^4$ times greater than for methaemoglobin. Coordination of the four nitrogen atoms of the tetramine on positions 1, 2, 5, and 6 leaves the adjacent positions 3 and 4 open for binding an OOH^- ion. The geometry of the complex is such that the O–O bond is stretched and the activation energy for splitting this bond is lowered. In common with the catalase reaction and decomposition by ferric ions, isotope experiments with the tetramine-catalyzed decomposition of H_2O_2 show that both atoms in a product oxygen molecule come from one peroxide molecule. The OOH^- ion stretched in a complex with the tetramine clearly does not provide the O_2, which must therefore arise from a second OOH^- ion reacting with the complex.

Metmyoglobin reacts with H_2O_2, MeOOH, and EtOOH at different rates to form the same compound, as evidenced by absorption spectrum, state of oxidation and magnetic moment. The detection by magnetic methods[28] of the free radicals produced in these reactions was not unexpected, since direct titration of the product oxidized haemoprotein showed it to have only one of the two equivalents of the hydroperoxides[29]. The latter experiment led to the extremely important titration of the oxidized compounds of peroxidase[30,31]. Other strong oxidizing agents such as potassium molybdicyanide, potassium chloriridate, and sodium chlorite produce the same oxidized metmyoglobin compounds as do hydroperoxides. The nature of the coordination of iron in this compound is discussed in Section 6. Methaemoglobin behaves like metmyoglobin in those reactions with strong oxidizing agents that have been studied. The rates of reaction of free peroxidases and catalase with hydroperoxides are much faster, the primary compounds of the enzymes retain both oxidizing equivalents of the hydroperoxides, and the formation of the primary compounds is not accompanied by free-radical formation.

The feeble peroxidase activities of the haemoproteins other than peroxidases can be enhanced by exposure to alkali, acid, and organic denaturing agents (*e.g.* formamide and guanidine)[69]. The promotion of activity through the binding of specific ligands to the haem groups of the haemoproteins suggests that non-protein haematin complexes might serve as models for peroxidase. A systematic investigation of this possibility revealed that, in the presence of various single reagents and combinations of reagents, haematin can show peroxidase activity[70]. For example, the complexes of haematin with histidine and guanidine separately behave peroxidatically, and the histidine–guanidine combination is more active. Several combinations (*e.g.* pyridine–guanidine) are found to have oxidase activity. For all of these models, the values of k_1 (the rate constant for reaction with H_2O_2) are orders of magnitude smaller than for common peroxidases, while the k_4 values (reaction with leucomalachite green as hydrogen donor) are comparable.

TABLE IV

SPECTRAL AND MAGNETIC PROPERTIES OF OXIDIZED PEROXIDASE, CATALASE, AND METMYOGLOBIN

Abbreviations as in Table II

Compound		*Absorption bands*					*Magnetic moment (Bohr magnetons)*	*Refs.*
		C.T.1	*α*	*β*	*C.T.2*	*Soret*		
Peroxidase (HRP)								
Free (pH 5.6)	λ_{max}	641	(~580)	(~530)	497	403	5.3	47,50
	ε_{mM}	2.8			10.0	91		
Compound I	λ_{max}	650	580	—	—	410	4.0	50,54,55
	ε_{mM}	5	6			55		
Compound II	λ_{max}	—	555	527	—	418 (pH 7)	3.5	47,50,56
	ε_{mM}		7	8		87		
Compound III	λ_{max}	—	583	546	—	416 (pH 7)	N.M.	47,56
	ε_{mM}		8.5	10		97		
Catalase								
Free (pH 7.0) (BMC)	λ_{max}	627.5	—	537	504	406	5.9	8,35
	ε_{mM}	7.0		9.7	11.1	103	(based on spectrum)	
Compound I (BMC)	λ_{max}	662	583	—	—	398	3.9	35,57
	ε_{mM}	9.4	6.8			44		
Compound II (BMC)	λ_{max}	—	568	530	—	428	2.9	50,51,56
	ε_{mM}		18	12.5		77	(HBC)	
Compound III (HBC)	λ_{max}	—	585	545	—	416	N.M.	56
	ε_{mM}		10.5	13		84		
Metmyoglobin (horse)								
Free (pH 6.4)	λ_{max}	630	(580)	(550)	502	408	5.7	50,52,61
	ε_{mM}	3.9			10.2	188		
"Compound III"	λ_{max}	—	590	549	—	420	2.9	50,58
	ε_{mM}		8	9		100		

6. Oxidized compounds of peroxidases and catalase

When free peroxidases and catalase, which are brown, react with hydroperoxides, a green compound, I, is first formed, and then other spectrophotometrically and magnetometrically distinct red compounds, II, III, and IV, may appear, depending upon the reagents present and other experimental conditions. The Roman numerals assigned to these compounds are related to order of appearance and do not represent a sequence of valence states. Compounds of peroxidases and catalase bearing the same number are spectrophotometrically similar, but not identical. There is also some variation among the different peroxidases and catalases. Table IV lists spectral and magnetic properties of free HRP, bacterial catalase, and metmyoglobin, and the oxidized compounds.

The early designation of these compounds as complexes was based upon the belief that the hydroperoxide molecules were bound intact, a natural viewpoint arising from the success of Michaelis–Menten mechanisms based upon enzyme–substrate complexes. When it was discovered that peroxidase II was not in equilibrium with the free enzyme, that it did not retain both oxidizing equivalents of the hydroperoxide, and that oxidizing agents (molybdicyanide, etc.) other than hydroperoxides can produce II and probably also I, the designation as complex was dropped in favor of the more accurate term compound[30].

In the absence of oxidizable material, compound I is fairly stable and can be studied by conventional means. Of course, H_2O_2 acts as a hydrogen donor for catalase I, and, when it is used as the oxidizing agent, only a 40% conversion to compound I occurs at optimum H_2O_2 concentration[32]. With methyl and ethyl hydroperoxide, it is possible to convert more than 90% of free catalase to the primary compound. The extent of conversion depends upon the freedom of both enzyme and peroxide preparations from hydrogen donors. Whether a true equilibrium rather than a steady-state occurs in a "clean" system has not yet been established, but recent experiments with very dilute solutions favor equilibrium[33].

TABLE V

REACTIONS OF COMPOUNDS I AND II OF CATALASE[34]

H-donor	*Catalase compound formed from*	
	Compound I	*Compound II*
H_2O_2	Free	III
Phenols	II	Free
Alcohols, formic acid	Free	No reaction
Nitrous acid	Free	Free
Ascorbic acid, ferrocyanide	II	No reaction
Sodium azide, hydroxylamine	NO-ferrocatalase	Free

References p. 478

Table V lists reactions of compound I. Quite generally compound I of peroxidase is reduced by one- and two-electron donors to compound II. Exceptional donors are alcohols and formic acid, with which peroxidase I and II do not react[2]. These donors are also unusual in that they reduce catalase I directly to the free enzyme without the intermediate formation of II. H_2O_2 and nitrous acid do the same, but other donors (phenols, ascorbic acid, ferrocyanide)[34] react with catalase I to produce catalase II. Free peroxidase can be converted completely to compound II by careful reduction of a solution containing a small excess of H_2O_2 over the enzyme. Peroxidase II is sufficiently stable for detailed spectral studies, titrations, and static magnetic susceptibility measurements.

Compound I of peroxidases and compound II of catalase have had to be studied in the presence of various amounts of oxidized compounds and free enzyme. The same is true of compound III when produced from peroxidase and catalase II by an excess of H_2O_2, and compound IV, which is a peroxidase compound prepared with an excess of MeOOH. Peroxidase can be converted directly to compound III by the addition of equimolar H_2O_2 to an aerobic solution containing dihydroxyfumarate[66].

Striking features of compound I are the very low absorbancy of the Soret band and the appearance of the band in the red at about 660 mμ. In the case of bacterial catalase the absorbancy coefficient of the 400-mμ peak of I is less than half that of the free-enzyme maximum at 406 mμ; $\varepsilon_{400\,m\mu} : \varepsilon_{662\,m\mu}$ (where 662 mμ is the location of the visible peak of longest wavelength) is smaller than corresponding ratios for other iron protoporphyrin compounds. Because of these spectral analogies of I with certain bile pigments, it was recognized early that the porphyrin ring was probably oxidized, and a methene bridge suggested as a likely site[32].

Another unusual property of I is the magnetic moment, which for both HRP and bacterial catalase is very close to that of a complex of spin 3/2 (3 unpaired electrons). Coupled with the fact that I has two oxidizing equivalents above the ferric state, the susceptibility data permits only the following possibilities for compound I:

1. an Fe(V) compound of spin 3/2
2. mixture of iron compounds of average spin 3/2
3. a low-spin (1) Fe(IV) compound with a free radical in the porphyrin ring or the protein moiety
4. a low-spin (1/2) ferric compound with a biradical in the porphyrin or protein.

While (3) and (4) cannot be ruled out, the stability of I does not favor a radical hypothesis. Furthermore a free radical in the protein moiety is excluded by negative paramagnetic resonance observations. The choice between (*1*) and (*2*) has to be made, at present, on the basis of spectrophotometric properties. There is no reason to expect the spectra of Fe(V) porphyrin complexes to have the unusual characteristics of the spectra of I. The latter characteristics can, however, nicely be explained in terms of (*2*), a mixture of compounds[35].

Peroxidase I has a spectrum more like that of a normal porphyrin than has catalase I, while the spectrum of catalase I has more bile pigment character. However, both compounds have peaks at ~ 400 mμ, 580–585 mμ, 650–662 mμ, and greater absorbancy than the free enzyme in the region around 450 mμ. Since only the intensities of the corresponding peaks are different and not the location, the spectra can be closely approximated by adding, with different weights, a pair of component spectra. One component can be viewed as arising from a porphyrin structure (POR), perhaps a simple complex with hydroperoxide in position 6, and the other as arising from an oxidized-ring compound (ROX). It is not essential that ROX have a methene bridge double bond oxidized, since interruption of any one of the double bonds of the porphyrin system could result in a decrease in the Soret band intensity and the appearance of a band in the red. As estimated from the spectra, peroxidase I is about 2/3 POR and 1/3 ROX; and conversely for catalase I. POR is expected to be of intermediate spin, since the changes in the absorption spectrum of peroxidase when it becomes compound I are those which have been found to occur in ferric haemoproteins as they change from the high-spin (5/2) type to types of intermediate spin (between 5/2 and 1/2)[11]. An exception is the increase in absorbancy at 630 mμ, which is due to the presence of ROX with a band at about 650 mμ. The magnetic properties of the iron in ROX-like compounds have not yet been investigated. The data on compound I require ROX to be of intermediate spin, but lower than POR. Nothing definite can be said about the group coordinated in position 6 until more is known about ROX-like structures.

The data available support the view that compounds II of peroxidase and catalase are quadrivalent iron compounds in which oxygen is bound in the sixth position, the ferryl ion structure, $Fe(IV)O^{2+}$ (Ref. 30). These compounds have one oxidizing equivalent above the free enzyme, and magnetic moments which low-spin quadrivalent iron would have. The only simple alternative explanation of these two facts is a low-spin ferric compound with a stable free radical in the porphyrin. However, oxidation of the porphyrin ring would reduce the intensity of the Soret band, which is not observed. A comparison of the absorption spectra of peroxidase II and catalase II shows the same kinds of difference as are found between complexes of peroxidase and catalase with simple ligands in which only the sixth position changes. This favors the ferryl ion structure for compound

References p. 478

II, where the coordination in position 1–5 remains the same, and a common change occurs in position 6. Unfortunately, simple ferryl complexes are at present unknown, and reference cannot be made to independently measured physical and chemical properties.

It should be recognized that while the above descriptions of compounds I and II encompass in simplest form the considerable data available, they do not represent established structures.

Compounds III of peroxidase and catalase have *very* similar spectra, and so much like those of the hydroperoxide compounds of methaemoglobin and metmyoglobin that the latter have been classified as compounds of type III. The likeness of the spectra suggests that position 5 as well as position 6 has the same group in all four oxidized haemoproteins. The oxidation state and magnetic moment of the metmyoglobin compound, and hence almost certainly for the other three compounds, are the same as for compound II of peroxide and catalase.

7. Kinetic studies

The formation and decay of compounds I and II of peroxidases and catalase have been observed spectrophotometrically, and mechanisms developed to explain the kinetic curves. Computer solutions of the non-linear differential equations arising from the mechanisms agree with the experimentally determined time courses and steady-state concentrations of the enzyme compounds under most conditions[36–40]. Calculations of overall reaction velocities, based upon the postulated mechanism and the measured rate constants of the component reactions, also generally agree with the observed activities[41]. Major differences occur at high concentrations of hydroperoxides[42]. Hydrogen donor free-radical intermediates, suggested as products of the reactions of compounds I and II in the kinetic mechanism[30], have been detected and identified in peroxidase reactions by paramagnetic resonance[19,43]. The measured concentration of free radicals as a function of enzyme concentration is predicted by a simple extension of the kinetic equations.

The reactions catalyzed by peroxidases and catalases will now be discussed from the kinetic viewpoint. Kinetic properties at high ($> 1\ M$) hydroperoxide concentrations have only been investigated in detail for the catalatic reaction, and will be treated in the section dealing with this reaction. It should be noted, therefore, that essentially all of the discussion relates to the performance of the system at relatively low hydroperoxide concentrations.

(a) *Peroxidase*

The mechanism (Eqns. 9–12) has associated with it the rate expressions (Eqns. 13–16) where the concentrations are [E], free enzyme; [S], hydroperoxide; $[E_I]$, compound I; $[E_{II}]$, compound II; $[AH_2]$, two-electron hydrogen donor; and [HA·], hydrogen-donor free radical. The rates of the reverse reactions are negligibly slow[32]. The steady-state solutions are given in Eqns. 17–20 where $[E]_0$ is the total enzyme concentration. One-electron donors presumably are oxidized without the formation of free radicals (paramagnetic resonance experiments have not been reported.)

$$E + S \xrightarrow{k_1} E_I \tag{9}$$

$$E_I + AH_2 \xrightarrow{k_2} E_{II} + HA\cdot \tag{10}$$

$$E_{II} + AH_2 \xrightarrow{k_3} E + HA\cdot \tag{11}$$

$$HA\cdot + HA\cdot \xrightarrow{k_4} HA{:}AH \text{ (or } A + AH_2) \tag{12}$$

$$-\frac{d[S]}{dt} = k_1[E][S] \tag{13}$$

$$\frac{d[E_I]}{dt} = k_1[E][S] - k_2[E_I][AH_2] \tag{14}$$

$$\frac{d[E_{II}]}{dt} = k_2[E_I][AH_2] - k_3[E_{II}][AH_2] \tag{15}$$

$$\frac{d[HA\cdot]}{dt} = k_2[E_I][AH_2] + k_3[E_{II}][AH_2] - 2k_4[HA\cdot]^2 \tag{16}$$

$$\left|\frac{d[S]}{dt}\right|_{ss} = \frac{1}{2}\left|\frac{d[AH_2]}{dt}\right|_{ss} = [E]_0\left\{\frac{1}{k_1[S]_{ss}} + \frac{1}{k_2[AH_2]_{ss}} + \frac{1}{k_3[AH_2]_{ss}}\right\}^{-1} \tag{17}$$

$$[E_I]_{ss} = [E]_0\left(1 + \frac{k_2}{k_3} + \frac{k_2[AH_2]_{ss}}{k_1[S]_{ss}}\right)^{-1} \tag{18}$$

$$[E_{II}]_{ss} = [E]_0\left(1 + \frac{k_3}{k_2} + \frac{k_3[AH_2]_{ss}}{k_1[S]_{ss}}\right)^{-1} \tag{19}$$

$$[HA\cdot]_{ss} = ([E]_0)^{1/2}\left\{k_4\left(\frac{1}{k_1[S]_{ss}} + \frac{1}{k_2[AH_2]_{ss}} + \frac{1}{k_3[AH_2]_{ss}}\right)\right\}^{-1/2} = \left\{\frac{1}{k_4}\left|\frac{d[S]}{dt}\right|_{ss}\right\}^{1/2} \tag{20}$$

Table VI lists ranges of rate constants. HRP can be prepared with modifications of the prosthetic group. In general the rate constants for formation of compound I from the various peroxides are thereby unaffected, but k_4 values are[71].

References p. 478

TABLE VI

RANGES OF RATE CONSTANTS AT 20°–30°C (Refs. 13, 15, 32, 34, 37, 59, 60)

Enzyme compound	*Substrate*	$k_n(M^{-1}sec^{-1})$	*pH*
A. Peroxidases			
Free	H_2O_2	$1–2 \cdot 10^7$	Independent
	MeOOH	$1–6 \cdot 10^6$	Independent
	EtOOH	$2–4 \cdot 10^6$	Independent
HRP I	Nitrous acid	$2 \cdot 10^7$	Free acid
	Guaiacol	$9 \cdot 10^6$	7
	p-Aminobenzoic acid	$5 \cdot 10^4$	(not given[60])
HRP II	Nitrous acid	$2 \cdot 10^5$	Free acid
	Guaiacol	$3 \cdot 10^5$	7
	p-Aminobenzoic acid	$2 \cdot 10^3$	(not given[60])
	Aniline	$7 \cdot 10^4$	7
	Ascorbic acid	$2 \cdot 10^4$	4.7
	NADH	$\sim 3 \cdot 10^3$	7
HRP and other II	Ferrocytochrome *c*	$1–10^2$	4.7
	Pyrogallol	$10^5–10^7$	7
B. Catalases			
Free	H_2O_2	$3–6 \cdot 10^7$	Independent
	MeOOH	$2–8 \cdot 10^5$	Independent
	EtOOH	$10^3–10^4$	Independent
I	H_2O_2	$> 2 \cdot 10^7$	Independent
	Nitrous acid	$\sim 10^7$	Free acid
	Pyrogallol	$> 10^3$	~ 7
	Formic acid	$\sim 10^6$	Free acid
	Methanol	$10^2–10^3$	Independent
	Ethanol	$10–10^3$	Independent
	n-Propanol	$10^{-2}–10$	Independent
II	Nitrous acid	$\sim 10^6$	Free acid
	Pyrogallol	$\sim 10^2$	~ 7
	p-Cresol	~ 10	~ 7

Note that the mechanism does not include a process which is independent of the substrate concentrations and hence rate-limiting when the concentrations of the substrates are high. In classical terms, there is no Michaelis–Menten type of intermediate. However, as yet no attempt has been made to determine the upper limits of concentration for which the scheme is valid.

Measurements of free-radical concentration as a function of the concentrations of enzyme and substrates have established Eqn. (20). When higher order mechanisms are ruled out, the proportionality of $[HA\cdot]_{ss}$ to $([E]_0)^{1/2}$ requires that the free radicals are produced at a rate linearly dependent upon $[E]_0$ and that they disappear in reaction with each other, as provided by Eqns. (10), (11), and (12). The paramagnetic resonance spectra of the free-radical intermediates identify them as derived from the hydrogen donors. Structures for the ascorbic acid oxidation sequence are given below:

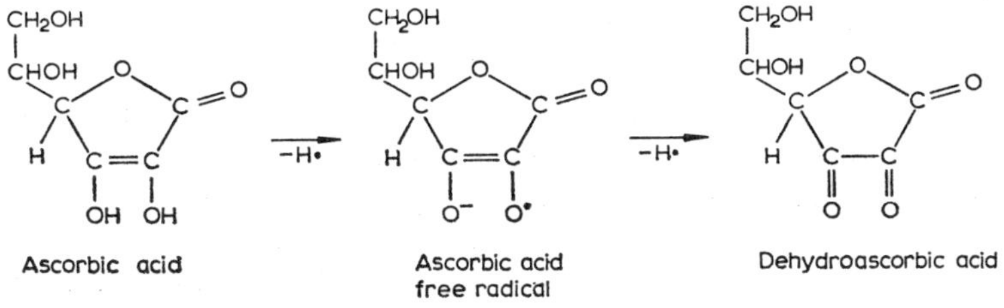

Ascorbic acid $\xrightarrow{-H\cdot}$ Ascorbic acid free radical $\xrightarrow{-H\cdot}$ Dehydroascorbic acid

The paramagnetic resonance spectra of the ascorbic acid free radicals produced enzymatically and during autoxidation are identical. (Conditions for the enzymatic reaction are chosen to minimize the rate of autoxidation of substrate.) The sharp doublet of the ascorbic acid free radical arises from interaction of the unpaired electron with the nuclear moment of the hydrogen on the carbon β to the double bond. The symmetrical triplet spectrum of the free radical from triose reductone arises from equal interactions with the two hydrogens; the quintet of reductic acid free radical from four equivalent hydrogens.

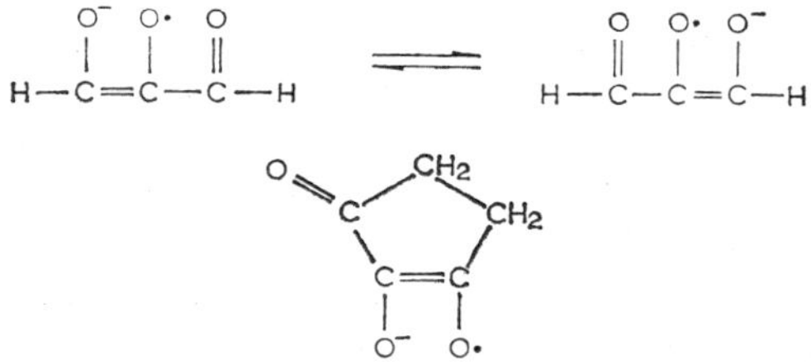

$$H{-}C(O^-){=}C(O\cdot){-}C({=}O){-}H \rightleftharpoons H{-}C({=}O){-}C(O\cdot){=}C(O^-){-}H$$

While the number of paramagnetic resonance experiments which have been performed is limited, and in a few cases the free-radical spectra and decay curves more complex than expected, there is little doubt that the essential features of the peroxidatic mechanism presented above are correct. The central unsolved problems are the nature of the atom transfers in the donor-oxidized enzyme reactions denoted by Eqns. (10) and (11), and the formation and release of the H_2O molecule (about which so little is known that the process has not been symbolized in this discussion).

(b) *Catalase*

Spectrophotometric studies of the *peroxidatic* reactions of catalase are not as extensive as those of peroxidase, and no paramagnetic resonance observations are available at present. However, two kinetic schemes have been

References p. 478

found, one of which is operative when the hydrogen donor is a phenol, and the other for the donors alcohol, formic acid, and nitrous acid. Excluded here are the special donors ascorbic acid and ferrocyanide which reduce I to II, but do not react with II, and hence cannot, alone, serve to complete the catalytic cycle. Other donors are known to be special (azide, hydroxylamine), and there are, probably, donors as yet uninvestigated which react according to one of the two schemes to be discussed below.

The data which have been obtained on phenols (Table VI lists rate constants) are in agreement with the kinetic mechanism of Eqns. (9), (10), and (11), where $[E]$, $[E_I]$, and $[E_{II}]$ are taken in terms of haem, rather than whole enzyme. H_2O_2 (in contrast with MeOOH and EtOOH), when used as the oxidant, also acts as a (second) hydrogen donor. The latter situation requires that Eqn. (21), which expresses the last step of the catalatic reaction, be included in the scheme.

$$E_I + S \xrightarrow{k_5} E + O_2 \qquad S \equiv H_2O_2 \tag{21}$$

When alcohols, formic acid, and nitrous acid react with compound I of catalase, the formation of compound II cannot be detected spectrophotometrically. The release of products and free enzyme appears to occur without the formation of a second enzyme compound. In the presence of a system which generates H_2O_2 continuously, endogenous donor (nature unknown) slowly converts I into II. Alcohols, formate, and nitrite, when added at the start of this process, prevent the formation of compound II. Furthermore, alcohols and formic acid do not react with II (although nitrous acid reduces II rapidly). For these reasons the following kinetic mechanism for the oxidation of alcohols, formate, and nitrite has been formulated to exclude the participation of compound II.

$$E + S \xrightarrow{k_1} E_I \tag{9}$$

$$E_I + AH_2 \xrightarrow{k_6} E + A \tag{22}$$

$$AH_2 \equiv \text{alcohols, formic acid, nitrous acid}$$

This scheme in conjunction with the measured rate constants predicts values which are consistent with the observed steady-state concentrations of the single catalytically active intermediate, compound I. Once again, if H_2O_2 is the oxidizing substrate, Eqn. (21) must be added to the two equations above. Eqn. (22) expresses a two-electron transfer: both oxidizing equivalents of compound I are received by a *single* hydrogen-donor molecule. It will now be shown that, whether the two electrons are transferred "simultaneously" or whether there are free-radical intermediates, the "lifetime" of the process is the same. The production of free-radical intermediates requires formation of compound II. While II is not observed, this could be because it is reduced to free enzyme at a great rate. Since II does not react with alcohols or formic acid, the reduction would have to take place by reaction with the free-radical intermediates. This situation is described by the scheme of Eqns. (23) and (24) of successive one-electron transfers.

$$E_I + AH_2 \xrightarrow{k_6} E_{II} + HA\cdot \tag{23}$$

$$E_{II} + HA\cdot \xrightarrow{k_7} E + A \tag{24}$$

The reducing equivalents of the free radicals cannot be expended in reactions with each other, otherwise compound II would accumulate. Therefore HA· produced in (23) must react with E_{II} before diffusing away, which is the operational definition of a simultaneous two-electron transfer.

The lifetimes of enzyme or free-radical intermediates involved in the sequence above are much shorter than can be measured by present techniques. The fraction of time, f_{II}, that catalase exists as II is

$$f_{II} = t_{II} \cdot (\text{T.N.}) \tag{25}$$

where t_{II} is the average lifetime of compound II and T.N. is the turnover number for the reaction. In terms of concentrations,

$$f_{II} = \frac{[E_{II}]_{ss}}{[E]_0} \tag{26}$$

and

$$t_{II} = \frac{[E_{II}]_{ss}}{[E]_0} \cdot \frac{1}{\text{T.N.}} \tag{27}$$

As an example, consider the reaction between MeOOH and ethanol as catalyzed by erythrocyte catalase[44]. In terms of haem, the T.N. is 20 sec^{-1} at a catalase (haem) concentration of 2.2 μM. The minimum (spectrophotometrically) detectable (haem) concentration of compound II is about $1 \cdot 10^{-3}$ μM, whence the inability to detect this compound means that

$$t_{II} < 2 \cdot 10^{-5} \text{ sec}$$

Thus the spectrophotometric determination of the upper limit for the lifetime of compound II is seen to be a poor measure for simultaneity of electron transfer, for 10^{-5} sec is many orders of magnitude longer than times suggested by criteria of diffusion and escape[45]. However, paramagnetic resonance cannot do even this well.

At sufficiently high concentrations of hydroperoxide and hydrogen donor, the step indicated by Eqn. (24) determines the turnover number.

References p. 478

Furthermore, the reactants E_{II} and HA· occur as a pair which may be viewed as a complex. It is clear that this complex is a typical Michaelis–Menten type of intermediate — that is, one which "dissociates" at a rate that is limiting when the concentration of substrate is high.

The general success of Eqns. (10) and (11) is a compelling reason to retain their main features. For the reactions just described, this implies that alcohol, formic acid and nitrous acid free radicals *are* formed in Eqn. (23), and are most excellent substrates for compound II.

Table VI demonstrates that comparison of rate constants does not permit any simple conclusions to be drawn about the accessibility of the active sites of peroxidases and catalase. For example, catalase I reacts with pyrogallol at a rate which is greater than with smaller alcohol molecules. H_2O_2 reacts more rapidly with catalases than with peroxidases, but EtOOH reacts 10^2–10^3 times more slowly with catalases. Nor is it possible to relate the marked differences between peroxidases and catalase toward alcohols and a few special donors, such as H_2O_2 and formic acid, solely to specific affinity for a group. The factors which affect the rate constant cannot be distinguished at present.

Because of the great vigor of the *catalatic* reaction, and the unique dual-role property of H_2O_2 in it, this reaction has been studied in greater detail than any of the preceding reactions. The kinetic mechanism, as established by spectrophotometric techniques, is given in Eqns. (9) and (21) and the steady-state solutions are given in Eqns. (28) and (29).

$$E + H_2O_2 \xrightarrow{k_1} E_I \tag{9}$$

$$E_I + H_2O_2 \xrightarrow{k_5} E + O_2 \tag{21}$$

$$\left|\frac{dx}{dt}\right|_{ss} = 2\,[E]_0\, x_{ss}\left(\frac{1}{k_1} + \frac{1}{k_5}\right)^{-1} \tag{28}$$

$$[E_I]_{ss} = [E]_0\left(1 + \frac{k_5}{k_1}\right)^{-1} \tag{29}$$

where

$$x \equiv [H_2O_2]$$

These expressions are in terms of concentration of haem rather than enzyme. The rate constant k of Eqn. (1) is traditionally based on the enzyme concentration $e = [E]_0/4$. From Eqn. (28) it follows:

$$k = 8\left(\frac{1}{k_1} + \frac{1}{k_5}\right)^{-1} \tag{30}$$

The scheme given by Eqns. (9) and (21) is believed correct because the derived relations (29) and (30) are obeyed by the experimentally determined parameters k_1, k_5, $[E_1]_{ss}/[E]$, and k. However, the range of peroxide concentrations studied is limited by the 10^{-3} sec mixing-chamber to observation-cell time of the accelerated-flow spectrophotometric technique. Since k_1 is of the order of $10^7/M$/sec, the kinetics of the formation of compound I can be followed only up to the relatively low H_2O_2 concentration[46] of 100 μM. Even the measurement of k by the activity test method of Section 1 fails for peroxide concentrations above 50 mM; k is found to decline rapidly with time, probably due to destruction of the protein.

It is possible to study the catalatic reaction[42] at $[H_2O_2]$ above 1 M. A rapid-flow two-mixer is used in which a reaction mixture 0.1–0.4 sec old is quenched by sulfuric acid. The velocities, for substrate concentrations from 0.1–5.0 M, depend upon $[H_2O_2]$ in accord with the Michaelis–Menten relation

$$v = \frac{v_{\max} x}{K_m + x} \tag{31}$$

where $v \equiv |dx/dt|$. At pH 7.0, 30°C, for horse-liver catalase, $K_m = 1.1$ M and $(\text{T.N.})_{\max} = 1.0 \cdot 10^7$ sec^{-1} on the basis of haem. K_m does not change with pH, and $v_{\max}$ decreases by only 50% from pH 7–10 and 20% from pH 7–4. Several possibilities exist for the rate-limiting step. In analogy with Eqns. (23) and (24), the reaction with the second H_2O_2 molecule might occur in two steps:

$$E_I + H_2O_2 \xrightarrow{k_5} E_{II} - HO_2\cdot \tag{32}$$

$$E_{II} - HO_2\cdot \xrightarrow{k_8} E + O_2 \tag{33}$$

On the basis of the observed turnover number, the lifetime of the E_{II}–$HO_2\cdot$ complex would be $1 \cdot 10^{-7}$ sec. While it is conceivable that the escape of $HO_2\cdot$ is somehow hindered, 10^{-7} sec would ordinarily be more than enough time for $HO_2\cdot$ to diffuse away, and the dissociation of an enzyme–free radical complex is unlikely to be the rate-limiting step.

Alternatively the formation of compound I might be a two-step reaction, or I might be the POR–ROX system discussed in Section 6:

$$E + H_2O_2 \xrightarrow{k_1} \text{POR} \tag{34}$$

$$\text{POR} \xrightarrow{k_9} \text{ROX} \tag{35}$$

followed by

$$\text{ROX} + H_2O_2 \xrightarrow{k_5} E + O_2 \tag{36}$$

References p. 478

Here POR is the Michaelis–Menten intermediate, and ROX alone reacts with the second H_2O_2 molecule. At sufficiently high substrate concentration there is no opportunity for ROX to revert to POR, while at the very low concentrations of spectrophotometric experiments the POR:ROX ratio approaches an equilibrium value:

$$\text{POR} \underset{k_{-9}}{\overset{k_9}{\rightleftharpoons}} \text{ROX} \tag{37}$$

$$\text{POR/ROX} = k_{-9}/k_9 \tag{38}$$

If this is the true situation, then the false picture of a *single* compound I is seen to arise from the restricted time resolution of the rapid-flow spectrophotometric technique. The spectrophotometric and magnetic properties of compound I are simply explained on the basis of a two-component equilibrium, and support a rate-limiting step of the kind expressed by Eqn. (35).

The rate-limiting step could also be involved in the formation of the water molecules. There are no experimental data which bear directly upon this possibility, and no discussion will be given of water formation.

It has been found that the degree of inhibition

$$H \equiv 1 - \frac{v_i}{v} \tag{39}$$

caused by cyanide, fluoride, and formate can be expressed by

$$H = \frac{i}{\Phi + i} \tag{40}$$

where i is the concentration of the inhibitor and Φ, the value of i for 50% inhibition, has the following properties:

(*1*) for $[H_2O_2]_s < K_m$, Φ is independent of $[H_2O_2]$
(*2*) for $[H_2O_2]_s > K_m$, Φ increases with $[H_2O_2]$
(*3*) for all three inhibitors, $\log \Phi\ (x = 4.5\ M) - \log \Phi\ (x = 0.017\ M) \approx 0.7$ log units

This behavior follows from

$$\Phi = K\left(1 + \frac{x}{K_m}\right) \tag{41}$$

which can be derived from both rate-limiting schemes given above, and hence the inhibition data does not favor either.

The temperature dependence of k_1 and k_5 have been measured[41] in water–glycerol media from $-20°$ to $45°$. k_5 increases linearly with temperature, yielding an Arrhenius energy of 5 kcal/mole. k_1 shows the same heat of activation between $-5°$ and $15°$, but is independent of temperature above $25°$ and decreases rapidly below $-10°$. Over the entire temperature range the velocity obeys Eqn. (28), which indicates that the complex behavior of k_1 is not related to a breakdown of the kinetic scheme of Eqns. (9) and (21). The interpretation of these data must also explain the unusual viscosity independence[41] of k_1. In the temperature range that k_1 is constant (activation energy $\sim$ 0), it is diffusion-independent up to viscosities of about 6 cPs. Reactions which are not limited by diffusion generally have activation energies above 6 kcal/mole. k_5 (at room temperature) is also not controlled by diffusion until the viscosity exceeds 6 cPs, and has a somewhat low heat of activation for this situation. On the basis of collision theory and the value of k_5 measured under diffusion control, the H_2O_2 molecule arrives at an active site of radius 0.6–1.2 Å for a solid angle of approach of 2π to π steradians. The exact nature of the processes which occur after this event remains a lively field of investigation.

REFERENCES

1 A. W. GALSTON, in R. L. WAIN AND F. WIGHTMAN (Eds.), *The Chemistry and Mode of Action of Plant Growth Substances*, Butterworth, London, 1956, p. 219.
2 D. KEILIN AND E. F. HARTREE, *Biochem. J.*, 60 (1955) 310.
3 B. CHANCE AND A. C. MAEHLY, in S. P. COLOWICK AND N. O. KAPLAN (Eds.), *Methods in Enzymology*, Vol. II, Academic Press, New York, 1955, p. 764.
4 H. THEORELL AND A. EHRENBERG, *Arch. Biochem. Biophys.*, 41 (1952) 442.
5 A. C. MAEHLY, *Nature*, 192 (1961) 630.
6 M. GOUTERMAN, *J. Mol. Spectr.*, 6 (1961) 138.
7 R. J. P. WILLIAMS, *Chem. Revs.*, 56 (1956) 299.
8 A. S. BRILL AND R. J. P. WILLIAMS, *Biochem. J.*, 78 (1961) 246.
9 A. C. MAEHLY, in J. T. EDSALL (Ed.), *Enzymes and Enzyme Systems*, Harvard University Press, Cambridge, Mass., 1951, p. 77.
10 K. G. PAUL, *Acta Chem. Scand.*, 13 (1959) 1239.
11 P. GEORGE, J. BEETLESTONE AND J. S. GRIFFITH, in *Haematin Enzymes*, Pergamon, London, 1961, p. 105.
12 H. A. HARBURY, *J. Biol. Chem.*, 225 (1957) 1009.
13 B. CHANCE, *J. Biol. Chem.*, 194 (1952) 483.
14 P. GEORGE, in D. E. GREEN (Ed.), *Currents in Biochemical Research*, Interscience, New York, 1956, p. 338.
15 P. NICHOLLS, *Biochim. Biophys. Acta*, 60 (1962) 217.
16 P. GEORGE AND R. L. J. LYSTER, *Proc. Natl. Acad. Sci. U.S.*, 44 (1958) 1013.
17 B. C. SAUNDERS, *Lectures, Monographs and Reports, The Royal Institute of Chemistry*, No. 1, 1957.
18 D. G. H. DANIELS, F. T. NAYLOR AND B. C. SAUNDERS, *J. Chem. Soc.*, (1951) 3433.
19 I. YAMAZAKI, H. S. MASON AND L. PIETTE, *J. Biol. Chem.*, 235 (1960) 2444.
20 D. KEILIN AND E. F. HARTREE, *Biochem. J.*, 39 (1945) 293.
21 P. NICHOLLS, *Biochem. J.*, 81 (1961) 365.
22 E. MARGOLIASH, A. NOVOGRODSKY AND A. SCHEJTER, *Biochem. J.*, 74 (1960) 339.
23 P. NICHOLLS, *Biochim. Biophys. Acta*, 59 (1962) 414.
24 W. G. BARB, J. H. BAXENDALE, P. GEORGE AND K. R. HARGRAVE, *Trans. Faraday Soc.*, 47 (1951) 591.
25 M. L. KREMER AND G. STEIN, *Trans. Faraday Soc.*, 55 (1959) 959.
26 P. JONES, R. KITCHING, M. L. TOBE AND W. F. K. WYNNE-JONES, *Trans. Faraday Soc.*, 55 (1959) 79.
27 J. H. WANG, in R. E. ZIRKLE (Ed.), *A Symposium on Molecular Biology*, University of Chicago Press, 1959, p. 137.
28 A. S. BRILL, A. EHRENBERG AND H. DEN HARTOG, *Biochim. Biophys. Acta*, 40 (1960) 313.
29 P. GEORGE AND D. H. IRVINE, *Nature*, 168 (1951) 184.
30 P. GEORGE, *Biochem. J.*, 54 (1953) 267.
31 P. GEORGE, *Biochem. J.*, 55 (1953) 220.
32 B. CHANCE, *Advan. Enzymol.*, Vol. 12, Interscience, New York, 1951, p. 153.
33 B. CHANCE AND G. R. SCHONBAUM, *J. Biol. Chem.*, 237 (1962) 2391.
34 D. KEILIN AND P. NICHOLLS, *Biochim. Biophys. Acta*, 29 (1958) 302.
35 A. S. BRILL AND R. J. P. WILLIAMS, *Biochem. J.*, 78 (1961) 253.
36 B. CHANCE, *J. Biol. Chem.*, 151 (1943) 553.
37 B. CHANCE, *Arch. Biochem. Biophys.*, 41 (1952) 416.
38 B. CHANCE, D. S. GREENSTEIN, J. HIGGINS AND C. C. YANG, *Arch. Biochem. Biophys.*, 37 (1952) 322.
39 J. HIGGINS, in S. L. FRIESS, E. S. LEWIS AND A. WEISSBERGER (Eds.), *Techniques of Organic Chemistry*, Vol. 8, Part I, Investigation of Rates and Mechanisms of Reactions, Interscience, New York, 1961, p. 285.
40 B. CHANCE, in S. L. FREISS, E. S. LEWIS AND A. WEISSBERGER (Eds.), *Techniques of Organic Chemistry*, Vol. 8, Part II, Investigation of Rates and Mechanisms of Reactions, Interscience, New York, 1961, p. 1314.
41 E. ACKERMAN AND G. K. STROTHER, *Biochim. Biophys. Acta*, 47 (1961) 317.

[42] Y. Ogura, *Arch. Biochem. Biophys.*, 57 (1955) 288.
[43] L. H. Piette, I. Yamazaki and H. S. Mason, in M. S. Blois Jr. *et al.* (Eds.), *Free Radicals in Biological Systems*, Academic Press, New York, 1961, p. 195.
[44] B. Chance, *J. Biol. Chem.*, 182 (1950) 649.
[45] F. H. Westheimer, in W. D. McElroy and B. Glass (Eds.), *The Mechanism of Enzyme Action*, Johns Hopkins, Baltimore, 1954, p. 321.
[46] B. Chance, in D. E. Green (Ed.), *Currents in Biochemical Research*, Interscience, New York, 1956, p. 308.
[47] D. Keilin and E. F. Hartree, *Biochem. J.*, 49 (1951) 88.
[48] E. F. Hartree, *Rept. Progr. Chem.*, 43 (1946) 295.
[49] A. S. Brill, unpublished data.
[50] A. Ehrenberg, *Svensk Kem. Tidskr.*, 74 (1962) 53.
[51] A. Maehly, *Biochim. Biophys. Acta*, 54 (1961) 132.
[52] W. Scheler, G. Schoffa and F. Jung, *Biochem. Z.*, 329 (1957) 232.
[53] H. Tauber, *Proc. Soc. Exptl. Biol. Med.*, 81 (1952) 237.
[54] P. George, *Science*, 117 (1953) 220.
[55] R. R. Fergusson, *J. Am. Chem. Soc.*, 78 (1956) 741.
[56] B. Chance, *Arch. Biochem. Biophys.*, 41 (1952) 404.
[57] A. S. Brill, in M. S. Blois (Ed.), *Free Radicals in Biological Systems*, Academic Press, New York, 1961, p. 53.
[58] P. George and D. H. Irvine, *Biochem. J.*, 55 (1953) 230.
[59] B. Chance, *J. Biol. Chem.*, 194 (1952) 471.
[60] B. Chance and R. R. Fergusson, in W. D. McElroy and B. Glass (Eds.), *The Mechanism of Enzyme Action*, Johns Hopkins, Baltimore, 1954, p. 389.
[61] H. Theorell and A. Ehrenberg, *Acta Chem. Scand.*, 5 (1951) 823.
[62] P. S. Braterman, R. C. Davies and R. J. P. Williams, in J. Duchesne (Ed.), *Advances in Chemical Physics*, Vol. 7, The Structure and Properties of Biomolecules and Biological Systems, Interscience, New York, 1964, p. 359.
[63] Peter O'D. Offenhartz, *J. Chem. Phys.*, 42 (1965) 3566.
[64] M. Gouterman, G. H. Wagniere and Lawrence C. Snyder, *J. Mol. Spectr.*, 11 (1963) 108.
[65] B. Swedin and H. Theorell, *Nature*, 145 (1940) 71.
[66] I. Yamazaki and L. H. Piette, *Biochim. Biophys. Acta*, 77 (1963) 47.
[67] M. L. Kremer, *Trans. Faraday Soc.*, 58 (1962) 702.
[68] I. Fridovich, *J. Biol. Chem.*, 238 (1963) 3921.
[69] T. Kurozumi, Y. Inada and K. Shibata, *Arch. Biochem. Biophys.*, 94 (1961) 464.
[70] Y. Nakamura, M. Tohjo and K. Shibata, *Arch. Biochem. Biophys.*, 102 (1963) 144.
[71] B. Chance and K. G. Paul, *Acta Chem. Scand.*, 14 (1960) 1711.

SUBJECT INDEX